Michael Micklin:

Tulane University

Population, Environment, and Social Organization: Current Issues in Human Ecology

The Dryden Press
Hinsdale, Illinois

Library of Congress Catalog Card Number: 73-754
ISBN: 03-089071-3
Printed in the United States of America
345 090 98765432

For Barbara
Connie
Willie
Ronnie
and Karen

Grateful acknowledgment is made to the following authors and publishers for permission to reprint selections from copyrighted material.

"Human Ecology" by Amos H. Hawley. Reprinted with permission of the Publisher from THE INTERNATIONAL ENCYCLOPEDIA OF THE SOCIAL SCIENCES, David L. Sills, Editor. Volume 4, pages 328 to 337. Copyright © 1968 by Crowell Collier and Macmillan, Inc.

"Toward a Thoretical System of Human Ecology" by Jack P. Gibbs and Walter T. Martin is reprinted from *Pacific Sociological Review*, Volume 2, Number 1 (Spring 1959) pp. 29-36, by permission of the Publisher, Sage Publications, Inc.

"The Adaptive Potentialities of Man" in Rene Dubos *Man Adapting*. Copyright © 1965 by Yale University.

"Social Morphology and Human Ecology" by Leo F. Schnore. Reprinted with permission of the Publisher and the Author from AMERICAN JOURNAL OF SOCIOLOGY, Volume 63, Number 6 (May 1958).

"A Long-Range View of World Population Growth" by John D. Durand. Reprinted with permission of the Publisher and the Author from THE ANNALS of the American Academy of Political and Social Science, January 1967.

"Man and His Environment" by Stanley Cain. Reprinted with the permission of the Publisher from POPULATION BULLETIN, November 1966, Volume 22, Number 4. Population Reference Bureau, Inc., 1755 Massachusetts Avenue, N.W. Washington, D.C.

"From Social System to Ecosystem" by Otis Dudley Duncan. Reprinted with permission from the Publisher, SOCIOLOGICAL INQUIRY, Volume 331, Number 2, 1961.

"Population and Panaceas: A Technological Perspective." Copyright 1969 by Paul R. Ehrlich and John P. Holdren. Reprinted by permission of the Authors and the Editors of Bioscience. *Bioscience* 19, Number 12, 1969.

"Some Environmental Effects of Economic Development" by John V. Krutilla. Reprinted by permission from DAEDALUS, Journal of the American Academy of Arts and Sciences, Boston, Massachusetts, Volume 96, Number 4.

"Global Ecology: Toward the Planetary Society: by John McHale is reprinted from *American Behavioral Scientist*, Volume 11, Number 6 (July/August 1968) pp. 29-34, by permission of the Publisher, Sage Publications, Inc.

"Norms for Family Size in Underdeveloped Areas" by Ronald Freedman is reprinted from *Proceedings of the Royal Society*, Series B, Volume 159, by permission of the Publisher and the Author.

"Cultural Differences in the Interpretation of Natural Resources" by Alexander Spoehr, in W. L. Thomas (ed.) MAN'S ROLE IN CHANGING THE FACE OF THE EARTH. Reprinted by permission of the Publisher, University of Chicago Press 1956.

"Microcosm—Macrocosm Relationships in North American Agrarian Society" by J. W. Bennett. Reproduced by permission of the American Anthropological Association from AMERICAN ANTHROPOLOGIST, Volume 39, Number 5, 1967.

"Population Policies in Developing Countries," by Dudley Kirk and Dorothy Nortman. Reprinted by permission of the Publisher, University of Chicago Press from ECONOMIC DEVELOPMENT AND CULTURAL CHANGE, Volume 15, Number 2, Part I (January 1967), pp. 129-42.

"Community Power and Urban Renewal Success" by Amos H. Hawley. Reprinted by permission of the Publisher, University of Chicago Press, from AMERICAN JOURNAL OF SOCIOLOGY, Volume 68, January 1963, pp. 422-431.

"Environmental Problems and Legislative Responses" by Jack C. Oppenheimer and Leonard A. Miller. Reprinted by permission of the publisher, from the ANNALS OF THE AMERICAN ACADEMY OF POLITICAL AND SOCIAL SCIENCE, Volume 389, (May 1970), pp. 77-86.

"Outmigration and the Depressed Area Problem," by John B. Parr. Reprinted by permission from the Publisher from LAND ECONOMICS, Volume 42, (May 1966), pp. 149-159.

"The Separation of Home and Work: A Problem for Human Ecology," by Leo F. Schnore. Reprinted by permission of the Publisher from SOCIAL FORCES, Volume 32, (May 1954) pp. 336-43.

"Urbanization and Natural Resources: A Study in Organizational Ecology," by Jack P. Gibbs and Walter T. Martin. Reprinted by permission of the Publisher, The American Sociological Association from THE AMERICAN SOCIOLOGICAL REVIEW, Volume 23, Number 3 (June 1958), pp. 226-77.

"The End of the Population Explosion" by Donald J. Bogue. Reprinted by permission of the Publisher, THE PUBLIC INTEREST, Number 7 (Spring 1967). Copyright National Affairs, Inc. 1967. This article is also reprinted in the Author's PRINCIPLES OF DEMOGRAPHY, John Wiley, 1970.

"Population Policy: Will Current Programs Succeed?" by Kingsley Davis. Reprinted by permission of the Publisher from SCIENCE, Volume 158, (10 November 1967) pp. 730-739.

"Beyond Family Planning" by Bernard Berelson. Reprinted by permission from The Population Council. STUDIES IN FAMILY PLANNING, No. 38, (February 1969), pp. 1-16.

"The U.S. Resource Outlook: Quantity and Quality" by Hans H. Landsberg. Reprinted by permission of DAEDALUS, Journal of the American Academy of Arts and Sciences, Boston, Mass., Fall 1967, America's Changing Environment.

"Population Pollution" by Francis S. L. Williamson. Reprinted by permission of the Publisher from *BioScience*, Volume 19, Number 11 (November 1969), pp. 979-83.

"Environment and the Shaping of Civilization" by Lynton K. Caldwell in Richard A. Cooley and Geoffrey Wandesforde-Smith (eds.) CONGRESS AND THE ENVIRONMENT, 1970. Reprinted by the permission of the Publisher, The University of Washington Press.

Contents

Preface

Human history is often calibrated in terms of a series of critical events that have marked drastic turning points in the evolution of society. At least three such "revolutions" are generally recognized: the tool-making, the agricultural, and the scientific-industrial; and one might well add a fourth, the nuclear. While the social implications of these developments are obviously numerous and diverse, two consequences common to each stand out in the broad picture of the evolution of social organization. First, man has become increasingly independent of the constraints of nature, and has developed successively greater capacities to manipulate and control his environment. Second, each of these revolutions has resulted in greatly expanded potential for supporting increasingly large populations.

It can be argued that we are now at another critical turning point in human history. There is a growing awareness that man's environment is being manipulated and utilized irresponsibly. Natural resources are being depleted, air and water are becoming increasingly unfit for human consumption, human settlements are deteriorating in organization as well as physical structure. At the same time, people are being born much more rapidly than they are dying, they are living longer, and human communities are becoming increasingly congested. Consequently the human population is reaching a point of imbalance with its environment. In short, the basic element of the human condition, the man-nature relationship, once again appears to be in a precarious state. As in the early period of social evolution, e.g., the hunting and gathering level, when nature was clearly dominant over man, the survival of human society is in question.

Were the outcome of man's current encounter with nature not still in doubt, one might refer to the present stage in human history as the "ecological revolution". But this would constitute an overly optimistic view, implying that human society had somehow resolved the problem, or at least was in the process of doing so. This is unfortunately not the case. Solutions to ecological problems are still being formulated and given trial runs. Ideas abound, but proven results are few. Understanding of the problems involved necessarily precedes their resolution, and much work remains to be done before the complexities of population-environment relationships can be fully comprehended.

During the early part of this century much attention was devoted to the development of human ecology as a social science.[1] Interest in the subject waned around 1940, picked up again in the mid-1950s, and has been steadily increasing since that time. Indeed, not since the mid-1930s has interest in human ecology been so great among social scientists as at present, and never before has the public been so aware of and so concerned about the topic.

Unfortunately, though, the conceptual and theoretical development of human ecology has not been cumulative. At least four different schools of thought have emerged in the discipline of Sociology alone. In addition, perspectives on the subject have been developed by anthropologists, geographers, political scientists and psychologists, as well as in hybrid fields such as demography, social psychiatry, public health and city planning. The result has been a variety of perspectives for approaching the subject matter, not all of which are compatible and some of which are contradictory. Probably the most serious deficiency of contemporary human ecology is its theoretical basis. Ecological "facts" are plentiful, but systematically reasoned explanations based upon an integrated body of assumptions and propositions have yet to be developed.

The massive increase in public concern over ecological problems has resulted in an avalanche of recent periodical publications. These discussions tend to be pragmatic, aimed at pointing out various aspects of the "ecological crisis" and/or suggesting ways in which these problems might be resolved. Another indication of the growing concern for ecology is the number of edited volumes on broad ecological themes that have appeared over the past few years. The lack of adequate theory in contemporary academic human ecology is strongly reflected in these problem-oriented discussions. Primarily evident is the failure to take adequate account of the social basis of such problems. Whether the concern be with pollution, urban deterioration, or overpopulation, one must view it in the context of some on-going social situation, with causes and consequences stemming from past and present forms of social organization.

The present volume is an attempt to derive and illustrate such a perspective for understanding current problems in human ecology. It is designed to provide a balance between the social scientist's concern with theoretical and conceptual issues and the concerned citizen's priority for practical matters. The basic theme of the book is that the relationships among the raw materials of human ecological systems—i.e., populations and their environments—are mediated through and largely determined by certain aspects of social organization. The primary questions to be explored involve the identification and delineation of the social processes through which human aggregates adapt themselves to the exigencies and contingencies of particular demographic and environmental conditions. Stated otherwise, emphasis is placed upon socially organized strategies for collective survival; hopefully such a focus will result in a better understanding of current ecological issues.

The volume begins with an introductory essay focusing on the structures and processes of ecological systems. A conceptual framework is developed which emphasizes the role of social organization in the process of ecological adaptation. Part I then develops this conceptual frame of reference. Chapter 1 deals with the problem of survival as an ecological issue. A connection is drawn between the basic concerns of general ecology and related developments in human ecology. It is suggested that the primary link between these disciplines is an emphasis on the importance of adaptations by organisms to their environments if collective survival is to be ensured. Chapter 2 contains a discussion of the principal components of ecological organization: population, environment and social organization.

Part II specifies further the relationship between particular adaptive mechanisms, demographic conditions, and environmental situations. Emphasis is placed upon clearly demonstrating the role of science and technology, ideology and culture, regulatory processes, and distributional phenomena in mediating ecological relationships. Thus Chapter 3 portrays the effects of scientific and technological strategies on selected demographic and environmental dimensions. Chapters 4 through 6 continue this theme, dealing with the effects of the remaining adaptive mechanisms on similar demographic and environmental problems.

Part III emphasizes unresolved issues currently facing human ecologists, especially those most critical for the survival of human society. Chapter 7 is devoted to demographic issues. The problem of population control is singled out for special consideration. The primary issue is whether or not the rate of population growth can be significantly reduced before it is too late. Chapter 8 continues the discussion of current issues with a consideration of selected environmental problems. Attention is focused on the apparently increasing depletion and contamination of the natural environment. The aim in these two chapters is primarily to focus attention on controversial aspects of these questions, but some attention is directed toward the evaluation of alternative strategies for resolving them.

As a final commentary on the current status of human ecology as an academic discipline as well as a matter of public concern, the Epilogue contains my speculations and suggestions regarding needed developments in the field. Attention is directed toward avenues for improving the theoretical basis of human ecology, especially in relation to the need for generating empirically grounded, non-trivial explanations for ecological phenomena. In addition, discussion is focused on means through which the consequences of adaptive mechanisms may be anticipated and utilized for resolving current ecological crises and preventing future ones.

I would like to express my appreciation to Joe Byers and Reece McGee for their enthusiasm and encouragement during the preparation of this volume. I am especially grateful for their patience and understanding while working with an author whose tendencies toward procrastination would drive most editors to the verge of mayhem. The administrative efficiency of Miss Linda Lezark, Mr. Byers' assistant, also contributed to the completion of this work and is greatly appreciated. Special thanks are of course due the authors and publishers who gave permission for articles to be reprinted here. I am particularly grateful to Professor John Bennett of Washington University who took time out from a busy summer in the field to revise and update his contribution to Chapter 4. The task of typing the final version of the manuscript was most adequately handled by Doris Segal. My wife, Barbara, has probably contributed as much to the completion of this volume as any single person; I would hesitate to count the hours she has spent in various libraries searching for renegade materials or hunched over a typewriter trying to decipher my generally illegible scrawl. Finally, I would like to acknowledge the considerable influence my own approach to human ecology has received from the published works of Professors Jack P. Gibbs, Leo F. Schnore, Otis Dudley Duncan, and Amos H. Hawley. It is my sincere hope that where I have drawn upon their ideas my interpretation has been accurate, and where I have been critical that my reservations have been justified.

Notes and References

1. For a review of this earlier work see A. B. Hollingshead, "Human Ecology," in *Outline of the Principles of Sociology*, ed. R. E. Park, New York: Barnes and Noble, 1939, pp. 63-170; James A. Quinn, "The Development of Human Ecology in Sociology," in *Contemporary Sociological Theory*, ed. H. A. Barnes and H. S. Becker, New York: Appleton-Century-Croft, 1940, pp. 212-244; Audrey Hawthorne and Emma Llewellyn, "Human Ecology," in *Twentieth Century Sociology*, ed. George Gurvitch and W. E. Moore, New York: The Philosophical Library, 1945, pp. 466-499; and Robert E. L. Faris, *Chicago Sociology 1920-1932*, San Francisco: Chandler Publishing Co., 1967. The classic critical analysis of this work is found in Milla Aissa Alihan, *Social Ecology: A Critical Analysis*, New York: Columbia University Press, 1938.

New Orleans, La.

Population, Environment, and Social Organization: Current Issues in Human Ecology

Introduction
A Framework for the Study of Human Ecology

Though varying widely in specific components, conceptions of human ecology are generally focused on " . . . the adjustments of human beings to their environments."[1] While at times these adjustments have been approached on the individual level of analysis,[2] most often they are viewed in terms of aggregate or population phenomena. The types of aggregates upon which ecological analyses have been focused include neighborhoods, cities and communities, regions, nations, and systems of nations. Given this emphasis it is not surprising that over the years the study of human ecology has been identified primarily, though certainly not exclusively, with the study of social organization.[3] The central question for ecological analysis may be generally stated as follows: *how do population aggregates, viewed as collectivities of socially interdependent actors, cope with concrete environmental conditions in the course of satisfying subsistence needs and maximizing conditions favorable to persistence of the aggregate?*

Answers to this basic question have been formulated in terms of a variety of theoretical systems that have evolved over the past half century or so. The earlier attempts at building a theory of human ecology were based upon the idea that the means through which human populations survived in their environmental settings were analogous with those underlying the survival of plant and animal communities.[4] In response to strong criticisms of these early "classical" approaches to human ecology,[5] positions were developed that reflected greater recognition of the social bases of adjustment among human populations.[6] In recent years further distinctions and clarifications have been added to the ecological perspective, particularly emphasizing the systematic nature of ecological relationships.[7]

The approach to human ecology upon which the present volume is based shares many features with these earlier efforts and should be interpreted as an attempt to draw together continuities in ecological thinking rather than present a totally new or revised formulation.[8] Examination of the various approaches to human ecology indicates the following general areas of agreement shared by most students of the subject:

1. The central focus is on relationships among human organisms and their environments. At times interest is centered on the processes by which men adjust directly to their environmental settings, while in other instances stress is laid upon inter-group relationships as modified by environmental conditions.[9]

2. The unit of analysis is the collectivity or the population, not isolated individuals. As indicated above, these aggregates may range from highly localized to widely dispersed groups.[10]

3. Relationships among members of populations as well as between distinct populations are socially organized, suggesting temporally persistent though highly modifiable patterns of social interaction. Indeed,

it is through social organization that populations are able to coordinate diverse skills and activities and thus satisfy the requisites of prolonged survival.[11]

4. An important aspect of ecological organization is reflected in regularities and variations in spatial and temporal patterns of relationships. It should be noted, though, that some of the most sterile work in the field has been focused on describing area distributions of social and demographic phenomena.[12]

5. Ecological relationships are best represented in terms of sets of activities, e.g., working, traveling, exploiting, etc. On the individual level these might well be viewed as "social roles," but on the collective level they are more adequately designated as "social processes."[13]

6. Ecological analysis should and can contribute to our understanding of social change. Neither environments nor populations are static phenomena and, as one or both undergo alteration, relationships between them are also transformed. Underlying these shifts in ecological organization is what is perhaps the most significant attribute of social organization: Its capacity for changing as well as adapting to external conditions.[14]

These principles of ecological organization are what otherwise might be called the theoretical assumptions underlying the subject.[15] In addition to those indicated above, the present work incorporates several additional assumptions that are perhaps not so widely agreed upon by students of human ecology.

7. Man's activities are affected by *both* material conditions and ideas. This premise serves to avoid an overly deterministic view of the factors that affect variations in ecological relationships.[16]

8. Conflict, as indicated by " . . . discord and opposition between two or more actors within the process of social organization,"[17] is an intrinsic part of social life, and must be taken into account in explaining differential aspects of collective behavior.[18] In ecological analysis, conflict is most evident in terms of the criteria by which groups define optimal adjustment to environmental conditions and the means through which they seek to achieve ecological goals.

9. Finally, ecological analysis may be focused on two analytically distinct outcomes of ecological systems. On the one hand, survival may be evaluated in terms of *quantitative* criteria—e.g., the size of the population supported, the prevailing level of life expectancy for members of the collectivity, or the relative endurance of various components of the environment. On the other hand, interest may be focused on the *qualitative dimensions* of collective survival—e.g., investigations focused on various aspects of population composition or on air and water pollution would fall in this category.[19]

To summarize, then: the assumptions guiding this examination of human ecology suggest a focus on relationships between collectivities and their environments. These relationships are mediated through socially organized activities aimed at satisfying the requisites of collective survival. Several constraints intrinsic to ecological relationships give rise to variations in prevailing modes of collective adaptation as well as empirical outcomes, these being space, time, and the ubiquitous organizational features of social conflict and change.

While establishing the parameters within which ecological systems may be approached, these assumptions do not address the central question of how it is that collectivities are able to meet the requisites of prolonged survival. Critical to an understanding of this problem is the specification and analysis of those aspects of social organization that influence and mediate population-environment relationships. The following section is devoted to this task.

The Human Ecological System: An Adaptation Perspective

A number of more-or-less explicit models have been proposed for representing and explaining ecological relationships. [20] Though varying considerably in content and form, these models are characterized by two primary difficulties that diminish their utility in accounting for variations in ecological patterns. First, they frequently fail to recognize that the nature of the population system itself is an important factor affecting adjustment to environmental conditions. [21] Second, these models generally fail to specify the dynamics of the adjustment process—i.e., how it is that survival is actually achieved and how conditions that threaten survival are dealt with. [22] Recognition of these issues is an explicit feature of the model described below.

The concept of adaptation has been defined as the ability for a social organization to "change or elaborate its structure as a condition of survival or viability"[23] and, alternatively, as " . . . the development of generalized means for pursuing a variety of goals and for meeting a variety of environmental conditions as they fluctuate and evolve over time." [24] Adaptation as well as related terms such as adjustment and accommodation have been part of the vernacular of sociology for many years, although they do not appear to be among its core concepts. [25] On the other hand, conceptual frameworks for the study of human ecology frequently stress the central importance of adaptation as an ecological process. Thus Hawley has argued that "Communal adaptation constitutes the distinctive subject matter of ecology. . . . That the community is the essential adaptive Mechanism may be taken as the distinctive hypothesis of ecology." [26] More recently, Klausner has stated that "Adaptation is the most important dynamic concept in human ecology." [27] This perspective is perhaps most concisely illustrated in the following passage from the work of Otis Dudley Duncan:

"Society exists by virtue of the organization of a population of organisms, each of which is individually unequipped to survive in isolation. Organization represents an adaptation to the unavoidable circumstance that individuals are interdependent and that the collectivity of individuals must cope with concrete environmental conditions—including, perhaps, competition and resistance afforded by other collectivities— with whatever technological means may be at its disposal. The 'social bond', in its most basic aspect, is precisely this interdependence of units in a more or less elaborated division of labor, aptly described as a 'functional integration'. Societies differ because, among other things, each territorially delimited aggregate confronts a special set of environmental circumstances and differs from other such aggregates in size and composition. Even more important: since most environmental and demographic situations permit alternative solutions to the problems of adaptation and since such solutions have a tendency to persist as they are embodied in organizational forms and technical apparatus, initial differences tend to produce continuing diversification. An ecological account of social change is attempted by referring to such instigating factors as environmental change (whether caused by man or other agencies), changes in size and composition of population, introduction of new techniques, and shifts in the spatial disposition or organization of competing populations. The interdependence of factors in the adaptation of a population implies that change in any of them will set up ramifying changes in the others."[28]

A concern with the process of collective adaptation raises a number of analytic questions, the most basic of which are the following:

1. What are the conditions to which the collectivity adapts?
2. What does the process of adaptation entail? For example, is the result an alteration in the organization of the collectivity itself, or is it rather a transformation of the conditions provoking the necessity for adaptation?[29]
3. What organizational mechanisms does the collectivity have at its disposal for achieving adaptation?
4. Finally, what are the criteria by which the relative success of the adaptive process may be evaluated?

In order to guide the reader in applying these questions to the substantive issues of human ecology, Figure 1 is presented as a schematic representation of the human ecological system. It should be emphasized that this is not intended to constitute a theory of human ecology in that no substantive propositions are evident, though such propositions could be derived on the basis of these components and several additional assumptions regarding so-

Figure 1
Relationships among Components of the Human Ecological System

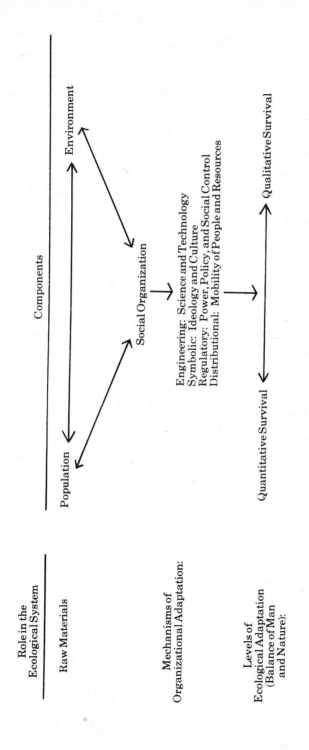

cietal goals. For the present this schema should be interpreted as a model, or perhaps a paradigm, which describes the structure of ecological systems and suggests relationships about which theoretical questions might be asked.[30]

From Figure 1 it is apparent that the human ecological system consists of three components: (1) the raw materials, (2) the mechanisms of organizational adaptation, and (3) the levels of ecological adaptation.

Raw Materials

The term raw materials implies that populations, their external environments, and the web of human relationships generally referred to as social organization constitute the basic elements of an ecological system, and this view is consistent with formulations of the general subject of ecology.[31] Each of these elements may be further subdivided into constituent structures and processes. The components of a population system are the basic processes of *fertility, mortality* and *migration*, and the structural features indicated by *population composition* (e.g., age, sex, marital status, race, occupation) and *population distribution*. The interaction of these constituent components determines the final feature of the system, population size.[32]

One finds much less agreement regarding the components of environmental systems, though they are generally described in terms of the things, conditions, and influences surrounding a given population.[33] For purposes of simplification one may divide the environment into its human and non-human components. The former would of course include all other human populations which are directly or indirectly consequential for the one in question. The non-human component may be further differentiated into natural and man-made phenomena. Included as elements of the natural environment are space, heat, available energy, mineral resources, water and food.[34] The man-made environment consists of man's living space—e.g., the buildings, recreational areas, streets and highways, towns, cities and regions he has carved out of the natural environment, as well as the synthetic materials he has created as substitutes for certain elements of that environment.[35]

The third fundamental component of the human ecological system is social organization, which may be defined as " . . . the process of merging social actors into ordered social relationships, which become infused with cultural ideas."[36] The structures of social organization consist of positions, roles, norms, groups, institutions, classes, and larger aggregates such as communities, nation-states and societies, while the processes are represented by activities and patterns of social interaction, the dynamic elements of organized human conduct.

The interaction of these three components, population, environment, and social organization, forms the basis for any human ecological system. The problematic issue lies in the nature of the interaction, whether this is considered at a single point in time or over a longer period. The central argument of the present conceptualization of human ecology is that the key to understanding ecological relationships is social organization, which stands in direct relationship to both populations and their environments and, moreover, serves to mediate relationships between the two. In fact, it is the ubiquitous presence of complex social organization and its emergent consequences that differentiates human ecological systems from those involving other forms of life. In contrast to non-human systems, neither population dynamics nor environmental conditions determine levels of ecological adaptation; rather, the primary causal relationships stem from variations in social organization.[37]

Mechanisms of Organizational Adaptation

As indicated earlier, the idea that social organization is crucial to man's ecological adaptation is certainly not new. What has been lacking, though, is a specification of those components of social organization that directly influence ecological relationships. Referring back to Figure 1, it may be seen that four mechanisms of organizational adaptation are proposed to serve this function. This concept may be defined as those organizational structures and processes through which population and/or environmental components are maintained, controlled or manipulated, resulting in an alteration in survival potential for the system as a whole. Stated otherwise, they consist of socially organized activities through which collectivities are able to influence the remaining components of the ecological system.

Four classes of adaptive mechanisms are singled out by reason of their impact on the ecological system. *Engineering mechanisms* [38] include the creative processes and discoveries of scientific activity as well as application of material technology developed from such activity. [39] It is hardly necessary to point out the adaptive potential inherent in science and technology. From the time of early man these have been highly consequential means for altering the conditions of human existence. [40] In recent years increasing attention has been given the social organizational bases and consequences of developments in science and technology, reflecting a growing concern that some or perhaps even many of the resulting changes create as many problems as they resolve. [41] An accurate assessment of contemporary ecological systems demands careful consideration of the variable effects of these engineering mechanisms.

Symbolic mechanisms include " . . . transmitted and created content and patterns of values, ideas, and other symbolic-meaningful systems as factors in the shaping of human behavior and the artifacts produced through behavior." [42] This dimension of human social organization is most frequently designated as culture, of which the key component is the process of "symboling". [43] It is through collectively recognized symbols that objective meanings are standardized, diffused, and transmitted from one generation to the next. Rather than viewing culture as determining the way of life in a society, it is more accurate to say that social values, norms, ideologies, customs, traditions, the entire range of shared meanings characteristic of the group, place *constraints* upon behavior. Referring specifically to social norms, Davis has argued that "They have arisen as a feature of cultural adaptation. . . . It is largely through them that [one's] conduct is regulated and integrated with the conduct of his fellows. It is through them that a society acquires a coherent structure and manages to get the business of group life tended to."[44] In many respects collective symbol systems may be viewed as developing in response to external conditions and historical experience. But this does not mean that they are always highly integrated or internally consistent. Indeed, as the exigencies of collective survival are subjected to increasingly rapid and drastic transformation, cultural systems may lose their adaptive quality.[45] As will be demonstrated in later Chapters, this is particularly evident with respect to contemporary ecological problems.

Regulatory mechanisms reflect the political dimensions of social organization—i.e., those processes that serve ". . . to combine sub-units into a societal unit, to make out of parts a whole, and to guide societal action toward the realization of societal values as expressed *via* the political processes."[46] Of central importance for understanding the capacity of a collectivity to regulate its internal organization, as well as its relationships with the external environment, is the concept of power, referring to the . . . "generalized capacity of an actor, in his relations with others, to reduce resistance in the course of action he prefers in a given field (i.e., in the presence of other actors) about a set of matters over a period of time."[47] The essence of power is the capacity for maintaining desirable conditions, altering those that are not so desirable, and generally controlling potentially disturbing influences. Reference to the preference and desirability attributes of power relationships suggests the importance of the purposes, goals or values, underlying the potential use of power. These criteria, which serve as generalized guides to action for the sub-units of a collectivity, are often formalized in terms of public or social policy.[48] Finally, the third dimension implicit in the concept of regulatory mechanisms is social control—i.e., "the achievement of modifications, or limitations of behavior of a group(s) or person(s) as a consequence of the actions—direct or indirect—of others."[49] In short, *policy* establishes formal guidelines for collective action, *power* constitutes the principal means through which policies are implemented, and *social control* is the intended result. Contemporary societies increasingly rely upon regulatory mechanisms in attempting to maximize conditions optimal for survival.[50] This proposition is no less true when one specifically considers problems of ecological adaptation.

The three mechanisms of organizational adaptation described thus far are widely recognized by students of social organization and are typically given considerable attention in any thorough treatment of the subject. The final mode of adaptation to be treated here, distributional mechanisms, is more typically limited to ecologically oriented discussions, though it will be suggested below that wider application is both possible and useful. *Distributional mechanisms* are composed of collective processes that result in the relocation of components of an ecological system in social and/or physical space. [51] These processes may be a consequence of purposively calculated strategies or they may result from sub-social forces inherent in the on-going process of social organization. [52] Distributional mechanisms take three principal forms. First, people may be redistributed through migration from one geographic location to another or through social mobility—i.e., movement among recognized categories of social status. [53] Second, the environment itself may be redistributed, as when natural resources and produced goods are exchanged and consumed. Since the materials necessary to sustain human life are generally available in limited supply, there is a " . . . constant process of human activity in which goods are produced, distributed, exchanged, and consumed in a constant economic battle against scarcity." [54] Third, units of social organization—e.g., institutions and activities—may themselves be redistributed. [55] The generalized adaptive significance of these forms of distribution and redistribution is that the balance between population, the environment, and socially organized activities may be altered such that the potential for collective survival is affected.

Since the preceding discussion of organizational adaptation was necessarily brief, two notes of caution are in order. First, the adaptive mechanisms identified do not include all those that can potentially operate within a social organization, nor are they necessarily the most useful analytic devices for the entire range of empirical problems. Other proponents of the adaptation frame of reference have identified alternative organizational sources of adaptation, and the critical reader should consult these models as well. [56] Moreover, the particular adaptive mechanisms emphasized here were selected specifically because of their impact, real as well as potential, on demographic and environmental phenomena. Were our concern here with organizational adaptation to the threat of attack by other populations, for example, the substance of the analytic model might have been different. Second, though each adaptive mechanism was discussed separately, only for analytic purposes may they be considered mutually exclusive. In the day-to-day process of social organization, the operation of each mechanism is influenced to some extent by each of the others. For example, the implementation of innovations in science and technology is affected by cultural norms and ideologies as well as collective decisions eminating from the political process. Likewise the redistribution of population and resources is partially dependent upon political decisions and developments in science and technology. Without reviewing all possible variations in the interrelationships among these adaptive mechanisms, the point is quite clear: at any point in time a given social organization is likely to be utilizing all four forms in the quest for survival, and the analytical issue becomes one of identifying the overall consequences of each as well as their interactive effects.

Levels of Ecological Adaptation
Having considered two components of the human ecological system, the raw materials and the mechanisms of organizational adaptation, we may now turn to the final element in the model, i.e., levels of ecological adaptation. This concept represents the various outcomes of the influence of the adaptive mechanisms on population and environmental phenomena. From Figure 1 it is evident that ecological adaptation may be evaluated from three points of view: quantitative, qualitative, and the overall balance between population and environment.

Consider first the population dimension, where the question of quantitative variation is at least as old as recorded history. [57] The primary issue has centered around the implications of population size and the rate of population growth for human welfare. Although at times the concern has been that populations were not large enough and/or were increasing too slowly, [58] more recently attention has been directed toward the advantages of smaller and less rapidly growing populations. [59] Within this context more specific inquiries have been developed regarding the components of population growth, especially fertility and mortality. [60] Historical experience indicates that mortality has been much more susceptible to control through human intervention than fertility but, paradoxically, levels of fertility have a much greater impact on rates of population growth. [61] Issues of quantitative survival with respect to population, then, deal with such matters as how many people are living at a given time, how rapidly their numbers are increasing over time, how frequently they are reproducing, how many are dying during a given time interval, and how long members of the population may be expected to live.

In recent years attention has been increasingly directed toward population quality. Unfortunately there is little agreement as to the substantive meaning of this concept. For some writers it refers to " . . . the level attained regarding various personal and social characteristics." [62] This is simply another way of defining population composition. Closely related to this view is the subject of eugenics, concerned with maximizing "desirable" traits in a population and minimizing "undesirable" ones through selective breeding. [63] Recently the meaning of population quality has been further broadened to convey a concern with the overall quality of life as it is influenced by quantitative factors. [64] From this perspective, problems of health, housing, education and family life, among others, emerge as important evaluative criteria. [65] It is impossible to speak of population quality, however the concept is defined, without making invidious distinctions among the various qualitative levels. Though the logic underlying such comparisons may seem reasonable, if not always apparent, to most observers, there are still many unresolved issues in formulating a universally acceptable classification of population quality.

We may now turn to the environmental side of the model. Once again it is evident that quantitative issues have received earlier and more extensive attention than qualitative ones. [66] Stemming from the pessimistic predictions of Malthus, [67] concern has been focused on whether the supply of resources necessary for sustaining the human population is available in sufficient quantity. Confounding this issue is the fact that many of these resources are renewable, while others can be replaced by substitute materials. It is now generally agreed that the qualitative aspect of the environment is a much more critical concern—e.g., " . . . the increasing pollution of water courses, the atmosphere, and the land itself, to the detriment of human and animal health, as well as to an aesthetically pleasing natural environment." [68] The general focus is on how the non-human environment is used, exploited, and transformed by man, and on the consequences of these activities for future environments. [69] As with population quality, any assessment of environmental quality is dependent upon relative goals and priorities, which are often only vaguely defined and frequently in conflict with one another.

Of course the problem of assessing levels of adaptation in human ecological systems is considerably more complex than is evident from the preceding discussion. Criteria for evaluation change over time and there is still little agreement regarding realistic possibilities for achieving optimal conditions for survival. But as Paul Sears has suggested

"Probably men will always differ as to what constitutes the good life. They need not differ as to what is necessary for the long survival of man on earth. Assuming that this is our wish, the conditions are clear enough. As living beings we must come to terms with the environment about us, learning to get along with the liberal budget at our disposal, promoting rather than disrupting those great cycles of nature—of water movement, energy flow, and material transformation that have made life itself possible. As a physical goal we must seek to attain what I have called a steady state. The achievement of an efficient dynamic equilibrium between man and his environment must always, in itself, have the challenge and the charm of an elusive goal." [70]

The task at hand, then, is to determine how man can structure his activities so as to most closely approximate this steady state, the elusive balance between man and nature.

Concluding Remarks

This Introduction has presented an analytic scheme for understanding human ecological systems. Emphasis has been placed on the role of selected aspects of social organization in the process of adapting to the exigencies of collective survival. The remainder of this volume is devoted to an explication of the model outlined in this introductory statement.

Notes and References

1. Mattie Dogan and Stein Rokkan, eds., *Quantitative Ecological Analysis in the Social Sciences*. Cambridge, Mass.: Massachusetts Institute of Technology Press, 1969, p. 4.

2. For example, see Roger G. Barker, *Ecological Psychology: Concepts and Methods for Studying the Environment of Human Behavior*. Stanford, Cal.: Stanford University Press, 1968; and Kenneth H. Craik, "Environmental Psychology," in *New Directions in Psychology 4*. New York: Holt, Rinehart and Winston, Inc., 1970, pp. 1-21.

3. Perhaps the most persuasive statement of this point of view is found in Otis D. Duncan and Leo F. Schnore, "Cultural, Behavioral, and Ecological Perspectives for the Study of Social Organization," *American Journal of Sociology*, Vol. 65 (September 1959), pp. 132-146.

4. See Robert E. Park, "Human Ecology," *American Journal of Sociology*, Vol. 42 (July 1936), p. 1-15.

5. For example, see Milla Aissa Alihan, *Social Ecology*. New York: Columbia University Press, 1938; and Walter Firey, *Land Use in Central Boston*. Cambridge, Mass.: Harvard University Press, 1947.

6. The best example is Amos H. Hawley, *Human Ecology: A Theory of Community Structure*. New York: The Ronald Press, 1950.

7. See Otis D. Duncan, "Social Organization and the Ecosystem," in Robert E. L. Faris, ed., *Handbook of Modern Sociology*. Chicago: Rand McNally Co., 1964, pp. 37-82.

8. One of the major problems inhibiting the development of cumulative theories and models of the social sciences is the over-emphasis on and much greater recognition for novel and unique explanations. We have yet to develop many paradigms of the type discussed by Thomas Kuhn in his illuminating work, *The Structure of Scientific Revolutions*. Chicago: University of Chicago Press, 1962. For a discussion of one set of ideas which *has* been subjected to cumulative revision, see James D. Miley and Michael Micklin, "Structural Change and the Durkheimian Legacy: A Macro-Social Analysis of Suicide Rates," *American Journal of Sociology*, Vol. 78 (November 1972), pp. 657-73.

9. R. D. McKenzie, "The Ecological Approach to the Study of the Human Community" in Robert E. Park, E. W. Burgess, and R. D. McKenzie, *The City*. Chicago: University of Chicago Press, 1925, pp. 63-64; James A. Quinn, *Human Ecology*. New York: Prentice-Hall, Inc., 1950, p. 3; Otis D. Duncan, "Human Ecology and Population Studies," in Philip M. Hauser and Otis D. Duncan, eds., *The Study of Population*. Chicago: University of Chicago Press, 1959, p. 681; and Otis D. Duncan, 1964, op. cit., p. 41.

10. Amos H. Hawley, 1950, op. cit., pp. 77-79; Otis D. Duncan, 1959, *Ibid*, p. 681; and Otis D. Duncan and Leo F. Schnore, op. cit., p. 144.

11. Otis D. Duncan, 1959, op. cit., pp. 682-83 and 1964, op. cit., p. 48; and Otis D. Duncan and Leo F. Schnore, 1959, op. cit., p. 144.

12. R. D. McKenzie, 1925, op. cit., p. 64; Walter Firey, 1945, op. cit., p. 3; Amos H. Hawley, 1950, op. cit., pp. 68-69; Otis D. Duncan and Leo F. S hnore, 1959, op. cit., p. 136. For a review of many earlier studies concentrating on spatial variations of ecological phenomena see George A. Theodorson, ed., *Studies in Human Ecology*. Evanston, Illinois: Row, Peterson and Co., 1961.

13. R. D. McKenzie, 1925, op. cit., pp. 72-79; Amos H. Hawley, 1950, op. cit., p. 72; and Otis D. Duncan and Leo F. Schnore, 1959, op. cit., pp. 136-37.

14. R. D. McKenzie, 1925, op. cit., p. 71; Amos H. Hawley, 1950, op. cit., pp. 319-23; Otis D. Duncan, 1959, op. cit., p. 682 and 1964, op. cit., pp. 45ff.; and Otis D. Duncan and Leo F. Schnore, 1959, op. cit., p. 142.

15. For a discussion of the importance and utility of specifying theoretical assumptions see Gideon Sjoberg and Roger Nett, *A Methodology for Social Research*. New York: Harper and Row, Publishers, 1968, pp. 58-69. For an instructive example see Amitai Etzioni, *The Active Society: A Theory of Societal and Political Processes*. New York: The Free Press, 1968, pp. 60-93.

16. The "materialist" approach to human ecology is exemplified by Jack P. Gibbs and Walter T. Martin, "Toward a Theoretical System of Human Ecology," *Pacific Sociological Review*, Vol. 2 (Spring 1959), pp. 29-36 (reprinted in Chapter 1 of this volume) and Otis D. Duncan and Leo F. Schnore, 1959, op. cit. The "idealist" position is represented by Walter Firey, "Sentiment and Symbolism as Ecological Variables," *American Sociological Review*, Vol. 10 (April 1945), pp. 140-48 and *Land Use in Central Boston*, 1947, op. cit., and Sidney M. Wilhelm, *Urban Zoning and Land-Use Theory*. New York: The Free Press of Glencoe, 1962. For an insightful critique and comparison of these and other theories of human ecology and urban sociology see Gideon Sjoberg, "Theory and Research in Urban Sociology," in Philip M. Hauser and Leo F. Schnore, eds., *The Study of Urbanization*. New York: John Wiley and Sons, 1965, pp. 157-89.

17. Marvin E. Olsen, *The Process of Social Organization*. New York: Holt, Rinehart and Winston, 1968, p. 134.

18. T. B. Bottomore, "Sociological Theory and the Study of Social Conflict," in J. C. McKinney and E. A. Tiryakian, eds., *Theoretical Sociology: Perspectives and Developments*. New York: Appleton-Century-Crofts, 1970, pp. 138-53. Also see Garhard Lenski, *Power and Privilege: A Theory of Social Stratification*. New York: McGraw-Hill Book Co., 1966, p. 34 and Marvin E. Olsen, 1958, op. cit., pp. 133-56. A similar assumption, based upon the more inclusive concept of "tension," is suggested by Walter Buckley in his *Sociology and Modern Systems Theory*. Englewood Cliffs, N. J.: Prentice-Hall, Inc., 1967, pp. 51-52. For an overview of contemporary approaches to conflict see Clagett G. Smith, ed., *Conflict Resolution: Contributions of the Behavioral Sciences*. Notre Dame, Indiana: University of Notre Dame Press, 1971.

19. An adequate assessment of any set of ecological relationships would of course include both quantitative and qualitative questions. The predominant emphasis has been on the quantitative dimensions of human survival; e.g., see Hawley, 1950, op. cit., pp. 149-74. In recent years attention has been turned more explicitly to qualitative criteria. See Lynton K. Caldwell, *Environment: A Challenge to Modern Society*. Garden City, N. Y.: The Natural History Press, 1970, pp. 27-62 and Joseph L. Fisher and Neal Potter, "The Effects of Population Growth on Resource Adequacy and Quality," in *Rapid Population Growth: Consequences and Policy Implications*. Baltimore and London: Johns Hopkins University Press, 1971, pp. 222-72.

20. Amos H. Hawley, 1950, op. cit.; Jack P. Gibbs and Walter T. Martin, 1959, op. cit.; Otis D. Duncan and Leo F. Schnore, 1959, op. cit., and Otis D. Duncan, 1964, op. cit.

21. This charge is not true of Gibbs and Martin who explicitly state that " . . . the sheer size of a population and its biological composition (sex and age) on the one hand set minimal sustenance needs of the population, and on the other fix the limits of the manpower resources for an organized effort to obtain these needs." *Ibid*, p. 33.

22. In most cases this problem lies in the tendency to treat "organization" as an undifferentiated concept and thus lose sight of the various activity complexes through which collective survival is made possible.

23. Walter Buckley, "Society as a Complex Adaptive System," in Walter Buckley, ed., *Modern Systems Research for the Behavioral Scientist*. Chicago: Aldine Publishing Co., 1968, p. 490.

24. Leon Mayhew, *Society: Institutions and Activity*. Glenview, Illinois: Scott, Foresman and Co., 1971, p. 28.

25. See, for example, Robert E. Park and Ernest W. Burgess, *Introduction to the Science of Sociology*. Chicago: University of Chicago Press, 1921, pp. 663-65; Talcott Parsons, *The Social System*. Glencoe, Illinois: The Free Press, 1951, pp. 167-69 and "An Outline of the Social System," in Talcott Parsons, Edward Shils, Kaspar D. Naegele, and Jesse R. Pitts, eds., *Theories of Society*, Vol. 1. New York: The Free Press of Glencoe, Inc., 1961, pp. 39-41; Walter Buckley, 1967, 1968, pp. 490-513, op. cit., and James D. Thompson and Donald R. Van Houten, *The Behavioral Sciences: An Interpretation*. Reading, Massachusetts: Addison-Wesley Publishing Co., 1970, pp. 211-46. Useful discussions of this concept have recently appeared in the work of anthropologists. See John Bennett, *Northern Plainsmen: Adaptive Strategy and Agrarian Life*. Chicago: Aldine Publishing Co., 1969, pp. 9-25 and Richard N. Adams, *Crucifixion by Power: Essays on Guatemalan National Social Structure, 1944-1966*. Austin: University of Texas Press, 1970, pp. 70-82.

26. Amos H. Hawley, 1950, op. cit., p. 31.

27. Samuel F. Klausner, *On Man in This Environment*. San Francisco: Jossey-Bass, Inc., 1971, p. 27.

28. Otis D. Duncan, 1959, op. cit., p. 683.

29. See Yehudi A. Cohen, ed., *Man in Adaptation: The Institutional Framework*. Chicago: Aldine Publishing Co., 1971, p. 4.

30. On the difference between "theories" and "models" see Mae Brodbeck, "Models, Meaning, and Theories," in Llewellyn Gross, ed., *Symposium on Sociology Theory*. New York: Harper and Row, 1959, pp. 373-403. For a discussion of the use of paradigms in sociological analysis see Robert K. Merton, *Social Theory and Social Structure*, rev. ed., New York: The Free Press of Glencoe, 1957, pp. 13-16.

31. For example, see Eugene P. Odum, *Fundamentals of Ecology*, 3rd ed. Philadelphia: W. B. Saunders Co., 1971, pp. 3-6.

32. A quite readable discussion of population systems is contained in Calvin Goldscheider, *Population, Modernization and Social Structure*. Boston: Little, Brown and Co., 1971, pp. 8-20. For a slightly variant and more technical presentation see Norman Ryder, "Notes on the Concept of a Population," *American Journal of Sociology*, Vol. 69 (March 1964), pp. 447-63.

33. Lynton K. Caldwell, 1971, op. cit., pp. 4-7. Also see F. Fraser Darling, "A Wider Environment of Ecology and Conservation," *Daedalus*, Vol. 96 (Fall 1967), pp. 1003-19; William W. Murdoch, "Ecological Systems," in W. W. Murdoch, ed., *Environment: Resources, Pollution and Society*. Stamford, Conn.: Sinauer Associates Inc., Publishers, 1971, pp. 1-28; and Ira J. Winn, ed., *Basic Issues in Environment*. Columbus, Ohio: Charles E. Merrill Publishing Co., 1972.

34. See Paul R. Ehrlich and Ann H. Ehrlich, *Population, Resources, Environment: Issues in Human Ecology*. San Francisco: W. H. Freeman and Co., 1970, pp. 51-80.

35. For an intricate classification and analysis of human settlement systems see C. A. Doxiadis, *Ekistics: An Introduction to the Science of Human Settlements*. London: Oxford University Press, 1968.

36. Marvin E. Olsen, op. cit., p. 3.

37. However, as indicated by the two-directional arrows in Figure 1, this model does not posit a completely deterministic system. Population and environmental characteristics alike exert some influence on social organization and thus place some limitation on its adaptive potential. For example, an already large and rapidly growing population is a decided obstacle to attempts to reinstate a balance between man and nature through socially organized strategies for economic development, as indicated in Ansley J. Coale and Edgar M. Hoover, *Population Growth and Economic Development in Low Income Countries*. Princeton, N. J.: Princeton University Press, 1958. Likewise, though certainly not advocating environmental determinism, one must recognize that "It is the physical environment that sets the possibilities for and the limitations of cultural development. Nature poses the problems for man, who is an animal that must live on earth. He must sustain himself with resources of the earth, and it is only within the range of potentialities presented by these resources that man can develop his culture. If the environment were too hostile, man would not survive; and it is certain that man puts his species in danger of extinction if he reproduces in numbers far beyond the potentiality of the earth to support." Richard A. Watson and Patty Jo Watson, *Man and Nature: An Anthropological Essay in Human Ecology*. New York: Harcourt, Brace and World, Inc., 1969, pp. 160-61.

38. Otis D. Duncan, 1964, op. cit., pp. 63-64, has suggested that the scientific-technological character of industrial society may be conveniently symbolized by the increasing significance of a single occupational role: the engineer.

39. Some writers would include science and technology within the scope of the concept of culture—e.g., this position is clearly evident in Yehudi A. Cohen, "Culture as Adaptation," in Y. A. Cohen, ed., *Man in Adaptation: The Cultural Present*. Chicago: Aldine Publishing Co., 1968, pp. 40-60. The strategy adopted here with reference to the specification of adaptive mechanisms has been to separate the material and the symbolic dimensions of culture, including the former under "engineering mechanisms" and the latter under "symbolic mechanisms," to be discussed below. This procedure is also followed by Marvin E. Olsen, 1968, op. cit., p. 57. Likewise, the knowledge upon which science is based would be part of symbolic culture, but the social organizational process of creating and utilizing scientific knowledge is more appropriately an engineering mechanism. See Leslie A. White, "Science is Sciencing," in L. A. White, *The Science of Culture*. New York: The Grove Press, 1949, pp. 3-21 (originally published 1938).

40. For example, see Francis R. Allen, Hornell Hart, Delbert C. Miller, William F. Ogburn, and Meyer F. Nimkoff, *Technology and Social Change*. New York: Appleton-Century-Crofts, 1957.

41. See Wilbert E. Moore, *The Impact of Industry*. Englewood Cliffs, N. J.: Prentice-Hall, Inc., 1965; Richard L. Meier, *Science and Economic Development: New Patterns of Living*, 2nd ed. Cambridge, Mass.: The MIT Press, 1966, pp. 144-249; Emanuel G. Mesthene, *Technological Change: Its Impact on Man and Society*, New York: New American Library, 1970; and Albert H. Teich, ed., *Technology and Man's Future*. New York: St. Martin's Press, 1972.

42. Alfred L. Kroeber and Talcott Parsons, "The Concepts of Culture and Social System," *American Sociological Review*, Vol. 23 (August 1958), pp. 582-83.

43. See Leslie A. White, "The Symbol: The Origin and Basis of Human Behavior," in L. A. White, *The Science of Culture*. New York: The Grove Press, 1949, pp. 22-39 and "Man and Culture," in L. A. White, *The Evolution of Culture*. New York: McGraw-Hill Book Co., 1959, pp. 3-32; and Fremont Shull and Andre Del Beque, "Norms, A Feature of Symbolic Culture," in William J. Gore and J. W. Dyson, eds., *The Making of Decisions: A Reader in Administrative Behavior*. New York: The Free Press of Glencoe, 1964, pp. 242-75.

44. Kingsley Davis, *Human Society*. New York: The MacMillan Co., 1949, p. 79. Cf. Marvin E. Olsen, 1968, op. cit., pp. 52-63.

45. For illustrations, see the discussion of "cultural lag" in William F. Ogburn, *Social Change*. New York: Dell Publishing Co., 1966, pp. 200-80 (originally published 1922) and "Cultural Lag as a Theory," *Sociology and Social Research*, Vol. 41 (January-February 1957), pp. 167-74.

46. Amitai Etzioni, 1968, op. cit., p. 76.

47. *Ibid.* pp. 314-15. Cf. Leon Mayhew, 1971, op. cit.; p. 127; Marvin E. Olsen, 1968, op. cit., p. 172; and Harold D. Lasswell and Abraham Kaplan, *Power and Society: A Framework for Political Inquiry*. New Haven, Conn.: Yale University Press, 1950, pp. 75-77.

48. See Martin Rein, *Social Policy: Issues of Choice and Change*. New York: Random House, 1970, pp. 3-20.

49. Paul E. Mott, "Power, Authority, and Influence," in Michael Aiken and Paul E. Mott, eds., *The Structure of Community Power*. New York: Random House, 1970, p. 4.

50. Perhaps the most exhaustive analysis of the processes employed is contained in Amitai Etzioni, 1968, op. cit. The non-professional reader is advised to consult the condensation and simplification of Etzioni's argument in Warren Breed, *The Self-Guiding Society*. New York: The Free Press, 1971.

51. An insightful discussion of distributional phenomena and their measurement is contained in Roderick D. McKenzie, "The Scope of Human Ecology," *American Journal of Sociology*, Vol. 32 (July 1926), reprinted in Amos H. Hawley, ed., *Roderick D. McKenzie on Human Ecology*. Chicago: University of Chicago Press, 1968, pp. 19-32.

52. The latter position was especially emphasized in the work of representatives of the "classical school" of human ecology, e.g., Robert E. Park, Ernest W. Burgess, and Roderick D. McKenzie.

53. See Maurice Halbwachs, *Population and Society: Introduction to Social Morphology*, trans. O. D. Duncan and H. W. Pfautz. Glencoe, Ill.: The Free Press, 1960, pp. 108-17 (Originally published 1938) and Leo F. Schnore, "Social Mobility in Demographic Perspective," *American Sociological Review*, Vol. 26 (June 1961), pp. 407-23.

54. Leon Mayhew, 1971, op. cit., p. 93. See also Neil J. Smelser, *The Sociology of Economic Life*. Englewood Cliffs, N. J.: Prentice-Hall, Inc., 1963, pp. 86-98.

55. This phenomenon was a primary concern evident in the work of the "classical" ecologists. See Robert E. L. Faris, *Chicago Sociology: 1920-1932*. San Francisco: Chandler Publishing Co., 1967, pp. 64-87. A theoretical justification for such an emphasis is presented in Roderick D. McKenzie, "The Ecology of Institutions," in Amos H. Hawley, ed., 1968, op. cit., pp. 102-17 (originally written about 1936).

56. Cf. Walter Buckley, 1967, 1968, op. cit.; John Bennett, 1969, op. cit.; and Richard N. Adams, 1970, op. cit.

57. See E. P. Hutchinson, *The Population Debate: The Development of Conflicting Theories up to 1900*. Boston: Houghton Mifflin Co., 1967.

58. An example is Joseph J. Spengler, *France Faces Depopulation*. Durham, N. C.: Duke University Press, 1938.

59. See the essays contained in *Rapid Population Growth*, 1971, op. cit. and Philip M. Hauser, ed., *The Population Dilemma*, 2nd ed. Englewood Cliffs, N. J.: Prentice-Hall, Inc., 1969.

60. For example, see Nathan Keyfitz, "Changes of Birth and Death Rates and Their Demographic Effects," in *Rapid Population Growth*, 1971, op. cit., pp. 639-80.

61. For an interesting empirical analysis of these relationships see Eduardo E. Arriaga, *Mortality Decline and Its Demographic Effects in Latin America*. Population Monograph Series, No. 6. Berkeley, California: Institute of International Studies, University of California, 1970.

62. Ralph Thomlinson, *Population Dynamics*. New York: Random House, Inc., 1965, p. 380

63. *Ibid*. pp. 380-88.

64. This is a central theme in Shirley Foster Hartley's *Population: Quantity vs. Quality*. Englewood Cliffs, N. J.: Prentice-Hall, Inc., 1972.

65. See *Rapid Population Growth*, 1971, op. cit., pp. 16-69.

66. See Joseph L. Fisher and Neal Potter, "Natural Resource Adequacy for the United States and the World," in P. M. Hauser, ed., 1969, op. cit., pp. 106-38 and "The Effects of Population Growth on Resource Adequacy and Quality," in *Rapid Population Growth*, 1971, op. cit., pp. 222-44.

67. See Thomas Robert Malthus, *On Population*, ed. Gertrude Himmelfarb. New York: The Modern Library, 1960 (originally published 1798 and 1872).

68. Joseph L. Fisher and Neal Potter, 1971, op. cit., p. 222.

69. See F. Fraser Darling and John P. Milton, eds., *Future Environments of North America: Transformation of a Continent*. New York: Natural History Press, 1966.

70. Paul B. Sears, "The Steady State: Physical Choice and Moral Law," *The Key Reporter*, Vol. 24 (January 1959). Reprinted in Paul Shepard and Daniel McKinley, eds., *The Subversive Science: Essays Toward an Ecology of Man*. Boston: Houghton Mifflin Co., 1969, p. 401.

Part I

**Ecological Adaptation:
Organizational Perspectives**

1 Organization for Survival: An Ecological Problem

Chapter 1 contains three selections that bear upon the adaptive problems of collective survival and their role in the study of human ecology. Hawley's article provides a brief overview of the development of the discipline as well as its central concepts and assumptions. In relation to the conceptual scheme presented above, Hawley similarly argues that populations must collectively adapt to their environments. Furthermore, he suggests that "organization arises from the interaction of population and environment," which is close to the view presented earlier that population, environment and social organization constitute the raw materials of collective ecological adaptation. It should be noted that in this essay Hawley departs from his earlier view[1] that the community should be the central unit of observation in ecological analysis; here he substitutes the term "social system" in recognition of the potentially confusing limitations of the former term.

In pointing out the indeterminacy of the human being's capacity to adapt, Hawley fails to give adequate emphasis to an important point: collectively, through socially organized activities, man greatly increases his ability to control and change the conditions of his existence. A set of principles of ecological organization are presented to further specify the means of collective adaptation. In some respects these overlap with the survival mechanisms indicated in the Introduction to the present volume. While Hawley's conceptual framework does clarify the matter somewhat, it tends to be a little confusing. For example, interdependence and differentiation are variable conditions of organization in a generic sense and do not clearly specify concrete means (or mechanisms) through which ecological adaptation may be achieved. The "principle of the key function" comes closer to getting at these mechanisms, but the functions themselves are never clearly identified. Dominance, rather than being considered on the same level of abstraction as the other principles, is more properly a type of key function, or in terms of the conceptual framework upon which the present book is based, a regulatory mechanism.

A further problem is seen in Hawley's consideration of ecological change. He implies that change is due to the fact that the environment is always in some state of flux. But this ignores changes inherent in the population itself, which are often independent of environmental change—e.g., changes in fertility, mortality, or migration rates. However, this observation does not negate Hawley's recognition of the importance of change in ecological adaptation.

Hawley's contribution is important for its emphasis on (1) the collective nature of ecological adaptation, (2) the interdependent relationships among population, environment, and social organization, (3) the recognition of a set of principles which determine variations in ecological organization, and (4) the importance of change, especially its cumulative and multi-phasic qualities. Further insight into the conceptual and theoretical development of human ecology may be gained from consideration of the second article in this chapter.

Gibbs and Martin argue that the central focus of the discipline ought to be on causes and consequences of variations in modes of sustenance organization. They present a theoretical system—actually a frame of reference[2]—for organizing the subject matter of human ecology. Essential to this position, like that of Hawley, is the assumption that "man survives through collective organization" and, as a consequence, human ecologists ought to be primarily concerned with phenomena at the societal level.

In developing their frame of reference the authors point up the importance of connecting mechanisms, or factors that determine the survival of populations, but they argue that these operate independently of cultural values and the individual motives of men. Here I must take issue with Gibbs and Martin from two points of view, one empirical, the other conceptual. First, there is considerable evidence to suggest that variations in cultural orientations (whether these be identified as norms, values, ideologies, or sentiments) do influence modes of collective survival, especially when one considers qualitative as well as quantitative dimensions.[3] Second, it is a mistake to view such factors as primarily individual phenomena. At the organizational level there exist what Durkheim called collective representations,[4] or, as Bohannen has translated the term, conventional understandings.[5] In sociological terms these are social norms, that serve to regulate and order human conduct by means of collectively communicated and agreed-upon symbols that define the parameters and boundaries of acceptable behavior.[6] *If* Gibbs and Martin are referring to individual representations[7] or purely private norms,[8] they are probably correct in excluding them from the domain of human ecology; but if they include the entire range of psychological phenomena, specifically what Durkheim referred to as collective psychology,[9] the validity of their position is dubious indeed. As indicated in the introduction, and amplified later in this book, collective symbols[10] play an important role in determining strategies and outcomes in man's struggle for survival.[11]

The foregoing comments are in no way meant to detract from the important contributions to human ecology contained in the Gibbs-Martin argument. Rather, they are included to indicate a point of departure from the frame of reference guiding my view of the subject. The primary significance of this second article is evident in: (1) the attempt to develop a theoretically based approach to the subject matter, (2) the emphasis on collective survival as a focus on attention, (3) the specification of a series of connecting mechanisms linking conditions with consequences, and (4) the rejection of purely descriptive views of human ecology, which deal with the spatial distribution of various phenomena.

The articles by Hawley and by Gibbs and Martin, while developing a broad picture of organizational adaptation as the central focus of human ecology, perhaps leave the reader with the impression that adaptation is a relatively unproblematic process, characterized by an increasingly desirable balance between man and nature. Certainly Hawley's contention that ecological systems approximate a state of equilibrium, though subject to continuous change, might give this impression. Unfortunately, such is not the case. Some of the potential problems and unforeseen consequences of adaptation are examined in the final selection in this chapter taken from the work of Rene Dubos. Though focused more on problems of individual adaptation, Dubos' comments often reflect a concern with the social mechanisms crucial to collective survival. Thus he states that human evolution will have to depend even more than in the past on cultural and social evolution. Central to Dubos' argument is the distinction between "adaptedness" and "adaptability," suggesting that any species, including man, must be able to adjust to changing conditions if it is to endure.

Several examples of the paradoxical nature of man's efforts to ensure survival are pointed out. On the one hand "there is no foreseeable limit to the variety and extent of the social adaptive mechanisms that man can bring to bear on the external world, in order to modify it according to his needs and wishes," but on the other, "the potential ability of mankind to survive crowding, emotional misery, environmental pollution, shortages of natural resources, and other kinds of environmental threats constitutes but a limited aspect of the problem of adaptation." Here Dubos begins to suggest some of the potentially deleterious and undesirable long-run consequences of more immediate solutions to problems of collective survival. Perhaps more important, though not dealt with by Dubos, are conflicts among various adaptive mechanisms *at the same point in time*. Thus, to draw upon the frame of reference suggested earlier, interests manifested in the operation of power and political decision-making may be quite contrary to collective cultural ideology, as when public laws facilitate the depletion of natural resources in spite of public norms which support their conservation. In short, though man's potential for ecological adaptation appears to be unlimited, his strategies for achieving this goal often show a lack of consistent organization. The main contribution of Dubos' discussion is to draw our attention to this problem.

Notes and References

1. Amos H. Hawley, *Human Ecology: A Theory of Community Structure*. New York: The Ronald Press, 1950.

2. To view this statement as a theoretical system is a bit premature, since no empirically testable propositions are generated. It is only fair to note, though, that Gibbs, in collaboration with Martin as well as others, has further developed this initial frame of reference in terms of a series of empirical studies which do test derived propositions. For example, see Jack P. Gibbs and Walter T. Martin, "Urbanization and Natural Resources: A Study

in Organizational Ecology," *American Sociological Review*, Vol. 23 (June 1958), pp. 266-277 (included in this volume, Chapter 7) and "Urbanization, Technology and the Division of Labor: International Patterns," *American Sociological Review*, Vol. 27 (October 1962), pp. 669-677; Sanford Labovitz and Jack P. Gibbs, "Urbanization, Technology, and the Division of Labor: Further Evidence," *Pacific Sociological Review*, Vol. 7 (Spring 1964), pp. 3-8; and Jack P. Gibbs and Harley L. Browning, "The Division of Labor, Technology, and the Organization of Production in Twelve Countries," *American Sociological Review*, Vol. 31 (February 1968), pp. 81-92.

3. Some of the supporting evidence is explicitly recognized by Gibbs and Martin, though they choose to disregard it, probably resulting from a confusion of the second point I discuss, below. See Milla Aissa Alihan, *Social Ecology: A Critical Analysis*, New York: Columbia University Press, 1938; Walter Firey, *Land Use in Central Boston*, Cambridge: Harvard University Press, 1945 and "Sentiment and Symbolism as Ecological Variables," *American Sociological Review*, Vol. 10 (April 1945), pp. 140-148; Christen T. Jonassen, "Cultural Variables in the Ecology of an Ethnic Group," *American Sociological Review*, Vol. 14 (February 1949); Sidney Wilhelm and Gideon Sjoberg, "Economic Versus Protective Values in Urban Land Use Change," *American Journal of Economics and Sociology*, Vol. 19 (January 1960), pp. 151-160; Lynn White, Jr., "The Historical Roots of Our Ecologic Crisis," *Science*, Vol. 155 (March 10, 1967), pp. 1203-07; William H. Michelson, *Man and His Urban Environment: A Sociological Approach.* Reading, Mass,: Addison-Wesley Publishing Co., 1970, esp. pp. 131-47; as well as the selections included in Chapter 5 of the present volume.

4. Emile Durkheim, "Individual and Collective Representations," in *Sociology and Philosophy*, trans. D. F. Pecock. Glencoe, Ill.: The Free Press, 1953, pp. 1-34. (Originally published in *Revue de Mexaphysique et de Morale*, Vol. 6 [May 1898].) For Durkheim these collective representations are " . . . produced by the action and reaction between individual minds that form the society, [though they] do not derive directly from latter and consequently surpass them." *Ibid*, pp. 24-25. He goes on to say that "While one might perhaps contest the statement that all social facts without exception impose themselves from without upon the individual, the doubt does not seem possible as regards religious beliefs and practices, the rules of morality and the innumerable precepts of law—that is to say, all the most characteristic manifestations of collective life." *Ibid*, p. 26. Also see Talcott Parsons, *The System of Modern Societies*. Englewood Cliffs, N. J.: Prentice-Hall, Inc., 1971, pp. 6 and 9.

5. Paul Bohannan, " 'Collective Conscience' and Culture," in Emile Durkheim et al., *Essays on Sociology and Philosophy*. Ed. Kurt H. Wolff. New York: Harper and Row, Publishers, 1964, p. 87.

6. In a later work Gibbs himself defines "norms" in terms of (1) a collective evaluation of behavior in terms of what it *ought* to be; (2) a collective expectation as to what behavior *will* be; and/or (3) particular *reactions* to behavior, including attempts to apply sanctions or otherwise induce a particular kind of conduct." See Jack P. Gibbs, "Norms: The Problem of Definition and Classification," *American Journal of Sociology*, Vol. 70 (May 1965), pp. 586-94.

7. Durkheim, 1953, op. cit.

8. Judith Blake and Kingsley Davis, "Norms, Values and Sanctions," in *Handbook of Modern Sociology*, ed. R. E. L. Faris. Chicago: Rand McNally Co., 1964, pp. 456-57.

9. In fact, Durkheim suggested that "Collective psychology is sociology, quite simply . . . ," 1953, op. cit., p. 34, fn. 1.

10. "From another point of view . . . collective representations originate only when they are embodied in material objects, things, or beings of every sort—figures, movements, sounds, words and so on—that symbolize them in some outward appearance. For it is only by expressing their feelings, by translating them into signs, by symbolizing them externally, that the individual consciousnesses, which are by nature, closed to each other, can feel that they are communicating and are in unison." Emile Durkheim, "Le dualisme de la nature et ses conditions sociales," *Scientia*, Vol. 15 (1914), pp. 216-217. (Reprinted as "The Dualism of Human Nature," trans. Charles Blend, in Emile Durkheim et al., *Essays on Sociology and Philosophy*, ed. Kurt H. Wolff. New York: Harper and Row, Publishers, 1964, pp. 325-40.)

11. Also see Leo Schnore's comments on the role of collective representations in Durkheim's thought in his "Social Morphology and Human Ecology," *American Journal of Sociology*, Vol. 63 (May 1958), pp. 620-34, reprinted in Chapter 2 of the present volume.

Human Ecology
Amos H. Hawley

The term "ecology," which has its root in the Greek word *oikos* (household or living place), came into use in the latter part of the nineteenth century in the works of zoologists and botanists to describe the study of the ways in which organisms live in their environments. Soon two branches of ecology were distinguished: *autecology* the study of the individual organism's inter-action with environment, and *synecology*, the study of the correlations be-tween the organisms engaged with a given unit of environment. The latter study has prevailed, however, and has become the principal connotation of ecology, since it became evident in numerous field studies that organisms, whether plant or animal establish viable relationships with environment, not independently but collectively, through the mechanism of a system of rela-tionships. Bioecologists were thus led to employ a set of concepts and tech-niques of investigation that imparted a markedly sociological coloration to their work.

Origins and History
The ecological approach was introduced as human ecology into the field of sociology at a critical period in the development of the latter discipline. In the 1920s the reformistic phase of sociology was drawing to a close, the subject was gaining acceptance as a respected discipline in the curricula of American universities. That the transition would have been effected so quickly without the aid of a theoretical framework lending itself to empirical research seems doubtful. Ecology opportunely provided the necessary theory. A period of vigorous research followed that was to prove instrumental in launching sociology on its career as a social science.

Sociologists made free use of analogy as they borrowed heavily from the concepts of plant and animal ecology. The Darwinian notion of animate nature as a web of life became at once a general orienting concept and a basic postulate; it directed attention to the necessary interdependence among men as well as among lower forms of life. A second concept, the balance of nature, denoting a tendency toward stabilization of the relative numbers of diverse organisms within the web of life and of their several claims on the environment, provided human ecology with its characteristic equilibrium position. The more or less balanced web of relationships, when viewed in a specific local area, presented the aspect of community, a concept with obvious appeal for students of human social life.

According to plant and animal ecologists, the community, or eco-system, is a population comprising a set of species whose reactions to the habitat and coactions between each other constitute an integrated system having some degree of unit character. Coactions involve members behaving both with reference to their similarities in an *intra*specific relationship known as commensalism and with reference to their differences in what is called symbiosis, an *inter*specific relationship. The community develops from simple to more complex forms through a sequence of stages described as succession. Each stage in the sequence is marked by an invasion of a new species or association of species, the series culminating in a climax stage in which a *dominant* species appears. The dominant species is related to the environment in such a way that it is able to control and maintain the community indefi-nitely. The community, then tends to approximate a self-maintaining, or "closed," system.

Community and Environment   The application of the concepts from plant and animal ecology to the human community carried with it the implication that the community was essentially a natural phenomenon, which meant that it had developed independently of plan or deliberation. From this it was a short, though uncritical, step to the interpretation of human ecology as a study of the biotic or subsocial aspect of human social organization (Park 1936), a view that was elaborated at some length by Quinn (1950). Not only did the subsocial characterization convey an excessively narrow concept of social organization, but it posed an operational problem for which there was no workable solution.

A somewhat different definition of human ecology, which ignored any reference to the cognitive level of events, was enunciated by McKenzie ([1924] 1925, pp. 63-64), whose formulation of the subject as a study of the spatial and temporal relations of human beings, affected by the selective, distributive, and accommodative forces of the environment, was widely ac-cepted as authoritative. Although McKenzie's definition inspired a large amount of fruitful research effort, it had the unfortunate effect of concen-trating attention almost exclusively on spatial distributions and correlations.

In consequence, many promising implications of ecological assumptions were neglected.

Hawley, in attempting to restore a conceptual continuity with plant and animal ecologies, advanced the view of human ecology as the study of the form and development of the human community (1950, p. 68). Community, in this connection, is construed as a territorially localized system of relationships among functionally differentiated parts; human ecology, then, is concerned with the general problem of organization conceived as an attribute of a population—a point of view that has been shown to be consistent with a long-standing sociological tradition (Schnore 1958). Although the emphasis is centered on the functional system that develops in a population, it is not intended to exclude concern with spatial and temporal aspects; rather, these aspects are regarded as useful dimensions for the measurement of organization.

A further step in making the orientation of human ecology explicit within the larger context of general ecological theory was made by Duncan (1959, pp. 683-684), who described four principal variables of human ecology—population, organization, environment, and technology—that constitute an ecosystem. In other words, while any one of the four may be treated as a dependent variable for certain purposes, it is also reciprocally connected with each of the other variables. The virtue of this perspective lies in the range of problems it opens to the student of human ecology. Yet it seems unlikely that that advantage can be fully enjoyed without a clear notion of how organization is constituted.

Other Applications   While sociologists were at work defining human ecology for their purposes and pursuing many of its research leads, the concept spread into various other fields of inquiry. Human geographers wondered if the term "human ecology" was not a more apt characterization of their discipline; but their historic preoccupation with the landscape and their general addiction to a macroscopic treatment of occupance led them to discard this notion. Archeologists, in their efforts to reconstruct population distributions, have made use of ecological concepts and techniques, but without attempting to give formal statement to the approach.

Studies of human evolution by anthropologists involved questions of the man—environment relationship, which, in turn, led them to describe their work as human ecology; indeed, social or cultural anthropologists have long engaged in various ecological studies, although not until recently have they so defined their activity. One definition by an anthropologist is that of Steward (1955), for whom human ecology is the study of the adaptation of specific items of culture to particular environments. This conception, which reduces ecology to something akin to a research technique, is shared by a number of Steward's contemporaries.

The language of human ecology has also made its appearance in economics, psychology, epidemiology, and other fields. In some instances, the term is used merely as a label for an environmental emphasis; in others, it is put forward in an effort to broaden the purview of a discipline.

But in spite of the widespread diffusion of ecological concepts, responsibility for systematic development of human ecology has been left to sociologists, who have drawn heavily on related fields for both theoretical and technical aid. The writings on real estate, finance, public administration, demography, planning, history, and other areas of inquiry, in addition to the literature of the fields previously mentioned, have at one time or another been exploited in the interest of human ecology. The reason for that catholicity of taste is not hard to find; human ecology is concerned with sociological problems in their fullest breadth. It overlaps, therefore, all the spheres of learning that concern the social life of man.

Distinctive Features of Human Ecology

As human ecology has moved toward a major concern with the general problem of social organization and thus closer to the central concern of sociology, it has retained certain distinctive features. Foremost among these is the importance attributed to environment.

The broad, positional hypothesis is that organization arises from the interaction of population and environment. Environment, however, defined as whatever is external to and potentially or actually influential on a phenomenon under investigation, has no fixed content and must be defined anew for each different object of investigation. Environment is seen both as presenting the problem of life and as providing the means for its resolution; to adopt this position is to place the problem in a time-space context.

A second distinguishing characteristic is the emphasis on population as the point of reference; organization, it is contended, is exclusively the property of a population taken as a whole and not of an assemblage of individuals. Obvious as this position may be, it has profound methodological and theoretical implications for the manner in which the ecological problem is put, the variables employed, and the data to be observed. The concreteness of population, however, in contrast with the seemingly ephemeral nature of organization, tends to beguile the student to a view of population as the independent variable in all things pertaining to organization. It is obviously more convenient to proceed from the more accessible to the less accessible by asking how a population makes a unitary response to its environment; yet that is merely a common-sense way of approaching the problem, and investigation soon makes it apparent that population is for many purposes better regarded as the dependent variable, delimited and regulated by organization.

A third characteristic is the treatment of organization as a more or less complete and self-sustaining whole. The interaction of population and environment is seen as culminating in a system of relationships between differentiated parts which gives the population unit character and enables it to maintain its identity. As the property of a population, organization lends itself most readily to a morphological, or structural, analysis. The parts are the units—individuals or clusters of individuals—that perform functions and the relationships by which these units are linked. Differing configurations of unit functions and relationships are expected to occur with differences in relationship to environment and at different stages in development.

A morphological concern does not exclude the problem of development. Presumably, any given form of organization had an earlier form and is capable of having a later form. Every organization has a history, perhaps a natural history, the knowledge of which may shed light on the nature of organizations by indicating, for example, at what points they are vulnerable to change and how change spreads through them.

Related to the conception of organization is a fourth distinctive, although by no means unique, attribute of human ecology: the central position given to an equilibrium assumption. Morphological change is assumed to be a movement toward an equilibrium state, whether through a succession-like sequence of stages or through a process of continuous modification. Unlike the equilibrium notion in some of its other applications, such as in functionalist theory, the ecological usage of the term harbors no teleological overtones; on the contrary, this usage merely implies that as an organization attains completeness, it acquires the capacity for controlling change and for retaining its form through time, although the interval need not be specified. To put it differently, to the extent that an organization possesses unit character, an approximation to equilibrium obtains.

There is a further implication that a stable relationship with environment is contingent on relative stability in the relationships between the parts of an organization. A population always remains open to environment, but the formation of organizations canalizes environmental influences and makes for increasing selectivity of response.

The term "community" has commonly been used to denote the unit of organization for ecological purposes. Operationally defined as that population which carries on its daily life through a given system of relationships, the community is regarded as the smallest microcosm in which all the parameters of society are to be found. For reasons that were largely fortuitous, human ecologists at first focused their attention on the city and its tributary area as the prototype of community; later, in an effort to encompass the antecedents of cities, they broadened their consideration to include all forms of nucleated settlement. The term "community," however, has the disadvantage of referring to the organization of a more or less localized settlement unit that does

not always approximate a self-maintaining whole. For example, in an extensively urbanized society, local settlement units are usually components of
more inclusive systems; in that event, the entire system must be treated as the
object of study. But the difference between a simple, compact organization
and a large, diffuse one is primarily a difference in scale; accordingly, the
principles of organization should be the same in each. Since the designation
of both simple and complex systems as communities threatens confusion, a
more neutral term, such as "social system," is to be preferred.

Principles of Ecological Organization

Inasmuch as principles of organization hinge on what is meant by population,
it is imperative that the concept be developed more fully.

A human population is an aggregate of individuals who possess the
following characteristics. As a living organism, every individual must have
access to environment, for that is the only possible source of sustenance.
Moreover, the interdependence of individuals is necessary; this condition,
which obtains for all forms of life, holds true to an exceptional degree in the
case of man, because of the naked state in which he comes into the world and
his long period of postnatal maturation. Interdependence is the irreducible
connotation of sociality.

The human being also possesses an inherent tendency to preserve and
expand his life to the maximum permitted by prevailing circumstances; this is
a general motive of which all other motives are special cases. In its most
elementary sense, expansion of life refers to the multiplication of man-years
through either the leaving of progeny or the extension of longevity; but it
also includes all that is involved in the realization of that objective. Another
important characteristic is the indeterminacy of the human being's capacity
to adapt; there is no known restriction on the kind or extent of refinement of
activity in which he can engage. Finally, the human individual, again like
other organisms, is time-bound; the recurring needs for food and rest fix the
fundamental rhythm of life and regulate the allocation of time to all other
activities. Accordingly, the time available for movement is limited and, in
consequence, the space over which activities can be distributed is correspondingly limited.

These several attributes of individuals not only define the kind of
population with which human ecology deals, but they also constitute a
cardinal set of assumptions from which principles of ecological organization
may be deduced. The following are some of the more salient of these principles of organization.

   Principle of Interdependence   Interdependence develops between
units on each of two axes: the symbiotic (on the basis of their complementary differences) and the commensal (on the basis of their supplementary similarities). That is, units that combine in a symbiotic union may

also enter into other combinations of a commensal character; the effect of each type of union is to raise the power of action above what it would be were the units to remain apart.

The effect, however, is not the same in each case. The symbiotic union enhances the efficiency of production or creative effort; the commensal union, since its parts are homogeneous, can only react and is suited, therefore, only to protective or conservative actions. Although commensalism is an elemental form of union, it is applicable to a wide array of situations. The point of importance at present is that a population tends to be knit together through an interwoven set of symbiotic and commensal relationships.

It should be evident that interdependence has temporal and spatial implications for the units involved. Relations of functional complementation and supplementation require mutual accessibility among units; since this is contingent on the time available for movement, the distance separating related units is always subject to some limitation. In general, for every set of related units, there should be, other things being equal, an appropriate pattern of distribution in the temporal and spatial dimensions.

Principle of the Key Function   A second principle may be described as the principle of the key function. That is, in every system of relationships among diverse functions, the connection of the system to its environment is mediated primarily by one or a relatively small number of functions, the latter being known as the key function or functions. To the extent that the principle of the key function does not obtain, the system will be tenuous and incoherent; in the extreme case, in which no system exists, every function has the same relationship to environment. Given a functional system, then, there are always some functions or functional units directly involved with environment and others that secure access to the environment indirectly, through the agency of the key function.

The notion of key function invokes the question of how to define the notion of environment, which can refer to many different kinds of things. For present purposes, these things may be classified in two broad categories: the natural and the social. Although every organized aggregate must contend with both, the relative importance of each may vary over a wide range. In some instances, because of the inaccessibility of the settlement, activities of necessity center on the exploitation of the local natural environment, while influences from the social field are relatively infrequent or of no great consequence. In this event, the key function is the activity that extracts the principal sustenance supply from local resources. But where the product from local resources, or a substantial part of it, is exchanged for other sustenance materials, whether through trade or other distributive mechanisms, the key function is determined by the comparative importance of production and of trade as sources of sustenance.

In many such instances, no distinction is necessary because the producer is also the trader—two functions combined in one functionary. But even before the two functions appear as separate specialties, the requisites of trade or distribution begin to regulate the uses of local resources. As the reliance on exchange advances, the social environment actually displaces the natural environment as the critical set of influences. A population is never emancipated from its dependence on physical and animate matters, but the importance of locale declines with increasing involvement in a network of intersystem relations; the natural environment is extended and diffused, and contacts with it are mediated through a variety of social mechanisms. Hence, the functions that link the local system to the social environment come to occupy the key position.

Principle of Differentiation   The extent of functional differentiation varies with the productivity of the key function or functions; this is the principle of differentiation. A corollary is that the size of population supportable by the system varies with the productivity of the key function. For given the simplifying assumption that each unit is fully occupied, the number of people is determined by the number of functions to be performed.

In a hunting and gathering community, for instance, productivity is usually low, even though the physical environment is richly endowed; hence, there is little time or opportunity available for the cultivation of more than a few specialized functions. Nor is it possible to support enough people to staff even a moderate extent of specialization. By contrast, where the key function is devoted to stable agriculture, the range of possibilities is much greater, while in an industrial system productivity is so great that there are no known upper limits on either the number of specializations or the size of the population that can be supported.

The productivity of the key funciton, then, constitutes the principal limiting condition on the extent to which a system can be elaborated, on the size of population that can be sustained in the system, and on the area or space the system can occupy.

A question of some importance has to do with the relative number of units engaged in each of several interrelated functions. That question remains unanswered at present. It may be suggested, however, that the number of units engaged in any given function is inversely proportional to the productivity of the function and directly proportional to the number of units that utilize the product of the function.

It follows, of course, that functional differentiation involves a differentiation of environmental requirements. As the materials and conditions used by diversely specialized units differ, so also will their needs for location in space and time. In general, units performing key functions have the highest priority of claim on location. Other units tend to distribute themselves about the key function units, their distances away corresponding to the number of degrees of removal separating their functions from direct relation with the key functions. The temporal spacing may be expected to reveal a similar pattern. Special location requirements, however, as for type of soil or other resource, may obscure the tendency to a symmetrical arrangement of functions by degree of indirectness of relationship with key functions.

An important implication of the principles of the key function and of differentiation is that of transitivity in the relation among functional units. Relations with environment are necessarily transitive for some units. By the same token, relations among many units are transitive. The advance of specialization increases transitive relations more than proportionally and lengthens the transitive sequences. Thus, it is possible for functional units widely removed from one another so far as direct encounters are concerned to be inextricably linked through their respective linkages with one or more units performing intervening functions. All functions, regardless of kind, are subject to the environmental nexus. They differ only in the immediacy with which influences reach them. Those which operate at or near the ends of chains of relationships may appear to have large degrees of independence of environment. The appearance is illusory, however. It is due, rather, to the time required for effects to reach them and, in complex systems, to their having positions in two or more relational sequences which expose them to countervailing influences.

Principle of Dominance   Given the principles stated above, it is a simple inferential step to a principle of dominance. According to this principle, functional units having direct relations with environment, and thus performing the key function, determine or regulate the conditions essential to the functions of units having indirect relations with environment. Dominance, in other words, is an attribute of function.

But while the power inherent in a system is unevenly distributed, it is not confined to the key function unit. Power is held in varying degrees by all other units, in measures that vary inversely with the number of steps of removal from direct relation with the unit performing the key function. A single power gradient running through all the units involved in a system assumes a very simple situation, of course, one in which a single unit occupies a key function position. Before introducing complications into this overly simplified conception, it is opportune to note some further implications of the dominance principle.

Where the progress of differentiation has distinguished a relatively large number of units, they tend to form clusters or complex units. A corollary to the dominance principle sheds light on how that comes about: the greater the extent to which variously specialized units are subject to the environmental conditions mediated by some one unit, the greater their tendency to coalesce in a corporate body. The interdependence among such units is manifestly close, and their requirements for mutual accessibility are correspondingly acute. A hierarchic pattern emerges in which the number of strata corresponds to the number of degrees that the parts are removed from direct relations with the key function; thus, symbiotic subsystems appear as components of a parent system. The nuclear family, although its origins are obscure, fits this principle. But instances with more proximate origins are found in the combinations of specialists to form producing enterprises, welfare agencies, governing bodies, etc., and again in the combinations of producing enterprises, retail establishments, or governments to constitute larger, more complex units. There is no restriction of scale or complexity in the formation of symbiotic or corporate units.

On the other hand, units that are of a given functional type and therefore occupy equivalent positions in the power hierarchy may raise their power potential by the formation of categoric unions. Any threat to a function or to the conditions of its performance can provoke such a response; groups of elders, the medieval guilds, labor unions, professional associations, councils of churches, retail associations, and associations of manufacturers are examples of categoric units. A social class is at most a loose form of categoric unit.

As with the corporate union, the categoric union may be composed of units of any size or kind. It may appear as a federation of categoric units or as an association of corporate units. So long as it retains its pure categoric form, however, such a unit can do little more than react to circumstances affecting it. Nor can it have more than a transitory existence, since in order to engage in positive action of any kind and to attain some measure of permanence, it must develop at least a core of specialists. Although the categoric unit tends to assume the characteristics of the corporate unit, it remains distinctive as long as its criterion for membership is possession of a given, common characteristic. In any event, the categoric unit is a source of rigidity in a social system, and once formed, its effect is to preserve the position of a functional category in the system.

The concept of dominance has been widely employed for the purpose of delimiting the boundaries of systems. It is argued that centers of settlement, such as cities, exercise dominance over their surrounding areas, in diminishing degrees as the distance from the center increases; the margin of influence marks the boundary of the system. Empirical support for this proposition is provided by the evidence of nonrandom distribution of related functions and by the gradient pattern that appears in the frequencies with which outlying functions are involved with central functions.

Two qualifications of this conclusion are needed; first, dominance is exercised from and not by centers, since it resides in functional units rather than in the places where they are located. Further, the apparent decline of dominance results less from an effect of distance in reducing control over related functions than from the increased difficulty of establishing dominance uniformly over an exponentially widening area.

   Isomorphism   A principle of isomorphism has been implied in much that has been said and needs now to be stated. Units subject to the same environmental conditions, or to environmental conditions as mediated through a given key unit, acquire a similar form of organization. They must submit to standard terms of communication and to standard procedures in consequence of which they develop similar internal arrangements within limits imposed by their respective sizes. Each unit, then, tends to become a replica of every other unit and of the parent system in which it is a subsystem.

   Since small units cannot acquire the elaborate organizations of which large units are capable, they jointly support specialized functions that complement their meager organizations. For example, whereas a large unit may include among its functionaries accountants, lawyers, engineers, public relations experts, and other specialists, the small unit must purchase comparable services from units specializing in each of the relevant functions. The principle of isomorphism also applies to the size of units, at least as a tendency; that is, all units tend toward a size that enables them to maintain contact with all relevant sectors of the parent system.

Closure and Social Change

Operation of the several principles mentioned thus far moves a system toward a state of closure. This term must be employed here with circumspection, for it cannot have its usual connotation of independence of environment. Closure can only mean that development has terminated in a more or less complete system that is capable of sustaining a given relationship to environment indefinitely. For closure to be realized, it is required not only that the differentiation of function supportable by the productivity of the key function has attained its maximum but also that the various functions have been gathered into corporate and categoric subsystems; moreover, the performance of the key function should have been reduced to one unit or to a number of units united in a categoric federation. Then a system is highly selective of its membership and capable of exercising some control over factors that threaten change in the system.

   Under these circumstances, certain conditions of equilibrium are held to obtain: the functions involved are mutually complementary and collectively provide the conditions essential to the continuation of each; the number of individuals engaged in each function is just sufficient to maintain the relations of the functions to each other and to all other functions; and the various units are arranged in time and space so that the accessibility of one to others bears a direct relation to the frequency of exchanges between them. Needless to say, equilibrium as thus defined is a logical construct; the conditions express an expected outcome if the principles of organization are allowed to operate without any external disturbances.

Origins and Effects of Change   Every social system is continuously subject to change, for since the environment is always in some state of flux, the equilibrium that can be attained is seldom more than partial. A system founded on nonreplaceable resources is faced with "immanent change"; sooner or later it will either pass into decline or shift perforce to a different resource base. Such, for instance, has been the experience of innumerable mining communities; in a similar manner agricultural communities often alter the soil composition of their lands by the uses they practice, with the ultimate result that the lands will no longer support the systems as they are constituted. Instances of maladaptation, such as the reliance of the Irish on the potato as a food staple in the nineteenth century, can lead to catastrophic consequences.

In general, however, change has an external origin, a proposition that follows by definition from an equilibrium position. Some influences emanate from the physical or biotic environment, such as variations in the growing season or invasion by parasites. To the extent that episodic occurrences of that order fail to modify one or more functions comprised in the system, their effects are transitory; the system returns to its original form. But where a function, particularly a key function, is substantially modified, the system must be reconstituted. The disappearance of a game supply, the silting of an estuary, or the eruption of a volcano may render a key function inoperative in its usual location. The population must relocate and work out a new system of activities. Unless there is an increase of productivity, new ways of acting will merely displace old ways, and the change will not be cumulative.

Cumulative Change   Cumulative change, or growth of the system, presupposes an increase in the productivity of a key function. Only in this way is it possible to multiply specialization, to employ a greater variety of techniques, and to support a larger population. The probability of the occurrence of disturbances having that effect rises with the number of points of contact with a social environment; location, therefore, is an important factor. A site on a traveled route is more exposed to external influences than one situated at a distance from an avenue of movement; a site at a conflux of routes is much more vulnerable to disturbances from without. Any location that fosters frequent meetings of people from diverse backgrounds is a gateway for the infusion of alien experiences and techniques into the social system centered there. Whether change is released through a deposit of numerous small additions to the culture or through a simple, dramatic innovation is immaterial.

The process of cumulative change may be generalized as a principle of expansion. Expansion is a twofold process involving, on the one hand, the growth of a center of activity from which dominance is exercised and, on the other hand, an enlargement of the scope of the center's influence. The process entails the absorption and redistribution of the functions formerly carried on in outlying areas, a centralization of mediating and control functions, an increase in the number and variety of territorially extended relationships, a growth of population to man a more elaborate set of activities, and an accumulation of culture together with a leveling of cultural differences over the expanding domain. After the revival of trade in Europe, from the tenth century onward, the favorably situated village with its narrow vicinage grew into a market town that served as a center of an enlarged territorial organization. That gave way, in turn, to the emergent city capable of exercising an integrating influence over an area of regional scope. Most recently, the metropolis has superseded the city and has brought under its dominion a vast interregional territory. Although the process is as old as recorded history, it has not advanced in a simple linear progression. It has moved and then stalled in one place, only to surge ahead in another; it has faltered and even on occasion has seemed to turn back upon itself, but it has always resumed its course with renewed vigor.

The limits to expansion are sometimes fixed by the facility of movement between center and periphery—by the maximum distance over which the exercise of dominance is feasible. More often than not, however, the limits are drawn at the points of juncture with the expanding domains of social systems in neighboring regions. As a system encounters its limits, however they are fixed, it loses capacity to absorb further change, and equilibrium tendencies begin to assert themselves once more.

Under conditions of closure, environmental effects, and particularly cultural innovations, would be expected to enter a system through the key function, for the obvious reason that it has the most direct connection with environment. And, presumably, change would spread through the system by affecting units successively in the order in which they are removed from direct relation with a key function. But in a system centered on a convergence of routes, many units may have direct, although not equal, access to the outside world. Change may therefore enter the system at many points, at least until its structure is fully developed with the parts systematically arrayed relative to a key unit. An expanding system, in other words, is an open system, and it remains so until the limits to expansion are reached.

In many instances, however, the first symptoms of change are experienced at the periphery of a system. Since the effects of dominance grow more uneven with increased distance from a center, boundaries are apt to be permeable at many points. Yet, in the degree to which a system is integrated, events at the boundary are transmitted directly to the key unit, from which they are communicated to ancillary units; it is always at the boundary that one system begins its absorption of another. Expansion may be resumed at any moment and in any of the systems that hem in one another. An innovation, even though it might present itself to all systems about the same time, gains admission to one or another by virtue of a more favorable location for its use, a more appropriate organization for its acceptance, or some other local advantage. The renewed expansion encroaches upon the territories of adjoining systems, sometimes reducing them to mere components of a single, greatly enlarged system.

Burgess' Hypothesis of City Growth   A hypothesis of city growth, stated by E. W. Burgess ([1925] 1961, pp. 37-44), pertains to a special case of the more general principle. According to that proposal, city growth takes the form of expansion from a zone centered on a highly accessible location. Growth involves increasing density of occupance of the central zone and, at the same time, a redistribution of activities or land uses scattered around the center to conform to a gradient pattern of variation of intensity of land use according to distances from the center. Redistribution results from increasing pressure at the center and a consequent encroachment by high-intensity uses into the spaces occupied by lower-intensity uses in a succession-like manner. Alternating periods of redistribution and stabilization of distribution, and those of growth and partial equilibrium, create a wavelike effect more or less visible in a set of concentric zones. By venturing to describe, in rather specific terms, the content of the zones and by thus reifying a set of statistical constructs, Burgess diverted attention from a growth process and caused it to be fixed on a specious distribution pattern. His argument, therefore, seemed to acquire a historical limitation that it need not have had.

The miscarriage of the import of the Burgess hypothesis is evident in criticisms that have opposed the preindustrial city to the industrial city as a qualitatively different phenomenon. Whereas Burgess suggested that the social-economic status of residents is higher in each successive concentric zone, critics have shown that in the preindustrial city the social-economic gradient runs in the opposite direction. Useful as that finding may be, it misses the essential point. That is, the significant gradient is one of dominance; units tend to distribute themselves over space in a way that reflects their relationships to the dominant unit. In this respect, both industrial and preindustrial cities are similar. The qualitative difference lies in the kinds of units that exercise dominance. In the preindustrial city, all functions are carried in familial or household units, and power is unevenly distributed among them. But in the industrial society, the household unit has been relegated to a minor position; specialized functions are performed by extra-familial units, and the separation of functions from the household has involved a spatial separation as well.

Furthermore, the notion of a monocentered system is applicable only to the simplest instances. All others include a constellation of settlement nuclei, that is to say, subsidiary service centers within cities, and villages, towns, or cities within hinterlands. Each serves as a locus of influence over a localized area, varying in scope with the types of functions centered in the nucleus. Thus, as Christaller observed, the constellation of nuclei forms a hierarchy by size and number of places and by order of functions performed. Small places provide low-order, or ubiquitous, functions, whereas each larger place performs, in addition to low-order functions, higher-order functions for broader domains. At the apogee of the hierarchy is the metropolis, in which the integrating and coordinating functions for the entire system are domiciled. Thus, dominance is exercised downward and outward through nested sets of subsidiary centers.

The least satisfactory aspect of the theory of change concerns its temporal incidence. The idea of succession, borrowed initially from bioecology, lingers in the dictionary of human ecology. Change as cyclical in form, consisting in movements between equilibrium stages, is clearly the most intelligible conception. Nevertheless, apart from the difficulty in empirically identifying an equilibrium stage, there are unsolved conceptual problems of the spacing of stages, and of the factors governing the intervals between stages. Thus far, succession has been applied only in retrospect. Its utility will remain uncertain until it can be projected into prediction. Quite possibly, that may have to wait for more extensive work on social system taxonomy.

The Limits of Human Ecology

Human ecology has progressed since its inception from an effort to apply the concepts of plant and animal ecology to human collective life, through an extended period of preoccupation with spatial configurations, to an increasing concern with the form and development of territorially based social systems. In the last phase, human ecologists have sought to clarify the assumptions of ecology and to draw out their implications for organization. Although the results of that work are far from complete, it seems clear that they indicate the direction in which human ecology will continue to develop.

As with most approaches in social science, human ecology has limited objectives. It seeks knowledge about the structure of a social system and the manner in which the structure develops. Hence, it is not prepared to provide explanations for all of the manifold interactions, frictions, and collisions that occur within the bounds of a social system. The findings of human ecology, however, define the context in which all such phenomena take place, and which is therefore pertinent to their full understanding.

Human ecology is not qualified to deal with the normative order in a social system. Yet consistent with its position is the expectation that a normative order corresponds to and reflects the functional order. The two are different abstractions from the same reality.

Toward a Theoretical System of Human Ecology
Jack P. Gibbs and Walter T. Martin

There is no aspect of society that is in greater need of sociological study than is man's increasingly efficient organization for providing himself with a quantity and variety of material goods. In recent decades human ecology has been the most notable attempt by sociologists to develop an analytical framework encompassing this sector of collective human behavior. But so widely accepted has become the self evident truth that the early great expectations for human ecology have not been fulfilled that even sociologists with an ecological orientation seem to lack faith in the value of their subject matter. Although each year demonstrates anew that this phenomenon remains too vital to be banished entirely from sociology, human ecologists have come to practice Uncle Tom postures in the presence of colleagues endowed with the current psychological orientation, and to spend their research hours assaying their data hopefully for values, sentiments, motivations, and other elusive psychological elements. The factors which have led to this unseemly situation are too complex to analyze here but, in brief, the difficulty lies in the absence of a coherent theoretical system developed specifically around man's organization for sustenance. The lack of such a system has led to fragmentation with consequent sterility in human ecology, and, correspondingly, a weakening of sociology itself. The development of a theoretical system would do more than anything else to further the advance of human ecology toward a logically sound, empirically productive, and sociologically meaningful discipline.

In attempting to move toward a theoretical system in the present paper, it has not been possible to give proper recognition to all those who have advanced similar ideas in the past. The parallels will be evident to persons familiar with the field. In particular it will be noted that the system offered here bears, at certain points, a close relationship to the conception of human ecology advanced by Hawley.[1] In contrast to Hawley, however, the writers see "the form and the development of the community"[2] as being both too broad and too narrow to be considered the proper subject matter of the field. For one thing, a community represents a configuration of widely diverse activities, phenomena which are far too heterogeneous to be treated in terms of one general theory. Furthermore, the community, for the purposes of human ecology, is only one unit of observation; more macroscopic units such as regions and nations must be included. There is nothing in the community that is intrinsically more "real" or "important" than is the case for countries. In fact, by placing its emphasis on societal organization human ecology is potentially capable of stemming the current trend which threatens to reduce sociology to social psychology. The necessity for a shift in units is further apparent when it is realized that the "biotic community" has no real equivalent in a complex society where the autonomy of the community is rapidly vanishing, and that it is increasingly difficult to ignore societal factors in seeking to explain events in a community.[3]

The Idea of a Theoretical System

Even though nebulous, the general idea underlying the concept of a theoretical system must play a leading role in any meaningful reconsideration of human ecology. It is useless to attempt to dodge the issue by holding that the idea of a system is beyond immediate concern. Research within any field takes place within some theoretical system, no matter how haphazardly located therein, and regardless of whether the system is explicit or implicit, complete or incomplete. It behooves the human ecologist, consequently, to work toward an explicit, articulated system. In so doing it is necessary to consider a most important question: What at a minimum should be incorporated in the statement of a system? Of the numerous questions that must eventually be answered only the four most relevant to human ecology at its present state of development can be considered here:

(1) What is the subject matter encompassed by the system?
(2) What is to be explained about this subject matter?
(3) What is the universe of inquiry?
(4) What mechanisms link the subject matter with the universe of inquiry?

While each of these questions appears most elementary, the present situation in human ecology requires that the work begin at this level. Even these four questions can be treated only superficially in this short statement.

Sustenance Organization as the Subject Matter of Human Ecology

In a sense human ecology had its origin when a particular biological question was asked of man: How does this species survive? That this question gave rise to a field of sociological interest is mainly due to the answer given: Man survives by collective organization in the exploitation of natural resources. The question, while biological in origin, was answered in terms that are central to sociology; namely, collective organization.

Looking at contemporary human ecology, it is apparent that whatever unity the field enjoyed from being confronted with a fundamental question has long since ceased to exist.[4] For those who see science in individualistic terms, human ecology now offers a congenial atmosphere; but for persons who strive for logical and empirical connections among the different theories and studies within a field, the situation is most regretable. For ecology to arrive at the ultimate goal of unified theory there must be some agreement as to what is and is not the subject matter of the field.

The most promising means to achieving a working unity within the field is through re-examining the answer given to the question posed above. That man survives through collective organization is fundamental to both sociology and human ecology. It is obvious, however, that not all populations organize themselves for the exploitation of natural resources in exactly the same manner. To the contrary, a wide variety of organizational forms are to be observed. It is in this variability in the characteristics of sustenance organization among populations that human ecology finds its fundamental problem. This subject matter—the nature of the sustenance organization of human populations—is largely ignored by contemporary ecology.

A brief consideration of what is entailed in sustenance organization can best begin with the conception of a population as an aggregate of individuals engaged in activities that provide them with a livelihood. These activities, here designated as *sustenance activities*, are abstracted from the total of human behavior and specifically exclude all activities not directly related to livelihood. While the sustenance activities of individuals are the primary data of human ecology, the ultimate goal is to describe the characteristics of sustenance organization for the population as a whole, that is, the patterning of social relationships within the population that are manifested in sustenance activities.

Sustenance activities have one outstanding property—they are highly organized in the sense of being regular, repetitive, and enduring; for this reason any pattern in the sustenance activities of a population constitutes an organization. The organization may involve the activities of thousands of persons, as does General Motors, or appear in the patterned but isolated activities of a trapper. It is not made up of individuals but rather of their activities, and any given person may be a participant in more than one sustenance organization.

The analysis of sustenance organization could begin, as shown in the illustrative taxonomy of Figure 1, with a distinction between those that are *collective* and those that are *non-collective*. In the former, individuals band together and coordinate their activities so as to obtain objects of consumption. Collective sustenance organization may be either undifferentiated, such as a hunting party in a preliterate society, or possess a high degree of division of labor as in the case of a modern factory or hospital. In non-collective sustenance organizations persons obtain objects of consumption through their individual effort. The farmer, the proprietor of a store with no employees, and the craftsman in a one-man shop are instances of this class.

Both non-collective and collective sustenance organizations may be characterized according to how their activities result in the acquisition of objects of consumption. In *isolated sustenance organizations* the individual or the collection of individuals merely produce for their own use. *Exchange sustenance organizations*, in contrast, are based on the production, processing, or distribution of objects of consumption for others. A coal mine company is an instance of a collective exchange sustenance organization, and the farmer who produces for a market represents a non-collective exchange sustenance organization. In a *service sustenance organization* the individual or collection of individuals obtain their objects of consumption by rendering a service as in the case of a doctor, a professional baseball club, or a firm of consulting engineers.

A further distinction is drawn in Figure 1 between two types of collective sustenance organization. In the one case there is differentiation—a division of labor calling for different types of activities and skills, along with a system of statuses. Thus, the configuration of sustenance activities found in a modern hospital constitutes a collective-service-differentiated sustenance organization. On the other hand, a hunting party in a preliterate society may lack a division of labor in this sense, and would be classified as a collective-isolated-undifferentiated sustenance organization.

The structure of sustenance organization embraces far more than is described above. Individual organizations (both collective and non-collective) can be distinguished and combined on the basis of the type of product or service which they produce. The various kinds and the basis of their distinctions are generally familiar as *industry categories*, and they appear as such in Figure 1. If a particular organization cannot function without the product or service of another, the two can justifiably be considered as forming a single unit in the over-all structure. These units are here designated as *organizational complexes*. Thus, while an airline company and an oil company which supplies it with fuel may be distinct and separate in the eyes of the law and may fall in different industry categories, from an ecological point of view they can be regarded as one. This applies to industry categories as well as to configurations of individual sustenance organizations. A great deal of research must be undertaken before organizational complexes can be delimited on a sound basis;[5] however, at least on a conceptual level, their position in the structure of sustenance organization warrants recognition.

The structure of sustenance organization, as described above, is applicable to any population, whether demarcated along territorial lines or

Figure 1

A Taxonomy of Sustenance Organization or Activities with Selected Examples[1]

By Type of Product or Service	Collective						Non-Collective		
	Isolated		Exchange		Service		Isolated	Exchange	Service
	D[2]	N-D[2]	D	N-D	D	N-D			
Domesticated Agriculture	A						F		
Undomesticated Agriculture[4]		B							
Other Extractive			C				G		
Retail Trade			D					H	
Wholesale Trade			E						
Finance									
Manufacturing									
Transport					I				J
Communication									
Other Utilities			K						
Construction									
Maintenance									
Education and Training					L				
Medical					M				N
Entertainment and Recreation									
Consultatory Other Than Medical					O				P
Protective					Q				
Administrative Governmental			R						S
Personal Services									T
Food Preparation									U

By Type of Social Relationship

A. Farmers' mutual aid harvesting crew with division of labor; producing for own use. B. Primitive hunting group without division of labor; producing for own use. C. Coal mine with division of labor among employees. D. Large department store. E. Wholesale grocery concern. F. Owner operated farm not producing for a market. G. Individual mining coal for his own use. H. Gift shop operated by owner without assistants. I. Large trucking concern. J. Independent taxi cab driven by owner. K. Municipal power company. L. Columbia University. M. Medical clinic comprising several specialists. N. General medical practitioner without associates or a nurse. O. Firm of income tax consultants employing specialists. P. Practicing marriage counselor. Q. City police department. R. U.S. Department of State. S. Justice of the Peace functioning without assistants. T. Valet. U. Housewife.

[1] Under ideal conditions this table would show in each cell the proportion of the sustenance activities of the total population falling in that particular category. The units would thus be activities rather than individuals and the different activities of a single person might fall in more than one cell.

[2] Differentiated

[3] Non-differentiated

[4] Includes hunting, fishing and gathering.

otherwise. In recognition of the importance of the spatial dimensions of sustenance behavior, however, the primary emphasis in ecology should be on the analysis of populations that have a territorial base. Two types of territorial units call for recognition—those demarcated along governmental lines (cities, countries, states, provinces, etc.) and those with an ecological rather than a governmental basis (communities, urban areas, metropolitan areas, regions, etc.).[6] It should be noted that each of the larger territorial units is something more than the sum of its areal parts. They are more than statistical averages of the component units in the sense that each of the units is conceived of as having a position in a more macroscopic structure of sustenance organization. On both the theoretical and research level much remains to be done, but it is clear that the concept organizational complex will play a crucial role in the delimitation of macroscopic structures. This should not be taken to mean that the study of sustenance organization in a nation must be delayed until the interrelationships of its component territorial units have been mastered; on the contrary, a nation can be characterized, for example, according to the proportion of its labor force found in collective sustenance organizations without making reference to its localities or regions. Such characterization is not merely a stopgap measure but is rather a supplement to other characterizations that do pertain to the areal parts. For that matter, the description of sustenance organization in a population, whether within a locality or a nation, is in final analysis a question of levels of abstraction. Thus, the proportion of behavior in a population that is devoted to sustenance activities is a relatively simple variable, but the number of organizational complexes in a population is much more abstract.

Each of the basic units in ecological analysis plays a role in the formation of the variables which characterize the mode of sustenance organization in a population. Examples of these variables are as follows: the average size of sustenance organization, the variety of sustenance organizations as to product or service, the degree of differentiation within collective sustenance organizations, the average number of sustenance organizations in organizational complexes, the proportion of sustenance organizations that are non-collective, the degree of territorial specialization as to type of product or service, and the amount of linkage among territorial units through organizational complexes. Certain combinations of the above variables serve to characterize a population in more abstract terms, such as the degree and basis of the division of labor.

While the question of the significance of the units and attributes of sustenance organization described here and the equally crucial question of their empirical applicability remains subject to debate, it would appear that sustenance organization lends itself to both logical and empirical analysis. It holds forth the promise of a coherent frame of reference for research and the generation of empirical propositions that are theoretically meaningful.

Explanation

One of the minimal requirements of a system is the specification of what is to be explained about the subject matter. The ecologist cannot be content to merely state that he seeks to explain human behavior. For one thing, human behavior is an impossibly broad category. Further, such a statement does not tell us what there is about human behavior that is to be explained. One may seek to explain why individuals behave differently, why populations behave differently, why human beings behave differently from other animals, or even why human beings behave at all, and on *ad infinitum*. Just as it is necessary to select certain forms of human behavior as the subject matter, so it is equally necessary to state what is to be explained about these forms. Without an explicit and precise statement of explanatory purpose, research and theory inevitably will be subject to misinterpretation. Confusion on this point is a major problem in human ecology.

With respect to this component of a system, the writers see human ecology as having two goals. First, *it seeks to explain the presence and absence of particular characteristics of sustenance organization among human populations*, i.e., to state the conditions under which a given characteristic will or will not appear. Second, *it seeks to establish the consequences of the presence or absence of particular characteristics of sustenance organization in human populations*. It is not concerned with origins, ultimate causes, or the association of motives and attitudes with the different characteristics of sustenance organization.

While it is not always clear what ecological studies seek to explain, it is apparent that the present specification differs radically from other statements[7] or is much more narrowly conceived.[8]

The Universe of Inquiry

The statement of a system should aim for the limitation of a universe of inquiry, that is, a designated body of events or empirical phenomena, which at any point in time represents a guess as to where the answers to questions about the subject matter are to be found.

At present the writers feel that the boundaries of the universe of inquiry for human ecology should be drawn so as to include all of the purely demographic characteristics of populations, geographical variables, the purely technological aspects of man's culture, and the different forms of sustenance organization. In the case of demographic characteristics, the sheer size of a population and its biological composition (sex and age) on the one hand set the minimal sustenance needs of the population, and on the other fix the limits of the manpower resources for an organized effort to obtain these needs. They also set the number of combinations and permutations that can occur in collective activities.[9] Geographical variables tend to determine the least amount of collective effort that is necessary to meet the minimal sustenance needs of a given population. The purely technological aspects of a population's culture place limits on the type of resources that can be exploited and on the effectiveness of exploitation.[10] Finally, the absence or presence of certain forms of sustenance organization in a population may determine the presence of other forms of sustenance organization. It should be noted that the variables incorporated in the universe of inquiry may also reflect or condition the consequences of different characteristics of sustenance organization being present or absent.

The Connecting Mechanisms

It will be noted that the non-material aspects of man's culture that do not pertain to technology or sustenance organization—whether conceived as values, motives, attitudes, or sentiments—have been excluded from the universe of inquiry. Since the exclusion of such variables has been considered in the past the ultimate weakness of human ecology, as witness Alihan[11] and Firey,[12] some justification must be given for their exclusion.

Underlying the subject matter of human ecology and serving as a connection between it and the variables included in the universe of inquiry, there is a mechanism that operates independently of cultural values and the individual motives of men; this mechanism is *selective survival*, the cornerstone of most ecological theory.

As a hypothetical illustration of the role of selective survival, let us suppose that under the condition of an infertile geographic situation, $G1$, a certain type of sustenance organization, $S1$, and a certain type of technological system, $T1$, are necessary to support a population of size $P1$ at a minimum level of subsistence. Faced with situation $G1$ and having neither $S1$ nor $T1$, a population larger than $P1$ has only four choices: change its mode of sustenance organization and technological system to types $S1$ and $T1$, decrease its size, leave the area, or perish. In neither case will the behavior of the population refute the empirical law that links the four variables. This remains true regardless of the cultural values prevailing in the population. In short, there are conditions which determine the survival of populations that are not subject to the "definition of the situation."[13]

The inference should not be drawn from the above illustration that human ecology deals only with populations that hover on a bare subsistence level. On the contrary, the writers maintain that the characteristics of sustenance organization are connected to the variables in the universe of inquiry through causal relationships as well as selective survival. These causal relationships, like the relationships that arise through selective survival, exist independently of motives or values; but, in addition, they also hold regardless of how far a population is above a bare subsistence level. As an instance of this let us consider the population of the United States with a view toward accounting for its high degree of division of labor (a characteristic of its sustenance organization) and high standard of living. It can be hypothesized that the high degree of division of labor in the United States has been made possible in part by certain technological developments (notably in transportation and communication) and population growth. It is possible that the population of the United States could survive without its present degree of division of labor, but this does not negate the fact that a certain population size and level of technological development is probably a necessary condition for a high degree of division of labor.

The standard of living enjoyed by a population is here considered to be an economic variable rather than a characteristic of sustenance organization; however, there is reason to believe that differential levels in the standard of living among populations is in large part the consequence of variability in the modes of sustenance organization. While it is possible to construct a very plausible explanation of the extraordinary standard of living in the United States by linking it to cultural values and the American character, such an explanation merely takes for granted the complex structure of sustenance organization which makes possible such an abundance of material things. The structure of sustenance organization in the United States may indeed not explain why Americans supposedly value an abundance of material things, but it probably goes a long way toward explaining how such an abundance is possible.

Other Conceptions of Human Ecology

The idea that sustenance organization is the appropriate subject matter of human ecology is not regarded by the writers as a radical departure from the main currents in the field. On the contrary, one of the reasons for taking this position is the promise it shows of bringing together many contrasting views. Such views have been aptly described by Quinn [14] and Hawley [15] and can only be referred to most briefly here.

Human ecology is not identical with human geography, [16] but all that is involved in human geography is of relevance to human ecology. The two fields differ in that human ecology incorporates more variables within its universe of inquiry and strives more for the status of a generalizing science, and, especially, in that it is primarily rather than secondarily concerned with the organizational characteristics of human populations. [17]

In a certain sense it is true that human ecology is an application of biological principles. [18] Biological variables are the key to one of the mechanisms that underlies ecological relations: If populations are to survive, their mode of sustenance organization must meet certain indispensable biological needs. The findings of the biological sciences in their study of these needs are of relevance to the human ecologist in that he sees in them the necessity for sustenance organization in a given population to take on certain characteristics ant not others.

The connection between biology and human ecology would not be construed as going beyond the fact that the former points to the physiological necessities for survival. This point is stressed because the writers feel that the field must not be tied too closely to the concepts of plant and animal ecology even though the obtaining of sustenance is a common interest in all cases. From Park [19] to Hawley [20] borrowed concepts have dominated theory without contributing to its advancement. Some of these concepts, "competition" being a prime example, have never had their empirical referents clearly established in the human sphere and consequently have produced only purely verbal explanations. Other concepts, such as invasion and succession, far from providing adequate explanations, have only served to further the almost exclusive concern with spatial distribution. [21] In either case, plant and animal concepts, taken as a whole, have a most questionable relevance for human ecology since they do not get at the fundamental attributes of sustenance organization in human populations. Sustenance organization *is* social and *is* cultural; but this does not mean that it is concerned with values, attitudes, or other variables of a psychological nature.

As stated earlier, the establishment of the consequences of the different characteristics of sustenance organization is the second goal of the human ecologist. This second goal may entail the analysis of social and cultural areas such as those studied by Frazier, [22] Anderson, [23] and Zorbaugh. [24] For studies of social and cultural areas to lay claim to having an ecological character, however, sustenance organization as the dependent variable must be the focus of attention. This was certainly not the case for most of the studies of the Chicago school, nor is it the case for contemporary "social area" studies. [25]

Human ecology as the study of sustenance organization has a very close relationship with economics. However, the two are by no means identical. Whereas economists are ordinarily interested in the interrelationships of such variables as supply, demand, cost, and prices within a given sustenance organization structure, ecologists are concerned with the characteristics of the structure itself. Furthermore, the structure of sustenance organization within a population is described by the human ecologist not in economic terms but by reference to certain types of social relationships. [26] The full import of this distinction can best be appreciated when one considers a comparison of the U.S.S.R. and the United States. The economic systems of the two are far more different than are the structures of their sustenance organization. The two nations are quite similar from the viewpoint of human ecology in that sustenance activities in both are characterized by a high degree of division of labor and the predominance of large collective sustenance organizations.

While maintaining that disproportionate emphasis has been placed in human ecology on the spatial distribution of phenomena, the writers do not suggest that it be ignored. For one thing, the particular pattern of the spatial location of society's sustenance organizations is probably of consideral importance to the efficiency of its operation. Furthermore, there is evidence to suggest that the characteristics of sustenance organization influence the spatial distribution of non-sustenance phenomena. In the study of the spatial distribution of the latter phenomena, however, as in the analysis of social and cultural areas, the ecologist should be seeking to establish the consequences of the different characteristics of sustenance organization. In so doing the ecologist goes beyond the purely descriptive studies of spatial distribution which have come to characterize much of contemporary human ecology.

Space as a physical phenomenon is within human ecology's universe of inquiry in that it is a geographical feature which confronts populations and individuals in organizing their sustenance activities. There is evidence to indicate that it has definite influence on both the location and development of sustenance organizations.[27] Where space is taken as a determinant in theory construction, as exemplified by Zipf,[28] Stewart,[29] and Dodd,[30] the theory would be regarded as ecological only if it was concerned with the relationships between space and sustenance organization.

The writers would insist that communities and regions[31] be regarded as ecological units, but they should be considered as units of observation, not as the subject matter of the field as is now frequently the case. The same may be said for cities and metropolitan regions. These areal units are of interest to human ecology not because they have spatial dimensions but rather because they represent a mode of sustenance organization and occupy positions in the structure of the sustenance organization of society as a whole. The ultimate goal for human ecology in the study of these areal units should be the same as that in the study of societies—to explain the presence or absence of the different characteristics of sustenance organization and to establish the consequences of their presence or absence.

The writers have not been successful in attempting to come to terms with each and all of the divergent points of view regarding the subject matter of human ecology. A case in point is the conception of human ecology offered by J. W. Bews who pictures the field as an inclusive synthesis of all of the human sciences.[32] Granted the desirability, it would appear that an attempt on the part of human ecologists to provide this synthesis could only be regarded as delusions of grandeur. In seeking a goal that is too far beyond them, human ecologists stand to lose what little unity is within their power to achieve.

Discussion and Conclusions

The conception of sustenance organization as the subject matter of human ecology provides a basis for bringing together many contrasting points of view in the field. While human ecology as described here draws on or is related to demography, biology, human geography, and economics it is not identical with any of these disciplines. It provides a rallying point for sociologists interested in a crucially important aspect of all social systems—organization to provide the population with a quantity and variety of material things. It provides a more specific subject matter than the all encompassing "adjustment to environment" advocated by some ecologists, and a more theoretically meaningful one than the spatial distribution of phenomena. But in each case it allows for divergent interests. On the one hand, organization for sustenance is one of man's most effective ways of adjusting to his environment; on the other hand, much more needs to be known about the spatial patterning of man's sustenance activities and the way it influences the spatial distribution of his other activities.

Above all, human ecology as considered here is deemed capable of achieving the status of a generalizing science, with its generalizations being testable propositions which are linked to a common frame of reference.

Notes and References

1. Amos Hawley, *Human Ecology*, New York: Ronald Press, 1950.

2. *Ibid.*, p. v.

3. For elaboration of this point see Gideon Sjoberg, "Urban Community Theory and Research: A Partial Evaluation," *American Journal of Economics and Sociology*, 14 (January, 1955), pp. 199-206.

4. Consider, for example, the heterogeneous nature of the subject matter of human ecology as suggested in the following publications: H. Warren Dunham, "The Ecology of the Functional Psychoses in Chicago," *American Sociological Review*, 2 (August, 1937), pp. 467-479; W. S. Robinson, "Ecological Correlations and the Behavior of Individuals," *American Sociological Review*, 15 (June, 1950), pp. 351-357; John A. Kinneman and Shirley E. Shipley, "The Ecology of Pluralities in Presidential Elections," *American Sociological Review*, 10 (June, 1945), pp. 382-389; Calvin F. Schmid, "Generalizations Concerning the Ecology of the American City," *American Sociological Review*, 15 (April, 1950), pp. 264-281.

A review of the literature leads one to the conclusion that human ecology is viewed by sociologists as nothing more than a method or as a field concerned only with the spatial distribution of phenomena, whether cemeteries or crimes. Of 51 articles listed in the ecology section of the last index to the *American Sociological Review*, no less than 30 give the impression that human ecology is the study of the spatial distribution of human phenomena; and there is little commonality among the remaining 21 articles, some of which treat ecology as a method. In the last index to the *American Journal of Sociology* 9 of the 17 articles in the ecology section suggest that spatial distribution is the subject matter of the field.

5. In this connection the method of input-output analysis holds forth a possible frame of reference for human ecology. See Walter Isard, Robert A. Kavesh, and Robert E. Kuenne, "The Economic Base and Structure of the Urban-Metropolitan Region," *American Sociological Review*, 18 (June, 1953), pp. 317-321.

6. While the distinction between governmental and non-governmental territories is not always distinct and relevant, it is sometimes crucial, and is usually associated with differential availability of data and other methodological problems.

7. For a treatment of human ecology as "the study of the spatial aspects of sociological events" see Don Martindale and Elio D. Monachesi, *Elements of Sociology*, New York: Harper and Brothers, 1951, pp. 676-677.

8. Noel P. Gist and L. A. Halbert, *Urban Society*, Fourth Edition, New York: Thomas Y. Crowell Company, 1956, pp. 75-76.

9. See Hawley, op. cit., pp. 101-102.

10. Of particular interest here are the works of Fred Cottrell, *Energy and Society*, New York: McGraw-Hill, 1955; Leslie A. White, *The Science of Culture: A Study of Man and Civilization*, New York: Farrar, Straus and Co., 1949; and William Fielding Ogburn, "Population, Private Ownership, Technology, and the Standard of Living," *American Journal of Sociology*, 56 (January, 1951), pp. 314-319.

11. Milla A. Alihan, *Social Ecology: A Critical Analysis*, New York: Columbia University Press, 1938.

12. Walter Firey, *Land Use in Central Boston*, Cambridge: Harvard University Press, 1947.

13. This does not deny that such socio-psychological factors may influence the selection of one alternative over others. That is, cultural values in one society may facilitate technological change but hamper it in another. "Sustenance activities are inextricably interwoven with sentiments, value systems, and other ideational constructs." (Hawley, op. cit., p. 73.) The problem of human ecology, however, is to develop generalizations about sustenance organization at a level that does not include individual motivations and attitudes. For a classic statement on the irrelevance of purposes and motives see William G. Sumner, "Purposes and Consequences" in Albert G. Keller (ed.), *Earth-Hunger and Other Essays*, New Haven: Yale University Press, 1913, pp. 67-75. An excellent example of this type of analysis is presented in Joseph B. Birdsell, "Some Environmental and Cultural Factors Influencing the Structuring of Australian Aboriginal Populations," *The American Naturalist*, LXXXVII (May-June, 1953), 171-207.

14. James E. Quinn, *Human Ecology*, New York: Prentice-Hall, 1950, pp. 4-11.

15. Hawley, op. cit., Chapter 4.

16. As instances of this view see Harlan H. Barrows, "Geography as Human Ecology," *Annals of the Association of American Geographers*, 13 (March, 1923), pp. 1-14; C. Langdon White and George T. Renner, *Geography: An Introduction to Human Ecology*, New York: D. Appleton-Century Co., 1936.

17. As an example of a geographic analysis placing emphasis on sustenance organization see Gunnar Alexanderson, *The Industrial Structure of American Cities*, Lincoln: University of Nebraska, 1956.

18. See Charles C. Adams, "The Relation of General Ecology to Human Ecology," *Ecology*, 16 (July, 1935), pp. 316-335; W. C. Allee, *The Social Life of Animals*, New York: W. W. Norton and Co., 1938, chapter 7.

19. Robert E. Park, "Human Ecology," *American Journal of Sociology*, 42 (July, 1936), pp. 1-15.

20. Hawley, op. cit., passim.

21. Actually, of course, these concepts were borrowed earlier by plant and animal ecology from the social sciences. The important point is that they made this round trip without adding to their value as explanatory concepts. All too frequently the act of labeling a phenomenon as "invasion" or "succession" is treated as explanation.

22. E. Franklin Frazier, *The Negro Family in Chicago*, Chicago: University of Chicago Press, 1932.

23. Nels Anderson, *The Hobo*, Chicago: University of Chicago Press, 1923.

24. Harvey W. Zorbaugh, *The Gold Coast and the Slum*, Chicago: University of Chicago Press, 1929.

25. See Eshref Shevky and Marilyn Williams, *The Social Areas of Los Angeles: Analysis and Typology*, Berkeley and Los Angeles: University of California Press, 1949; Eshref Shevky and Wendell Bell, *Social Area Analysis: Theory, Illustrative Application and Computation Procedures*, Stanford: Stanford University Press, Stanford Sociological Series, No. 1, 1955; Robert C. Tyron, *Identification of Social Areas by Cluster Analysis: A General Method with an Application to the San Francisco Bay Area*, Berkeley: University of California Press, 1955.

26. There are, of course, many economic analyses that are of relevance to human ecology. It is important to note, however, that the most relevant works are those in which "economy" and "economics" are conceived in very broad terms. See N. S. B. Gras, *An Introduction to Economic History*, New York: Harper and Brothers, 1922.

27. See Walter Isard, *Location and Space Economy*, Cambridge: Technology Press of Massachusetts Institute of Technology, 1956, chapter III.

28. George Kingsley Zipf, *Human Behavior and the Principle of Least Effort*, Cambridge: Addison-Wesley Press, 1949, pp. 386-409.

29. John Q. Stewart, "The Development of Social Physics," *American Journal of Physics*, 19 (May, 1950), pp. 239-253.

30. Stuart Carter Dodd, "The Interactance Hypothesis: A Gravity Model Fitting Physical Masses and Human Groups," *American Sociological Review*, 15 (April, 1950), pp. 245-256.

31. For examples of the conception of human ecology as the study of communities and/or regions see Howard W. Odum and Harry E. Moore, *American Regionalism*, New York: Henry Holt and Co., 1938; R. K. Mukerjee, "Social Ecology of a River Valley," *Sociology and Social Research*, 12 (March-April, 1928), pp. 341-347 and *The Regional Balance of Man: An Ecological Theory of Population*, Madras: Indian University of Madras, 1938; C. J. Galpin, *The Social Anatomy of an Agricultural Community*,

Madison: Agricultural Experiment Station of the University of Wisconsin, Research Bulletin 24, May, 1915; Quinn, op. cit.; Hawley, op. cit.

32. J. W. Bews, *Human Ecology*, London: Oxford University Press, 1935, p. 14.

The Adaptive Potentialities of Man
Rene Dubos

Adaptedness vs. Adaptability

Throughout prehistory and history, *Homo sapiens* and his societies have utilized many different genotypic, phenotypic, psychic, and social mechanisms in order to adapt to new environmental situations. This biological and social versatility accounts for the spectacular and continued success of the human species. Now that man can alter his physical environment so profoundly and modify it so rapidly to his ends, there is a tendency to believe that the biological mechanisms on which he has depended for adaptation in the past have become of negligible importance. It is commonly stated that the human species can without danger afford to lose the physical and mental qualities that used to be essential for its survival, because it can create an environment in which these attributes are no longer needed.

It is true indeed that Western man is able through his technology to shut out many of the environmental insults he could not avoid until a few decades ago and to which he had therefore to react adaptively. Air conditioning allows him to work in an office, at the North Pole or in Timbuktu, dressed as if he were in a South Seas paradise; he is almost unconcerned with seasonal shortages of food; he need never experience actual hunger and thirst and may have the diet of his choice anywhere in the world at any time of the year. He can in theory make his environment so free of pathogens and other microbes that his immune mechanisms come less and less into play. He can control illumination, both quantitatively and qualitatively, filter out some of the solar radiations in summer, and expose himself to the southern sun or to artificial radiation in winter. He can withdraw from noise in a cork-lined room, yet maintain the desired degree of auditory stimulus with background music if he so wishes. He is learning to control his biological and emotional responses by the use of drugs that selectively inhibit or stimulate various biochemical and physiological processes. In brief, modern man can almost orchestrate at will the nature and intensity of the stimuli he receives from the external world, and he can exercise some measure of control over his responses to them.

Because he can manipulate so many aspects of his environment, and also govern to some extent the operations of his body and his mind, modern man has entered a phase of his evolution in which many of his ancient biological attributes are no longer called into play and may therefore atrophy through disuse. As a whole, the human race has lost much of the physical strength it had in the days of the caveman, when survival required the ability to fight savage beasts with clubs, or even with bare fists.

For all his strength and primitive resourcefulness, on the other hand, the caveman would not get along well in a modern city. The present environment demands a different kind of man. Natural selection cannot possibly maintain the state of adaptiveness to an environment that no longer exists, any more than it can adapt human populations to environments that have not yet been created. Yet because of technological advances, such new environments will continue to appear at an accelerated rate. In order to keep pace with them, human evolution will therefore have to depend even more than in the past on cultural and social evolution.

Since man is able to eliminate or avoid many of the struggles and stresses which used to be his fate, it seems to follow that his biological mechanisms of adaptation have become useless, or at least obsolete. Paradoxically, however, the very avoidance of stresses may in itself constitute a new kind of threat to health if it is carried too far, because the body and the mind are geared for responding to challenges; they lose many of their essential qualities in an environment that is so bland as to make life effortless. [M]an retains in his biological and emotional make-up the structures, functions, and needs that emerged during his evolutionary past, and it is certain that some form of challenge continues to be necessary for his normal development and performance. For example, the personality structure breaks down as a result of sensory deprivation and the intestinal tract fails to develop normally in animals raised under germ-free conditions. The complete absence of challenge can thus be as deleterious as excessive intensity of environmental stimuli.

Human history shows, furthermore, that the same kind of knowledge that permits man to alter his environment for the purpose of minimizing effort, achieving comfort, and avoiding exposure to stress also gives him the power to change his environment and ways of life in a manner that often entails unpredictable dangers. The ability to adapt to the unforeseeable—threats of the future therefore remains an indispensable condition of survival and biological success. Even if it were possible for man to achieve a perfect state of adaptedness to the environmental conditions which prevail now, such a state would not be suited to the conditions of the future. The state of adaptedness to the world of today may be incompatible with survival in the world of tomorrow.

Paleontological studies have established that narrow adaptation of a species is a frequent prelude to its extinction because it jeopardizes its ability to adapt itself to changing conditions. Similarly, it is dangerous to assume that man need be adapted only to the conditions of the present, created by today's form of urban living and industrial technology. This state of adaptedness gives a false sense of security because it does not have a lasting value and does not prepare for the future. It must be supplemented by the attribute of adaptability.

Balanced polymorphism provides a basis for a kind of adaptability based on genetic mechanisms. But adaptability involves, in addition, many phenotypic processes which have not been defined, let alone studied experimentally. The most that can be done at the present time perhaps is to approach the evaluation of adaptability through measurements of the tolerance or reserve of body processes for various inputs, loads, and resistances.

The various tolerance tests used in clinical medicine make it possible to acquire some quantitative knowledge of the range of activities of which a person is potentially capable. Mild physiological defects that otherwise remain unnoticed can be revealed by the application of increased loads or resistances on body processes. For example, administration of glucose, or evaluation of effect of cortisone on its utilization, can reveal levels of diabetes so low as to be inapparent under basal conditions. Similarly, an increased venous inflow load, or aortic outflow resistance, can bring out unsuspected hemodynamic evidence of cardiac failure. More generally, it can be said that when input load and opposing resistances exceed available capacity, the process fails to deal effectively with all of the input presented to it, and disease ensues. Conversely, when available capacity exceeds input load and resistances, the process exhibits a high degree of reserve or tolerance.[1]

Tolerance tests, in their various forms, have been systematically developed so far only for a few physiological systems, and their use has been considered only with regard to the diagnosis of disease states. It would seem possible, however, that their extension could enlarge the knowledge of man's potentialities. In other words, judicious utilization of tolerance tests might make it possible to obtain some objective knowledge of what a particular person, or mankind in general, is capable of doing, overcoming, and learning, both physically and mentally. Such an approach might provide data for the evaluation of adaptability, i.e. of the potential ability for adaptation to new environmental circumstances and new challenges.

Adaptation to Modern Life

The social history of man leaves no doubt that he was in the past endowed with a wide range of adaptive potentialities and that he has retained most of this attribute at least until very recent times. Pollution of the air in the industrial cities of Northern Europe provides a striking illustration of the extent to which modern man can make some kind of successful adjustment to environmental conditions that appear at first sight extremely hostile to both his body and his mind.

Ever since the beginning of the nineteenth century, certain parts of Northern Europe have experienced a characteristic kind of smog determined by the cold humidity of the Atlantic weather and by the burning of large amounts of soft coal for domestic and industrial purposes. This smog, loaded with soot, sulfur oxides, and mineral acids, is extremely unpleasant to breathe and creates an atmosphere of gloom that is almost unbearable for those who are not accustomed to it. But the inhabitants of the industrial areas of Northern Europe have come to accept their dark, polluted skies as a matter of course. They grumble, of course, against soot, grit, and irritating fumes, but they manage nevertheless to create a stimulating and satisfying human atmosphere out of their dreary surroundings—witness the following description, written in 1963, of Huddersfield, the Yorkshire town where the technical revolution began two centuries ago:

> The long huddle of the textile mills, creeping away to the moor's edge; the marching file of tall brick chimneys, their vapours drifting into the dusk; the coveys of cramped terrace houses, jammed hugger mugger against the hillsides; the dingy red brick everywhere, the patina of dirt, labor and middle age. . . . Here in these grim moorlands of Northern England, the technical revolution began. . . .
>
> She is now a clubable town, rich in choral societies and brass bands—she has evolved a society that is, as human institutions go, strong, decent and kindly. . . .
>
> So she looks, two centuries after the event, and this is a comfort. In Cairo or Kiruna or the Indian steel towns—they can draw upon her for encouragement. The cruelty, she seems to say, need not be permanent. The degradation will not last.[2]

A recent social survey of the Lancashire city of Leigh, near Manchester (England), provides a similar picture of human adaptation to unhealthy and dreary surroundings. The mill dominates the town, the air is gritty, obscured by smog, but human life is not defeated by the murky environment. The sociologists found in Leigh a vigorous, thriving culture, and a deep involvement in community affairs. Everywhere in Northern Europe the people of the industrialized areas have indeed managed to create a way of life that is spirited and emotionally warm despite soot, grit, and gloomy skies. They have remained highly active and productive physically, biologically, and intellectually. Their expectancy of life is not very different from that of people of the same stock and economic status living in uncontaminated areas, nor is their birth rate smaller. Two hundred years of history thus demonstrate that human beings can become adjusted to contaminated and darkened atmospheres. The raping of nature by technology does not necessarily make the environment incompatible with human life.

Much the same story can be told of other forms of threats created by technological innovations. There is little doubt concerning the toxicity of most of the pesticides, food additives, and other synthetic chemicals that contaminate air, food, water, and many of the objects with which the people of Western civilization now come into daily contact. But paradoxically, it is also true that the countries in which these potentially dangerous synthetic chemicals are most widely used are also the ones in which life expectancy is now the longest. We shall see later that there is another side to this picture. But for the time being, and in the Western world at least, mankind seems to take environmental pollution in stride.

The dangers posed by the agitation and tensions of modern life constitute another topic for which public fears are not based on valid evidence. Most city dwellers seem to fare well enough under these tensions; their mental health is on the whole as good as that of country people. Indeed, there is no proof whatever that mental diseases are more common or more serious among them now than they were in the past, or than they are among primitive people. They are not even different in kind.

The experience of urbanized and industrialized societies bears witness therefore to the fact that everywhere man can make some sort of adjustment to crowding, to environmental pollution, to emotional tensions, and certainly to many other kinds of organic and emotional stresses. It is not difficult to imagine how the people of the pre-industrial era would have reacted if they had been suddenly transported to our world of automobile traffic, polluted air, shrill noises, blinding artificial lights, and intense competition. All would have suffered, physically and mentally; many would have died; only very few would have been capable of functioning effectively in our "unnatural" environment. Yet, people of all origins, races, and colors, have now become adjusted to the artificial world created by modern industrial and urban civilization. In fact, city dwellers would find it difficult to return to the ways of life of not so long ago. The mechanized world of the modern city, which would have appeared so unnatural to our ancestors, has now become the natural environment, outside of which Western man can hardly survive.

The Price of Adaptation
If the ability to survive, multiply, and function were the only criteria by which to evaluate the dangers posed by modern technology, or by demographic and economic growth, the future of mankind would provide little

cause for worry at the present time. On the one hand, there still exist in human nature large untapped reservoirs of biological adaptive potentialities, genotypic as well as phenotypic. In addition, there is no foreseeable limit to the variety and extent of the social adaptative mechanisms that man can bring to bear on the external world, in order to modify it according to his needs and wishes. Short of nuclear warfare, it would seem therefore that mankind will be able to take the stresses of the future in stride, just as it has survived destructive famines and epidemics in the past. One can almost take it for granted that mankind will adapt itself to the new ways of life created by the second industrial revolution, and even to the crowding, shortages, and other ordeals likely to result from the much dreaded increase in the world population.

Recent history confirms indeed that modern man can still make adjustments to an astonishingly wide range of threatening situations, even to some that appear at first sight almost incompatible with life. During the last war, many different kinds of persons managed to survive and to function, under circumstances so appalling as to be almost beyond the range of human imagination and belief—either the exhausting and frightening experience of combat, or starvation and torture in concentration camps.

However, the potential ability of mankind to survive crowding, emotional misery, environmental pollution, shortages of natural resources, and other kinds of threats constitutes but a limited aspect of the problem of adaptation. Other aspects have their origin in the fact that human life involves values which have little to do with biological needs and which transcend the survival of individual persons. All too often, the biological and social changes that enable mankind to overcome the threats posed by the modern world must be eventually paid for at a cruel price in terms of human values.

Sudden and profound changes in the ways of life, whatever their nature, always bring about a decrease in the resistance of the body and the mind to almost any kind of insult. But the social and medical problems associated with this early phase of change tend to be transitory. More important in the long run, even though less dramatic, are the distant consequences of some of the adaptive processes that make it possible for man to survive the deleterious consequences of the rapid changes brought about by technological innovations and by social revolutions.

One of these consequences is the accumulation of hereditary defects brought about by medical and technological procedures that allow many persons to survive and reproduce who would have left no progeny in the past. While it is likely that mutation rates are increasing, the modern ways of life are interfering with the elimination of undesirable genes; natural selection is more and more embarrassed by social and medical practices. True enough, the effects of genetic degeneration are so slow that they are usually overlooked or are accepted as a part of the natural order; but the most destructive operations of the living world are precisely those of a creeping, secular character.

It is misleading, of course, to speak of biological defectives without regard to the kind of environment in which man lives and functions. Medical techniques can make up for many forms of genetic and other deficiencies that would be lethal in the wilderness. While it is certain that the physically handicapped could not long survive under "natural" conditions, it is also true that medical and other social skills make it possible for men to live long and function effectively in the modern world even though they be tuberculous, diabetic, blind, crippled, or psychopathic. Fitness is not an absolute characteristic, but rather must be defined in terms of the total environment in which the individual has to spend his life.

On the other hand, it is often overlooked that fitness achieved through constant medical care has grave social and economic implications that will become manifest only in the future. We can expect that the cost of medical care will continue to soar, because each new discovery calls into use more specialized skills and more expensive equipment and products. There is certainly a limit to the percentage of society's resources that can be devoted to the prevention and treatment of disease. Furthermore, it must not be taken for granted that the power of science is limitless. Only during the past few decades and in but a few situations has medical treatment enabled the victims of genetic disabilities to survive and to reproduce on a large scale. If the numbers of biologically defective individuals continue to increase, therapy may not be able to keep pace with the new problems that will inevitably arise.

The possibility of genetic deterioration is not the only threat that arises from the biotechnological advances through which mankind becomes adapted to the modern world. Many of the processes thereby set in motion have phenotypic effects that remain unnoticed at first, but eventually play havoc with the human values of life. Environmental pollution illustrates the fact that many of the adjustments that facilitate life in a hostile environment commonly express themselves at a later date in disease and human misery. As mentioned earlier, the inhabitants of the industrial areas of Northern Europe behave as if they had made a successful adjustment to massive air pollution. But while they function effectively despite the presence of irritating substances in the atmosphere they breathe, the linings of their respiratory tracts register the insult. Each exposure leaves its marks, and after several years the cumulative effects of the irritation result in irreversible pulmonary disease.

Chronic bronchitis in the industrial areas of Northern Europe provides a model for the kind of medical problems likely to arise in the future from the various forms of environmental pollution in our own communities. In the great majority of cases, control over chemical pollution of air, water, and food is sufficiently strict to prevent obvious toxic effects. But while neither the acute toxicity nor the nuisance value of environmental pollution is great enough to interfere seriously with social and economic life, a vastly more important danger comes from the likelihood that repeated exposure to low levels of toxic and irritating agents will eventually result in a great variety of delayed pathological manifestations.

As in the case of environmental pollution, the possibility exists that the apparently successful adjustments to the emotional stresses caused by competitive behavior and crowding can result in delayed organic and mental disease. Through the experience of social intercourse, man learns to control the outward manifestations of his emotional responses. He usually manages to conceal his impatience, irritations, and hostile feelings behind a mask of civil behavior. But inwardly he still responds to emotional stimuli by means of physiological mechanisms inherited from his Paleolithic ancestry and even from his animal past. The ancient fight and flight response still operates in him, calling into play the autonomic nervous system and various hormonal mechanisms that generate useless and potentially dangerous physiological reactions. It is probable, as we have seen, that these misguided responses leave scars which eventually threaten the body and the mind as they accumulate through the years.

The fight and flight response is only one of the many traits that man has retained from his evolutionary past. His bodily mechanisms are still linked to the daily rotation of the earth around its axis and to its annual rotation around the sun, as well as to other cosmic events. The natural rhythms that are built into his body fabric thus often conflict with those which govern his social life. Man is so adaptable, true enough, that he can carry his day into the night and move at supersonic speed from one latitude to another, unconcerned with the instructions of biological rhythms. But while he can usually make the necessary physiological adjustments, these always involve severe hormonal disturbances. It is not unlikely that the ultimate outcome of these disturbances will become more serious, as life becomes more mechanized and more acutely dissociated from the natural cycles. In fact . . . evidence of pathological effects has been obtained in experimental animals maintained for prolonged periods under physical conditions differing from those of their natural rhythms.

A last example will suffice to illustrate the wide range of threats to health arising from the adjustments that man makes to the new ways of life. Immense strides have been made toward the control of the acute infectious diseases which used to be responsible for so many deaths. However, many other kinds of diseases are still caused by microbes that are ubiquitous and become active when the resistance of the body is lowered. Yet, physicians, as well as laymen, have come to accept as a matter of course a situation in which many days every year are sacrificed to so-called "minor" infections, despite the fact that these ailments have an importance that goes beyond their nuisance value. They erode the functional integrity of the organism, progressively damaging the respiratory, digestive, or urinary tracts, as well as the kidneys and perhaps also the blood vessels. They too probably play their part in the so-called diseases of civilization.

The aspect of the problem of adaptation that is probably the most disturbing is paradoxically the very fact that human beings are so adaptable. This very adaptability enables them to become adjusted to conditions and habits which will eventually destroy the values most characteristic of human life.

Millions upon millions of human beings are so well adjusted to the urban and industrial environment that they no longer mind the stench of automobile exhausts, or the ugliness generated by the urban sprawl; they regard it as normal to be trapped in automobile traffic, to spend much of a sunny afternoon on concrete highways among the dreariness of anonymous and amorphous streams of motor cars. Life in the modern city has become a symbol of the fact that man can become adapted to starless skies, treeless avenues, shapeless buildings, tasteless bread, joyless celebrations, spiritless pleasures—to a life without reverence for the past, love for the present, or hope for the future.

Man is so adaptable that he could survive and multiply in underground shelters, even though his regimented subterranean existence left him unaware of the robin's song in the spring, the whirl of dead leaves in the fall, and the moods of the wind—even though indeed all his ethical and esthetic values should wither. It is disheartening to learn that today in the United States schools are being built underground, with the justification that the rooms are easier to clean and the children's attention not distracted by the outdoors!

The frightful threat posed by adaptability when the concept is applied to human beings in a purely biological context is that it implies so often a passive acceptance of conditions which really are not desirable for mankind. The lowest common denominators of existence tend to become the accepted criteria, merely for the sake of a gray and anonymous peace or tranquility. The ideal environment tends to become one in which man is physically comfortable, but progressively forgets the values that constitute the unique qualities of human life.

The biological view of adaptation is inadequate for human life because neither survival of the body, nor of the species, nor fitness to the conditions of the present, suffice to encompass the richness of man's nature. The uniqueness of man comes from the fact that he does not live only in the present; he still carries the past in his body and in his mind, and he is concerned with the future. To be really relevant to the human condition, the concept of adaptability must incorporate not only the needs of the present, but also the limitations imposed by the past, and the anticipations of the future. Above and beyond all, man is still of the earth, earthy, notwithstanding all the technological and medical advances that superficially seem to dissociate him from his evolutionary past. As happened to Anteus of the Greek legend, his strength will probably wane if he loses contact with the biological ground from which he emerged and which still feeds him, physically and emotionally.

Notes and References

1. Fenster, J. H. Load Tolerances: A Quantitative Estimate of Health. *Annals of International Medicine*, Vol. 57, pp. 788-94. (1962)

2. Morris, J. Ticket to Huddersfield. *Encounter*, Vol. 20, pp. 16-27. (1963)

Selected References for Chapter 1

Duncan, Otis Dudley, "Social Organization and the Ecosystem," *Handbook of Modern Sociology*, ed. R. E. L. Faris. Chicago: Rand-McNally Co., 1964, pp. 36-82. A comprehensive introduction to the sociological approach to ecosystem analysis.

Hawley, Amos H., *Human Ecology*. New York: The Ronald Press, 1950. Still the most useful introduction to the field.

Lenski, Gerhard, *Human Societies: A Macrolevel Introduction to Sociology*. New York: McGraw-Hill Book Co., 1970. An introduction to the field of Sociology based upon an "ecological-evolutionary" perspective.

Odum, Eugene P., *Fundamentals of Ecology*, 3rd ed. Philadelphia: W. B. Saunders Co., 1971. A thorough and readable introduction to general ecology.

Having considered these broad parameters of ecological organization, we will now turn to a more specific examination of the basic elements involved. These consist of (1) population structure and process, (2) the external, non-human environment, and (3) socially organized activities and relationships. Chapter 2 presents a brief consideration of the relationships among these components of ecological systems.

2 Population, Environment, Social Organization: The Raw Materials of Collective Survival

The readings for Chapter 2 begin with an essay on social organization. More specifically, it is an attempt by Leo Schnore to spell out the continuities between Emile Durkheim's concept of "social morphology," as illustrated in his early study of the division of labor in society, and some current perspectives on human ecology. The author not only outlines the major features of Durkheim's position, but also fills in gaps in the original argument and demonstrates linkages with more recently formulated ecological schemes.

Two aspects of Schnore's argument require further comment. The first concerns his observation that Durkheim did not give adequate attention to the role of the physical environment as a vital and permissive factor with respect to human activities. Schnore suggests that environmental considerations are important because the environment may be both cause and consequence of organizational structure and change. His approach differs from mine in that he appears to emphasize the environment as an independent variable affecting social morphology rather than viewing morphological arrangements as mechanisms for dealing with the environment. Both views are legitimate but, for reasons mentioned earlier and expanded below, the latter approach seems to be more productive for building ecological theory and understanding organizational aspects of human survival.

Schnore's second important revision of the Durkheimian scheme is contained in his discussion of the role of competition in relation to the division of labor. Durkheim viewed increased differentiation (and concomitant functional specialization) as a resolution to the struggle for survival. But Schnore indicates a series of alternative mechanisms available to human populations, specifically focusing on (1) demographic, (2) technological, and (3) organizational changes, though recognizing that his list of alternatives is not exhaustive. This is an important point, as it is a step toward identifying the specific socially-organized strategies through which collective survival is achieved. Schnore's position differs from that utilized in the present book in terms of the specific mechanisms identified and the place of demographic and organizational variables in the model.

Schnore's argument makes a key contribution to the development of contemporary human ecology. First, it directly links Durkheim's early ideas on the causes and functions of structural variations to more recent conceptual frameworks, while at the same time modifying them in light of subsequent developments. Second, it highlights the central role of social organization in mediating ecological arrangements. Finally, it suggests one possible approach to developing a systematic theory of human ecology.[1]

The second contribution to this chapter outlines some of the historical developments and anticipated changes in the demography of human populations. It is evident from Durand's discussion that excessive population growth has emerged as a crucial problem affecting human survival only within the twentieth century, and significantly so only since the early 1950s. Furthermore, projections for the future do not suggest much basis for optimism regarding a reduction in man's numbers.

Two demographic conditions are proposed to account for the aforementioned growth trends. First, and of primary significance, is the drastic reduction in mortality that has resulted from man's increased ability to control disease and famine. Second, only in the more economically developed nations have reductions in fertility been achieved; in the vast majority of African, Asian, and Latin American countries birth rates remain at preindustrial levels. The net result is that the world's population is now growing at an average annual rate of approximately 1.8 per cent, with the less developed countries accounting for close to eighty per cent of the total.

Durand concludes that "The crux of the present problem of world population is in the association of persistent poverty and technological retardation with unremitting rapid growth of numbers in the less developed regions." At the same time, he suggests that the problem of rapid growth itself may be a stimulus to seeking creative solutions. What these creative solutions might be, however, is a question that lies at the heart of the current ecological crisis, and will be one of the major emphases in the remainder of this volume.

The third essay, by Stanley Cain, is focused on the remaining component of our basic ecological model, the environment. While this author's discussion is quite general, he makes several key points regarding the role of the environment in human ecology. First, we are reminded that human and man-made, as well as natural, phenomena should be considered, thus resulting in the complex set of relationships often referred to as the ecosystem. At the same time Cain clearly recognizes that man has increasingly become master of his environment, to an extent that human actions—man's ability to organize for cooperative effort—have resulted in often dramatic changes in the non-human component. Reference to man's attack on nature as effective and ruthless forcefully conveys the net result of the process of adaptation in human ecosystems.

But, as Cain points out, this "single-purpose" approach has not had altogether beneficial results. As has so often been suggested, man's attempts at planning often appear, in retrospect, to have been short-sighted. Thus, we are now beginning to recognize the gap between the needs of rapidly expanding populations and the inadequacy of existing human ecosystems to meet such needs, at least at standards of living that are acceptable today. Observations of this nature point up the importance of considering environmental quality as being *at least* as significant an issue as environmental quantity. Management of the environment must take into account all the diverse dimensions of the ecosystem, not simply those which contribute to the immediate needs of technology and the economy.

The final contribution to this chapter represents an attempt to illustrate the interrelationships among components of the human ecosystem. Using urban air pollution as a concrete example, and the "ecological complex" as an analytic model, O. D. Duncan suggests the intricate connections of cause, influence, and response operating among population, organization, environment, and technology.

While this article successfully conveys the advantages of an ecosystem perspective, it also points to the need for further specification of the ecological processes at work. Particularly evident is the failure to clearly differentiate among alternative forms of organizational response to ecosystem imbalances. From the perspective elaborated in the Introduction to this volume, one might argue that the problematic condition, air pollution, is the result of the interaction of changing demographic structure, primarily through population concentration, exacerbated by technological change in the form of industrialization and motorized transportation, within the confines of a fixed natural environment. Organizational responses have included (1) a collective definition that a "problem" exists and increasing consensus that something should be done about it, (2) direction of scientific and technological activities toward various solutions, (3) organized political and legal action aimed at regulating underlying causes and, finally (4) attempts to alleviate the problem through redistribution of population (e.g., the "flight to the suburbs") or human activities (e.g., relocation of industry). By identifying these specific organizational responses one might, were the necessary data available, be able to determine which have been more or less successful and why. The point to be emphasized is that attempts to understand contemporary ecosystems must pay close attention to the organization of human activities as these constitute, in large part, both the causes of problematic imbalances and the hope for their ultimate resolution.

Notes and References

1. This approach has been outlined more fully in Otis Dudley Duncan and Leo F. Schnore, "Cultural, Behavioral, and Ecological Perspectives in the Study of Social Organization," *American Journal of Sociology*, Vol. 65 (September, 1959), pp. 132-46.

Social Morphology and Human Ecology
Leo F. Schnore

Introduction

Emile Durkheim, of course, was not himself a human ecologist. The ecological viewpoint did not develop within sociology until near the end of Durkheim's life, and then in America.[1] There is no evidence that this new approach to social phenomena exerted any profound influence upon his thought, despite the fact that he regarded "social morphology" as one of the major branches of sociology. In Durkheim's scheme, this field was to be devoted to two major inquiries: (1) the study of the environmental basis of social organization and (2) the study of population phenomena, especially size, density, and spatial distribution.[2] These areas of interest obviously converge with those of human ecology as it was originally formulated.

This paper consists of an exegesis and a critique of one of his major theoretical contributions and a consideration of the broad implications of his "morphological" analysis for contemporary human ecology. It is concerned, for the most part, with Durkheim's doctoral dissertation, *De le division du travail social: étude sur l'organisation des sociétés supérieures*, first published in 1893.[3] More particularly, the discussion is largely limited to Book II, where he dealt with the "causes" of division of labor and where the morphological approach was most explicitly used. The brief exegesis is based on a selective restructuring of his main argument, which is unfortunately scattered through many pages. We trust that taking up the crucial elements in his thought in somewhat different order does no violence to the essential logic of his position. This procedure has been adopted in order to point up the contrasts between his morphological theory of differentiation and the alternative explanations that were available at the time that he wrote.

Exegesis

First, it must be emphasized that Durkheim's intention in Book II of *Division* was to account for differentiation and its obvious increase in Western societies. The very subtitle is the key: "A Study of the Organization of Advanced Societies." Second, it is necessary to preserve the historical context of his work. The division of labor had long interested social philosophers, especially in the West. As early as 1776, Adam Smith had pointed to division as the main source of "the wealth of nations," and the concept itself can be traced at least to the Greeks. Unfortunately, these earlier writers gave scant attention to the determinants of differentiation, contenting themselves with analyses of its nature and its implications for economic efficiency and productivity.

In the latter half of the nineteenth century, however, increasing effort was given to explaining the process, with special reference to the "advanced" societies of the time. Comte dealt with the matter at some length, discussing the nature of differentiation as a generic social phenomenon.[4] Tönnies and Simmel also examined the problem in publications that preceded Durkheim's by only a few years.[5] By the time that Durkheim began his work, however, the dominant views in intellectual circles were still a peculiar admixture of utilitarian and evolutionary "explanations," both best represented in the works of Herbert Spencer. In large part, Durkheim's analysis must be seen as a reaction against the Spencerian view.

Durkheim's own analysis actually began in Book I, with a distinction between two forms of organization somewhat similar to the types sketched by Maine and Tönnies. The first type ("mechanical") was used by Durkheim to describe the relatively undifferentiated or "segmented" mode of organization characteristic of small and isolated aggregates, in which little control has been achieved over the local environment. The basis of social unity is likeness or similarity. There is minimal differentiation, chiefly along age and sex lines, and most members are engaged most of the time in the same activity—collecting, hunting, fishing, herding, or subsistence agriculture. The "social segments" of the community (families and kinship units) are held together by what they have in common, and they derive mutual support from their very likeness. Unity is that of simple "mechanical" cohesion, as in rock forms, and homogeneity prevails.[6]

Durkheim was fully aware that structural differentiation is a variable characteristic of aggregates, for he recognized another and fundamentally different mode of organization. He saw that modern Western society was based increasingly upon differentiation, and his concept of the "organic" type of organization was designed to describe the complex and highly differentiated structural arrangements of his own time. According to Durkheim, a complex and heterogeneous society, like all but the most rudimentary organisms, is based on an intricate interdependence of specialized parts. Labor is divided; all men do not engage in the same activities, but they produce and exchange different goods and services. Moreover, not only are individuals and groups differentiated with respect to functions, but whole communities and nations also engage in specialized activities. In short, there has been a breakdown of internal "segmentation" *within* communities and societies and a reduction of isolation *between* them, although mechanical solidarity never completely disappears.[7]

Transition from Mechanical Organization or Organic

With this distinction between major types of organization in mind, Durkheim's task in Book II was to explain the conditions under which "mechanical" organization is superseded by the "organic" form. According to the mode of analysis that prevailed at the time that he wrote, Durkheim viewed this change in social organization as comprising a kind of "evolutionary" sequence, and much of his theory was cast in these terms. However, it would be extremely misleading to portray his work as that of an uncritical evolutionist, for Durkheim possessed a sensitive, critical mind and he considered and rejected a number of alternative hypotheses that had been widely accepted as explanations of increasing differentiation.[8]

With respect to the popular utilitarian version, Durkheim vigorously attacked the idea that differentiation was somehow the product of man's rational desire to increase his own happiness. In fact, he rejected all individualistic interpretations. The notion that social structure is merely the product of the motivated actions of individuals was apparently almost repugnant to him. It ran directly counter to his conception of society as an entity *sui generis*, and it obviously violated his most famous principle: that "the determining cause of a social fact should be sought among the social facts preceding it and not among the states of the individual consciousness."[9]

Durkheim then turned his attention to the evolutionary portion of the Spencerian argument. The organismic analogy, of course, was in vogue at the time, and Spencer had used it brilliantly. As to the division of labor in society, Spencer had held that "along with increase of size in societies goes increase of structure. . . . It is also a characteristic of social bodies, as of living bodies, that while they increase in size they increase in structure. . . . The social aggregate, homogeneous when minute, habitually gains in heterogeneity along with each increment of growth; and to reach great size must acquire great complexity."[10] In other words, Spencer's theory of differentiation— despite its cosmic overtones and utilitarian underpinnings—reduced to an explanation based on sheer population size. At the very least he pointed to a universal association between size and differentiation.

Durkheim recognized the potential role of population increase in bringing about further differentiation. Along with Adam Smith, he was aware of the permissive effect of sheer size.[11] Large aggregates allow greater differentiation to emerge, but Durkheim concluded that the population-size factor was a necessary, but not a sufficient, cause. His reasons for this conclusions are particularly instructive. In contrast to Spencer, who exemplified the deductive method of proceeding from first principles, Durkheim was very much the inductive analyst. In fact, he showed the underlying weakness of Spencer's theory by pointing to "deviant cases." Concretely, he called attention to large, densely settled areas in China and Russia clearly characterized, not by extreme differentiation (organic solidarity), but by homogeneity (mechanical solidarity).[12]

Durkheim's Sociological Concepts
Having thus rejected the Spencerian argument on empirical grounds, Durkheim tried to explain the absence of any marked differentiation in these

places in the face of great size and density. It is at this point that Durkheim introduced a series of essentially sociological concepts, the first of which must be seen as an "intervening variable." First, he noted that social segmentation had not broken down (i.e., that there was minimal contact between the constituent parts of Chinese and Russian society). In the face of limited contact, these parts remained homogeneous, very much like each other with respect to structure and functions, representing a proliferation of essentially similar village units. Durkheim asserted that this "segmentation" disappears and that division increases only with an increase in "moral" or "dynamic density." In contrast to physical density—the number of people per unit of space—"dynamic density" refers to the density of social intercourse or contact or, more simply, to the rate of interaction—the number of interactions per unit of time. Until this rate of interaction reaches a high (although unspecified) level, the constituent social segments or parts remain essentially alike. According to Durkheim: "The division of labor develops . . . as there are more individuals sufficiently in contact to be able to act and react upon one another. If we agree to call this relation and the active commerce resulting from it dynamic or moral density, we can say that the progress of the division of labor is in direct ratio to the moral or dynamic density of society." [13] In other words, differentiation tends to increase as the rate of social interaction increases.

Durkheim then asked the next logical question: Under what conditions does this rate of interaction increase? In answer, he first observed that dynamic density "can only produce its effect if the real distance between individuals has itself diminished in some way." [14] He then pointed to two general ways in which this might come about: (1) by the concentration of population, especially in cities, i.e., via increases in *physical density*; (2) by the development of more rapid and numerous means of transportation and communication. These innovations, "by suppressing or diminishing the gaps separating social segments . . . increase the [dynamic] density of society." [15]

Thus, to demographic factors (essentially the Spencerian explanation), Durkheim added a technological emphasis. An increase in population size and density *plus* more rapid transportation and communication bring about a higher rate of interaction. However, the crucial questions still remain: what brings about differentiation? Why should a simple increase in the rate of interaction produce greater division of labor? If social units (whether individuals or collectivities) are brought into more frequent contact, why should they be obliged to specialize and divide their labor? A simple identification of "factors" obviously was not enough; Durkheim was also compelled to indicate the mechanism that would produce further differentiation under the prescribed circumstances. As it turns out, he had in mind a particular type of interaction, viz., competition.

It is in his identification of competition as the vital mechanism that Durkheim borrowed most heavily upon Darwinian thought, and it is this part of his theory that has been most widely distorted. Durkheim's argument was based on Darwin's observation that, in a situation of scarcity, increased contact between like units sharing a common territory leads to increased competition. Being alike, they make similar demands on the environment. Inspired by the Malthusian account of population pressure on limited resources, Darwin had been led to stress the resultant "struggle for existence" as the essential condition underlying the differentiation of species. In the human realm, Durkheim reasoned in turn, individuals or aggregates offering the same array of goods or services are potential, if not active, competitors. Thus, according to Durkheim,

> If work becomes divided more as societies become more voluminous [i.e., larger in size] and denser, it is not because external circumstances are more varied, but because struggle for existence is more acute. Darwin justly observed that the struggle between two organisms is as active as they are analogous. . . . Men submit to the same law. In the same city, different occupations can co-exist without being mutually obliged to destroy each other, for they pursue different objects. . . . The division of labor is, then, a result of the struggle for existence, but it is a mellowed dénouement. Thanks to it, opponents are not obliged to fight to a finish, but can exist one beside the other. Also, in proportion to its development, it furnishes the means of maintenance and survival to a greater number of individuals who, in more homogeneous societies, would be condemned to extinction.[16]

The division of labor is thus seen by Durkheim as essentially a mode of resolving competition and as an alternative both to Darwinian "natural selection" and to Malthusian "checks."

Critique

One might conclude from the foregoing that Durkheim merely substituted one variety of evolutionism for another, by pointing to a Darwinian struggle for existence between competitors as the mainspring of differentiation, rather than Spencerian cosmic forces leading inexorably to increased division. Indeed, the common interpretation of *Division* has been along these lines. Consider, for example, Benoit-Smullyan's remarks:

> Having disposed of the psychologistic and individualistic explanations of the division of labor, Durkheim now turns to his own morphological explanation. . . . Division of labor is due to changes in social structure arising out of an increase in material and moral density. The increase in population intensifies competition and thus forces individuals to spe-

cialize, in order to survive. Thus Durkheim, rather reluctantly, comes to rest his entire explanation upon the factor of an assumed natural increase in population. This is obviously a biologistic rather than a sociologistic type of explanation.[17]

On the contrary, Durkheim tried to spell out the conditions under which one variety of "social evolution" would occur, by pointing to the factors underlying increased structural complexity. Far from assuming natural increase and then using population growth as the explanation (à la Spencer), Durkheim clearly asserted that differentiation will accompany growth only if interaction increases concomitantly; moreover, he suggested that this intensification of interaction ordinarily occurs as a result of technological changes that facilitate contact, exchange and communication.[18] Thus Durkheim rejected a single-factor explanation—whether it be the individual's desire for happiness, cosmic evolutionary force, or population size—and proceeded to construct a multiple-factor theory.

But what of the charge that Durkheim disobeyed his own rules and thus became guilty of "biological reductionism"? This question can be answered best by recalling the explanatory concepts that he employed (i.e., dynamic density and competition). Both refer to interaction and can hardly be called intrinsically biological constructs without stretching the meaning of "biological" to the point where it loses all discriminatory value. If anything, these are clearly sociological concepts. Moreover, Durkheim's technological emphasis—his stress upon the role of improvements in transportation and communication—cannot properly be called "biological" reasoning.

As to the dependence of the theory upon an assumed natural increase, Durkheim's critics have again fallen into error. An increase in effective population size can obviously occur in several ways, of which natural increase is only one. Following out the implications of Durkheim's thought, it is readily apparent that improvements in transportation and communication can bring into sustained contact previously separate areas and populations. Historically, such "growth by merger" has frequently involved political merger, whether by violent subjugation or peaceful assimilation, and often has witnessed an extension of the area of regular economic exchange. These political and economic changes can be subsumed under the "biological" rubric only with difficulty, if at all.[19]

Although Merton is also inclined to view parts of Durkheim's explanation as biological, he has pinpointed the truly sociological character of Durkheim's analysis in the following passage:

> It is true that he finds the "determining cause" of increased division of labor in the growth and heightened density of populations, which is primarily a biological factor, but it is only in so far as this demographic

change is associated with increased social interaction and its concomitant, enhanced competition, that the stipulated change will occur.
*It is this social factor—the "dynamic density" as he terms it—which
Durkheim finds actually determinant.* ... To the extent that this differentiation is generalizable as a social process it may be said to be
associated with competition between individuals and between groups,
whatever the factors leading to such competition.[20]

Even Durkheim's "evolutionism" is not really biological in orientation.
Although he did use the language of evolutionary thought, he clearly rejected
most of the prevailing evolutionist views on the nature of social change. There
is no idea here of unilinear, irreversible development in a fixed sequence of
stages, no suggestion of "progress" as a necessary consequence of greater
complexity, no hint of blind cosmic forces animating the whole process, as in
Spencer's thought.[21] Durkheim simply attempted to specify the social conditions under which a particular change in social organization tends to occur. In
addition, he attempted to identify the general mechanism by which like units
become unlike, through the resolution of competition. Unfortunately, the
process is not described in any detail. Presumably the unsuccessful competitors (individuals, groups, or territorial aggregates) take up new functions and
somehow become integrated in a more inclusive and complex system.

At any rate, it should be evident by this point that most criticisms of
Durkheim's theory of differentiation have been misplaced. As they have been
stated, they might better be aimed at Spencer—the theorist against whom
Durkheim was contending throughout his entire analysis. The unfortunate
effect of these errors of interpretation is plain: to the extent that these
secondary sources are read in place of the original work, a whole generation
of American sociologists has been given an essentially incorrect image of one
of Durkheim's most important theoretical contributions. American sociology
is probably the poorer for it. Durkheim clearly viewed "the origin of social
species" as the product of social and not biological forces. If his analysis were
not so clear on this issue, the apparent unanimity of his critics would be more
compelling.

To say that most of the prevailing criticisms of Durkheim's theory are
themselves unsound, however, is not to say that the theory is entirely satisfactory as it was originally stated. The major difficulty stems from his treatment of competition. In view of the great importance that he attached to it,
his discussion is surprisingly brief. If differentiation is the resolution of competition that does occur and if a more complex organizational pattern does
emerge to integrate the new specialties, it may be correct to view these
developments as due to increases in effective size and improvements in the
facilities for movement. However, a number of writers have suggested that
differentiation is not the only resolution of competition.[22]

"Competition" occurs whenever the number of individuals or units with similar demands exceeds the supply, whether it be food, raw materials, markets, or occupational positions. As Durkheim suggested, differentiation represents a less harsh resolution of competition than that stressed by Darwin and Malthus. But in the case of human populations, the competition resulting from an increase in demand (population) theoretically can be resolved in a number of ways. Among them are the following:

Demographic Changes
(1) As Durkheim recognized, following Darwin and Malthus, an increase in the death rate can bring population into line with resources. (2) Similarly, a decrease in the birth rate can have the same effect, although not so immediately. (3) Migration may remove excess numbers at least temporarily and thus reduce demand.

Technological Changes
A number of possible developments may redefine and expand the effective environment, thus altering the supply. (4) Previously unused local resources may be brought into use via technological innovation or diffusion; the result is a more intensive use of environmental elements already present but unexploited. (5) Technological changes in transportation and communication, whether indigenous or borrowed, can make new areas and new resources available; such changes may also improve the internal distribution of commodities. (6) The substitution of mechanical for human energy may increase production and release manpower for other pursuits, including new occupations; thus the shift in the energy base of modern societies can be viewed as a process of displacement of the affected sectors of the population.

Organizational Changes
As noted above, previously isolated areas, resources, and peoples can be absorbed by conquest or assimilation. However, internal reorganization of a given population can also result in supporting increased numbers. (7) "Revolutionary" changes may occur; the surplus formerly held by the few may be distributed among the many, and increased numbers can be supported, with perhaps an even higher average level of living. (8) The converse can also occur; for a variety of specific reasons, the average level of living may be lowered, permitting a given area and its resources to support even greater numbers. (9) Finally, as Durkheim suggested, occupational and territorial differentiation may occur.

This list of "alternatives" is probably not exhaustive, but it suggests that further differentiation is only one of a number of ways to resolve competition. It is also clear that these alternatives are not mutually exclusive, for a number of them have occurred simultaneously in the Western world. [23] This observation suggests that the changes that have occurred are concomitants of differentiation itself. Indeed, closer analysis reveals that each of these "alternatives" involves either (1) elimination of excess numbers, (2) expansion of the resource base, or (3) functional differentiation, or some combination of these changes.

In view of the importance that Durkheim attached to competition, however, it is unfortunate that he did not present a more explicit and systematic treatment of its resolution. He was inclined to invoke competition and to let it go at that. In passing, he remarked that "Spencer ably explains in what manner evolution will be produced, if it does take place, but he does not tell us the source producing it." [24] Durkheim, on the other hand, pointed to the sources of differentiation but offered little in the way of a detailed account of the manner in which it is to be produced. In fairness, of course, it must be said that such a statement has yet to appear.

A more serious weakness in Durkheim's theory is the inadequate attention accorded the physical environment. He apparently was reluctant to give such factors as climate and topography any major role in his analysis. In part, this probably is due to the restrictive character of his own rules, adherence to which obliged him to seek the explanation of social facts in other social facts. He tended to dismiss the physical environment as a relevant variable and to regard the "social environment" as the ultimate source of differentiation. But this procedure has its own blind alleys; for one thing, the analyst does not get "outside the system" in his search for relevant variables.

Variability of the Environment

To accept Durkheim's view of the limited role of environmental variability is to ignore two key considerations, the first of which is implicit in his own thought. (1) As suggested above, the effective environment can be altered by technological and organizational changes. These changes redefine the environment by bringing new resources into use—local resources already "there" but unexploited or resources found at sites that were previously inaccessible because of limited transportation facilities and exchange mechanisms. Although the initial impetus may not be the environment itself, it may become an important condition with respect to further organizational change. (2) Environmental variability must be viewed in static as well as dynamic terms. The plain fact of the matter is that the physical environment confronting mankind is almost infinitely variable, in the sense that there are enormous geographical differences from place to place. Some of these differences may favor organizational change. Long before Durkheim's time, Adam Smith perceived the significance of this factor, pointing to the greater likelihood of differentiated units appearing at the water's edge. [25] Since Durkheim wrote, the role of a favorable geographic position has been stressed frequently in discussions of the sites of early civilizations and of the deep-water orientation of most great cities throughout history. This emphasis also appears in Cooley's famous "break-in-transportation" theory, and it can be easily merged with Durkheim's own views on the crucial role of transportation and communication technology.[26]

Nonetheless, Durkheim's own theory clearly minimizes the potential relevance for organization of variations in physical environment. The corrective probably lies in adopting the modern geographer's concept of the environment as a vital permissive factor with respect to human activities. This approach is best summed up in the view known as *possibilisme*, wherein the environment is viewed as a set of limiting conditions, which may be narrow or broad, depending upon the technological devices and modes of organization that prevail in a given population.[27]

Despite these minor shortcomings, Durkheim provided a highly useful framework for the analysis of social structure and particularly for the examination of changes in structure. From the ecological standpoint, *Division*'s major contribution is its stress upon the significance of technological advances for the development of a more elaborate division of labor. As Durkheim correctly pointed out, the efficiency of transportation and communication affects the degree to which spatially separate and functionally dissimilar activities may be interrelated. This is especially evident in the case of territorial differentiation, in which whole areas are devoted to specialized functions. Such a development clearly depends upon the loss of isolation and the establishment and maintenance of sustained contact.

Division provides, though only in outline, a framework for studying one of the most salient aspects of social organization, viz., the degree of structural differentiation. It can be applied to static, cross-sectional analysis as well as to dynamic, longitudinal study. Although it stands in need of certain modifications, his morphological theory seems particularly useful in approaching the problem of structural differentiation within and between areally based aggregates, i.e., communities. It is to this contention that the following section is addressed.

Implications for Human Ecology
The very first point to be made is that ecologists concern themselves with precisely the same problem as that attacked by Durkheim in Book II of *Division*. Just as he tried to explain one aspect of social structure, contemporary ecologists try to identify the factors determining variations in structure. Hawley, for example, defines human ecology as the study of the form and development of the community. At one point, he adopts Durkheim's exact phraseology and describes the ecologist's objective as the elucidation of

"the morphology of collective life in both its static and dynamic aspects." [28] Although he represents a more traditional ecological viewpoint, Quinn also declares that the logic of ecological inquiry points to the study of "the occupational pyramid" as essential subject matter, despite the unfortunate preoccupation of some ecologists with spatial distributions. [29] Thus modern human ecology deals with the Durkheimian problem of "morphology" and takes the same dependent variable (structure) as its *explanandum*. This is despite the fact that ecologists of Hawley's persuasion frequently limit themselves to discussing community structure, avoiding Durkheim's broader concern with society.

Second, once the environment is brought into the picture, modern ecology can be regarded as working with essentially the same array of *independent* variables—most broadly, population, technology, and the environment. Building on Hawley's theory, Duncan has labeled the resulting scheme "the ecological complex." [30] Although it tends to be implicit rather than explicit, Hawley's own effort seems to consist of treating community structure as the product of the interaction of these broad factors. The structure of a given community is viewed as a collective adaptation on the part of the population to its total environment (including other organized populations, as well as physical features), an adaptation that is strongly modified by the technological equipment in use and by certain "purely" demographic attributes of the population itself, notably its size, rate of growth, and biological (age-sex) composition. [31]

Thus the general relevance of Durkheim's thought to modern ecology is clear. He worked with essentially the same broad factors, taking one of them (structure) as his dependent variable. Moreover, his general mode of analysis is highly similar to that employed in current ecological theory. This becomes particularly apparent when one considers Hawley's treatment of differentiation, which clearly follows Durkheim in its major outlines. [32] Moreover, there are obvious formal parallels between Durkheim's *mechanical-organic* typology and the concepts of *commensalism* and *symbiosis, categoric* and *corporate groups*, and *independent* and *dependent communities* in Hawley's work. [33] Both writers point to (1) two modes of relationship, or forms of interaction, between like and unlike unit parts and to (2) two major forms of organization, depending upon which type of relationship is most prominent. Also deserving stress here is their common search for the factors that explain the progressive breakdown of isolation, the welding-together of larger and more inclusive functional units, and the emergence of a more complex structure.

Cultural Ecology
An even more recent variety of ecological thought—Julian Steward's "cultural ecology"—is amenable to interpretation along the lines suggested here. In

other words, the "ecological complex" appears to be in use throughout much of Steward's work, despite the fact that he does not consciously focus upon organization as the *explanandum*, preferring to work with "culture," a much broader dependent variable, and despite the fact that he gives a much larger role to the physical environment than either Durkheim or Hawley.[34] Durkheim's influence on Steward is apparently more indirect, via Durkheim's contribution to the development of "functional anthropology."

But we need not confine ourselves to the most recent statements of ecological thought. A Durkheimian approach has informed human ecology since its inception. In one of his most influential essays—"The Urban Community as a Spatial Pattern and a Moral Order"—Robert E. Park identified the subject matter of human ecology as "what Durkheim and his school call the morphological aspect of society."[35] It has probably also occurred to the reader that the use of the concept of competition in Durkheim's work is highly similar to Park's. To quote Park: "Competition determines the distribution of population territorially and vocationally. The division of labor and all the vast organized economic interdependence of individuals and groups of individuals characteristic of modern life are a product of competition."[36] Thus both Durkheim and Park saw structure as ultimately emerging out of competition in a context of scarcity, although Park was no more helpful than Durkheim in providing a detailed account of the process as a whole.[37]

In addition, it should be pointed out that Durkheim anticipated much of McKenzie's theoretical work, especially the latter's treatment of the rise of "metropolitan" communities. In Durkheim's analysis, we have seen that great stress is given to advances in transportation and communication technology, which lessen isolation and break down "social segmentation." McKenzie showed that this theory can be readily given an areal referent, since formerly isolated and territorially distinct populations are frequently brought into more intimate contact by virtue of improvements in transportation and communication. McKenzie saw the key feature of metropolitan development as the emergence of an intricate territorial division of labor between communities that were formerly almost self-sufficient, and he viewed the whole process as mainly due to technological improvements. In fact, McKenzie went so far as to characterize the metropolitan community as "the child of modern facilities for transportation and communication."[38]

Although Durkheim's analysis was largely at the societal level and dealt mainly with occupational differentiation, McKenzie used an essentially similar model in treating communities and regions, analyzing the problem of territorial differentiation. The process of differentiation is presumably the same in each case. Units that are brought into contact via technological improvements become competitors; such units necessarily compete to the extent that they offer the same goods and services to the same population. In the communal or regional context, the resolution of this competitive situation is frequently effected by territorial differentiation. Certain areal units, including whole communities, then give up certain functions and turn to new specialties. A case in point is the historical "flight" of certain specialties, particularly infrequently purchased goods and services, from nearby smaller cities to the metropolis, following the development of the automobile. In the process, formerly semi-independent centers, which once offered a rather full range of services, came to take up more narrowly specialized roles in a larger and more complex division of labor—the metropolitan community as a whole.[39]

At any rate, whether we examine earlier or more recent versions of human ecology, Durkheim's stamp is clearly imprinted.[40] In order to provide maximum utility in ecological analysis, Durkheim's theory needs certain modifications, particularly along the lines of bringing the environment into the schema as a factor worthy of recognition. As a result of its conceptual heritage from biology, human ecology has a rather full appreciation of the role of the physical environment as it affects social structure. This is not to say, however, that the ecologist is an environmental determinist; rather, he points to the relevance of the environment as it is modified and redefined by the organized use of technology. To paraphrase a recent compendium of valuable ecological data, man has a key role in changing the face of the earth.[41] Although the human ecologist's initial concern may be with the interaction between "man and his total environment," as a sociologist he inevitably turns to a study of the organized relations between man and man in the environmental setting, i.e., to morphological considerations. As Park said for ecology, it is "not man's relation to the earth which he inhabits, but his relations to other men, that concerns us most."[42] And in following out the interaction of a given aggregate with other organized populations, the ecologist necessarily concerns himself with what Durkheim called "the social environment."

Conclusions

The only American sociologists to make any intensive use of Durkheim's earliest and most ambitious work are those who have adopted the ecological perspective. Very little attention has been given to Durkheim's "social morphology," and his theory of differentiation has been widely misunderstood. Most American writers who have discussed *Division* have drawn upon Book I, where Durkheim treated the effects of division with his customary insight. His later works, especially those dealing with suicide and religion, have been much more influential in this country. In these later studies Durkheim was more frequently dealing with individual behavior, especially as it is "normatively defined" and modified by group ties.

This selective emphasis by American writers is probably related to the main drift of American sociology in this century (i.e., toward increasing concern with social-psychological considerations). Instead of taking social structure as the phenomenon to be explained—the dependent variable—most American sociologists habitually deal with social structure as an independent variable with respect to individual behavior. More particularly, structure is usually treated as it is perceived by the individual.

Now it must be made very clear that this procedure is an entirely legitimate enterprise; the variables with which one works and their analytical status depend upon the problem to be investigated. Moreover, this approach has vastly illuminated the human situation. Since the individual is somehow regarded as a less abstract unit than the organized aggregate and as a more interesting subject for study, social psychology has grown rapidly and has made giant strides toward acceptance in the scientific community. Witness the present status of "behavioral science." For all its past progress and future promise, however, the social-psychological sector of sociology still deals with some of the consequences of structural arrangements, leaving the determinants of structure to someone else.

In the light of these considerations, Durkheim's conception of *collective representations*—"shared norms and values" in the contemporary lexicon—provides an interesting sidelight on the position of social psychology within sociology. Durkheim regarded these social phenomena as mere "emanations" of underlying social morphology or structure.[43] If one accepts this position, then he holds that the social psychologist be concerned with little more than the derivative manifestations or passive reflections of underlying structural arrangements. Such a view clearly poses the analysis of structure itself as a logically prior problem. However, if current sociological output is any measure, few of us are inclined to grant any kind of priority to a morphological approach.

It is true that Durkheim himself turned more and more to the analysis of individual behavior in his later years, but he rarely departed from his original position regarding the undesirability of attempting to explain "social facts" by reference to individual characteristics.[44] This is in dramatic contrast to the direction taken in American sociology: toward the view that has been labeled "voluntaristic nominalism." As the most significant characteristic of American sociology, our fundamental postulates have recently been identified as follows: "The feeling, knowing, and willing of individuals—though limited by cultural prescriptions and social controls—are taken to be the ultimate source of human interaction, social structure, and social change. . . . Social behavior is interpreted voluntaristically. Social structures are real only as they are products of individuals in interaction."[45] One must be impressed by the fact that so many American theorists now acknowledge a heavy indebtedness to Durkheim. If this voluntaristic position is actually dominant, however, we have only succeeded in turning Durkheim upside down.

Be that as it may, Durkheim's conception of "social morphology" suggests that one of the most promising areas of structural analysis lies in the development of a general taxonomy of aggregates and collectivities. Few sociologists seem to have addressed themselves to this task in recent years. To the extent that "types of society" are used today, they represent minor variants of the dichotomies presented long ago by Tönnies, Durkheim, and other writers of the nineteenth century. More important, most of the refinements and reformulations of these typologies in recent years have been left to writers like Redfield and Steward. In other words, a genuinely sociological tradition is being kept alive by the efforts of anthropologists.

With respect to "types of community," the initiative has been taken by economists and geographers, despite the fact that many areas of current sociological interest absolutely require close attention to the community context. To choose only the most obvious example, community studies of stratification would probably be enormously improved if the overall structure and functions of the selected research sites were indicated with some precision according to their taxonomic types. For one thing, the overgeneralizations that seem to emerge from many such studies might be far less frequent.[46] It is probably unfortunate that the few sociologists currently attempting to develop a systematic taxonomy of communities appear to be those who employ an ecological framework.[47]

As for types of groups within communities and societies, we have not advanced very far beyond the rather rudimentary notions of "in-" and "out-groups" and "primary" versus "secondary" groups. Both of these dichotomies, of course, tend to be employed within a social-psychological context. The only notable recent addition to this limited array of group types is the notion of "membership" versus "reference" groups. However, the latter turn out not to be groups at all, for the distinction rests not upon structural or functional attributes of aggregates but upon the identifications and aspirations of individuals. It would be difficult to find a better index of just how far we have gone in bartering our sociological heritage for a mess of psychological pottage.

Morphological problems, including the development of fundamental structural taxonomies, deserve far greater attention than they have received in recent years. These are the tasks that have been largely ignored since Durkheim's day. Moreover, Durkheim's earliest work offers a challenge to those interested in the most neglected area of sociology—the analysis of the determinants of structure. As we have tried to suggest, Durkheim also provided a fascinating view of the problematics of social psychology. Given the current division of labor within American sociology, Durkheim's morphological theory of structural differentiation is probably of greatest value to ecologists, although not without relevance to other students of social organization. In this age of specialization, that he saw developing so rapidly, the sheer breadth and scope of Durkheim's achievement becomes all the more impressive with the years.

Notes and References

1. Durkheim died in 1917, and the first use among sociologists of the term "human ecology" did not appear until 1921, in Robert E. Park and Ernest W. Burgess (eds.), *Introduction to the Science of Society* (Chicago: University of Chicago Press, 1921), pp. 161-216. However, Durkheim was familiar with the work of Ernst Haeckel, who coined the word "ecology" in 1868 and who is often described as the father of plant ecology.

2. Taken from Durkheim's essay, "Sociologie et sciences sociales" (1909); cited in Harry Alpert, *Émile Durkheim and His Sociology* (New York: Columbia University Press, 1939), p. 51. Durkheim's own discussion of social morphology appears in scattered essays and reviews in *L'Année sociologique* (old series), e.g., "Note sur la morphologie sociale," 2 (1897-98), 520-21.

3. Paris: Alcan, 1893; translated by George Simpson as *The Division of Labor in Society* (New York: Macmillan Co., 1933; Glencoe, Ill.: Free Press, 1947). All citations to *Division* hereafter refer to the 1947 edition. Occasional reference will also be made to *Les Régles de la méthode sociologique* (Paris: Alcan, 1895), a collection of essays that had appeared in *Revue philosophique* in 1894. *Les Régles* was translated by Sarah A. Solovay and John H. Mueller and edited by George E. G. Catlin as *The Rules of Sociological Method* (Chicago: University of Chicago Press, 1938; Glencoe, Ill.: Free Press, 1950). All subsequent citations to *The Rules* refer to the 1950 edition.

4. August Comte, *The Positive Philosophy*, translated and edited by Harriet Martineau (New York: D. Appleton, 1853).

5. Ferdinand Tönnies, *Gemeinschaft und Gesellschaft* (1887), translated and edited by Charles P. Loomis as *Fundamental Concepts of Sociology* (New York: American Book Co., 1940). Although it is not cited in this work, Durkheim had previously reviewed *Gemeinschaft und Gesellschaft* in highly favorable terms (see *Revue philosophique*, 27 [1889], 416-22). George Simmel's *Uber soziale Differenzierung* appeared in 1890, but Durkheim indicated that he did not see it until after 1893, when *Division* first appeared. For a general critique of Simmel see Durkheim's "La Sociologia ed il suo dominio scientifico," *Revista Italiana di sociologia*, 4 (1900), 127-48.

6. "We say of these societies that they are segmental in order to indicate their formation by the repetition of like aggregates in them" (*Division*, p. 175). This type is not to be understood as somehow lacking any differentiation whatsoever (see pp. 129, 173, 177, 180). As Redfield has suggested, homogeneity in simpler societies is more than merely "occupational," extending to biological characteristics and even to outlook. Small size and extreme isolation appear to be crucial factors in the development of both genetic and cultural homogeneity (see Robert Redfield, "The Folk Society," *American Journal of Sociology*, 52 [1947], 292-308).

7. See *Division*, p. 229, and Durkheim's assertion that "mechanical solidarity persists even in the most elevated societies" (p. 186). Some critics erroneously accuse him of failing to see that both forms of integration can be found in every society.

8. Durkheim usually tried to dispose of competing hypotheses before setting out his own views. *Division* contains a perfect example of his didactic style, which Alpert calls the method of "argumentum per eliminationem" (op. cit., pp. 84-87).

9. *The Rules*, p. 110. In the course of his argument, Durkheim cited comparative suicide rates as "proof" to the contrary. Whatever the merits of this argument, it is interesting to note that Durkheim here anticipated his later work in this area. At another point, he dealt with religious phenomena (Book I). A number of writers have observed that *Division* contained the seeds of all his later work.

10. Herbert Spencer, *Principles of Sociology* (London, 1876; New York: D. Appleton & Co., 1884 and 1892), I, 459 (1892 ed.).

11. See Smith's famous aphorism to the effect that "the division of labor is limited by the extent of the market" (*The Wealth of Nations* [New York: Modern Library], p. 17).

12. *Division*, p. 261. This thought is further developed in *The Rules*, p. 115.

13. *Division*, p. 257. Later, Durkheim graciously credited Comte with the basic idea (see *ibid.*, pp. 262-63). In the quoted passage and elsewhere, Durkheim spoke as if the individual were the referent. However, the treatment of change that he applied to inter-individual relations appears to be even more appropriate in the analysis of the changing relations between areal units or whole aggregates in the process of differentiation.

14. *Ibid.*, p. 257.

15. *Ibid.*, pp. 259-60. Durkheim went on to say that one can usually substitute physical density ("this visible and measurable symbol" or index) for dynamic density, but that they are not inevitably correlated (see n. 11, p. 260). The point apparently troubled Durkheim, for in *The Rules* he repeats this idea in the form of an apology for having confused the two types of density (see *The Rules*, p. 115).

16. *Division*, pp. 266-70.

17. Émile Benoit-Smullyan, "The Sociologism of Émile Durkheim and His School," in Harry Elmer Barnes (ed.), *An Introduction to the History of Sociology* (Chicago: University of Chicago Press, 1948), p. 508. This point has been widely misunderstood. Sorokin, for example, says that "as soon as Durkheim puts this problem, he has to recognize at once its dependence on the factor of procreation and multiplication of the people—a factor essentially biological. Increase of labor division is principally the result of an increase of population. Such is his answer" (Pitirim Sorokin, *Contemporary Sociological Theories* [New York and London: Harper & Bros., 1928], p. 480). In a similar vein, Parsons says: "What he ends up with is population pressure, not in any analytical sense a social element at all, but essentially biological. In so far as this is Durkheim's main line of thought it is a familiar one here; it is the breakdown of utilitarianism into radical positivism, in this case the 'biologizing' of social theory" (Talcott Parsons, *The Structure of Social Action* [New York: McGraw-Hill Book Co., 1937; Glencoe, Ill.: Free Press, 1949], p. 323). Regarding Durkheim's explanation, Alpert has written: "If we accept this statement at face value, we must conclude that Durkheim's causal explanation of the division of labor is couched, contrary to his own methodological postulate that social facts must be explained socially, in biological, or, more exactly, in demographical terms. It is no wonder, then, that his book has been qualified as Malthusian" (op cit., p. 91).

18. It is true that he did not go on to "explain" growth or technological innovation. The task that he had set for himself was the explanation of differentiation, and to confine his

discussion to the implications of increase in size and density—whatever their sources—was an entirely legitimate scientific procedure.

19. The critics cited above do not seem to appreciate the fact that changes in effective population size need not depend upon natural increase or decrease. Demographers have long been aware that the organizational response to population pressure in a given area has frequently taken the form of a splitting-off process, in which a whole segment of a local community moves off to establish a new colony. This process, to which biblical reference may be found, apparently had a large role in the spread of mankind over the earth; it may be labeled "fission." Growth by merger, however, presents a contrasting phenomenon. Although it often generates substantial migratory streams, migration is not intrinsic to the process, nor is natural increase or decrease necessarily involved. To preserve the metaphor, this form of increase may be called growth by "fusion." Both processes, of course, refer to sociological (organizational) changes and not to biological changes.

20. Robert K. Merton, "Durkheim's Division of Labor in Society," *American Journal of Sociology*, 40 (1934), 325-26; italics added. In addition to calling population change "biological," Merton is in error regarding the implied universality of the association between competition and differentiation.

21. See *Division*, pp. 141-42. Merton has erroneously identified Durkheim as a unilinear evolutionist (op. cit., pp. 324-25). Marjolin provides a more accurate view of Durkheim's position: "For him there does not exist any single general human society, but only particular societies which have diverse evolutions, and it is not possible to consider the conditions which they have reached as stages in a single developmental sequence" (see Robert Marjolin, "French Sociology—Comte and Durkheim," *American Journal of Sociology*, 42 [1937], 694).

22. As Parsons has noted, Durkheim "recognizes the fact that there is more than one possible outcome of this intensification [of competition]. It might lead simply to the elimination by natural selection of a larger proportion of those born" (op. cit., p. 322). Benoit-Smullyan indicates emigration or war as additional alternatives (op. cit., p. 530). Alpert extends the list: "Of course, there are many other ways out, such as migration, suicide, civil war, crime, etc." (op. cit., p. 94).

23. When they occur, it is clear that these changes need not "run in the same direction." The modern nations of the West have lowered their birth rates, extended the environment in breadth and in depth, substituted machines for men, and have become more highly differentiated at the same time that gigantic streams of migration were set loose. Meanwhile, death rates did not rise but declined, and the level of living did not fall but rose dramatically. Whether or not these other changes are intrinsic to differentiation, Durkheim took a rather over-simplified view of the entire process. It must be noted that he clearly recognized the first alternative listed above and that others (especially the fifth) are implicit in his analysis. It will be seen that alternatives 1, 2, 3, 7, and 8 have their primary effect upon the population, or "demand ' side of the competitive equation, while alternatives 4, 5, and 6 have their major impact upon the resource, or "supply" side. Interestingly enough, alternative 9 (differentiation) has important effects upon *both* supply and demand; not only is the number of competitors effectively reduced, but the efficiency of differentiation presumably increases the supply.

24. *Division*, p. 265.

25. Smith, op. cit., chap. i.

26. Charles Horton Cooley, "The Theory of Transportation," *Publications of the American Economic Association*, 9 (May, 1894), entire issue; reprinted in Robert Cooley Angell (ed.), *Sociological Theory and Social Research* (New York: Henry Holt & Co., 1930). In fairness, it should be pointed out that Spencer appreciated the role of environmental variation, although his thinking on this issue is not easily reconciled with his general theory of differentiation. Spencer observed that all physical resources are not perfectly ubiquitous and that some areas are better suited to specialization in a narrow range of production (Spencer, *First Principles*, p. 381; cited in Durkheim, *Division*, p. 263). Durkheim's rejection of the environment as a significant factor in differentiation led him away from a potentially fruitful line of analysis—the study of territorial division of labor. He did note that "since the 14th century, the interregional division of labor has been developing" (*ibid.*, p. 188). In addition, his most detailed example involves an instance of territorial differentiation (*ibid.*, pp. 268-69).

27. This view is commonly associated with the names of Jean Brunhes and Paul Vidal de la Blache. For a recent statement along these lines see Robert S. Platt, "Environmentalism versus Geography," *American Journal of Sociology*, 53 (1948), 351-58.

28. Amos H. Hawley, *Human Ecology: A Theory of Community Structure* (New York: Ronald Press, 1950), p. 67.

29. James A. Quinn, *Human Ecology* (New York: Prentice-Hall, 1950), p. 14.

30. Otis Dudley Duncan, "Human Ecology and Population Studies," in Philip M. Hauser and Otis Dudley Duncan (eds.), *The study of Population* (Chicago: University of Chicago Press, 1959).

31. In contrast to earlier ecological emphases, spatial distributions of population and human activities enter into Hawley's thinking only as convenient indexes of organizational form; in this view, space is of interest only to the extent that it reflects structure. The same thing can be said for temporal patterns, which also have value as indexes of organization (see Amos H. Hawley, "The Approach of Human Ecology to Urban Areal Research," *Scientific Monthly*, 73 [1951], 48-49).

32. Hawley, *Human Ecology*, chap. xi.

33. *Ibid.*, chap. xii.

34. Steward criticizes Hawley as "uncertain in his position regarding the effect of environmental adaptations on culture" and indicates that he prefers to give this factor a larger causal role (Julian H. Steward, *Theory of Culture Change* [Urbana: University of Illinois Press, 1955], p. 34). This greater stress on physical-environmental factors is undoubtedly related to the fact that ethnologists are more frequently concerned with simpler societies, where the physical environment is literally a more fundamental determinant, pressing upon small and stable local populations that survive by means of relatively simple and unchanging technology and organization. To use Duncan's "ecological complex" once again, where technology and population are relatively constant, the environment assumes the position of the dynamic causal variable with respect to organization.

35. Originally published in 1925 as "The Concept of Position in Sociology" (see Robert E. Park, *Human Communities: The City and Human Ecology* [Glencoe, Ill.: Free Press, 1952], p. 166).

36. Park and Burgess, op. cit., p. 506.

37. On the use of competition as an all-explanatory concept in the earlier ecological literature see Amos H. Hawley, "Ecology and Human Ecology," *Social Forces,* 23 (1944), 398-405.

38. See R. D. McKenzie, *The Metropolitan Community* (New York: McGraw-Hill Book Co., 1933); see also Leslie Kish, "Differentiation in Metropolitan Areas," *American Sociological Review,* 19 (1954), 388-98.

39. That differentiation is not the only mode of resolution of competition is again dramatically demonstrated by the experience of many rural service centers and hamlets after the coming of the automobile. With their markets usurped by larger centers now within easy access, a great number of these smaller places literally disappeared.

40. This review has been confined to American developments. In France, Durkheim's morphological interests were carried on by his students, especially Maurice Halbwachs. In addition to extending Durkheim's analysis of suicide and "collective representations," Halbwachs' *Morphologie sociale* (Paris: Armand Colin, 1938) drew heavily upon his mentor's views and—at the same time—incorporated an ecological perspective that is often strikingly similar to Park's. Halbwachs visited the United States and taught at the University of Chicago in 1930 (see his "Chicago, expérience ethnique," *Annals d'histoire economique et sociale,* 4 [1932], 11-49).

41. William L. Thomas, Jr. (ed.), *Man's Role in Changing the Face of the Earth* (Chicago: University of Chicago Press, 1956).

42. Park, *Human Communities,* p. 165.

43. See Durkheim's "Representations individuelles et représentations collectives." *Revue de métaphysique et de morale,* 6 (1898), 273-302.

44. Durkheim's shifting interests are mirrored not only in the subjects of his later books but also in his writings in the old series of *L. Année sociologique.* Although references to "social morphology" are less frequent after about 1905, it should be noted that it was maintained as a major caption as long as Durkheim himself held the editorship.

45. Roscoe C. Hinkle, Jr., and Gisela J. Hinkle, *The Development of Modern Sociology* (New York: Doubleday, 1954), p. 73.

46. See Seymour M. Lipset and Reinhard Bendix, "Social Status and Social Structure: A Re-examination of Data and Interpretations," *British Journal of Sociology,* 2 (1951), 150-68 and 230-54; Harold W. Pfautz and Otis Dudley Duncan, "A Critical Evaluation of Warner's Work in Community Stratification," *American Sociological Review,* 15 (1950), 205-15; and Ruth Kornhauser, "Warner's Approach to Stratification," in Reinhard Bendix and Seymour M. Lipset (eds.), *Class Status and Power* (Glencoe, Ill.: Free Press 1953), pp. 224-55.

47. See Otis Dudley Duncan and Albert J. Reiss, Jr., *Social Characteristics of Urban and Rural Communities, 1950* (New York: John Wiley & Sons, 1956), pp. 215-370; for a more limited set of sub-community types see Leo F. Schnore, "Satellites and Suburbs," *Social Forces,* 36 (1957), 121-27.

A Long-Range View of World Population Growth
John D. Durand

The human species is now undergoing a phase of extraordinary numerical expansion which began about 200 or 250 years ago among the peoples of several parts of the earth and in which virtually all humanity has since become involved. From about 1700 or 1750 until 1900, the number of the earth's human inhabitants increased at a rate distinctly above the long-term average of earlier centuries. The growth rate rose higher during the first half of the present century and higher yet after World War II, so that the population is now increasing at a speed without precedent in human experience. Although the figures cannot be determined exactly, the following estimates probably represent the form of the trend fairly well.

Table 1
Growth Rate of World Population*

World Population (Millions)		Average Annual Growth Rate (Per Cent)	
1750	791	1750-1800	0.4
1800	978	1800-1850	0.5
1850	1,262	1850-1900	0.5
1900	1,650	1900-1950	0.8
1950	2,515	1950-1965	1.8
1965	3,281		

*The estimates shown here for 1750, 1800, 1850, and 1900 are from the author's article, "The Modern Expansion of World Population" (forthcoming in *Proceedings of the American Philosophical Society*), where an explanation of their basis will be found. The estimates for 1950 and 1965 and projections for the year 2000 quoted farther on are from the United Nations publication, *World Population Prospects as Assessed in 1963*, Population Studies, No. 41, (New York: United Nations, 1966).

The rise of the annual growth rate may now be near its climax, but it is apparent that the growth is by no means yet finished. Barring a catastrophe, an enormous further increase of the world population is almost certainly still in store. If the events of the next few decades bear out the assumptions of the United Nations projections,[1] the population in the year 2000 will be in the range of approximately 5,500 to 7,000 million and still increasing, according to the most conservative assumptions ("low" variant), at an annual rate of about 1¼ per cent. This would be appreciably less than the present growth rate but still well above the average for the first half of this century. It does not seem impossible that the increase during the twenty-first century might exceed that of the twentieth in absolute number, although probably not in proportionate measure. One can only conjecture how long the growth may continue and how many human beings the earth may hold when this growth comes to an end, as ultimately it must.

Population Growth in Earlier Epochs of World History

The increase which has already taken place since the beginning of the present growth phase is mammoth compared with the increases during earlier periods of history and prehistory. If the population trend could be traced back to the time, nearly ten thousand years ago, when the earliest known farming communities made their appearance, the form of the long-range growth curve would resemble what is shown in Figure 1.

For this chart, an estimate of five million has been taken to represent the order of magnitude of the world population in 8000 B.C., when, according to present archaeological information, all human societies were still living mainly by hunting, fishing, and collecting wild-plant food, insects, and the like. For the population at the birth of Christ, the order of magnitude is represented by an estimate of 300 million. If these estimates are near the truth, the population doubled approximately six times between 8000 B.C.

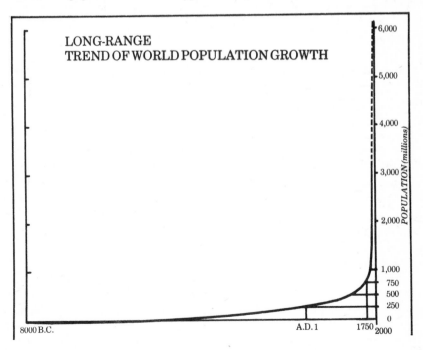

LONG-RANGE
TREND OF WORLD POPULATION GROWTH

and A.D. 1;[2] in other words, the average doubling time was more than a thousand years. During the first seventeen and a half centuries after Christ, according to the population estimates of 300 million as of A.D. 1 and approximately 800 million as of 1750, the average growth rate again corresponded to a doubling time of more than a thousand years. Contrasted against this background are the approximate doubling in 150 years indicated by the estimates for 1750 and 1900 and in 65 years by those for 1900 and 1965.

The contrast can be drawn from another angle by calculating the shares of the modern period and of earlier periods in the total increase of the human species since its origin. If the total increase is considered as a net figure, not including whatever gains have been cancelled out by subsequent losses, its measure is the present number of the population, estimated at 3,281 million as of 1965. Three-fourths of this increase (about 2,500 million) has taken place since 1750, about one-sixth or one-seventh (500 million) accumulated during the seventeen and a half centuries from A.D. 1 to 1750, and about one-tenth (300 million) during the eighty centuries from 8000 B.C. to A.D. 1, according to the estimates given above. Only an insignificant fraction of the increase took place before 8000 B.C., during the many thousands of centuries from the origin of the species up to the time of the "agricultural revolution."

Reliability of Estimates

A word should be said about the basis of these estimates and their reliability. The size of the world population even at the present time is not known exactly. There are countries with estimated population totalling more than sixty million where no census has yet been taken, and, more important, the census records for some of the more populous countries are dubious for accuracy or badly out of date. In the estimate for Mainland China alone (695 million as of 1965), an error of 100 million is not out of the question. In the historical estimates, margins of error widen in proportions (though not always in absolute magnitudes) as time lengthens. Few countries have precise statistical records of the population trend extending back beyond the nineteenth century. The world population in 1750 has been estimated to a large extent by working back from more recent benchmarks for various countries, and it is not impossible that the total of about 800 million might be off the mark by as much as 200 million in either direction.[3] For the estimate of population at the beginning of the Christian era, some statistical basis exists in ancient Chinese and Roman census records, and the probable magnitude of India's population about that time has been calculated roughly by reference to other kinds of historical information. Estimates for the regions outside the limits of literate civilization at the time of Christ's birth are mostly guesswork, but it is safe to say that their share of the world population was a minor one. The estimated total of 300 million as of A.D. 1 might be too small or too large by as much as 100 million.[4] Of course, there are no statistics on the population in any part of the world 8,000 years before Christ. The estimate for that date is based on what is known about the population densities of primitive hunting, fishing, and food-gathering peoples observed during recent times in various kinds of natural environments. The total of 5 million implies an average density of about 15 persons per 100 square miles of land in regions where the climate was favorable to human habitation. This corresponds approximately to estimates of average density of the aboriginal population at the times of early European contacts, in the nondesert regions of Australia, and also in the temperate-climate regions of North America where the Indians did not practice agriculture (with the exception of the extraordinarily populous northwestern coastal region). The estimate of the world total as of 8000 B.C. could be raised as high as ten million or reduced as low as one or two million without much strain on credibility.[5]

By selecting different estimates within the ranges indicated for each date, one would get somewhat different measures of average doubling times and shares of time-periods in the increase of world population up to the present. But the shape of the long-range growth curve would not be greatly changed, and the outstanding feature would remain—growth during the modern period far surpassing that of all previous periods for speed and sheer magnitude of added numbers.

Improvement of Mortality Conditions
The quickening proliferation of humanity in the modern period has not been brought about by an increase in the rate of reproduction but by an improvement in the conditions of mortality. The world's average birth rate has not risen; on the contrary, it is almost certainly lower now than it was two centuries ago, since birth rates in the economically more developed countries have been greatly reduced, while there is no evidence of any great changes having occured in the rest of the world. The impetus for growth of population has come from a decreasing trend of death rates which appears to have begun during the eighteenth century in several parts of the world and has since developed as an almost universal movement.

The improvement in mortality conditions is measured by gains in the expectation of life at birth, which have been most impressive in the countries leading in modern economic development but in which virtually the whole world has had a share. At present, life expectation at birth typically exceeds seventy years in the economically more developed countries and ranges down possibly as low as thirty-five years in areas where conditions of health and survival are least favorable (parts of tropical Africa, for instance). Formerly, a

35-year expectation of life at birth represented an enviable condition among human societies; it is doubtful whether the inhabitants of any large area before the modern era achieved a much greater expectation than this as an average over an extended period of time. The life expectation of slightly over twenty years estimated for India during the early decades of the present century is probably more nearly representative of the experience of humanity in general during past epochs of history and prehistory. The ancient Greeks and Romans fared little if at all better according to the indications obtained from the study of ages at death inscribed on their tombstones. Life expectation even below twenty years is indicated as the typical condition of early agricultural societies and primitive hunting, fishing, and food-gathering peoples, according to the results of studies of their skeletal remains.

The maximum span of life was no shorter in former times than it is today, but the risks of premature death were far greater. That one out of every four or five children born should die within the first year seems to have been the common experience of human societies in the past, whereas now infant mortality has been reduced to less than one out of fifty in countries where the best conditions of health have been achieved. Mortality risks in later childhood and the early and middle adult years were also fearfully high in the past by modern standards. The causes were largely in hazards of disease and famine, inherent in the natural or social environment, against which the societies of the past had little defense. Now, thanks to modern technology and organization for producing, transporting, and preserving food supplies, the threat of famine has been virtually eliminated in economically developed countries, while modern medicine has provided a measure of protection against disease which was unknown in the past.

The biological power of multiplication of the species has been greatly enhanced by the increased probabilities of survival to and through the reproductive years of life. When expectation of life at birth was no greater than twenty-five years, it took a high reproduction rate merely to replace the population, and growth at such rates as are now being recorded in much of the world was beyond the limits of reproductive capacity. With life expectation at that level and a reproduction rate near the highest level known to have been reached in human populations (such that women surviving to the end of the potentially reproductive period of life would bear eight children on the average), population would grow only at a modest rate of about 1½ per cent per annum. On the other hand, such a reproduction rate with life expectation at seventy years would bring galloping growth at annual rates approximating 5 per cent.[6] Reproduction rates at the levels typical of a majority of less developed countries at present (and probably of most of the world in the past), corresponding to averages of five or six births per woman in a full reproductive life-span, were scarcely more than enough to balance mortality under the former regimes. Now such reproduction rates are generating growth in less developed countries at annual rates of 2 to 3 per cent or higher, which double population in two or three decades.

Moderation of Reproduction Rates

In the countries of more advanced economic development, the change in mortality has been countered by tightening control of reproduction. In the United States, where the average number of births per woman surviving to the end of the reproductive period was probably about seven in the early nineteenth century, it has now been reduced to three; and the average is down to two or a fraction more in several European countries and Japan. Thus the impetus to population growth from the decline of mortality rates has been checked in varying degrees throughout Europe, in the Soviet Union, northern America, Australia, New Zealand, Japan, Argentina, Uruguay, Israel, and a few other areas of relatively advanced economic development. In some cases, the recent decrease of reproduction rates have overbalanced continuing decreases of mortality rates so that the population is now growing somewhat more slowly than it did in the early decades of the present century, while in other cases such a change in the growth trend has not yet been established.

There is little sign as yet of any tendency toward moderation of reproduction rates in the less developed countries, including most of those in Asia, Latin America, and Africa. With few exceptions, the present reproduction rates in those parts of the world appear to be as high as ever; and so, as mortality rates have decreased, their rates of population growth have accelerated incessantly.

The figures in Table 2 sum up the evolution of the contrasting pattern of growth in the less developed and more developed segments of the world and the prospect for its continuation in the decades ahead as indicated by the United Nations projections.[7]

Implications of Current and Prospective Trends

The crux of the present problem of world population is in the association of persistent poverty and technological retardation with unremitting rapid growth of numbers in the less developed regions. Demographers, economists, sociologists, and the members of other disciplines concerned with the study of these matters cannot yet claim to have defined unequivocally the basic causal relationships in this disquieting association and what it portends for the future of the economically disadvantaged nations and the world as a whole. Some of the implications, though, can be spelled out clearly enough. One which deserves particular notice is the need for increased international

Table 2
**Population Growth in More Developed
and Less Developed Regions of the World**

Time-Periods	Less Developed Regions (Asia Except Japan, Africa, Latin America)	More Developed Regions (Europe, U.S.S.R., Northern America, Oceania, and Japan)
Population (Millions)		
1850	925	343
1900	1,088	561
1950	1,682	833
1965	2,288	999
Range of projections for 2000	4,204-5,478	1,245-1,516
Average Annual Growth Rate (per cent)		
1850-1900	0.3	1.0
1900-1950	0.9	0.8
1950-1965	2.1	1.2
Range of projections for 1965-2000	1.8-2.5	0.6-1.2
Share of World Total Growth (per cent)		
1850-1900	44	56
1900-1950	69	31
1950-1965	78	22
Range of projections for 1965-2000	86-89	11-14

sharing of resources which results from the disproportion in population growth between the "have" and the "have-not" nations as well as from the opposite disproportion in the growth of their income and wealth.

Those who would attempt a long-range view of the future are well advised to turn their eyes also upon the long vista of the past, and there some comfort may be found in the observation that growth of population has played a positive part in the evolution of civilization and economy in the long run. While it is obvious that the increase of man's numbers since the days of prehistoric hunters and food-gatherers has depended on the growth of his power to convert nature's resources to satisfaction of his needs, the same proposition holds equally true in reverse. In the preindustrial phase, a certain numerical strength was prerequisite to the progressive specialization of functions and the growth of cities, those incubators of the arts and sciences, and industrial civilization depends on larger numbers to furnish the labor force for mass-production industries and markets for their products. In fact, as the evolution of technology and forms of economic organization has progressed, both the optimum and the necessary minimum size of population have increased along with the maximum number that could be supported. Increasing population may also, at times, have furnished a motive force for progressive innovations of technology and productive organization, in accordance with the principle that necessity is the mother of invention. Such is the hypothesis proposed by certain economic historians to explain the coincidence of quickening population growth with the advent of the Industrial Revolution in eighteenth-century Europe. It is tempting to hope that the pressures now being generated by growth of population in less developed countries might soon evoke an equally creative response. If the progress of industrialization and related economic and social developments could be greatly accelerated in the near future in the regions of the world that are lagging in these respects, and if numerical stability were attained without a very great delay, the population problem might thereby be solved. On the other hand, if the multiplication of numbers should continue into a more distant future, a more novel response to its imperatives might be required.

Notes and References

1. M. A. El-Badry, "Population Projections for the World, Developed and Developing Regions: 1965-2000." *The Annals of the American Academy of Political and Social Science*, Vol. 369 (January 1967), pp. 9-15.

2. Six doublings would correspond to a sixty-four-fold multiplication (in the ratios $1 : 2 : 4 : 8 : 16 : 32 : 64$), whereas a multiplication of sixty-fold is indicated by the estimates.

3. Walter F. Willcox, *Studies in American Demography* (Ithaca, N. Y.: Cornell University Press, 1940), estimated the world total as of 1750 at 694 million, and A. M. Carr-Saunders, *World Population: Past Growth and Present Trends* (New York: Oxford University Press, 1936) put it at 728 million. A somewhat larger estimate now appears preferable in view of the results of recent research, particularly on the population history of China and India.

4. A range of 200 to 300 million for the world population as of A.D. 1 was suggested in: United Nations, *The Determinants and Consequences of Population Trends* (New York: United Nations, 1953), p. 8. In the present author's opinion, the information available as regards China, the Roman Empire, and India makes it appear prudent to raise the upper limit of the range to 400 million and to take the round number of 300 million as a "medium" estimate.

5. Several writers have given estimates in this range for the world population just before the development of the first agricultural societies. See Julian Huxley, "Population and Human Destiny," *World Review* (January 1950) and *Harper's Magazine* (September 1950); Edward S. Deevey, Jr., "The Human Crop," *Scientific American* (September 1960).

6. Growth rates and other vital indices corresponding to different combinations of reproduction rates and expectation of life at birth in model stable populations are tabulated in detail in: A. J. Coale and P. Demeny, *Regional Model Life Tables and Stable Populations* (Princeton, N. J.: Princeton University Press, 1964).

7. This division between less developed and more developed regions is a crude one. Within Latin America, for instance, Argentina and Uruguay should be placed in the category of more developed areas, while the minority of Oceania's population outside Australia and New Zealand belongs in the less developed category. Such refinements require a more detailed areal classification of historical estimates than the author has attempted. In the United Nations estimates, the total given for less developed and more developed regions are 1,658 and 858 million, respectively, as of 1950; 2,249 and 1,032 million, as of 1965.

Man and His Environment
Stanley A. Cain

Most of us have some feeling that we are experts on man. After all, we do belong to the species. We do react to human behavior, often man's foibles, by saying: "But that is human nature." However, I am sure that sociologists, anthropologists, and psychologists would challenge this general assumption of expertise by the rest of us.

But although we pose as experts on human emotions, good and bad, our analyses do not extend very far when we view the environment. As a matter of fact, most of us would not profess to have much knowledge of the environment beyond opinions on the weather, many of them unprintable.

Environment consists of all of the things, conditions, and forces to which living matter is sensitive and capable of reacting, including changes in the intensity and direction of stimuli. In simpler terms, if there is no response, there has been no effective stimulus, and anything in the surroundings that does not provide a stimulus is not a part of the environment of living organisms. The rest of the surroundings, whatever they may be, have no significance for life because no stimulus to protoplasm is a consequence of their existence. They elicit no biological response.

If I am walking in the dark and stumble over a rock, it is part of my environment. If I pass it by without knowing it is there, it is only part of my surroundings. In the daytime, if I were to see the rock and step around it, it would be part of my environment. I would be responding to its presence.

The distinction between surroundings and environment does not depend upon consciousness, however. If the rock were strongly radioactive and I stayed near it long enough, it would be part of my environment if there were any physiological consequence to me. Regardless of whether I was aware of the stimulus, my cells and their chemicals could be affected.

It follows that happenings remote from an individual organism, both in space and time, may have consequences for that organism because of the intricate interconnected web of causes and effects that ties together the biotic units, all features of the abiotic world, and the interrelations of the living and non-living.

The ecologist, or whoever practices ecological thinking, must keep in mind that single-factor operations do not occur in biological nature, that the environment cannot be completely analyzed, and that diverse analytic data cannot at present be synthesized back into anything like the ecosystems as a whole.

These are awkward facts, but we need to do the best we can with them. Rene Dubos, the bacteriologist, said: "The physician could not deal with the problems of disease if he did not concern himself with the integrated reactions of man to environmental forces. He would have little chance to help his patient if he did not try to comprehend the effects of the total environment on the human condition."

The complicated, diverse mixes of environmental factors have always been an embarrassment to ecologists because of the difficulty of reassembling analytical data into meaningful wholes. But an organism, by the very fact of its successful life, does represent just such an integration, now beyond the power of computers. It is for this reason that man takes vegetation and certain species of plants and animals as indicators of a particular environmental complex.

As to the physical environment, variability of component factors is well illustrated by the intemperate character of the climate of the temperate zone. The weather can be "hot as the dickens" at one time and, paradoxically, "cold as the dickens" at another time in the same place.

Consider the earth shells, the lithosphere, the hydrosphere, and the atmosphere; that is, soil, water, and air. They are interpenetrating and interacting as shown by such labels as "soil water," "soil atmosphere," "dust," "water vapor," "silt," and "dissolved oxygen." The topography of the earth affects the oceans through erosion and sedimentation, as it does the circulation of the atmosphere. The earth's astronomic phenomena of rotation and revolution affect movements in the sea and the air as well as light and temperature in the air, water, and soil. Aquatic and atmospheric circulations distribute the gaseous components and suspended materials (including allergens, pesticides, and radio nucleids), while they accomplish mass transfer of heat. Heat changes affect the solubility of materials in air and water and hence their holding capacity.

Although we may be concerned with physical conditions as they affect purely physical processes, our thoughts about environment are clearly in relation to living beings and, unless we are naturalists of some special sort, in relation to ourselves. Although all living organisms may be said to be egocentric, we may very well be the only consistently egotistical species in nature.

The heart of the biological environment in the sense of interrelations among living organisms lies in the food chains. I know that there are other inter-organismal relationships, but the crux of the matter is the cycling of matter and the flow of energy, and that is what is worked out among the primary producers, herbivores, carnivores, degraders, and decomposers.

The interactions among the abiotic components of the environment, those among the living components, and those between the biotic and abiotic result in what many persons consider the fundamental unit of nature—the ecosystem that is a consequence of such actions, reactions, and coactions.

The Balance of Life

Ecology, which is observational natural history supplemented by the use of modern concepts and technology, deals with these complexes of merging and overlapping features of the environment, and with species occurrences, behavior patterns, and community structure. This inescapable complexity lies in the inseparable aspects of all ecosystems, whether we consider them natural because of little human modification, or human because attention is centered on man's role and fate in them.

Under such conditions, natural or human, there is always a considerable element of abstraction and even of subjective judgment shown by students of the natural sciences, whether they approach ecosystems primarily as systematists, physiologists, environmentalists, geographers, foresters, wildlife managers, agriculturists, horticulturists, or some other. It is the same in human ecology whether the ecosystem is viewed in terms of environment and the natural resources it can be made to yield for human use, or the community and the human resources that can be marshaled to accomplish a certain end, and is approached from the point of view of economists, engineers, chemists, investors, educators, politicians, or others.

Biotic communities and the ecosystems of which they are a part are never studied in their entirety and throughout their areal extent. Thus the result is that we deal with partial descriptions and incomplete understandings that are the best that we have. As Dubos said of the physician, we must try to comprehend the effects of the total environment on the human condition, or whatever species we may focus attention on.

Whatever the scale of our views of nature, we are met with the phenomenon of variability in all regards. The consequence is that we deal with generalizations and probabilities, not with certainties and definiteness. A residual difficulty, of course, is that few persons other than scientists are acquainted with the statistical requirements for generalization, or with the nature of evidence. Hopefully, after a generation or two of experience with the "new math," the general public will realize that an individual's chance and parochial experience is insufficient basis for a meaningful generalization. If such a happy day arrives, our lives may be more sensible but less interesting.

Human ecology and the functioning of human ecosystems are further complicated when compared with more natural ecosystems because of the high degree of institutionalization of human actions. No other species comes close to human social structure. There was a time before man, even before the earlier hominoids, when there were species with some degree of social organization. But it is only man who has carried very far the individual specialization, division of labor, and, because of that, organization for cooperative effort. Social action, institutionalized, is the core of human ecological functioning. Individual drives remain, but they are generally directed toward the population as a whole. Man unites against all of nature as he wrests from her the products and services of other animals, plants, and the physical environment. Man is the preeminent predator and, with modern technology, the greatest living force for changing the character of the earth.

Man's Attack on Nature

Man's social organization ranges over all the facets of culture, using the term in its broadest sense, from family and religion to political and economic life.

While inescapably dependent upon food for the energy that supports him and enables him to get his work done, as are all other living things, technological man is distinguished by his ability to harness and put to work the energy derived from earth forces such as wind and flowing water, from fossil fuels such as coal and oil, from the combustion of contemporary organic matter such as wood, and quite recently, the nuclear energy of the sun and nuclear and radioactive elements found on earth. As these capabilities have developed, some over the centuries, some during the past few decades, human specialization, division of labor, and the details of social organization have multiplied in complexity and interrelatedness.

During this span, which is only a moment in the history of the species, man's attack on nature has become more effective and generally more ruthless. Potential natural resources of the environment have been brought to usefulness at an ever-accelerating rate. Economic growth has become a visible progress, changing within a generation for those people who have embraced the analytic sciences and their technological applications. This is in stark contrast to the imperceptible changes of the previous millennia of human history.

Depending largely on the analytic sciences—leaving synthesis to poets, philosophers, and cosmologists—industrial nations have made impressive economic advancement. Many millions of people work shorter hours and have

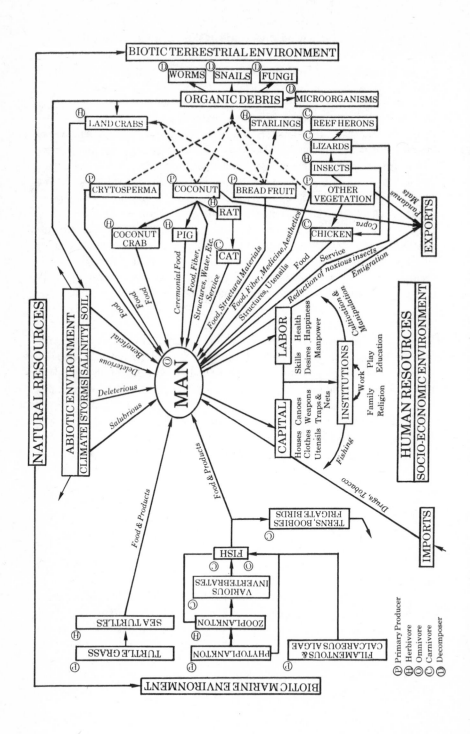

more comfort—even luxuries—than ever before. In this process some nations have been fortunate in having expanding frontiers and rich virgin lands from which the raw materials of this kind of progress could be extracted. The United States and Canada are outstanding examples, and more recently the U.S.S.R. At the same time, others of the industrial nations have profited from the raw material richness of colonial empires.

Recent history has changed this 19th century experience, but some of the developing countries are repeating it within their national boundaries. However, what the world is discovering at this time in history is that the single-purpose approach to the environment has produced costs as well as benefits. As long as natural wealth seemed boundless, the costs of profligacy were not apparent. Today these costs are seen on all sides in the gap between the needs of rapidly expanding populations and the inadequacy of existing human ecosystems to meet such needs, at least at standards of living that are acceptable today.

There is, of course, a critical difference between "standard of living" that is commonly interpreted as level of income, consumption, and related quantities, and standards in the sense of the qualities of life. Today we are concerned not only with the levels of living as they exist, but with the standards that are essentially goals that are desired. It is at this point that we become concerned with the quality of the environment. It is one thing to know what a human ecosystem is producing in factories and mills and power plants, and another to know what pollution of air, water, and soil these works are also producing.

We have historically proceeded as though the facts of nature and the raw materials of our economy were discrete entities and not parts of complex interacting systems. Doing things this way, we have had bookkeeping on the benefits, but generally not on the costs of our procedures. We have mined each mineral, cut each tree, farmed each acre, and used each body of water as though there would be no significant effect on any other part of the environment. In so doing, we have bought economic progress out of nature's capital. The short-term benefits have been phenomenal, but the long-term consequences are proving unhappy for man.

The Cost of Right Living

Today's question is whether we are rich enough to afford conservation management and maintain an environment of quality. Rich enough in dollars? Rich enough in socio-economic and political knowledge? Rich enough in wisdom and the will to do what is needed doing? Devoted enough to the synthesizing sciences, such as ecology and economics, and the humanities? Have we really discovered that there are no single resources only resource complexes? Do we yet know that there are no independent and isolated socio-economic and political actions? Do we really appreciate that all things are linked by actions in the continuous web of the ecosystem?

The ascendancy of ecology as a synthesizing rather than an analytic science during recent years seems to be due to certain very human concerns. Among them:

The Rise of Environmental Health   The medical profession, including its practitioners in industry and the armed forces, has been accumulating indications that there is more to disease than pathogenic organisms, and that even the systemic diseases, such as cardiovascular ailments, have relations to environmental conditions.

The Acceleration of Human Population Growth   Both the causes and the consequences of an exploding population are being found related not only to the physical environment but also to social, economic, and political influences working within culture. Neo-Malthusianism has a broader base than Malthus appreciated at the end of the 18th century.

The Shock of the Nuclear Age   The bombs over Hiroshima and Nagasaki brought more than destruction. The people became aware of the insidiousness of radioactive isotopes that find their way into water and food. Linkages in the ecosystem are being understood by people who never heard of ecology.

The Impact of Silent Spring   It was Rachel Carson's book that did more than technical studies to alert the public and public agencies to the fact that no more than a small part of the poisons hit the target, and that we should find out where the rest of them go and what they do.

The Concern for Natural Beauty   Still more recent than these other concerns is the wider awareness that quality of the environment includes natural beauty for which we have a record of gross unconcern.

I do not wish to be misunderstood. I do not propose that we short-change in any way the scientific specialties or the engineering and other technologies that depend upon basic science. But I do hope that the recent respectability of ecology, itself a field ranging from the intracellular to the global and microcosms in space, will receive appropriately balanced support by public and private institutions.

I would expect a payoff from such an investment of manpower and money equal to the phenomenal success of agriculture in the United States, and I include, of course, livestock, horticulture, and related fields. Agriculture has always had its intuitive ecology. For more than a century now the United States has supported agricultural research, education, and extension together with the several states. There has been principal attention to the separate scientific disciplines such as genetics, pathology, soils, biochemistry, and the like, but there has always been also the necessity of integrating such knowledge into the management of species populations in the given total environment. The agricultural mission has been clear, and it is one that can be attained only in terms of the population and the community together with the total environment.

More and more the fields of fish and wildlife, oceanography, water management, land management, and broad environmental areas are being forced to more adequate considerations of the ecological parameters within which they must work. This is coming slowly and painfully to road building, dam construction, and real estate development, but it is coming because we can no longer afford tunnel vision of our problems.

From Social System to Ecosystem
Otis Dudley Duncan

The concern of human ecology for the "central problem of sociology" is well stated in Professor Schnore's paper.[a] His statement, nonetheless, is unduly conservative insofar as it seeks merely to explicate and clarify the inter-relations of certain conventional "modes of analysis" in current sociology. The description of human ecology as a "type of macrosociology" may be reassuring to students attracted to ecological problems but anxious to preserve their membership in good standing in the sociological fraternity. Such a description could, however—though I am sure this is not the effect Schnore is after—foster a new "myth," that human ecology is just a different name for what sociologists are already doing, and are perfectly capable of doing, without benefit of ecological ideas. (This is certainly implied in the remarks of Peter Rossi cited in Schnore's paper.)

I shall be less diplomatic than Professor Schnore. I believe that the real problems confronting man in the contemporary world can best be illuminated—insofar as social science can illuminate them—by stating them and attacking them as ecological problems. It will be taken for granted that illumination of these problems is "central" to the task of sociology; if not, then sociology is itself "peripheral" to what is going on in the world and is not worthy of cultivation by responsible scholars.

Levels and Systems
All science proceeds by a selective ordering of data by means of conceptual schemes. Although the formulation and application of conceptual schemes are recognized to entail, at some stage of inquiry, more or less arbitrary choices on the part of the theorist or investigator, we all acknowledge, or at least feel, that the nature of the "real world" exercises strong constraints on the development of schemes in science. Some schemes, used fruitfully over

long periods of time, come to seem so natural that we find it difficult to imagine their being superseded. One type of scheme is deeply ingrained by our training as social scientists, to wit, the organization of data by *levels*. Kroeber is only voicing the consensus of a majority of scientists when he writes:[1]

> The subjects or materials of science ... fall into four main classes or levels: the inorganic, organic, psychic, and sociocultural. ... There is no intention to assert that the levels are absolutely separate, or separable by unassailable definitions. They are substantially distinct in the experience of the totality of science, and that is enough.

MacIver gives substantially the same classification, but instead of using the relatively colorless term "levels," he chooses to segregate the several "nexus of causation" into "great dynamic realms."[2]

It is significant that scientists, insofar as they do accept the doctrine of levels, tend to work *within* a level, not *with* it. The scheme of levels does not itself produce hypotheses; it can scarcely even be said to be heuristic. Its major contribution to the history of ideas has been to confer legitimacy upon the newer scientific approaches to the empirical world that, when they were emerging, had good use for any kind of ideological support.

Quite another type of conceptual scheme, the notion of *system*, is employed by the scientist in his day-to-day work. Conceptions of interdependent variation, of cause and effect, or even of mere patterning of sequence, derive from the idea that nature (using the term broadly for whatever can be studied naturalistically) manifests itself in collections of elements with more than nominal properties of unity.

No doubt there are many kinds of system, reflecting the kinds of elements comprising them and the modes of relationship conceived to hold among these elements. The point about this diversity that is critical to my argument is this. When we elect, wittingly or unwittingly, to work *within* a level (as this term was illustrated above) we tend to discern or construct— whichever emphasis you prefer—only those kinds of system whose elements are confined to that level. From this standpoint, the doctrine of levels may not only fail to be heuristic, it may actually become anti-heuristic, if it blinds us to fruitful results obtainable by recognizing *systems that cut across levels*.

One such system, probably because it is virtually a datum of immediate experience, is rather readily accepted by social scientists: personality. Manifestly and phenomenologically an integration of nonrandomly selected genetic, physiologic, social, and psycho-cultural elements, personality has a kind of hard reality that coerces recognition, even when it can be related to other systems only with difficulty or embarrassment. If I am not mistaken, however, the concept of personality system enjoys a sort of privileged status.

We do not so readily accede to the introduction into scientific discourse of other sorts of system concept entailing integration of elements from diverse levels. The resistance to such concepts is likely to be disguised in charges of "environmental determinism" or "reductionism." An example: The working assumption of some human ecologists that the human community is, among other things, an organization of activities in physical space is criticized (though hardly refuted!) by the contention that such a conceptual scheme is contrary to "essentially and profoundly social" facts, i.e., "conscious choice of actors who vary in their ends and values."[3] We must resist the temptation to comment here on the curious assumption that the "essentially and profoundly social" has to do with such personal and subjective states as "ends and values," rather than with objective relations among interdependent living units. (Surely the latter is the prior significance of the "social," in an evolutionary if not an etymological sense.) The point to emphasize at present is, rather, that such a reaction to ecological formulations is tantamount to a denial of the crucial possibility that one can at least conceive of systems encompassing both human and physical elements. The "dynamic realm" of the psycho-social has indeed become a "realm," one ruled by an intellectual tyrant, when this possibility is willfully neglected or denied.

The Ecosystem

Acknowledged dangers of premature synthesis and superficial generalization notwithstanding, ecologists have been forced by the complexity of relationships manifested in their data to divise quite embracing conceptual schemes. The concept of ecosystem, a case in point, has become increasingly prominent in ecological study since the introduction of the term a quarter-century ago by the botanist, A. G. Tansley. "The *ecosystem*," according to Allee and collaborators, "may be defined as the interacting environmental and biotic system."[4] Odum characterizes the ecosystem as a "natural unit . . . in which the exchange of materials between the living and nonliving parts follows circular paths."[5] The first quotation comes from an enlightening synthesis of information now available on the evolution of ecosystems; the second prefaces an exposition of principles concerning the operation of "biogeochemical cycles" in ecosystems. Social scientists whose acquaintance with general ecology is limited to gleanings from the essays of Park[6] or the polemic by Alihan[7] might do well to inform themselves concerning current developments in ecological theory by consulting such sources as these. Even more readily accessible is the statement of Dice:[8]

> Ecologists use the term ecosystem to refer to a community together with its habitat. An ecosystem, then, is an aggregation of associated species of plants and animals, together with the physical features of their habitat. Ecosystems . . . can be of any size or ecologic rank. . . . At

the extreme, the whole earth and all its plant and animal inhabitants together constitute a world ecosystem.

Later in his text (ch. xv) the same author undertakes a classification of "human ecosystems." This classification presents in elementary fashion much material familiar to social scientsts; but it also conveys an unaccustomed emphasis on the "diverse relationships" of human societies "to their associated species of plants and animals, their physical habitats, and other human societies."[9]

Popularization of the ecosystem concept is threatened by the felicitous exposition by the economist, K. E. Boulding,[10] of "society as an ecosystem." The word "threatened" is well advised, for Boulding uses "ecosystem" only as an analogy, illustrating how human society is "something like" an ecosystem. His ecosystem analogy is, to be sure, quite an improvement over the old organismic analogy. But ecosystem is much too valuable a conceptual scheme to be sacrificed on the altar of metaphor. Human ecology has already inspired a generation of critics too easily irritated by figures of speech.

If the foregoing remarks suggest that general ecologists have come up with cogent principles concerning the role of human society in the ecosystem, then the discussion has been misleading. Actually, the writing of Dice is exception as a responsible attempt to extend general ecology into the human field. Most biological scientists would probably still hold with the caution of Clements and Shelford, that "ecology will come to be applied to the fields that touch man immediately only as the feeling for synthesis grows."[11] There is abundant evidence in their own writing of the inadvisability of leaving to biological scientists the whole task of investigating the ecosystem and its human phases in particular. As a discipline, they clearly have not heeded the plea of the pioneer ecologist, S. A. Forbes, for a "humanized ecology":[12]

> I would humanize ecology ... first by taking the actions and relations of civilized man as fully into account in its definitions, divisions, and coordinations as those of any other kind of organism. The ecological system of the existing twentieth-century world must include the twentieth-century man as its dominant species—dominant, that is, in the sense of dynamic ecology as the most influential, the controlling member of his associate group.

Symptomatically, even when discussing the "ecology of man," the biologist's tendency is to deplore and to exhort, not to analyze and explain. The shibboleths include such phrasings as "disruption," "tampering," "interference," "damage," and "blunder," applied to the transformations of ecosystems wrought by human activities. Such authorities as Elton, Darling, and Sears state very well some of the dilemmas and problems of human life in the ecosystem. [13] They evidently need the help of social scientists in order to make intelligible those human behaviors that seem from an Olympian vantage point to be merely irrational and shortsighted. Insofar as they recommend reforms—and surely some of their suggestions should be heeded—they need to be instructed, if indeed social science now or ultimately can instruct them, in "The Unanticipated Consequences of Purposive Social Action." [14] If social science falls down on its job, a statement like the following will remain empty rhetoric: "Humanity now has, as never before, the means of knowing the consequences of its actions and the dreadful responsibility for those consequences." [15]

Illustration

Now, it is all very well to assert the possibility of conceptual schemes, like ecosystem, ascribing system properties to associations of physical, biological, and social elements. But can such a scheme lead to anything more than a disorderly collection of arbitrarily concatenated data? I think the proof of the ecosystem concept could be exemplified by a number of studies, ranging from particularistic to global scope, in which some such scheme, if implicit, is nevertheless essential to the analysis. [16] Instead of reviewing a sample of these studies, however, I would like to sketch a problematic situation that has yet to be analyzed adequately in ecosystem terms. This example, since it is deliberately "open-ended," will, I hope, convey the challenge of the concept.

The framework for the discussion is the set of categories suggested elsewhere [17] under the heading, "the ecological complex." These categories, population, organization, environment, and technology (P, O, E, T), provide a somewhat arbitrarily simplified way of identifying clusters of relationships in a preliminary description of ecosystem processes. The description is, by design, so biased as to indicate how the human elements in the ecosystem appear as foci of these processes. Such an anthropo-centric description, though perfectly appropriate for a *human* ecology, has no intrinsic scientific priority over any other useful strategy for initiating study of an ecosystem.

The example is the problem of air pollution, more particularly that of "smog," as experienced during the last two decades in the community of Los Angeles. Southern California has no monopoly on this problem, as other communities are learning to their chagrin. But the somewhat special situation there seems to present a configuration in which the role of each of the four aspects of the ecological complex, including its relation to the others, is salient. I have made no technical investigation of the Los Angeles situation and have at hand only a haphazard collection of materials dealing with it, most of them designed for popular rather than scientific consumption. (The personal experience of living through a summer of Los Angeles smog is of value here only in that it permits sincere testimony to the effect that the problem is real.) The merit of the illustration, however, is that ramifying influences like those postulated by the ecosystem concept are superficially evident even when their nature is poorly understood and inadequately described. I am quite prepared to be corrected on the facts of the case, many of which have yet to come to light. I shall be greatly surprised, however, if anyone is able to produce an account of the smog problem in terms of a conceptual scheme materially *less* elaborate than the ecological complex.

During World War II residents of Los Angeles began to experience episodes of a bluish-gray haze in the atmosphere that reduced visibility and produced irritation of the eyes and respiratory tract (E→P); it was also found to damage growing plants (E→E), including some of considerable economic importance, and to crack rubber, accelerating the rate of deterioration of automobile tires, for example (E→T). In response to the episodes of smog, various civic movements were launched, abatement officers were designated in the city and county health departments, and a model control ordinance was promulgated (E→O). All these measures were without noticeable effect on the smog. At the time, little was known about the sources of pollution, although various industrial operations were suspected. By 1947, a comprehensive authority, the Los Angeles County Air Pollution Control District, was established by action of the California State Assembly and authorized to conduct research and to exercise broad powers of regulation. Various known and newly developed abatement devices were installed in industrial plants at the instance of the APCD, at a cost of millions of dollars (O→T).

Technical Considerations
Meanwhile, research by chemists and engineers was developing and confirming the "factory in the sky" theory of smog formation. Combustion and certain other processes release unburned hydrocarbons and oxides of nitrogen into the atmosphere (T→E). As these reach a sufficiently high concentration and are subjected to strong sunlight, chemical reactions occur that liberate large amounts of ozone and form smog. In particular, it was discovered that automobile exhaust contains the essential ingredients in nearly ideal proportions and that this exhaust is the major sources of the contaminants implicated in smog formation. It became all the more important as a source when industrial control measures and the prohibition of household open incinerators (O→T) reduced these sources (T→E). Also implicated in the problem was the meteorological situation of the Los Angeles Basin. Ringed by mountains and enjoying only a very low average wind velocity, the basin frequently is blanketed by a layer of warm air moving in from the Pacific. This temperature inversion prevents the polluted air from rising very far above ground level; the still air hovering over the area is then subject to the afore-mentioned smog-inducing action of Southern California's famous sunshine (E→E).

The problem, severe enough at onset, was hardly alleviated by the rapid growth of population in the Los Angeles area, spreading out as it did over a wide territory (P→E), and thereby heightening its dependence on the already ubiquitous automobile as the primary means of local movement (T↔O). Where could one find a more poignant instance of the principle of circular causation, so central to ecological theory, than that of the Los Angelenos speeding down their freeways in a rush to escape the smog produced by emissions from the very vehicles conveying them?

A number of diverse organizational responses (E→O) to the smog problem have occurred. In 1953 a "nonprofit, privately supported, scientific research organization, dedicated to the solution of the smog problem," the Air Pollution Foundation, was set up under the sponsorship of some 200 business enterprises, many of them in industries subject to actual or prospective regulatory measures. The complex interplay of interests and pressures among such private organizations and the several levels and branches of government that were involved (O→O) has not, to my knowledge, been the subject of an adequate investigation by a student of the political process. Two noteworthy outcomes of this process merit attention in particular. The first is the development of large-scale programs of public health research and action (O→P, E) concerned with air pollution effects (E→P). Comparatively little is known in this field of epidemiology (or as some research workers would say nowadays, medical ecology), but major programs have been set up within the last five years in the U.S. Public Health Service (whose interest, of course, is not confined to Los Angeles) as well as such agencies as the California State Department of Public Health. Here is a striking instance of interrelations between medical ecology and the ecology of medicine illustrating not merely "organizational growth," as studied in conventional sociology, but also an organizational response to environmental-demographic changes. Second, there has been a channeling of both public and private research effort into the search for a "workable device," such as an automatic fuel cutoff, a catalytic muffler, or an afterburner, which will eliminate or reduce the noxious properties of automobile exhaust. California now has on its statute books a law requiring manufacturers to equip automobiles with such a device if and when its workability is demonstrated (O→T).

Some engineers are confident that workable devices will soon be forthcoming. The Air Pollution Foundation has gone so far as to declare that the day is "near when Los Angeles' smog will be only a memory." Should the problem be thus happily resolved, with reduction of pollution to tolerable levels, the resolution will surely have to be interpreted as the net result of an intricate interaction of factors in the ecological complex (P, O, T→E). But if the condition is only partially alleviated, how much more growth of population and increase in automobile use will have to occur before even more drastic technological and organizational changes will be required: redevelopment of mass transit, introduction of private electric automobiles, rationing of travel, limitation of population expansion, or whatever they may be? What will be the outcome of experience with increasing air pollution in other communities, whose problems differ in various ways from that of Los Angeles? And the question of questions—Is the convulsion of the ecosystem occasioned by smog merely a small-scale prototype of what we must expect in a world seemingly destined to become ever more dependent upon nuclear energy and subject to its hazards of ionizing radiation?

I must assume that the reader will be kind enough to pass lightly over the defects of the foregoing exposition. In particular, he must credit the author with being aware of the many complications concealed by the use of arrows linking the broad and heterogeneous categories of the ecological complex. The arrows are meant only to suggest the existence of problems for research concerning the mechanisms of cause, influence, or response at work in the situation so sketchily portrayed. Even the barest account of that situation, however, can leave no doubt that social change and environmental modification occurred in the closest interdependence—so close, in fact, that the two "levels" of change were *systematically* interrelated. Change on either level can be comprehended only by application of a conceptual scheme at least as encompassing as that of ecosystem.

The reader's imagination, again, must substitute for documentation of the point that smog, though a spectacular case and full of human interest, is no isolated example of how problems of human collective existence require an ecosystem framework for adequate conceptualization. I do not intend to argue, of course, that sociologists must somehow shoulder the entire burden of research suggested by such a conceptualization. Science, after all, is one of our finest examples of the advantages of a division of labor. But labor can be effectively divided only if there is articulation on the several sub-tasks; in scientific work, such articulation is achieved by employment of a common conceptual framework.

Sociologists may or may not—I am not especially optimistic on this score—take up the challenge to investigate the social life of man as a phase of the ecosystem, with all the revisions in their thought patterns that this kind of formulation will demand. If they shirk this responsibility, however, other disciplines are not unprepared to take the leadership. Anthropology of late has demonstrated its hospitality to ecological concepts.[18] Geography, for its part, cannot forget that it laid claim to human ecology as early as did sociology.[19]

Of even greater ultimate significance may be the impending reorientation of much of what we now call social science to such concepts as welfare, level of living, and public health. Programs to achieve such "national goals" (to use the former President's language), like the studies on which such programs are based, are finding and will find two things: first, each of these concepts is capable of almost indefinite expansion to comprehend virtually any problem of human collective life; and, second, measures or indicators of status or progress in respect to them must be multi-faceted and relational. Public health, to take that example, is surely some sort of function of all elements in the ecological complex; it is observable in any sufficiently comprehensive sense only in terms of interrelations of variables located at all levels of the ecosystem. Extrapolation of current trends over even a short projection period is sufficient to suggest the future preoccupation of the sciences touching on man with much more macroscopic problems than they now dare to set for themselves. It is perhaps symptomatic that spokesmen for the nation's health programs now declare that the "science of health is a branch of the wider science of human ecology," [20] and that expositions of the problem of economic development have come to emphasize the necessary shift "From Political Economy to Political Ecology." [21] Even the literati proclaim that the "fundamental human problem is ecological." [22] (Cf. the similar remark of Kenneth Burke: "Among the sciences, there is one little fellow named Ecology, and in time we shall pay him more attention." [23]) If one holds with Durkheim that the basic categories of science, as well as the interpretive schemes of everyday life, arise from the nature and exigencies of human collective existence, it cannot be long before we are forced to conjure with some version of the ecosystem concept. The question is whether sociology will lead or lag behind in this intellectual movement.

Notes and References

a See Leo F. Schnore, "The Myth of Human Ecology," *Sociological Inquiry*, Vol. 31 (Spring 1961), pp. 128-39.

1. A. L. Kroeber, "So-Called Social Science," ch. vii in *The Nature of Culture* (Chicago: University of Chicago Press, 1952), pp. 66-67.

2. R. M. MacIver, *Social Causation* (Boston: Ginn & Co., 1942), pp. 271-72.

3. Arnold S. Feldman and Charles Tilly, "The Interaction of Social and Physical Space," *American Sociological Review*, 25 (December, 1960), p. 878.

4. W. C. Allee, Alfred E. Emerson, Orlando Park, Thomas Park, and Karl P. Schmidt, *Principles of Animal Ecology* (Philadelphia: W. B. Saunders Co., 1949), p. 695.

5. Eugene P. Odum, *Fundamentals of Ecology* (Philadelphia: W. B. Saunders Co., 1953), p. 9.

6. Robert E. Park, *Human Communities: The City and Human Ecology* (Glencoe, Ill.: The Free Press, 1952).

7. Milla Aïssa Alihan, *Social Ecology: A Critical Analysis* (New York: Columbia University Press, 1938).

8. Lee R. Dice, *Man's Nature and Nature's Man: The Ecology of Human Communities* (Ann Arbor: University of Michigan Press, 1955), pp. 2-3.

9. *Ibid.*, pp. 252-53.

10. Kenneth E. Boulding, *Principles of Economic Policy* (Englewood Cliffs, N. J.: Prentice-Hall, Inc., 1958), pp. 14-16.

11. Frederic E. Clements and Victor E. Shelford, *Bio-ecology* (New York: John Wiley & Sons, 1939), p. 1. Cf. F. Fraser Darling, "Pastorialism in Relation to Populations of Men and Animals," in *The Numbers of Man and Animals*, edited by J. B. Cragg and N. W. Pirie (Edinburgh: Oliver & Boyd, 1955).

12. Stephen A. Forbes, "The Humanizing of Ecology," *Ecology*, 3 (April, 1922), p. 90.

13. Charles S. Elton, *The Ecology of Invasions by Animals and Plants* (London: Methuen & Co., Ltd., 1958); F. Fraser Darling, *West Highland Survey: An Essay in Human Ecology* (Oxford: Oxford University Press, 1955); Paul B. Sears, *The Ecology of Man*, "Condon Lectures" (Eugene: Oregon State System of Higher Education, 1957). See also, F. Fraser Darling, "The Ecology of Man," *The American Scholar*, 25 (Winter, 1955-56), pp. 38-46; Donald F. Chapp, "Ecology—A Science Going to Waste," *Chicago Review*, 9 (Summer, 1955), pp. 15-26.

14. Title of an early essay by Robert K. Merton, *American Sociological Review*, 1 (December, 1936), pp. 894-904; a recent statement, pertinent to ecology, is Walter Firey's *Man, Mind and Land: A Theory of Resource Use* (Glencoe, Ill.: The Free Press, 1960).

15. Sears, op. cit., p. 50.

16. The following are merely illustrative: A. Irving Hallowell, "The Size of Algonkian Hunting Territories: A Function of Ecological Adjustment," *American Anthropologist*, 51 (January-March, 1949), pp. 34-45; Laura Thompson, "The Relations of Men, Animals, and Plants in an Island Community (Fiji)," *American Anthropologist*, 51 (April-June, 1949), pp. 253-76; Edgar Anderson, *Plants, Man and Life* (Boston: Little, Brown & Co., 1952); Fred Cottrell, *Energy and Society* (New York: McGraw-Hill Book Co., 1955); Harrison Brown, *The Challenge of Man's Future* (New York: Viking Press, 1954).

17. Otis Dudley Duncan, "Human Ecology and Population Studies," ch. xxviii in *The Study of Population*, edited by Philip M. Hauser and Otis Dudley Duncan (Chicago: University of Chicago Press, 1959).

18. Marston Bates, "Human Ecology," in *Anthropology Today*, edited by A. L. Kroeber (Chicago: University of Chicago Press, 1953); J. G. D. Clark, *Prehistoric Europe: The Economic Basis* (New York: Philosophical Library, 1952); Julian H. Steward, *Theory of Culture Change* (Urbana: University of Illinois Press, 1955).

19. H. H. Barrows, "Geography as Human Ecology," *Annals of the Association of American Geographers*, 13 (March, 1923), pp. 1-14; William L. Thomas, Jr., editor, *Man's Role in Changing the Face of the Earth* (Chicago: University of Chicago Press, 1956).

20. President's Commission on the Health Needs of the Nation, *America's Health Status, Needs and Resources. Building America's Health*, vol. 2 (Washington: Government Printing Office, 1953), p. 13.

21. Title of an essay by Bertrand de Jouvenel, *Bulletin of the Atomic Scientists*, 8 (October, 1957), pp. 287-91.

22. Aldous Huxley, *The Devils of Loudon,* "Torchbook edition" (New York: Harper & Bros., 1959), p. 302.

23. Kenneth Burke, *Attitudes toward History*, Vol. I (New York: The New Republic, 1937), p. 192.

Selected References for Chapter 2

Goldscheider, Calvin, *Population, Modernization, and Social Structure*. Boston: Little, Brown, and Co., 1971. An analysis of social organizational causes and consequences of population change; a particularly good introduction to social demography.

Hartley, Shirley Foster, *Population: Quantity Vs. Quality*. Englewood Cliffs, N. J.: Prentice-Hall, Inc., 1972. An examination of contemporary population trends and problems.

Johnson, Huey D., ed., *No Deposit—No Return. Man and His Environment: A View Toward Survival*. Reading, Mass.: Addison-Wesley Publishing Co., 1970. Readings depicting ecological problems in various components of man's environment.

Olsen, Marvin E., *The Process of Social Organization*. New York: Holt, Rinehart and Winston, Inc., 1968. A comprehensive discussion of the structure and dynamics of human social organization.

Thomas, William L., Jr., ed., *Man's Role in Changing the Face of the Earth*. Chicago: University of Chicago Press, 1956. Proceedings of a symposium dealing with man's impact on his physical-biological environment.

This chapter has been focused on the interrelationships among three components of a basic ecological model: population, environment, and social organization. It has been suggested that through social organization man is able to exert some degree of control over the structuring and dynamics of population and environment, as well as their interrelationships.

Part II of this volume, comprising Chapters 3 through 6, is directed toward further explication of the framework for ecological analysis presented in the Introduction. In this section the focus is on the role of particular aspects of social organization in the process of ecological adaptation. Thus Chapter 3 examines ways in which science and technology affect demographic adjustment, on the one hand, and environmental usage on the other. Succeeding chapters similarly deal with the effects of symbolic, regulatory, and distributional mechanisms on the components of ecological systems.

Part II

Organizational Aspects of Ecological Adaptation: Mediating an Equilibrium between Population and Environment

3

**Engineering Mechanisms:
The Role of Science
and Technology**

Probably the most significant demographic effects of science and technology are seen in the revolution in death control that took place following the industrial revolution. But we have already examined (Chapter 2) recent trends in population growth, and it was concluded that the major demographic problem facing the world is not saving lives, but rather slowing down the rate at which people are being born. Does it not seem reasonable, then, that science and technology ought to be focused on this more pressing problem? Increasingly such research and development is being funded, but results are singularly unimpressive except in a few areas of the world. As yet science and technology have not provided solutions to problems of excessive population growth.

More typically, scientific and technological developments are seen as means of supporting the world's inhabitants *in spite of* high birth rates. The initial article included in this chapter is addressed to evaluating this possibility. Ehrlich and Holdren focus their attention on four potential technological "solutions" to over-population. Briefly, these are (1) increased food production, (2) increased capacity to supply water, (3) development of nuclear sources of energy, and (4) increased transportation (redistribution) of food, material, and people. Upon closer examination, none of these panaceas proves to be much of a resolution.

Generally, the authors conclude that it is abundantly clear that in terms of cost, lead time, and implementation on the scale required, technology without population control will be too little and too late. More specifically, with respect to food production, they conclude that conventional agriculture cannot possibly yield significantly increased crops, that present uncultivated land is neither plentiful nor economically feasible, and that alternative sources, such as the sea, are overrated as to their potential contribution. Regarding additional sources of water, they note that technological solutions again fall short. As the authors say: "serious shortages arising from problems of quality, irregularity, and distribution already plague much of the world." Schemes for making use of sea water present more problems than they resolve. Developments in nuclear energy production are exceedingly expensive and, in many respects, still on the drawing board. Furthermore, secondary effects, such as excess heat production, may in themselves threaten man's survival. Finally, transportation solutions would be hard pressed to affect any more than a temporary balance between population and resources. The net result of these considerations is to reject science and technology as effective resolutions to problems of human survival. Ehrlich and Holdren conclude that there is no alternative but the cessation of our irresponsible, all-demanding, and all-consuming population growth.

Having seen that science and technology have contributed significantly more to population growth than to its control, we now turn to the other side of the ecological balance, the environment. In the preceding article Ehrlich and Holdren observed in passing that many so-called technological improvements may have deleterious consequences for environmental quality. This theme is pursued in the following essay by John Krutilla.

Attention is focused on man's increasing technological devastation of his natural surroundings, though implicit is the proposition that the human environment is also suffering. Perhaps the thesis of Krutilla's argument is best summarized in his contention that the change in the face of North America by reason of industrial man's dominance has resulted in a high standard of material well-being, but the ecological consequences may not yet be understood nor the ultimate cost appreciated. Such is the paradox of man's progressive mastery over nature. Natural resources, wildlife, open space—all have been grist for a technological mill whose output, measured largely in terms of "economic development," has been heretofore judged primarily in terms of market value. But, as the author suggests, industrialization has its unintended or socially unwarranted side effects, which may ultimately negate the material advances thus far achieved.

What are these side effects? Erosion and depletion of natural resources, proliferation of ugly and polluting waste materials and potential extinction of wildlife head a growing list. Is the continuation of undesirable consequences necessary? No, but resolution of the problem would involve a drastic reorganization of production and governmental processes. Essentially this would require industrialists and politicians alike to view "resource configurations not as individual cases but as parts of systems with an appropriate allocation of resources within the system in proportion to their representation." Some resources, those that technology cannot recreate or replace, will have to be protected no matter what their value to scientific and industrial production.

Krutilla's essay suggests further limitations on the adaptive value of technology in ecological systems. While no one can rationally dispute the contention that technological development has been a major factor in man's quest for material, social and psychological well-being, there have been certain "costs" involved. These are especially evident in the deterioration of the non-human environment. More importantly, further technological advancement does not appear to be a viable solution to this problem.

The major question, how best to gear technology for optimum use of the environment, will not be easily resolved. Modern society is organized around and dependent upon available technology, so any calls for a return to simpler modes of existence generally fall upon deaf ears. More reasonable and potentially successful are detailed strategies for fully assessing the implications of technology for other components of the ecosystem. Harmful effects can thus be anticipated, and perhaps even be prevented or at least minimized.

The final contribution to this chapter deals with such an outlook, focusing on the technological dimension. John McHale argues that ecological balance must be viewed in global, or world, proportions, not simply the more transient value systems and vested interests of any local society! Man's technological capacity to adapt nature to his needs and to increase the survival potential for his species has developed largely without benefit of conscious planning. The time has arrived—indeed, is probably long overdue—to assess the ecological impact of technological evolution.

Generally, the balance seems to be weighted toward the debit side of the ledger. McHale indicates how extensively industry and agriculture alike have depleted the resources upon which they depend, including land, minerals, fossil fuels, and water. In addition, the environment has been increasingly polluted with industrial wastes and residues. These observations are hardly new and should surprise no one. But even so, simple solutions are nowhere in sight.

McHale's approach to the problem of technological destruction of the environment stresses a socio-agri-industrial ecology. He offers several means by which man can reorganize technological imputs to the ecosystem and thus minimize (eliminate?) harmful consequences. These include recycling metals and materials, increasing use of non-fossil fuels (but see the comments by Ehrlich and Holdren, earlier in this chapter), refashioning food-producing and -distribution systems, and the establishment of monitoring systems for detecting and evaluating long-range effects on the ecosystem.

The utility of such a strategy can be determined only after it has been extensively implemented, and at present we have little evidence of applications along these lines. Whether man controls or is controlled by technology is still an open question, but the future of our global ecosystem is significantly dependent upon the answer.

Population and Panaceas: A Technological Perspective
Paul R. Ehrlich
John P. Holdren

Today more than one billion human beings are either undernourished or malnourished, and the human population is growing at a rate of 2% per year. The existing and impending crises in human nutrition and living conditions are well-documented but not widely understood. In particular, there is a tendency among the public, nurtured on Sunday-supplement conceptions of technology, to believe that science has the situation well in hand—that farming the sea and the tropics, irrigating the deserts, and generating cheap nuclear power in abundance hold the key to swift and certain solution of the problem. To espouse this belief is to misjudge the present severity of the situation, the disparate time scales on which technological progress and population growth operate, and the vast complexity of the problems beyond mere food production posed by population pressures. Unfortunately, scientists and engineers have themselves often added to the confusion by failing to distinguish between that which is merely theoretically feasible, and that which is economically and logistically practical.

As we will show here, man's present technology is inadequate to the task of maintaining the world's burgeoning billions, even under the most optimistic assumptions. Furthermore, technology is likely to remain inadequate until such time as the population growth rate is drastically reduced. This is not to assert that present efforts to "revolutionize" tropical agriculture, increase yields of fisheries, desalt water for irrigation, exploit new power sources, and implement related projects are not worthwhile. They may be. They could also easily produce the ultimate disaster for mankind if they are not applied with careful attention to their effects on the ecological systems necessary for our survival (Woodwell, 1967; Cole, 1968). And even if such projects are initiated with unprecedented levels of staffing and expenditures, without population control they are doomed to fall far short. No effort to expand the carrying capacity of the Earth can keep pace with unbridled population growth.

To support these contentions, we summarize briefly the present lopsided balance sheet in the population/food accounting. We then examine the logistics, economics, and possible consequences of some technological schemes which have been proposed to help restore the balance, or, more ambitiously, to permit the maintenance of human populations much larger than today's. The most pertinent aspects of the balance are:

1) The world population reached 3.5 billion in mid-1968, with an annual increment of approximately 70 million people (itself increasing) and a doubling time on the order of 35 years (Population Reference Bureau, 1968).

2) Of this number of people, at least one-half billion are undernourished (deficient in calories or, more succinctly, slowly starving), and approximately an additional billion are malnourished (deficient in particular nutrients, mostly protein) (Borgstrom, 1965; Sukhatme, 1966). Estimates of the number actually perishing annually from starvation begin at 4 million and go up (Ehrlich, 1968) and depend in part on official definitions of starvation which conceal the true magnitude of hunger's contribution to the death rate (Lelyveld, 1968).

3) Merely to maintain present inadequate nutrition levels, the food requirements of Asia, Africa, and Latin America will, conservatively, increase by 26% in the 10-year period measured from 1965 to 1975 (Paddock and Paddock, 1967). World food production must double in the period

1965-2000 to stay even; it must triple if nutrition is to be brought up to minimum requirements.

Food Production

That there is insufficient additional good quality agricultural land available in the world to meet these needs is so well documented (Borgstrom, 1965) that we will not belabor the point here. What hope there is must rest with increasing yields on land presently cultivated, bringing marginal land into production, more efficiently exploiting the sea, and bringing less conventional methods of food production to fruition. In all these areas, science and technology play a dominant role. While space does not permit even a cursory look at all the proposals on these topics which have been advanced in recent years, a few representative examples illustrate our points.

Conventional Agriculture   Probably the most widely recommended means of increasing agricultural yields is through the more intensive use of fertilizers. Their production is straightforward, and a good deal is known about their effective application, although, as with many technologies we consider here, the environmental consequences of heavy fertilizer use are ill understood and potentially dangerous[1] (Wadleigh, 1968). But even ignoring such problems, we find staggering difficulties barring the implementation of fertilizer technology on the scale required. In this regard the accomplishments of countries such as Japan and the Netherlands are often cited as offering hope to the underdeveloped world. Some perspective on this point is afforded by noting that if India were to apply fertilizer at the per capita level employed by the Netherlands, her fertilizer needs would be nearly half the present world output (United Nations, 1968).

On a more realistic plane, we note that although the goal for nitrogen fertilizer production in 1971 under India's fourth 5-year plan is 2.4 million metric tons (Anonymous, 1968a). Raymond Ewell (who has served as fertilizer production adviser to the Indian government for the past 12 years) suggests that less than 1.1 million metric tons is a more probable figure for that date.[2] Ewell cites poor plant maintenance, raw materials shortages, and power and transportation breakdowns as contributing to continued low production by existing Indian plants. Moreover, even when fertilizer is available, increases in productivity do not necessarily follow. In parts of the underdeveloped world lack of farm credit is limiting fertilizer distribution; elsewhere, internal transportation systems are inadequate to the task. Nor can the problem of educating farmers on the advantages and techniques of fertilizer use be ignored. A recent study (Parikh et al., 1968) of the Intensive Agriculture District Program in the Surat district of Gujarat, India (in which scientific fertilizer use was to have been a major ingredient) notes that "on the whole, the performance of adjoining districts which have similar climate but did not enjoy relative preference of input supply was as good as, if not better than, the programme district. . . . A particularly disheartening feature is that the farm production plans, as yet, do not carry any educative value and have largely failed to convince farmers to use improved practices in their proper combinations."

As a second example of a panacea in the realm of conventional agriculture, mention must be given to the development of new high-yield or high-protein strains of food crops. That such strains have the potential of making a major contribution to the food supply of the world is beyond doubt, but this potential is limited in contrast to the potential for population growth, and will be realized too slowly to have anything but a small impact on the immediate crisis. There are major difficulties impeding the widespread use of new high-yield grain varieties. Typically, the new grains require high fertilizer inputs to realize their full potential, and thus are subject to all the difficulties mentioned above. Some other problems were identified in a recent address by Lester R. Brown, administrator of the International Agricultural Development Service: the limited amount of irrigated land suitable for the new varieties, the fact that a farmer's willingness to innovate fluctuates with the market prices (which may be driven down by high-yield crops), and the possibility of tieups at market facilities inadequate for handling increased yields.[3]

Perhaps even more important, the new grain varieties are being rushed into production without adequate field testing, so that we are unsure of how resistant they will be to the attacks of insects and plant diseases. William Paddock has presented a plant pathologist's view of the crash programs to shift to new varieties (Paddock, 1967). He describes India's dramatic program of planting improved Mexican wheat, and continues: "Such a rapid switch to a new variety is clearly understandable in a country that tottered on the brink of famine. Yet with such limited testing, one wonders what unknown pathogens await a climatic change which will give the environmental conditions needed for their growth." Introduction of the new varieties creates enlarged monocultures of plants with essentially unknown levels of resistance to disaster. Clearly, one of the prices that is paid for higher yield is a higher risk of widespread catastrophe. And the risks are far from local: since the new varieties require more "input" of pesticides (with all their deleterious ecological side effects), these crops may ultimately contribute to the defeat of other environment-related panaceas, such as extracting larger amounts of food from the sea.

A final problem must be mentioned in connection with these strains of food crops. In general, the hungriest people in the world are also those with the most conservative food habits. Even rather minor changes, such as that from a rice variety in which the cooked grains stick together to one in which the grains fall apart, may make new foods unacceptable. It seems to be an unhappy fact of human existence that people would rather starve than eat a nutritious substance which they do not recognize as food.[4]

Beyond the economic, ecological, and sociological problems already mentioned in connection with high-yield agriculture, there is the overall problem of time. We need time to breed the desired characteristics of yield and hardiness into a vast array of new strains (a tedious process indeed), time to convince farmers that it is necessary that they change their time-honored ways of cultivation, and time to convince hungry people to change the staples of their diet. The Paddocks give 20 years as the "rule of thumb" for a new technique or plant variety to progress from conception to substantial impact on farming (Paddock and Paddock, 1967). They write: "It is true that a *massive* research attack on the problem could bring some striking results in less than 20 years. But I do not find such an attack remotely contemplated in the thinking of those officials capable of initiating it." Promising as high-yield agriculture may be, the funds, the personnel, the ecological expertise, and the necessary years are unfortunately not at our disposal. Fulfillment of the promise will come too late for many of the world's starving millions, if it comes at all.

Bringing More Land Under Cultivation   The most frequently mentioned means of bringing new land into agricultural production are farming the tropics and irrigating arid and semiarid regions. The former, although widely discussed in optimistic terms, has been tried for years with incredibly poor results, and even recent experiments have not been encouraging. One essential difficulty is the unsuitability of tropical soils for supporting typical foodstuffs instead of jungles (McNeil, 1964; Paddock and Paddock, 1964). Also, "the tropics" are a biologically more diverse area than the temperate zones, so that farming technology developed for one area will all too often prove useless in others. We shall see that irrigating the deserts, while more promising, has serious limitations in terms of scale, cost, and lead time.

The feasible approaches to irrigation of arid lands appear to be limited to large-scale water projects involving dams and transport in canals, and desalination of ocean and brackish water. Supplies of usable ground water are already badly depleted in most areas where they are accessible, and natural recharge is low enough in most arid regions that such supplies do not offer a long-term solution in any case. Some recent statistics will give perspective to the discussion of water projects and desalting which follows. In 1966, the United States was using about 300 billion gal of water per day, of which 135 billion gal were consumed by agriculture and 165 billion gal by numicipal and industrial users (Sporn, 1966). The bulk of the agricultural water cost the farmer from 5 to 10 cents/1000 gal: the highest price paid for agricultural water was 15 cents/1000 gal. For small industrial and municipal supplies, prices as high as 50 to 70 cents/1000 gal were prevalent in the U.S. arid regions, and some communities in the Southwest were paying on the order of $1.00/1000 gal for "project" water. The extremely high cost of the later stems largely from transportation costs, which have been estimated at 5 to 15 cents/1000 gal per 100 miles (International Atomic Energy Agency, 1964).

Irrigating the Desert

We now examine briefly the implications of such numbers in considering the irrigation of the deserts. The most ambitious water project yet conceived in this country is the North American Water and Power Alliance, which proposes to distribute water from the great rivers of Canada to thirsty locations all over the United States. Formidable political problems aside (some based on the certainty that in the face of expanding populations, demands for water will eventually arise at the source), this project would involve the expenditure of $100 billion in construction costs over a 20-year completion period. At the end of this time, the yield to the United States would be 69 million acre feet of water annually (Kelly, 1966), or 63 billion gal per day. If past experience with massive water projects is any guide, these figures are overoptimistic; but if we assume they are not, it is instructive to note that this monumental undertaking would provide for an increase of only 21% in the water consumption of the United States, during a period in which the population is expected to increase by between 25 and 43% (U.S. Dept. of Commerce, 1966). To assess the possible contribution to the *world* food situation, we assume that all this water could be devoted to agriculture, although extrapolation of present consumption patterns indicates that only about one-half would be. Then using the rather optimistic figure of 500 gal per day to grow the food to feed one person, we find that this project could feed 126 million additional people. Since this is less than 8% of the projected world population growth during the construction period (say 1970 to 1990), it should be clear that even the most massive water projects can make but a token contribution to the solution of the world food problem in the long term. And in the crucial short term—the years preceding 1980—*no* additional people will be fed by projects still on the drawing board today.

In summary, the cost is staggering, the scale insufficient, and the lead time too long. Nor need we resort to such speculation about the future for proof of the failure of technological "solutions" in the absence of population control. The highly touted and very expensive Aswan Dam project, now nearing completion, will ultimately supply food (at the present miserable diet level) for less than Egypt's population growth during the time of construction (Borgstrom, 1965; Cole, 1968). Furthermore, its effect on the fertility of the Nile Delta may be disastrous, and, as with all water projects of this nature, silting of the reservoir will destroy the gains in the long term (perhaps in 100 years).

Desalting for irrigation suffers somewhat similar limitations. The desalting plants operational in the world today produce water at individual rates of 7.5 million gal/day and less, at a cost of 75 cents/1000 gal and up, the cost increasing as the plant size decreases (Bender, 1969). The most optimistic firm proposal which anyone seems to have made for desalting with present or soon-to-be available technology is a 150 million gal per day nuclear-powered installation studied by the Bechtel Corp. for the Los Angeles Metropolitan Water District. Bechtel's early figures indicated that water from this complex would be available at the site for 27-28 cents/1000 gal (Galstann and Currier, 1967). However, skepticism regarding the economic assumptions leading to these figures (Milliman, 1966) has since proven justified—the project was shelved after spiralling construction cost estimates indicated an actual water cost of 40-50 cents/1000 gal. Use of even the original figures, however, bears out our contention that the *most* optimistic assumptions do not alter the verdict that technology is losing the food/population battle. For 28 cents/1000 gal is still approximately twice the cost which farmers have hitherto been willing or able to pay for irrigation water. If the Bechtel plant had been intended to supply agricultural needs, which it was not, one would have had to add to an already unacceptable price the very substantial cost of transporting the water inland.

Significantly, studies have shown that the economies of scale in the distillation process are essentially exhausted by a 150 million gal per day plant (International Atomic Energy Agency, 1964). Hence, merely increasing desalting capacity further will not substantially lower the cost of the water. On purely economic grounds, then, it is unlikely that desalting will play a major role in food production by conventional agriculture in the short term.[5] Technological "break-throughs" will presumably improve this outlook with the passage of time, but world population growth will not wait.

The Oak Ridge Studies

Desalting becomes more promising if the high cost of the water can be offset by increased agricultural yields per gallon and, perhaps, use of a single nuclear installation to provide power for both the desalting and profitable on-site industrial processes. This prospect has been investigated in a thorough and well-documented study headed by E. A. Mason (Oak Ridge National Laboratory, 1968). The result is a set of preliminary figures and recommendations regarding nuclear-powered "agro-industrial complexes" for arid and semiarid regions, in which desalted water and fertilizer would be produced for use on an adjacent, highly efficient farm. In underdeveloped countries incapable of using the full excess power output of the reactor, this energy would be consumed in on-site production of industrial materials for sale on the world market. Both near-term (10 years hence) and far-term (20 years hence) technologies are considered, as are various mixes of farm and industrial products.

The representative near-term case for which a detailed cost breakdown is given involves a seaside facility with a desalting capacity of 1 billion gal/day, a farm size of 320,000 acres, and an industrial electric power consumption of 1585 Mw. The initial investment for this complex is estimated at $1.8 billion, and annual operating costs at $236 million. If both the food and the industrial materials produced were sold (as opposed to giving the food, at least, to those in need who could not pay),[6] the estimated profit for such a complex, before substracting financing costs, would be 14.6%.

The authors of the study are commendably cautious in outlining the assumptions and uncertainties upon which these figures rest. The key assumption is that 200 gal/day of water will grow the 2500 calories required to feed one person. Water/calorie ratios of this order or less have been achieved by the top 20% of farmers specializing in such crops as wheat, potatoes, and tomatoes; but more water is required for needed protein-rich crops such as peanuts and soybeans. The authors identify the uncertainty that crops usually raised separately can be grown together in tight rotation on the same piece of land. Problems of water storage between periods of peak irrigation demand, optimal patterns of crop rotation, and seasonal acreage variations are also mentioned. These "ifs" and assumptions, and those associated with the other technologies involved, are unfortunately often omitted when the results of such painstaking studies are summarized for more popular consumption (Anonymous, 1968b, 1968c). The result is the perpetuation of the public's tendency to confuse feasible and available, to see panaceas where scientists in the field concerned see only potential, realizable with massive infusions of time and money.

It is instructive, nevertheless, to examine the impact on the world food problem which the Oak Ridge complexes might have if construction were to begin today, and if all the assumptions about technology 10 years hence were valid *now*. At the industrial-agricultural mix pertinent to the sample case described above, the food produced would be adequate for just under 3 million people. This means that 23 such plants per year, at a cost of $41 billion, would have to be put in operation merely to keep pace with world population growth, to say nothing of improving the substandard diets of between one and two billion members of the present population. (Fertilizer production beyond that required for the on-site farm is of course a contribution in the latter regard, but the substantial additional costs of transporting it to where it is needed must then be accounted for.) Since approximately 5 years from the start of construction would be required to put such a complex into operation, we should commence work on at least 125 units post-haste, and begin at least 25 per year thereafter. If the technology *were* available now, the investment in construction over the next 5 years, prior to operation of the first plants, would be $315 billion—about 20 times the total U.S. foreign aid expenditure during the past 5 years. By the time the technology *is* available the bill will be much higher, if famine has not "solved" the problem for us.

This example again illustrates that scale, time, and cost are all working against technology in the short term. And if population growth is not decelerated, the increasing severity of population-related crises will surely neutralize the technological improvements of the middle and long terms.

Other Food Panaceas   "Food from the sea" is the most prevalent "answer" to the world food shortage in the view of the general public. This is not surprising, since estimates of the theoretical fisheries productivity of the sea run up to some 50-100 times current yields (Schmitt, 1965; Christy and Scott, 1965). Many practical and economic difficulties, however, make it clear that such a figure will never be reached, and that it will not even be approached in the foreseeable future. In 1966, the annual fisheries harvest was some 57 million metric tons (United Nations, 1968). A careful analysis (Meseck, 1961) indicates that this might be increased to a world production of 70 million metric tons by 1980. If this gain were realized, it would represent (assuming no violent change in population growth patterns) a small per capita *loss* in fisheries yield.

Both the short- and long-term outlooks for taking food from the sea are clouded by the problems of overexploitation, pollution (which is generally ignored by those calculating potential yields), and economics. Solving these problems will require more than technological legerdemain; it will also require unprecedented changes in human behavior, especially in the area of international cooperation. The unlikelihood that such cooperation will come about is reflected in the recent news (Anonymous, 1968d) that Norway has dropped out of the whaling industry because overfishing has depleted the stock below the level at which it may economically be harvested. In that industry, international controls were tried—and failed. The sea is, unfortunately, a "commons" (Hardin, 1968), and the resultant management problems exacerbate the biological and technical problems of greatly increasing our "take." One suspects that the return per dollar poured into the sea will be much less than the corresponding return from the land for many years, and the return from the land has already been found wanting.

Synthetic foods, protein culture with petroleum, saline agriculture, and weather modification all may hold promise for the future, but all are at present expensive and available only on an extremely limited scale. The research to improve this situation will also be expensive, and, of course, time-consuming. In the absence of funding, it will not occur at all, a fact which occasionally eludes the public and the Congress.

Domestic and Industrial Water Supplies

The world has water problems, even exclusive of the situation in agriculture. Although total precipitation should in theory be adequate in quantity for several further doublings of population, serious shortages arising from problems of quality, irregularity, and distribution already plague much of the world. Underdeveloped countries will find the water needs of industrialization staggering: 240,000 gal of water are required to produce a ton of newsprint; 650,000 gal, to produce a ton of steel (International Atomic Energy Agency, 1964). Since maximum acceptable water costs for domestic and industrial use are higher than for agriculture, those who can afford it are or soon will be using desalination (40-100 + cents/1000 gal) and used-water renovation (54-57 cents/1000 gal [Ennis, 1967]). Those who cannot afford it are faced with allocating existing supplies between industry and agriculture, and as we have seen, they must choose the latter. In this circumstance, the standard of living remains pitifully low. Technology's only present answer is massive externally-financed complexes of the sort considered above, and we have already suggested there the improbability that we are prepared to pay the bill rung up by present population growth.

The widespread use of desalted water by those who *can* afford it brings up another problem only rarely mentioned to date, the disposal of the salts. The product of the distillation processes in present use is a hot brine with salt concentration several times that of seawater. Both the temperature and the salinity of this effluent will prove fatal to local marine life if it is simply exhausted to the ocean. The most optimistic statement we have seen on this problem is that "*smaller plants* (our emphasis) at seaside locations may return the concentrated brine to the ocean if proper attention is paid to the design of the outfall, and to the effect on the local marine ecology." (McIlhenny, 1966) The same writer identifies the major economic uncertainties connected with extracting the salts for sale (to do so is straightforward, but often not profitable). Nor can one simply evaporate the brine and leave the residue in a pile; the 150 million gal/day plant mentioned above would produce brine bearing 90 million lb. of salts daily (based on figures by Parker, 1966). This amount of salt would cover over 15 acres to a depth of one foot. Thus, every year a plant of the billion gallon per day, agro-industrial complex size would produce a pile of salt over 52 ft deep and covering a square mile. The high winds typical of coastal deserts would seriously aggravate the associated soil contamination problem.

Energy

Man's problems with energy supply are more subtle than those with food and water: we are not yet running out of energy, but we are being forced to use it faster than is probably healthy. The rapacious depletion of our fossil fuels is already forcing us to consider more expensive mining techniques to gain access to lower-grade deposits, such as the oil shales, and even the status of our high-grade uranium ore reserves is not clearcut (Anonymous, 1968c).

A widely held misconception in this connection is that nuclear power is "dirt cheap," and as such represents a panacea for developed and under-developed nations alike. To the contrary, the largest nuclear-generating stations now in operation are just competitive with or marginally superior to modern coal-fired plants of comparable size (where coal is not scarce): at best, both produce power for on the order of 4-5 mills (tenths of a cent) per kilowatt-hour. Smaller nuclear units remain less economical than their fossil-fueled counterparts. Underdeveloped countries can rarely use the power of the larger plants. Simply speaking, there are not enough industries, appliances, and light bulbs to absorb the output, and the cost of industrialization and modernization exceeds the cost of the power required to sustain it by orders of magnitude, regardless of the source of the power. (For example, one study noted that the capital requirement to consume the output of a 70,000 kilowatt plant—about $1.2 million worth of electricity per year at 40% utilization and 5 mills/kwh—is $111 million per year if the power is consumed by metals industries, $270 million per year for petroleum product industries [E. S. Mason, 1957].) Hence, at least at present, only those underdeveloped countries which are short of fossil fuels or inexpensive means to transport them are in particular need of nuclear power.

Prospects for major reductions in the cost of nuclear power in the future hinge on the long-awaited breeder reactor and the still further distant thermonuclear reactor. In neither case is the time scale or the ultimate cost of energy a matter of any certainty. The breeder reactor, which converts more nonfissile uranium (^{238}U) or thorium to fissionable material than it consumes as fuel for itself, effectively extends our nuclear fuel supply by a factor of approximately 400 (Cloud, 1968). It is not expected to become competitive economically with conventional reactors until the 1980s (Bump, 1967). Reductions in the unit energy cost beyond this date are not guaranteed, due both to the probable continued high capital cost of breeder reactors and to increasing costs for the ore which the breeders will convert to fuel. In the latter regard, we mention that although crushing granite for its few parts per million of uranium and thorium is possible in theory, the problems and cost of doing so are far from resolved.[7] It is too soon to predict the costs associated with a fusion reactor (few who work in the field will predict whether such a device will work at all within the next 15-20 years). One guess puts the unit energy cost at something over half that for a coal or fission power station of comparable size (Mills, 1967), but this is pure speculation. Quite possibly the major benefit of controlled fusion will again be to extend the energy supply rather than to cheapen it.

A second misconception about nuclear power is that it can reduce our dependence on fossil fuels to zero as soon as that becomes necessary or desirable. In fact, nuclear power plants contribute only to the electrical portion of the energy budget; and in 1960 in the United States, for example, electrical energy comprised only 19% of the total energy consumed (Sporn, 1963). The degree to which nuclear fuels can postpone the exhaustion of our coal and oil depends on the extent to which that 19% is enlarged. The task is far from a trivial one, and will involve transitions to electric or fuel-cell powered transportation, electric heating, and electrically powered industries. It will be extremely expensive.

Nuclear energy, then, is a panacea neither for us nor for the underdeveloped world. It relieves, but does not remove, the pressure on fossil fuel supplies; it provides reasonably-priced power where these fuels are not abundant; it has substantial (but expensive) potential in intelligent applications such as that suggested in the Oak Ridge study discussed above; and it shares the propensity of fast-growing technology to unpleasant side effects (Novick, 1969). We mention in the last connection that, while nuclear power stations do not produce conventional air pollutants, their radioactive waste problems may in the long run prove a poor trade. Although the AEC seems to have made a good case for solidification and storage in salt mines of the bulk of the radioactive fission products (Blanko et al., 1967), a number of radioactive isotopes are released to the environment, and in some areas such isotopes have already turned up in potentially harmful concentrations (Curtis and Hogan, 1969). Projected order of magnitude increases in nuclear power generation will seriously aggravate this situation. Although it has frequently been stated that the eventual advent of fusion reactors will free us from such difficulties, at least one authority, F. L. Parker, takes a more cautious view. He contends that the large inventory of radioactive tritium in early fusion reactors will require new precautions to minimize emissions (Parker, 1968).

A more easily evaluated problem is the tremendous quantity of waste heat generated at nuclear installations (to say nothing of the usable power output, which, as with power from whatever source, must also ultimately be dissipated as heat). Both have potentially disastrous effects on the local and world ecological and climatological balance. There is no simple solution to this problem, for, in general, "cooling" only moves heat: it does not *remove* it from the environment viewed as a whole. Moreover, the Second Law of Thermodynamics puts a ceiling on the efficiency with which we can do even this much, i.e., concentrate and transport heat. In effect, the Second Law condemns us to aggravate the total problem by generating still *more* heat in any machinery we devise for local cooling (consider, for example, refrigerators and air conditioners).

The only heat which actually leaves the whole system, the Earth, is that which can be radiated back into space. This amount steadily is being diminished as combustion of hydrocarbon fuels increases the atmospheric percentage of CO^2 which has strong absorption bands in the infrared spectrum of the outbound heat energy. (Hubbert, 1962, puts the increase in the CO^2 content of the atmosphere at 10% since 1900.) There is, of course, a competing effect in the Earth's energy balance, which is the increased reflectivity of the upper atmosphere to incoming sunlight due to other forms of air pollution. It has been estimated, ignoring both these effects, that man risks drastic (and perhaps catastrophic) climatological change if the amount of heat he dissipates in the environment on a global scale reaches 1% of the solar energy absorbed and reradiated at the Earth's surface (Rose and Clark, 1961). At the present 5% rate of increase in world energy consumption,[8] this level will be reached in less than a century, and in the immediate future the direct contribution of man's power consumption will create serious local problems. If we may safely rule out circumvention of the Second Law or the divorce of energy requirements from population size, this suggests that, whatever science and technology may accomplish, population growth must be stopped.

Transportation

We would be remiss in our offer of a technological perspective on population problems without some mention of the difficulties associated with transporting large quantities of food, material, or people across the face of the Earth. While our grain exports have not begun to satisfy the hunger of the underdeveloped world, they already have taxed our ability to transport food in bulk over large distances. The total amount of goods of *all* kinds loaded at U.S. ports for external trade was 158 million metric tons in 1965 (United Nations, 1968). This is coincidentally the approximate amount of grain which would have been required to make up the dietary shortages of the underdeveloped world in the same year (Sukhatme, 1966). Thus, if the United States *had* such an amount of grain to ship, it could be handled only by displacing the entirety of our export trade. In a similar vein, the gross weight of the fertilizer, in excess of present consumption, required in the underdeveloped world to feed the additional population there in 1980 will amount to approximately the same figure—150 million metric tons (Sukhatme, 1966). Assuming that a substantial fraction of this fertilizer, should it be available at all, will have to be shipped about, we had best start building freighters! These problems, and the even more discouraging one of internal transportation in the hungry countries, coupled with the complexities of international finance and marketing which have hobbled even present aid programs, complete a dismal picture of the prospects for "external" solutions to ballooning food requirements in much of the world.

Those who envision migration as a solution to problems of food, land,

and water distribution not only ignore the fact that the world has no promising place to put more people, they simply have not looked at the numbers of the transportation game. Neglecting the fact that migration and relocation costs would probably amount to a minimum of several thousand dollars per person, we find, for example, that the entire long-range jet transport fleet of the United States (about 600 planes [Molloy, 1968] with an average capacity of 150), averaging two round trips per week, could transport only about 9 million people per year from India to the United States. This amounts to about 75% of that country's annual population *growth* (Population Reference Bureau, 1968). Ocean liners and transports, while larger, are less numerous and much slower, and over long distances could not do as well. Does anyone believe, then, that we are going to compensate for the world's population growth by sending the excess to the planets? If there were a place to go on Earth, financially and logistically we could not send our surplus there.

Conclusion

We have not attempted to be comprehensive in our treatment of population pressures and the prospects of coping with them technologically; rather, we hope simply to have given enough illustrations to make plausible our contention that technology, without population control, cannot meet the challenge. It may be argued that we have shown only that any one technological scheme taken individually is insufficient to the task at hand, whereas *all* such schemes applied in parallel might well be enough. We would reply that neither the commitment nor the resources to implement them all exists, and indeed that many may prove mutually exclusive (e.g., harvesting algae may diminish fish production).

Certainly, an optimum combination of efforts exists in theory, but we assert that no organized attempt to find it is being made, and that our examination of its probable eventual constituents permits little hope that even the optimum will suffice. Indeed, after a far more thorough survey of the prospects than we have attempted here, the President's Science Advisory Committee Panel on the world food supply concluded (PSAC, 1967): "The solution of the problem that will exist after about 1985 *demands* that programs of population control be initiated now." We most emphatically agree, noting that "now" was 2 years ago!

Of the problems arising out of population growth in the short, middle, and long terms, we have emphasized the first group. For mankind must pass the first hurdles—food and water for the next 20 years—to be granted the privilege of confronting such dilemmas as the exhaustion of mineral resources and physical space later.[9] Furthermore, we have not conveyed the extent of our concern for the environmental deterioration which has accompanied the population explosion, and for the catastrophic ecological consequences which would attend many of the proposed technological "solutions" to the population/food crisis. Nor have we treated the point that "development" of the rest of the world to the standards of the West probably would be lethal ecologically (Ehrlich and Ehrlich, 1970). For even if such grim prospects are ignored, it is abundantly clear that in terms of cost, lead time, and implementation on the scale required, technology without population control will be too little and too late.

What hope there is lies not, of course, in abandoning attempts at technological solutions; on the contrary, they must be pursued at unprecedented levels, with unprecedented judgment, and above all with unprecedented attention to their ecological consequences. We need dramatic programs now to find ways of ameliorating the food crisis—to buy time for humanity until the inevitable delay accompanying population control efforts has passed. But it cannot be emphasized enough that if the population control measures are *not* initiated immediately and effectively, all the technology man can bring to bear will not fend off the misery to come. [10] Therefore, confronted as we are with limited resources of time and money, we must consider carefully what fraction of our effort should be applied to the cure of the disease itself instead of to the temporary relief of the symptoms. We should ask, for example, how many vasectomies could be performed by a program funded with the 1.8 billion dollars required to build a single nuclear agro-industrial complex, and what the relative impact on the problem would be in both the short and long terms.

The decision for population control will be opposed by growth-minded economists and businessmen, by nationalistic statesmen, by zealous religious leaders, and by the myopic and well-fed of every description. It is therefore incumbent on all who sense the limitations of technology and the fragility of the environmental balance to make themselves heard above the hollow, optimistic chorus—to convince society and its leaders that there is no alternative but the cessation of our irresponsible, all-demanding, and all-consuming population growth.

Acknowledgments
We thank the following individuals for reading and commenting on the manuscript: J. H. Brownell (Stanford University); P. A. Cantor (Aerojet General Corp.); P. E. Cloud (University of California, Santa Barbara); D. J. Eckstrom (Stanford University); R. Ewell (State University of New York at Buffalo); J. L. Fisher (Resources for the Future, Inc.); J. A. Hendrickson, Jr. (Stanford University); J. H. Hessel (Stanford University); R. W. Holm (Stanford University); S. C. McIntosh, Jr., (Stanford University); K. E. F. Watt (University of California, Davis). This work was supported in part by a grant from the Ford Foundation.

Notes

1. Barry Commoner, address to 135th Meeting of the AAAS, Dallas, Texas (28 December 1968).

2. Raymond Ewell, private communication (1 December 1968).

3. Lester R. Brown, address to the Second International Conference on the War on Hunger, Washington, D.C. (February 1968).

4. For a more detailed discussion of the psychological problems in persuading people to change their dietary habits, see McKenzie, 1968.

5. An identical conclusion was reached in a recent study (Clawson et al., 1969) in which the foregoing points and numerous other aspects of desalting were treated in far more detail than was possible here.

6. Confusing statements often are made about the possibility that food supply will outrun food demand in the future. In these statements, "demand" is used in the economic sense, and in this context many millions of starving people may generate no demand whatsoever. Indeed, one concern of those engaged in increasing food production is to find ways of increasing demand.

7. A general discussion of extracting metals from common rock is given by Cloud, 1968.

8. The rate of growth of world energy consumption fluctuates strongly about some mean on a time scale of only a few years, and the figures are not known with great accuracy in any case. A discussion of predicting the mean and a defense of the figure of 5% are given in Gúeron et al., 1957.

9. Since the first draft of this article was written, the authors have seen the manuscript of a timely and pertinent forthcoming book, *Resources and Man*, written under the auspices of the National Academy of Sciences and edited by Preston E. Cloud. The book reinforces many of our own conclusions in such areas as agriculture and fisheries and, in addition, treats both short- and long-term prospects in such areas as mineral resources and fossil fuels in great detail.

10. This conclusion has also been reached within the specific context of aid to underdeveloped countries in a Ph.D. thesis by Douglas Dactz: "Energy Utilization and Aid Effectiveness in Nonmechanized Agriculture: A Computer Simulation of a Socioeconomic System" (University of California, Berkeley, May 1968).

References

Anonymous. 1968a. India aims to remedy fertilizer shortage. *Chem. Eng. News*, 46 (November 25), p. 29.

———. 1968b. Scientists Studying Nuclear-Powered Agro-Industrial Complexes to Give Food and Jobs to Millions. *New York Times*, March 10, p. 74.

———. 1968c. Food from the atom. *Technol. Rev.*, January, p. 55.

———. 1968d. Norway—The end of the big blubber. *Time*, November 29, p. 98.

———. 1968e. Nuclear fuel cycle. *Nucl. News*, January, p. 30.

Bender, R. J. 1969. Why water desalting will expand. *Power*, 113 (August), p. 171.

Blanko, R. E., J. O. Blomeke, and J. T. Roberts. 1967. Solving the waste disposal problem. *Nucleonics*, 25, p. 58.

Borgstrom, Georg. 1965. *The Hungry Planet*, Collier-Macmillan, New York.

Bump, T. R. 1967. A third generation of breeder reactors. Sci. Amer., May, p. 25.

Christy, F. C., Jr., and A. Scott. 1965. *The Commonwealth in Ocean Fisheries*. Johns Hopkins Press, Baltimore.

Clawson, M., H. L. Landsberg, and L. T. Alexander, 1969. Desalted seawater for agriculture: It is economic? *Science*, 164, p. 1141.

Cloud, P. R. 1968. Realities of mineral distribution. *Texas Quart.*, Summer, p. 103.

Cole, LaMont C. 1968. Can the world be saved? *BioScience*, 18, p. 679.

Curtis, R., and E. Hogan. 1969. *Perils of the Peaceful Atom*. Doubleday, New York, p. 135, 150-152.

Ennis, C. E. 1967. Desalted water as a competitive commodity. *Chem. Eng. Progr.*, 63:(1), p. 64.

Ehrlich, P. R. 1968. *The Population Bomb*. Sierra Club/Ballantine, New York.

Ehrlich, P. R., and Anne H. Ehrlich. 1970. *Population, Resources, and Environment*. W. H. Freeman, San Francisco (In press).

Galstann, L. S. and E. L. Currier. 1967. The Metropolitan Water District desalting project. *Chem. Eng. Progr.*, 63,(1), p. 64.

Gúeron, J., J. A. Lane, I. R. Maxwell, and J. R. Menke. 1957. *The Economics of Nuclear Power. Progress in Nuclear Energy*. McGraw-Hill Book Co., New York. Series VIII. p. 23.

Hardin, G. 1968. The tragedy of the commons. *Science*, 162, p. 1243.

Hubbert, M. K. 1962. Energy resources, A report to the Committee on Natural Resources. National Research Council Report 1000-D, National Academy of Sciences.

International Atomic Energy Agency, 1964. Desalination of water using conventional and nuclear energy. Technical Report 24, Vienna.

Kelly, R. P. 1966. North American water and power alliance. In: *Water*

Production Using Nuclear Energy, R. G. Post and R. L. Seale (eds.). University of Arizona Press, Tucson, p. 29.

Lelyveld, D. 1968. Can India survive Calcutta? *New York Times Magazine*, October 13, p. 58.

Mason, E. S. 1957. Economic growth and energy consumption. In: *The Economics of Nuclear Power. Progress in Nuclear Energy*, Series VIII, J. Gúeron et al. (eds.). McGraw-Hill Book Co., New York, p. 56.

McIlhenny, W. F. 1966. Problems and potentials of concentrated brines. In: *Water Production Using Nuclear Energy*, R. G. Post and R. L. Seale (eds.). University of Arizona Press, Tucson, p. 187.

McKenzie, John. 1968. Nutrition and the soft sell. *New Sci.*, 40, p. 423.

McNeil, Mary. 1964. Lateritic soils. *Sci. Amer.*, November, p. 99.

Meseck, G. 1961. Importance of fish production and utilization in the food economy. Paper R11.3, presented at FAO Conference on Fish in Nutrition, Rome.

Milliman, J. W. 1966. Economics of water production using nuclear energy. In: *Water Production Using Nuclear Energy*. R. G. Post and R. L. Seale (eds.). University of Arizona Press, Tucson, p. 49.

Mills, R. G. 1967. Some engineering problems of thermonuclear fusion. *Nucl. Fusion*, 7, p. 223.

Molloy, J. F., Jr. 1968. The $12-billion financing problem of U.S. airlines. *Astronautics and Aeronautics*, October, p. 76.

Novick, S. 1969. *The Careless Atom*. Houghton Mifflin, Boston.

Oak Ridge National Laboratory, 1968. Nuclear energy centers, industrial and agro-industrial complexes. Summary Report. ORNL-4291, July.

Paddock, William. 1967. Phytopathology and a hungry world. *Ann. Rev. Phytopathol.*, 5, p. 375.

Paddock, William, and Paul Paddock. 1964. *Hungry Nations*. Little, Brown & Co., Boston.

———. 1967. *Famine 1975!* Little, Brown & Co., Boston.

Parikh, G., S. Saxena, and M. Maharaja. 1968. Agricultural extension and IADP, a study of Surat. *Econ. Polit. Weekly*, August 24, p. 1307.

Parker, F. L. 1968. Radioactive wastes from fusion reactors. *Science*, 159, p. 83. Parker, F. L. and D. J. Rose, *Science*, 159, p. 1376.

Parker, H. M. 1966. Environmental factors relating to large water plants. In: *Water Production Using Nuclear Energy*, R. G. Post and R. L. Seale (eds.). University of Arizona Press, Tucson, p. 209.

Population Reference Bureau. 1968. Population Reference Bureau Data Sheet. Pop. Ref. Bureau, Washington, D.C.

PSAC. 1967. *The World Food Problem*. Report of the President's Science Advisory Committee. Vols. 1-3. U.S. Govt. Printing Office, Washington, D.C.

Rose, D. J., and M. Clark, Jr. 1961. *Plasma and Controlled Fusion*. M.I.T. Press, Cambridge, Mass., p. 3.

Schmitt, W. R. 1965. The planetary food potential. *Ann. N.Y. Acad. Sci.*, 118, p. 645.

Sporn, Philip. 1963. *Energy for Man*. Macmillan, New York.

———. 1966. *Fresh Water from Saline Waters*. Pergamon Press, New York.

Sukhatme, P. V. 1966. The world's food supplies. *Roy. Stat. Soc. J.*, 129A, p. 222.

United Nations. 1968. *United Nations Statistical Yearbook for 1967*. Statistical Office of the U.N., New York.

U.S. Dept. of Commerce. 1966. *Statistical Abstract of the U.S.* U.S. Govt. Printing Office, Washington, D.C.

Wadleigh, C. H. 1968. Wastes in relation to agriculture and industry. USDA Miscellaneous Publication No. 1065. March.

Woodwell, George M. 1967. Toxic substances and ecological cycles. *Sci. Amer.*, March, p. 24.

Some Environmental Effects of Economic Development
John V. Krutilla

American culture and character have been influenced profoundly by the open rural countryside and the wilderness beyond. The further we are removed from the conditions of a more primitive America, the greater is our nostalgia for the conditions of earlier times. But despite the many influential and eloquent advocates for preserving the American scene—and especially the wilderness and rural countryside—the assaults upon America's landscape and the erosion of its natural environment continue.

In the past, the degradation of the landscape has been associated principally with mining, logging, and agricultural activities. Open pits abandoned after completion of strip-mining operations seriously deface a natural landscape, but strip mining is certainly not alone, nor is it first among the mining methods that have such an adverse consequence. The dredging of stream beds and hydraulic mining, particularly in connection with the recovery of gold, create unsightly mounds of debris along streams. By its very nature, mining is inimical to natural environments. Mining operations annually produce solid wastes amounting to 3.3 billion tons.[1] The discharge into streams used in washing and in transporting wastes often degrades the water quality for miles along the watercourse. Occasionally, as in the case of zinc-recovery operations, escape of flue gases destroys the vegetation in the surrounding area. Ducktown, Tennessee, and Sudbury, Ontario, are the classic examples here, and more recent experience in the Trail, British Columbia, area reminds us that mine-mill activities threaten the maintenance of the vegetative cover and topographic equilibrium in surrounding areas.

Together, logging and agricultural activities, including livestock grazing, have most probably had a more extensive effect on natural environments than mining. Where soils were initially thin, or slopes so steep that clearing and converting to cropland was, at best, questionable, early ignorance of or disregard for the equilibrium of topography, soil, and vegetation transformed many an Appalachian landscape into a series of denuded slopes and gullied ridges. Clear-cutting in some private forest holdings often fails to ensure the maintenance of bases for viable biotic communities. In the western portions of North America, the pressure of grazing on the carrying capacity of the range is transforming, and in some cases has transformed, grasslands into areas of desert shrubs, forbs, and other wasteland vegetation.

Such activities are not alone in changing the character of the landscape. Highways, dams, reservoirs, railroads, and utilities all alter the landscape, and their effects on the natural environment are probably greatest in primitive or wilderness areas. Ironically, recreationists, many of whom are lovers of nature, and students of natural history pose the greatest threat to some fragile ecosystems by the intensity of recreation activities in areas of unique geologic, biotic, or recreational interest, in national parks and forests.

Effects of Nearby Cities
Rural areas that lie within easy reach of urbanites are subject to a variety of different factors. The refuse of our increasingly "containerized" society litters the landscape along the corridors between urban places. Currently the most pressing problem may be disposing of discarded automobiles—whether they are concentrated in junk yards or abandoned at random along rural roads and country woodlands. Automobile graveyards are, however, evidence

of only one kind of littering. Frequently there are no sanitation departments in rural villages and counties, so that household trash gets dumped wherever convenient, without regard for appearance. Streambanks, in particular, appear to invite the disposal of refuse, doubtless with the thought that freshets will periodically remove the trash from view.

Americans often observe that the European landscape appears to be graced by reason of human habitation. Structures erected for their utility to man are often disguised ingeniously or blended into the landscape so that they do not mar the harmony of the pastoral setting. And certainly some of New England, notably the Dorset Valley, also exhibits pastoral scenes that provide a landscape aesthetically more pleasing in some respects than the original forest. But in areas of submarginal agriculture, in New England no less than elsewhere, America is strewn with the unsightly evidence of deteriorating farmsteads and dying and dilapidated communities. Derelict coal tipples and abandoned trucks further insult the landscape in areas where mines have shut down.

The opening up and development of the country has, of course, affected the natural environments for the survival and reproduction of wildlife.[2] Changes in the landscape have wrought fundamental changes in habitat, thereby altering greatly the numbers, distribution, and character of wildlife in the United States. Some species adaptable to village and farm conditions have increased in numbers since the advent of the white man in America, but these represent a small minority.

Changing Patterns of Wildlife
Before the Atlantic Seaboard, the Appalachian Highlands, and the Ohio Valley were settled, the eastern portion of the United States abounded with game. Most of the species that have survived are now restricted to greatly reduced ranges in the West. The American elk once roamed all the areas of the New England and Middle Atlantic states and the forest areas to the west. By 1850, no elk were left in the eastern United States, being reduced in range to the western mountain regions. The woods bison was also in evidence in great numbers throughout the forested areas along the Atlantic, the Appalachians, and the Ohio Valley as late as 1750; by 1800, however, the great herds of Pennsylvania had disappeared, and within twenty-five years, the bison were gone from West Virginia, the last refuge of the eastern herds. A half century later, the plains bison, too, had all but disappeared. Woodland caribou, found in New England until after the Civil War, persisted in Maine until 1890. Of the moose that originally ranged through New England, New York, and Pennsylvania, only remnants still survive in the Maine woods.

For the large game mammals, as well as for such fowl as turkey (which are deep-woods species), logging and, perhaps even more, the conversion of

forest to cropland altered the conditions of survival beyond immediate re-
trieval. Not only did these practices change the character of the vegetation,
they broke the continuity of the range. Even when large areas of forest land
remained, the species that require conditions remote from human habitation
disappeared from these areas.

Among the predators, the populations of lynx, cougar, and bobcat have
diminished with the wilderness. The gray wolf, formerly found everywhere
except desert areas, disappeared from the East by 1905, was still abundant in
the intermountain area of the West until 1915, but had almost disappeared by
the early 1940s. Only remnants continue to exist in northwestern Michigan,
Minnesota, Wisconsin, and Oregon. The red wolf is still found in small numbers in portions of Louisiana, Texas, Arkansas, Missouri, and Oklahoma. The
cougar, with a natural range extending throughout the continental United
States, is now confined largely to the Rocky Mountains, the Sierras, the
Cascades, the Olympic Mountains, and, in drastically diminished numbers, the
cypress swamps and Everglades in Florida where the "panther" is threatened
with extirpation.

The depredation of bird populations is partly associated with the adaptation of natural environments to the requirements of agriculture and industry. Some species have disappeared entirely; others are vastly reduced in
numbers and range. An early victim was the great auk, the last of these being
seen and slaughtered in 1844. Only three decades later, the Labrador or
sand-shoal duck was last seen and shot on Long Island. The passenger pigeon
was gone by 1900; the Guadalupe petrel and the masked bobwhite, by the
second decade of the present century, although the latter may have been
rediscovered as a small flock of domesticated fowl in Mexico. Of the three
recognized races of prairie chicken which collectively occupied a large area of
the United States from Maine to Virginia on the Atlantic Seaboard across the
continent to the western Gulf states and the Great Plains of the Southwest,
the heath hen is extinct, Attwater's prairie chicken is found only in a small
area of Texas, and the common prairie chicken of the northern United States
and Canada is still declining in numbers. As with the masked bobwhite, the
conversion of grasslands to agricultural purposes and overgrazing have been
responsible for the demise or decimation of these once large populations.

Among the birds of prey with the greatest geographic distribution, the
kites seem to have suffered the greatest depredation. Originally seen on both
continents of the Western Hemisphere, the several races now occupy only the
most restricted areas—the swallow-tail kite appearing principally in the
swamps of South Carolina, Florida, and Louisiana, and the white-tail in California. Only the Mississippi kite appears out of danger of extinction. Of
greatest irony is the threat to the continued survival of the bald eagle, proud
symbol of American freedom and power.

The condition of some species, on the other hand, has improved during the last several decades. The whitetail deer and the raccoon have made an excellent adjustment to conditions associated with rural human habitation, and the opossum has even adapted to modern urban conditions. Moreover, much of the marginal cropland in the Appalachians has gone back to forest. In New England, the reversion began with the introduction of the trans-Appalachian railroads in the last century, and some of the long abandoned cropland is now supporting forest growth approaching climax conditions. In the southern Appalachians where the shift did not begin until the turn of the century, the timber stands are in earlier stages of succession, but some have matured sufficiently to produce mast and cover hospitable to some species of woodland wildlife. Consolidation of lands into comparatively large public holdings for parks, wildlife management, and hunting, and the establishment of large national forests have made it possible to reintroduce some woodland species in a limited way. The wild turkey, for example, has been reintroduced to forested areas of the Pennsylvania and Virginia Appalachians and elsewhere in the South with the spread of new forests. Reintroduction of elk in a more limited way has also been accomplished with some success.

Except for the few species mentioned above, however, not only has the original range been reduced drastically, but the survival of the species itself is threatened. A systematic survey by the U.S. Fish and Wildlife Service has identified seventy-eight species of mammals, birds, fishes, and reptiles that are endangered, forty-four others that have become rare, and twenty-one whose occurrence in the United States represents the outer edges of their natural ranges.[3] In some instances, the threat is not necessarily to continued existence of the species itself, but to its survival in the United States. Another category includes fifty or sixty species on which there is insufficient information to warrant such classification, but among which there may be species whose survival is precarious.

The Problem in Perspective: Past and Current

Large, and in many cases, irreversible changes in the American landscape and biota have taken place, but one should not conclude that all of these changes should not have occurred. The extractive activities that have contributed to the deterioration of the natural environment have promoted in a significant way the growth of the national economy and the material well-being of human society. Without them, a modern industrial nation could not have developed.

Earlier in the nation's history, the level of material well-being was quite low relative to present standards, technology was in its infancy, and the wilderness was large in relation to the lands under cultivation and the domesticated varieties of plant and animal life. Under these circumstances, the reduction in the size of the wilderness and the wildlife populations represented a conversion of resources that were abundant, and hence of limited value *at the margin*, into goods and services of high marginal value for the development of the economy. Today we have a large accumulation of capital and a level of living unparalleled in other cultures and previous periods. Moreover, the sophisticated technology that has made this possible appears to have reached a stage where the rate of advance can be manipulated, within limits, by research and development. The continued advance in material well-being now seems to depend more on programming technological advance than on converting the remaining wilderness into material inputs for agricultural and industrial production. If this is so, may we now relax, satisfied that the preservation of the remaining natural environments is assured? On the contrary, there are reasons to fear that additional and unnecessary degradation of natural environments may continue. This is due partly to the imperfection in the economic organization of production and partly to the imperfection with which the governmental processes work.

The organization of industrial production by means of the free market spins off *some* consequences for natural environments that would not be accepted by members of the community were they to have a choice, even if the choice involved costs that they would be required to share. Certain economic choices threaten the continued existence of an irreplaceable asset, while others create nuisances or fail to take advantage of feasible opportunities for enhancing human welfare, primarily because there is no incentive mechanism to reward entrepreneurs for taking action.

Scenario of Development
Consider first a natural environment that is unique and non-reproducible: Let it be a landscape of commanding beauty overlying mineral deposits of commercial value. To harvest the timber, to work the mineral deposits, and to beneficiate the ores at the site of the mining activity would irreparably destroy the aesthetic quality of the landscape. Preserving the landscape would, however, have no irreversible consequence. It would provide opportunity to harvest the timber and mine the minerals in the future *were circumstances to warrant*.

A private entrepreneur could realize a return from his investment either by marketing the aesthetic features of the landscape and associate biota as a scientific resource or recreational product, or by resorting to mining and logging. In a private-enterprise system, a rational profit-motivated entrepreneur would choose the alternative from which he expected the highest returns. His choice would be based on market values, but the market would register the full value only in a competitive situation.

Under competitive conditions, the value of the output of a good or service is measured by the price of the commodity and the amount sold. There are enough sellers and buyers so that no one seller or buyer can affect the price of the good or the supply appreciably by entering or withdrawing from the market. But when there is no close substitute for a commodity, no alternative source of supply, the value of the output is greater than the product of the price and the quantity, because the price represents only the value per unit that the marginal buyer attaches to the commodity. All buyers who would be willing to pay more than the market price rather than do without receive a bonus represented by the difference between the price and their valuations. This value is not captured by the seller.[4] Thus, if a unique commodity is removed from the market, the social loss is not what the seller could have received, but the sum of the maximum each buyer would have been willing to pay rather than go without. If in our hypothetical example the receipts from mining and other extractive activities correspond to competitive returns, while the receipts from the use of the resources for scientific and recreational purposes correspond to returns from sale of rare commodities for which no adequate substitutes exist, the returns expected by the entrepreneur from the two alternatives are not comparable indices of social value. What do economic observations tell us about the two possibilities?

The continuous decline in the price of natural-resource commodities relative to prices of commodities in general suggests the existence of numerous alternative sources of supply and roughly competitive conditions in the extractive industries.[5] But conditions of extreme congestion at scenic landmarks in the national parks suggest that there are no adequate substitutes for these unique natural environments.

The market has another potential deficiency as the mechanism for allocating rare natural environments among competing uses. Individuals who have no definite plans to visit a particular natural wonder may be willing to pay some price in order to retain the option. Large sums change hands in commercial transactions trading in options of one sort or another, not all of which are ultimately exercised. This is a way of hedging against uncertainty by postponing a decision in the hopes that some of the uncertainty will be reduced with time. In the present context, there is a value associated with deferring a decision that will have an irreversible consequence potentially inimical to human welfare. A decision in favor of converting the landscape through commercial exploitation by extractive industries permanently forecloses the opportunity to use the landscape itself as an amenity that gratifies aesthetic interests or psychological needs.

A parallel rationale can be advanced for protecting species threatened with extinction or an entire ecosystem essential to the survival of a species. Such biotic communities represent banks of genetic information required by a species for survival as it competes for the finely graduated niches in nature.

Such competition is absent in domestic counterparts; indeed, modern agriculture provides so highly protected an environment that the energy released from some of the genetic characteristics no longer needed for survival is redirected toward greater productivity. At the same time, the instability that results from progressive reduction of biological diversity through monoculture and the application of pesticides occasionally requires a reintroduction of some genetic materials that have been lost in the domestic strains.

Substantial use is also made of biological specimens for medicinal purposes; indeed, approximately half of the new drugs being produced have botanical sources.[6] Because only a small part of the potential medicinal value of biological sources has been realized, preserving the opportunity to examine all species among the natural biota for this purpose is a matter of no little importance.

There may be substantial commercial value in preserving wild species and natural environments, but the market cannot communicate the option demand nor can the resource owners appropriate the option value. The conventional market operation does not provide adequate information or rewards to ensure the preservation of rare and irreproducible natural phenomena.[7] If the disposition of irreproducible natural environments is determined through normal market transactions, we cannot be confident that the results will represent the most highly valued disposition—either economic or social. At the same time, it must be recognized that only a small proportion of the market allocation of resources involves rare natural environments. And the deficiencies of the market's organization of industrial production detailed above occur only when a rare and irreplaceable asset is involved.

Certain cases of resource use threaten no irreplaceable asset, but neither do the prices by which the economy responds in organizing production reflect the social costs and benefits of such use. These situations have external, offsite, or spillover effects that compromise the efficiency of the market in allocating resources to their highest socially-valued uses. External effects occur in three forms. In the first case, one consumer's behavior affects the enjoyment another may obtain from a consumption activity. If, for example, one household keeps feline pets that regularly call upon the neighbor children's sandbox, the enjoyment of the neighbor is adversely affected by the consumption behavior of the household in question. In the second case, a production activity affects the consumer's enjoyment. The discharge of mill wastes into a watercourse may, for instance, spoil a sport fishery. In the third case, the production activity of one firm directly affects another's output. The release of water from a storage facility upstream to increase the production of power at the site of the dam during the dry season may increase the power generated at some independent hydro projects downstream or make available an improved flow for irrigation or another productive purpose.

Effects of External Events on Natural Systems

Where such external effects occur—and they appear to be concentrated in the natural resources field—benefits are enjoyed by some without cost to themselves, and uncompensated costs are inflicted on others. These costs and benefits do not get reflected in market prices of goods and services to which entrepreneurs respond in making their production decisions. Accordingly, when the spoliation of a natural environment occurs to the advantage of, but without cost to, the despoiler, the market offers no incentive to do otherwise. Without public supervision, continued assaults on the natural environment can be expected. Alternately, when a benefit is conferred on all members of an area if it is provided for any one member—for example, elimination of air pollution in the area—the conditions for a market to develop for the good do not exist. No one in the area can be excluded from benefiting by failure to pay a price. If a private entrepreneur cannot expect to appropriate enough of the value to compensate for his costs, no incentive exists for him to provide such services.

The market mechanism does not everywhere provide entrepreneurs or resource owners with appropriate information or incentives to adopt actions that are socially optimal while still privately remunerative. Thus, there are imperfections in the way the market organizes production, and the government usually intervenes in particular situations to offset this deficiency. The prime example is the need for public action to offset the absence of adequate market signals or incentives in the field of water-resources development. Development, however, almost always conflicts with the preservation of the natural environment. In such situations, the implementing of collective decisions by public agencies may itself spawn difficult problems which neither the market nor the government is yet equipped to handle adequately. Reservoirs of the Bureau of Reclamation's proposed Bridge and Marble Canyon Dams would, for example, encroach on the Grand Canyon National Park.

When a public agency undertakes a mission necessitating the resolution of conflicting interests, a decision in favor of the predominant viewpoint as a reflection of majority rule often appears to be required.[8] This reasoning does not hold, however, when public intervention is made in order to improve the allocation of resources because often it would lead to an uneconomic allocation contrary to the justification for public intervention. Nevertheless, a public agency will generally provide a good or service that appeals to many over an alternative that pleases a small minority. If such decisions come up *one at a time*, and each decision in favor of the commonly held preference pre-empts one of the remaining opportunities for indulging an esoteric taste, all of the resources or configurations of land forms and biota necessary to indulge less common tastes will be extinguished over time.[9]

Deciding Between Competing Demands

No adequate mechanism exists in the public sector for automatically allocating among the qualitatively different demands in their relative proportions. Since the government is deeply involved in the resources field and dominates, to a large extent, the remaining wildlands, many of the grand panoramic landscapes, and all navigable streams, such machinery is required if we wish to safeguard rare natural environments. It is not just a question of, say, adjusting the margins between hydro-power production and more water-based recreation. Catering to the mass demand for lakes for swimming, boating, and water-skiing is not all of the problem. Provision should also be made for those who prefer to canoe in white water or to fish in free-flowing streams, even if such activities require some resources of use in the more popular water sports.

While public servants might be expected to respond to the predominant viewpoint when they consider a given case, the problem can be structured more meaningfully. We can visualize an explicit policy that takes into account the intensity of both the dominant and minority demands as well as the number of individuals nurturing each. *This procedure requires viewing resource configurations not as individual cases but as parts of systems with an appropriate allocation of resources within the system to accommodate the widest range of demands in proportion to their representation.*

Irreplaceability of Resources

If we are to have an economic assignment of resources within a system, we must have a far more discriminating ecological survey than any yet contemplated. Such a survey should identify and classify all terrestrial and aquatic communities as a basis for appropriate reservations in the interest of scientific research and education as well as recreational experiences. A great deal of research in the behavioral sciences would also need to be undertaken to enable us to distinguish between the significant constituents of demand for outdoor recreation.

Earlier I suggested that the modern industrial economy is winning its independence from the conventional resource base through advances in technology. The more optimistic students of the problem, in fact, hold that ultimately only mass and energy are relevant inputs to an ever increasing production of goods.[10] Yet even these optimists acknowledge that the quality of the environment is deteriorating.[11] Implicit in this paradox of plenty and impoverishment is the asymmetry in the implication of technological advance for manufacturing goods, on the one hand, and for producing natural environments, on the other. In spite of the remarkable advances in technology, rare natural features cannot be created. Producing a replica of the Grand Canyon or Yosemite Valley is as out of the question as the resurrection of an extinct species. Technology can make only a limited contribution to re-establishing natural environments. Modern earth-moving technology can help remedy the ravages of open-pit mining, but even so it takes time and the co-operation of nature to restore the landscape and its natural fauna. Technology thus promises liberation from dependence on natural environments as a source of industrial inputs, but not from dependence on natural environments for the amenities associated with personal contacts with nature.

The differential capability for increasing the supply of industrial goods as compared to natural amenities has important implications. As manufactured goods become more abundant and natural amenities more scarce, the trade-off between them will progressively favor the latter. Natural environments, hence, represent assets of appreciating future value.

This leads to a final comment. Modern economic research has established that heads of households are motivated by a desire not only to gain satisfaction from consumption but to leave an estate.[12] An estate may be left either as private goods (or the assets to purchase such goods and services), or as public goods. An aesthetically attractive, scientifically valuable natural endowment of appreciating future value may be an efficient way for the bulk of the population to leave its heirs an estate of maximum value. This is unlikely to occur if we rely solely on the operation of the private market. It can be done only by a policy directed toward the protection of natural environments against unjustified encroachment.

The change in the face of North America by reason of industrial man's dominance has resulted in a high standard of material well-being, but the ecological conseqvences may not yet be understood fully nor the ultimate cost appreciated. Some of the degradation—but certainly not all—is the necessary price of the high material standard of living achieved through industrialization. There have been unintended or socially unwarranted side effects of the organization of industrial production that we should have avoided. Yet the information on which decisions are made is not always adequate, nor are the incentives to individuals always in harmony with the larger public interest, often because the mechanisms for harmonizing private and public purposes have not been developed. Some of the environmental deterioration, although sought by no one, cannot be avoided by individual action. Thus, public authority must help to achieve collectively what cannot be attained individually. This involves, in part, the acquisition of greater knowledge in the natural as well as the behavioral sciences. Such knowledge would enable both private and public managers of natural resources to make more discriminating judgments about matters that might have adverse and irreversible consequences. It also involves a need for the creation of social institutions or mechanisms that will not produce results inimical to the preservation of natural environments simply because of the way the machine is assembled.

Notes and References

1. I owe this estimate to Dr. Richard J. Frankel of Resources for the Future, Inc.

2. The following summary sketch of the effect of human dominance on wildlife populations is based principally on Peter Mathiessen, *Wildlife in America* (New York, 1959) and Raymond Camp, ed., *The Hunter's Encyclopedia* (Harrisburg, Pa., 1954).

3. U.S. Department of the Interior, Fish and Wildlife Service, Bureau of Sport Fisheries and Wildlife, *Survival or Surrender for Endangered Wildlife* (Washington, D.C., 1965).

4. The student of economics will recognize this as Jules Dupuit's discovery and the value in excess of the entrepreneur's receipts as Alfred Marshall's consumer surplus, a real part of the social valuation of the services of the resource in question. Of course, if there were no substitute for the services of the resources used in one way, monopoly pricing could be practiced, but this would not alter the result that pricing would not appropriate the total social value of the resources in their specialized uses.

5. Neal Potter and Francis T. Christy, Jr., *Trends in Natural Resource Commodities: Statistics of Prices, Output, Consumption, Foreign Trade, and Employment in the United States, 1870-1957* (Baltimore, 1962).

6. Margret B. Kreig, *Green Medicine–The Search for Plants That Heal* (New York, 1964).

7. John V. Krutilla, "Conservation Reconsidered," *The American Economic Review* (forthcoming).

8. For an alternative explanation, see Julius Margolis, "The Economic Evaluation of Federal Water Resource Development," *The American Economic Review*, Vol. 49, No. 1 (March, 1959), pp. 99-100. For a different view of what transpires in government decision-making, see Roland McKean, "The Unseen Hand in Government," *American Economic Review*, Vol. 55, No. 3 (June, 1965).

9. For an interesting development of a similar point, see Alfred E. Kahn, "The Tyranny of Small Decisions: Market Failures, Imperfections, and the Limits of Economics," *Kyklos,* Vol. 19-1966-Fasc. 1, pp. 23-47.

10. Harold J. Barnett and Chandler Morse, *Scarcity and Growth–The Economics of Natural Resource Availability* (Baltimore, 1963), p. 238.

11. *Ibid.*, p. 254 ff.

12. Franco Modigliani and Richard Brumberg, "Utility Analysis and the Consumption Function: An Interpretation of Cross Section Data," *Post-Keynesian Economics*, ed. Kenneth K. Kurihara (New Brunswick, N. J., 1954).

Global Ecology: Toward the Planetary Society
John McHale

In the second half of the twentieth century, there is a perceptible shift in human consciousness and conceptuality which begins to alter man's overall relations, both to his fellowmen and to his planetary habitat. Aspects of this change in conceptuality extend inward, from unraveling of the micro lifecode at the molecular level, to the successful maintenance of men beyond the earth's atmosphere and under its oceans and the outward monitoring of other worlds and galaxies.

A new awareness of the origins, parameters, and possible limits of human life and intelligence is engendered in these explorations. In our relation to time, we now begin to probe and plan forward into the future, almost in due ratio to the extent that we successively locate the beginnings of life itself even more remotely in the past.

At the daily level of experience, we may note this increased awareness in more popular acceptance of a "one world" view. Even where this lacks any positive action, and is most often qualified in "their world" or "our world" terms, it still marks a shift toward recognition of the planetary inter-dependence of the human community and the sustaining system of natural forces within which it exists. In no small measure, such awareness is due to the swift and myriad diffusion of images and messages in the world communications networks. The repercussions of local events of any large-scale consequence for the whole community are rapidly felt and reacted to around the world.

Where tribal man became disoriented when separated from his immediate group and surroundings, and early city or local-state man could barely conceive of any larger territory, we are now in a period when many men think casually in terms of the whole earth. The planet as "life space" comes as naturally to the grasp as did the previous successive conceptual extensions of childhood area, home town, region, or country.

Accompanying these various expansions of the levels of conceptual awareness is a significant recourse to ecology, or ecologically oriented thinking, as a defining framework for their containment and interrelation. This transdisciplinary approach now begins to encompass the study of large-scale regional ecosystems and global interactions and distributions. The role of man, both as symbiotic component and disruptive agency, has been particularly focused upon in recent years.

The various major problems evidenced in the present disparities between developed and less developed regions of the world—food, shelter, health, life expectancy, and education—may be more clearly defined in terms of ecological imbalances. In adopting such a viewpoint, we can more sharply outline them in operational terms. The urgency of their solution thereby broadens from its present evaluative level—of appeals to the humanitarian concern of the more fortunate few—to the common self-preservation of all.

Within the closely knit interdependence of our now global community, the continued disparities between have and have-not nations may be viewed as a grave threat to the overall maintenance of the human community. The explosive rises in population, the pressures on food lands and other resources, the scale of wastage, disorganization, and pestilence now accompanying our "local" wars are also linked in due measure to the revolution in human expectations—a further, even if negative, aspect of the increase in awareness referred to above. As physical events, these press ever more critically upon the total resources and social energies of the developed regions. As world problems, they go increasingly beyond the capacity of any locally organized effort to mitigate or solve them, in anything but the shortest range.

In these terms, there are no "local" problems any more—such as may be left to the exigencies and dangerous predilections of local economic or political "convenience." We have now reached the point in human affairs at which the ecological requirements for sustaining the world community take precedence over, and are supererogative to, the more transient value systems and vested interests of any local society!

> The world, then, which the expanding network of electronic communication is fast reducing to a complex but single ecosystem, confronts the technological civilization with a profound and growing imbalance. . . . The first step towards a human future is the acceptance of responsibility for meeting the emergency in our total environment by creating those generalized human conditions which will at least prevent the system from degenerating further. In the immediate term, the only way we know how to do this is by devoting the necessary physical resources to feeding the hungry; in the mediate term, we must do it by inventing the necessary means to graft our technological knowledge on all branches of the human trees.[1]

As we examine not only the local aspects of such problems within the less developed areas, but also their global effects on the more fortunate, it is clear that they form part of a larger context of ecological mismanagement. Wasteful resource-usage, soil exhaustion and spoliation, air, water, and earth pollution, etc., are world phenomena. They have all been contingent factors on human occupancy of the earth during historical time. Until recently, however, their effects were more localized and their scale relatively small. Now they may affect a whole region or continent in a few years—or in a few days, in the case of radioactive fallout. Most of the problems of the less

Figure 1
The Global Ecosystem
(From *The Ecological Context: Energy and Materials,* John McHale, Illinois: World Resources Inventory, 1965, p. 23.)

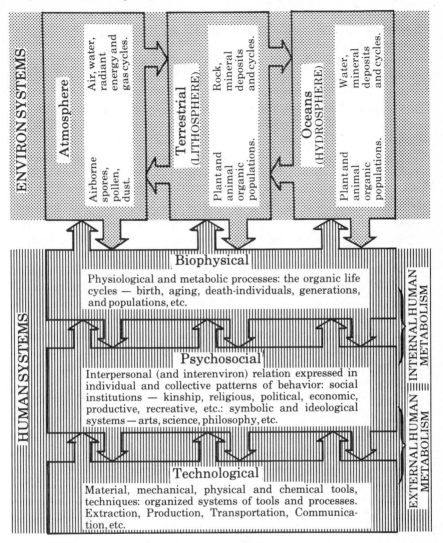

We need to extend the physical and biological concepts of ecology to include the social behaviors of man—as critical factors in the maintenance of his dynamic ecological balance. Nature is not only modified by human action as manifested in science and technology—through physical transformations of the earth to economic purpose—but also by those factors, less amenable to direct perception and measure, which are political-ethical systems, education, needs for social contiguity and communication, art, religion, etc. Such 'socio-cultural' factors have played and will increasingly continue to play a considerable role in man's forward evolutionary trending and its effects on the overall ecology of the earth.

developed regions are all present in greater or lesser degree in the so-called developed regions. All are, in varying measure, contingent upon the "piece-meal" nature of our present modes of knowledge integration, the gaps between such knowledge, its diffusion and effective application, and the lack of a consistent body of agreement on the physical "stewardship" of the planet.

An Overview

Life on earth has been possible during the past billions of years only through the relatively stable interrelationships of the variables of climate, the composition of the atmosphere, the oceans, and the life-sustaining qualities of the land surface, the natural reservoirs and cycles.

Within the thinly spread biofilm of air, earth, and water space around the planet, all living organisms exist then in various systems of delicately balanced symbiotic relations. The close tolerances of many of these relationships have only become known to us, generally through their disruption, in recent times.

Apart from the comparatively local disturbances of natural cycles brought about through hunting, herding, and primitive agricultural practices, man, until quite recently, did not have the developed capacities to interfere seriously with the major life-sustaining processes of the planet. He could live and find food only under conditions restricted by his technological development. The earth surface available to him, with breathable air, water, and arable land, was less than one-eighth of the earth's area; the remainder—of the seas, mountain peaks, glacial and desert areas—was mainly inaccessible to human habitation or large-scale use. Though the evidence of ancient disruption of natural balance is still with us in the form of man-made deserts, e.g., de-forested lands, etc., these were essentially local in their scope and consequences. It is only in the most recent and brief historical period that man has developed sufficient power to be actually, and even more potentially, dangerous to the overall ecosystem—hence, to the maintenance of the human community within that system.

As earlier inventions increased the amount of energy and survival advantage available to man, so they had adjusted the ecological balance to favor his increase, with corresponding adjustments in all other living populations within the system. The latest growth change in human population since the onset of the industrial revolutions is, within all previous contexts, an extremely "abnormal" one: "It represents, in fact, one of the greatest biological upheavals known in geological, as well as in human, history."[2] In the longer range, of course, this expansion may be viewed as the "natural" evolutionary development of a unique species.

The first century of this new phase, of adaptation and "species extension" through intensive industrialization, seemed to confirm the notion that man could indeed conquer nature—could free himself from the biological laws governing other species' development. As the series of such technological revolutions has multiplied in frequency and power amplification, this has been somewhat tempered by the equivalent increase of knowledge about the overall effects on the planetary habitat. Both the extended possibilities of human control of the environment and its present and potential limitations have become the focal point of our mid-twentieth century dialogues.

Though it has been obvious, for some time, that we cannot simply extrapolate human development in terms of "natural laws," and that Malthusian and other limits may not strictly apply, there are still more central questions remaining. Since man, as a species, side-stepped the normal biological sequence of evolutionary adaptation through his capacity to externalize his intellectual and physical means, in symbolic and technological systems, he is, in this sense, more directly in control of his own future evolvement. The extent of that control, over the environment and over his "uncontrolled" activities within it, rests on his capacity to apply himself consciously to an adaptive process which has been largely unconscious.

Through his intelligence, man has enlarged his "ecological niche" to include the whole planet. His activities are no longer constrained to horizontal deployments around its surface, but go increasingly into and beyond the atmosphere and beneath the oceans and include the transformation of vast amounts of the material resources of the planet to his purposes.

The scale of these activities and the expansion, and proliferation, of man-made systems now approach magnitudes in which they directly affect larger and larger areas, sectors, and relationships of the overall ecosystem.

Negative and Positive Aspects

Where such extended controls of man have increased survival advantage for greater numbers of men, and thus forwarded the human enterprise, we may count the overall balance till now as favorable. Our next priority—toward enormously extending such survival advantage to the greatest number of men—requires an even more rapid and extensive growth in scientific and technological undertaking on a world scale. This will require not only taking cognizance of the great positives of our recent acquisition of sufficient material power to carry out such a task, but also an immense stocktaking of the negatives which are inherent in the present lack of conscious integration and planning of our major technological systems.

Such systems now comprise not only local industrialization, in the sense of mass production factory facilities, but all the globally interrelated systems complexes of transportation, communication, production, and distribution facilities. There is no longer a division possible between factory and farm or, in this sense, town and country; all are closely interlocked in a close symbiotic relation—a man-made ecology which we now see, almost for the first time, as an integrally functioning "organic" sector within the overall ecosystem.

Agriculture, until recently seen as a sector of human activity separate from industry, is now more clearly viewed as a frontier area of scientific and technological attention. It is one, particularly, in which traditional modes are no longer adequate to the complexity and size of immediate requirements.

Though the growth of population has been accompanied by more intensive cultivation and higher food yields per acre, the amount of presently usable soil per capita is declining, and, in many areas, becomes impoverished through ill use. As the historical pattern of deforestation, which produced many of the great desert areas, continues, there is added to this the increasing amount of arable land claimed for building dams, roads, industrial installations, mining, etc.—all the necessary uses of an increasing technological system. In the United States alone, urbanization and transportation have been calculated to draw more than a million acres of soil, each year, from cultivation.

Other uses of the earth, incident on our developed technological capacities, have also increased enormously in the past hundred years. As against approximately 50 tons of raw materials per person consumed in 1880, we now use over 300 tons per person annually. When this is translated into amounts of iron, coal, oil, wood and other products "harvested" from the earth, processed, and redistributed elsewhere, the operation becomes of considerable ecological magnitude. For example, of all the coal mined by 1960, only 20% was mined before 1900, and the remaining 80% since that time. The energies used in the extraction, processing, transportation, and use cycles of all the industrial materials are obtained mainly from burning the fossil fuels—each ton of which used releases large amounts of carbon dioxide and other gases into the atmosphere. From 1860 to 1960, this has been calculated to have increased the atmosphere carbon dioxide concentration by 14%; during the eight years from 1954 to 1962, the average rate of increase was 5%. Sulphur oxides, a more immediately harmful aerial pollutant in highly industrialized countries, are expected to show a 75% increase over present critical levels by 1980. A single fossil fuel, power-generating plant may emit several hundred tons of sulphur dioxide per day and, under certain weather conditions, locally overburden the air of a whole city. When this effect is increased by larger multiple fuel uses in dense urban concentrations, the results may be lethally apparent—four thousand persons died, directly or indirectly, from one week of such intense pollution in London in 1952, and one thousand in 1956. The annual emission into the atmosphere of such pollutants, other than carbon dioxide, is estimated at 125 million tons for the

United States alone. Even if present generating and production power technologies were converted 50% to nonfossil fuels, it has been estimated that pollutant by-products from the remainder would still double present levels every twenty years.

The dependence of one-sixth of the world's food supply on "artificial" nitrogen from the chemical industry is another factor in the overall ecosystem function. There is a tendency to separate agriculture from industry in everyday thinking, but the image of the farmer as conserver, and industry as the spoiler, of nature is no longer true—if it ever was. To make each million tons of such nitrogenous fertilizer annually, we use, in direct and related industries, a million tons of steel and five million tons of coal. Some fifty million tons of such support nitrogen are estimated to be required annually by 2000 A.D. The amounts of other agricultural chemicals which will require equally massive support technologies, to further maintain and increase crop yields, is only now becoming apparent.

Problems of Disposal
When air, water, and earth uses are compounded with mounting waste and sewage disposal, the emphasis on the required re-design of all such human systems becomes acute. The natural systems of air/water/soil purification are now so overburdened, through increase and misuse in many areas of the world, that concern is now expressed about their overall malfunction in greater areas. These are no longer "local" problems, as each subsector of the overall ecosystem eventually affects other sectors, if misuse occurs on a large enough scale.

Water disposal, even in the most advanced countries, is still archaic. Those methods used in our larger urban concentrations are little improved from the traditional systems evolved for much smaller and less waste-productive communities of the pre-industrial period. The average city of a half million people now disposes of fifty million gallons of sewage daily and produces solid waste of about eight pounds per person each day.

The use of watercourses, or rivers, streams, and lakes has also been grossly affected, not only in the "discard/residue" process of sewage disposal from cities and the increasing discharges of industrial wastes, but from intensified agricultural practices. Large amounts of soil additives in the form of fertilizers and chemical nutrients are washed off the lands through rainfall, irrigation, and drainage into the natural watercourses, where they disturb the aquatic life balances. The undue growth of algae and plant growths decreases the oxygen supply for fish and other organisms, thus attenuating the self-renewal of the water system. Again, such problems are not localized. In the case of pesticide "spin-offs" and other toxic agents, introduced into upper river reaches, their concentrated effects may only be felt thousands of miles away, e.g., the massive fish fills, of around twelve million, in the Mississippi River and Gulf of Mexico in recent years.

Inadvertent poisoning of organic life through the unplanned and unco-ordinated introduction of various toxins into the environment is not re-stricted to plants and animals. The effects on man are, in many cases, greater—but receive less direct attention. Some 500 new chemical compounds each year go into widespread usage in highly industrialized countries with little attention to their long-term deleterious effects. Without going into the more publicized aspects of radioactive fallout, a simpler case may be adduced of "lead fallout"—from tetra-ethyl lead in auto fuel additives. After almost fifty years of rapidly increasing use, such lead contamination is now being monitored at levels approaching toxicity in waters, crops, and the human system.

Returning to the more positive aspects of man's ecological activities, it is necessary to redress, in part, the semantic bias on "pollutants, garbage, and poisons." This usually tends to suggest vast quantities of alien substances being injected into an otherwise perfectly functioning system. Rather—pollutants are as we perceive and designate them: poisons and natural sub-stances "out of place," or in excess of tolerable levels. The gases and dust of forest fires, volcanic ashes, pollens, marsh effluents, etc., are all "natural" pollutants of natural environments. Our concern here is to more fully ap-praise the role of man-made systems which are also *natural systems* in the overall integral functioning of the ecosystem.

The problem aspects which we have stressed are only problems through lack of "design" and more thorough anticipatory planning. The naturally occurring forces operative in the environment can be more selectively and systematically used to absorb pollutants, reduce sewage/garbage, and re-process discards and residue on a much vaster scale.

Our lack of adequate knowledge and equal lack of foresight and control are the main factors which overburden the natural regulatory systems and lead to their malfunction and breakdown. Some large-scale sectors, such as the global atmosphere, have enormous absorptive and regenerative capacities —others, such as a local soil area, forest, lake, or watershed, are more pre-cariously balanced and may *not* be renewable or recoverable in anything but very long-range terms.

Some of the mandatory requirements for the merely adequate main-tenance of the ecosystem are already clear.

We need to re-design our major social, industrial, and agricultural under-takings toward their more efficient and systematic functioning—as ecologi-cally operating systems, rather than "piecemeal" aggregates of unrelated processes. This would apply not only to environmental controls—such as houses, cities, and other facilities—but to all of our environmental control facilities which now comprise within themselves a vast "socio-agri-industrial ecology." We need to refashion this system so that it can serve many more people at better standards and at higher performance levels than ever before:

a.   *To "recycle" the metals and materials in the system*—so that there is a swifter turnover with the least lag in scrapping and processing cycles. In high-grade technological process, each use cycle tends, through overall development, to achieve more, not less, performance per invested unit of materials.

b.   *To employ increasingly our "income" energies* of solar, water, wind, tidal, and nuclear power, rather than the hazardous and depletive fossil fuels. The latter represent major "capital" investments, which once used are not replaceable. They are too precious to "burn up" in our currently prodigal fashion, but they may be more efficiently—and more fractionally—employed in indirect conversion to plastics, foodstuffs, etc.

c.   *To refashion our food cycle* that we may more swiftly augment the present starvation diets of more than half the developing world. We need, however, to go also beyond emergency satisfaction of immediate needs toward the more extensive ecological re-design of our whole agri-industrial system; employing the most efficient "natural" means of food conversion through the plant/ animal chains *and* the possibilities inherent in microbiological, biosynthetic, and other processes.

d.   *To set up eco-monitoring and control centers* which will act as "early warning" systems in relation to our large-scale scientific and technological undertakings—analyzing and evaluating their immediate and long-range effects on the overall ecological matrix and their positive and negative implications on the quality of the human environment.

In essence, we have to re-design the presently chaotic elements of our developed and "externalized" human metabolic system into a series of "closed" ecological loops phased in with, and taking gainful symbiotic advantage of, the overall ecosystem. The wastes of one type of production cycle become the raw materials of another; thus energy converted and dissipated for one purpose may serve many more. The noxious "garbage" of several processes may be valuable "nutrients" materials in another sector. Each component subsystem now requires critical evaluation and re-design in terms of such higher performance and more economical function. The directly quantitative gains implied in this re-design are also qualitative in terms of more "useful" function, in the reduction of pollution hazards, in less "destruction" of the natural environment—and in the increased social and physical advantages available to all men.

Our thinking must obviously go beyond immediate preoccupation with locally vested interest in the prior solution of this or that isolated problem! The only context for all of our major problems is the global context. The range of our thinking is that which may extrapolate human ecological requirements, beyond subsistence survival, to the maximal advantage of all. It must also accept the challenge of designing not only for "tomorrow" but for a century of tomorrows.

This may often entail "non-use" as well as re-use. The scale of our present technological capacities is such that we cannot act without more accurate gauges of their immediate and long-range effects. Where it may be pleaded, for example, by special interest groups that we have enough coal, oil, and gas reserves for five hundred years, any *expanded* use at the present rate and level of technology is obviously precluded by their adverse side effects on the ecosystem. In such cases, a resource, an invention or process which is evaluated as dangerous to the maintenance of the life systems should be left in "storage"—until a more evolved society may use it less prodigally and less dangerously!

Need for Global Thinking

Such an orientation leads to further considerations involving our global, rather than local, commitments. As stated, there is no large-scale human problem which may not be solved outside of this context. Air, water, and soil pollution are not local—the air is not restrained within municipal or national boundaries, nor are the waters.

Where massive imbalances occur—whether bio-physical in terms of earthquakes and other natural catastrophes or socio-physical in terms of hunger, disease, and the catastrophe of war—we need to recall that the resources of the planet can no more belong, by geographical chance, to any individual, corporation, country, or national group than can the air we breathe. National ownership of a key watershed, mineral deposit, or scientific discovery is as farcical, and dangerous, a proposition as our supposedly national sovereignty of an "air space."

The evolutionary transition toward "world man" now faces a situation analogous to that of emerging national or empire man in the preceding two centuries. Then, the local ideological issues revolved around national control of public health, or child welfare, education, pure food and water legislation, etc. The same arguments now prevail at the world level, regarding the rights and privileges of individual nations—as if they were isolated, self-contained, and wholly autonomous physical and social entities. Though such a fiction may be a comforting "prop" for local individual and social identity in a rapidly changing world, it is dangerously removed from reality.

The scale of our global systems of production/distribution, communication/transportation, etc., has now gone beyond the capacities of any single national or even regional group to wholly sustain and operate. They require, and are dependent upon, the resource range of the entire planet for the metals and materials of which they are built—and in which no nation is now self-sufficient. Each system is intricately and complexly interlocked with all others—production with transport, transport with communications, etc. The whole is increasingly dependent on the global interchange, not only of physical resources and finished products, but of the "knowledge pool"—of research, development, technical and managerial expertise, and the highly trained personnel who sustain and expand this.

Ours is possibly one of the most critical periods in human experience up till this time. Poised in the transition from one kind of world to another, we are literally on the hinge of a great transformation in the whole human condition. The next fifty years may be the most crucial in all of man's history. We have few guides to follow and almost no historical precedents. "Many of the old moralities have suddenly become immoralities of the most devastating character."[4] All of our previously local actions are now writ large on a planetary scale. The knowledge with which we might make the correct decisions is barely adequate—yet our gross ecological errors may reverberate for many generations.

Notes and References

1. Hasan Ozbekhan, *Technology and Man's Future*, Systems Development Corp., Sp-2494, May, 1966.

2. National Academy of Sciences, *Energy Resources*, N.R.C. Pub. No. 1000-D, 1962.

3. G. Borgstrom, "The Human Biosphere and Its Biological and Chemical Limitation," in Mortimer P. Starr (ed.), *Global Impacts of Applied Microbiology* (Stockholm: Almqvist & Wiksell, 1964).

4. R. C. Cook, "Truth and Consequences in a New Era," *Population Bull.*, XXII, 4 (Nov., 1966).

Selected References for Chapter 3
Cottrell, Fred, *Energy and Society: The Relation Between Energy, Social Change, and Economic Development.* New York: McGraw-Hill Book Co., 1955. An insightful and comprehensive discussion of man's progress in manipulating energy sources for purposes of environmental exploitation.

Keyfitz, Nathan, "The Impact of Technological Change on Demographic Patterns," *Industrialization and Society*, B. F. Hoselitz and W. E. Moore (eds.), The Hague: Mouton and Co., 1963, pp. 218-36. Focuses on influences of technological development on mortality patterns and reproductive behavior.

Leiss, William, "Utopia and Technology: Reflections on the Conquest of Nature," *International Social Science Journal*, Vol. 22, No. 4, 1970, pp. 576-88. A critical examination of utopian designs for human betterment through the technological exploitation of the natural environment.

Meier, Richard L., *Science and Economic Development: New Patterns of Living*, 2nd ed. Cambridge, Mass.: The MIT Press, 1966. A wide-ranging discussion of the impact of recent developments in science and technology on a variety of demographic and environmental problems.

Siu, Ralph G. H., "Role of Technology in Creating the Environment Fifty Years Hence," *Environment and Change: The Next Fifty Years*, W. R. Ewald (ed.). Bloomington, Indiana: Indiana University Press, 1968, pp. 81-98. Speculations regarding environmental changes which may result from future technology.

In this chapter we have reviewed some aspects of the role of science and technology in ecological adaptation. The demographic consequences of technological development are seen primarily in man's ability to control morbidity and mortality. Other things being equal, this results in a greater proportion of all births surviving to adulthood and longer life expectancy. Increasingly, this appears to be a world-wide trend, and is reflected in relatively high rates of population growth for the majority of nations. On the other hand, science and technology have contributed relatively little to man's ability to affect reductions in birth rates. And, finally, science and technology show little promise for adequately maintaining the world's population if it continues to grow at the present rate. Not only is food production insufficient, but other natural resources necessary for currently desirable levels of living probably cannot be supplied through technological means.

Our consideration of technological effects on the environment results in similarly pessimistic conclusions. We are now to the point in scientific-technological development where environmental resources for the production of energy and materials are nearing dangerously low levels of supply. In addition, technological processes are seriously polluting the remaining components of the environment. As yet, inadequate attention has been paid to reducing the harmful effects of scientific and technological development on the ecosystem.

Our evaluation of the role of science and technology in ecological adaptation is hardly encouraging, especially when one considers how significant these have been in getting man to his present stage of socio-cultural evolution. Is it possible that technological mechanisms are to be superseded as the primary means through which man ensures his survival? Will drastic changes in the social organization of science and technology have to be implemented if we are not to destroy civilization through unintended side-effects and unrecognized consequences? Or need man merely shift the focus of his efforts in developing new technology, perhaps toward a more explicit emphasis on the quality of life rather than its quantitative dimensions? These questions are only suggestive of many issues that need to be explored regarding the role of science and technology in man's future. Certainly not all of the attendant problems are ecological, but those that are have serious implications for human survival. This topic will be given further attention in the Epilogue.

4

Symbolic Mechanisms:
The Role of Ideology
and Culture

We now turn to the question of how man's capacity to represent and evaluate his activities and surroundings in terms of abstract symbols is related to the problem of ecological adaptation. Ronald Freedman's contribution deals with the question of how collective norms regarding reproduction influence family size. Though his discussion is focused on the developing areas, the underlying principles uncovered are probably relevant to societies at all stages of evolution. Fundamental to the argument presented is the proposition that, since the problem of how many children a couple should have is so widely shared and has so many personal and social consequences, all societies tend to develop normative solutions for it. Stated otherwise, all societies manifest through their system of social norms a collective idealization of permissible and desirable levels of reproductive performance. Evidence suggests that in few situations are questions about these values viewed as meaningless or irrelevant.

Freedman argues that norms for high fertility are largely an adjustment (adaptation) to situations where mortality takes a significant toll among young children and where family and kinship ties play a major role in community organization. Such norms have been highly resistant to change, in spite of the drastic reduction in fetal and infant mortality so evident in the Twentieth Century. This is not to say that personal norms have remained correspondingly high. Indeed, as the author points out, women with three or four children often show more favorable attitudes toward fertility control than those with fewer children. But this is only after the cultural norm has resulted in a relatively large family; thus the prior influence of collective ideals nullifies the potential demographic consequences of emerging personal preferences.

Attention is also focused on the relationship between fertility norms and societal goals. To the extent that numbers of children are useful in maximizing the family's ability to achieve culturally prescribed ends, high levels of reproduction will be reflected in the normative order. One implication to be drawn from this observation is that lowered reproductive norms may result from an altered perception of the social utility of children. In other words, and speaking pragmatically, if fewer children are associated with material advantages in achieving desired societal goals, this may stimulate changes in collective standards.

The reader must be careful not to assume that social norms are the sole determinant of levels of reproductive performance. Rather, norms are integrally associated with institutional arrangements, thus making difficult the specifying of cause-and-effect relationships. The point to be made is that norms regarding family size do exert some influence independent of changes in other dimensions of social organization. As such they constitute an additional mechanism by which societies adapt to the exigencies of collective survival.

With the second contribution in this chapter we turn to an examination of collective views of the environment. Alexander Spoehr's essay contrasts modern man's interpretation of natural resources with that prevalent in preindustrial societies. Recognizing the more limited and specialized nature of so-called primitive man's technology, Spoehr nevertheless points out that his survival is contingent upon an understanding of man's relationship to those environmental resources upon which the technology depends. Furthermore, social structural arrangements appear to reflect collective views regarding proper and efficient use of natural resources—as seen, for example, in the organization of production and distribution. Of fundamental importance here is the structure of beliefs regarding man's place in nature. In preindustrial societies a holistic view seems to predominate: "Man . . . is not set apart from nature, but is part of a single order, combining man, nature, and the gods. When man utilizes the resources of nature, it is within the framework of this system of ideas."

Modern man, on the other hand, as we have seen earlier, tends to set himself apart from the natural universe. This view is reflected in his constant attempt to dominate, control, and exploit the elements of his environment. Spoehr suggests that these differences in normative views of natural resources have important implications for our understanding of contemporary conservation movements. Preindustrial man has little need to be concerned with the possibility of destroying his habitat since this would be interpreted as *destroying himself*. There is little potential for such a view among industrial societies, given our prevailing conception of the universe as dichotomized into human and non-human components. Modern man has paradoxically come to the conclusion that his survival is dependent upon his ability to obtain maximum control over natural resources, yet increasingly recognizing that, once depleted, they are gone forever.

Spoehr's discussion indicates how collective views of the environment may influence the ways in which it is utilized. Clearly, preindustrial man's perception of natural resources resulted in greater curbs on environmental exploitation, even considering his less elaborate technology. But the modern world is culturally quite distant from "primitive" society, and the complexities of cultural adaptations are better understood in terms of situations facing contemporary communities. Accordingly, the final contribution to this chapter reports a case study of ecological relationships in a North American rural setting.

In terms of the theoretical framework guiding our approach to human ecology, Bennett's analysis illustrates several ways in which the symbolic components of culture—norms, values, ideologies—affect ecosystem relationships. Running throughout his discussion are considerations that reflect the fact that contemporary communities, be they local, regional, or national, are continually faced with the necessity to adapt their internal organization to externally imposed conditions. This is the essence of "complex" society. It is the flexibility of cultural systems that allows men collectively to manipulate external relationships (e.g., with bureaucracies) in the interests of personal and group welfare.

Bennett's discussion suggests that the role played by cultural values in adaptive strategies is one of defining appropriate courses of action for satisfying collective goals and preferences. In agrarian societies the allocation of natural resources (e.g., land and water) largely determines material outcomes in the quest for survival, and thus it is to be expected that normative considerations will be focused on this issue. This analysis clearly demonstrates how these concerns are manifested in on-going social processes. Thus the instrumental values of individualism, egalitarianism, and particularism are shown to structure collective views on the use of natural resources and to mediate relationships with external agencies. One must nevertheless keep in mind that these influences are by no means completely consistent; as the author points out, the system has contradictions between values and actuality, with the result that consequences are not always desirable from the point of view of the participants.

Further insight into the role of culture as an adaptive strategy for acquiring needed resources emerges from Bennett's discussion of game-playing. As participants, local agricultural populations must learn the rules of the game, the norms that structure relationships between agrarian operators and external agencies. Though styles of play vary—e.g., among the farmer, rancher, and Hutterite groups in question—winning (obtaining the desired resources) is contingent upon the ability to manipulate potentially disruptive external relationships.

While this essay is focused primarily on man-land relationships, the general principles illustrated may be useful for understanding a wide range of ecosystem problems. Adaptive actions are typically based upon adaptive strategies, and the latter, whether explicitly recognized or not, are closely connected to prevailing systems of social norms. As suggested by Bennett, if we are to understand *why* man uses and abuses his environment in particular ways, we must first examine how he cognitively transforms these phenomena into natural resources.

Norms for Family Size in Underdeveloped Areas
Ronald Freedman

It is a commonplace observation that fertility is high in the so-called underdeveloped societies. Sometimes this leads to the erroneous view that their fertility is limited only by what is biologically possible so that birth rates reach a mythologically high natural level. In this idealized view free and unrestrained sexual unions beginning at an early age produce very high fertility as an incidental result without deliberate intent and without much individual or social concern about family size.

A more plausible general proposition is that reproduction, whether at high or low levels, is so important to the family and to society everywhere that its level is more or less controlled by cultural norms about family size and such related matters as marriage, timing of intercourse, and abortion. In each society the cultural norms about these vital matters are consistent with social institutions in which they are deeply embedded. Changes in fertility are unlikely without prior or, at least, simultaneous changes in these institutions.

Variations in Fertility Rates

Before developing these ideas, it may be useful to consider briefly the variability in fertility among underdeveloped societies. A recent study of the Cocos Island population[1] provides a unique example of exceptionally high fertility expected in the model of virtually unrestrained fertility. The Cocos Islanders, living between 1870 and 1947 under an exceptionally favourable paternalistic regime married early, and about two-thirds of their brides were pregnant at marriage. The birth rates between 1880 and 1947 averaged about 55 per thousand and reached 60 in several years. This may be contrasted with birth rates of about 35 per thousand in pre-industrial England. The gross reproduction rate for the Cocos Islands was about 4.2, perhaps the highest ever recorded with reliable data.

This is an exceptionally high fertility level. It is not characteristic of all underdeveloped areas, although it is not unlikely that there are many populations with a biological potential for a similar performance. Some African populations may reach similar levels.[2] In Appendix I estimated gross reproduction rates are listed for a number of high fertility populations, underdeveloped by most criteria. These reproduction rates are very high in comparison with the rates for the developed low-fertility countries shown for contrast. But, the rates generally are well below the Cocos rate or that for the American Hutterites. The rates do not conform to any uniform level.

The range of fertility rates currently found among underdeveloped areas is wide enough to include rates which characterized Western Europe before its modern fertility decline but long after social and economic development were under way. For example the gross reproduction rate of 2.4 for England in 1861, shortly before fertility began to decline, is lower than the rates for most but by no means all of the high fertility societies today. Married women born in England in 1841-45 had just under six children on the average,[3] if they survived to the end of the child-bearing period. This is about the same as the figure reported for India now,[4] although it is significantly less than the average of more than eight children born to the Cocos

Island mothers and the average of more than ten to the American Hutterite mothers.[5]

These selected data are intended only to illustrate the idea that fertility, however measured, varies from moderately to very high levels in under-developed societies, even after allowing for inaccuracies for base data.

Genetic differentials in fecundity eventually may be shown to account for some of the existing variation between societies, but I think they are unlikely to explain the major variations in time or between societies. They are unlikely to explain why fertility is relatively high in underdeveloped societies and declines with development.

Fertility and Cultural Norms

As a more plausible explanation, I begin with the thesis that societal levels of fertility are related to variations in cultural norms about reproduction, and these, in turn, are related to the nature of the society.

One of the fundamental principles of sociology is that when many members of a society face a recurrent common problem with important social consequences they tend to develop a normative solution for it. This solution, a set of rules for behaviour in a particular situation, becomes part of the culture, and the society indoctrinates its members to conform more or less closely to the norms by explicit or implicit rewards and punishments.

The problem of how many children a couple should have is so widely shared and has so many personal and social consequences that it would be a sociological anomaly if social norms regarding it did not develop. This is also true for such related problems as when to marry and when sexual intercourse is permitted. In view of the special importance attached to kinship ties in the underdeveloped societies, it would be particularly strange if the reproductive level of the familial unit were not a matter of normative concern.

Norms about family size are likely to be in terms of a range in numbers of children that are permissible or desirable. While specifying clearly that childlessness is an unspeakable tragedy and an only child very undesirable, the norm for a particular culture or group may be as vague as 'at least three or four children' or 'as many as possible'. But I know of no organized society, primitive or modern, in which the question of how many children are born is a matter of indifference either to the reproducing unit or to the community.

In various underdeveloped societies, a large number of sample interview surveys[6] have been made since the Second World War in which peasant populations have been asked such questions as how many children they want for themselves, how many are right for others, etc. In almost all of these studies only a small minority of the respondents found the questions ridiculous or meaningless or answered that such matters were up to fate or God, etc. Even where the answers invoke the Deity or fate, further inquiry frequently indicates that the respondent has rather firm ideas of what he desires that fate or divine providence should bring. In most such surveys the answers tend to be clustered about a moderate modal value rather than to be randomly distributed. Appendix II contains some illustrative frequency distributions of attitudes about family size and family growth from surveys in several different countries. Of special significance are data in a number of these studies indicating that a majority of those with three or four children want no more and many prefer a smaller number than they have. (Illustrations are found in Appendix II.)

There are a few studies in which it is reported that questions about the desired number of children are regarded by respondents as ludicrous. This is reported, for example, by Richards & Reining for the Bahaya of Africa.[7] But, the attitude expressed apparently does not result from the absence of a norm. The report is that, under existing conditions, most women do not have the four to six children in the household which they consider ideal and would approximate if they could. And even in this instance, the authors report that there are voluntary practices limiting reproduction during certain periods.

The exact meaning and accuracy of the answers obtained in such surveys is open to question, but there is little doubt that there is considerable consensus in such populations about desirable family size.

It must be admitted that much of the survey evidence is from societies that have been in touch with the West for many years, but some of the samples studied have been in village areas of India, the Near East and other places where illiteracy and immobility have isolated much of the population from modern ideas.

It is possible, but unlikely, that all of the populations studied through sample surveys have already been considerably influenced by modern Western values about reproduction. The same cannot be said for a large number of primitive societies whose ethnology with respect to sexual and reproductive behaviour was studied by Ford.[8] He concluded that childbirth is by no means universally accepted as either natural or inevitable. Many women are ambivalent about childbirth, so that considerable social pressure may be necessary to insure adequate reproduction.

Obviously, social norms encouraging reproduction at less than the physiological maximum can be implemented only if one or more practices are available. A variety of controls are possible and are used. In addition to such deliberate and obvious practices as contraception and abortion, there are a large number of others; for example, the age at first sexual union, timing and frequency of intercourse, voluntary or involuntary fecundity impairments, foetal mortality, etc.

Factors Controlling Fertility   Davis & Blake[9] have provided a useful classification of such control factors immediately determining the fertility level of a society. They call them 'intermediate variables' because they are the means of fertility control standing intermediate between the social institutions and norms on the one hand and actual fertility on the other. Any social influences on fertility can only operate by affecting one or more of these 'intermediate variables'. The Davis & Blake classification is shown in Appendix III. I will not duplicate the detailed discussion of these variables given in their excellent paper.

Different combinations of values for these intermediate variables may produce identical fertility levels. On the other hand, societies with very different fertility levels may have similar values on some though, of course, not all of the intermediate variables. It is unnecessary and often incorrect to assume that levels of these control variables always are manipulated deliberately to limit fertility. The limiting effect on fertility is often, probably usually, an unintended consequence of one or more cultural patterns that have no explicit connexion with fertility.

Contemporary data for high fertility societies make it evident that a combination of very different control variables may produce high fertility. Coale & Tye [10] have recently shown that high fertility in some Chinese populations results from late marriage followed by very high reproduction rates into the later child-bearing years. On the other hand, high fertility in India results from very early marriage and high reproduction rates in the early child-bearing years, with a sharp decline in the later years. While both types of controls may lead to similar average family size, the 'Chinese' pattern will result in a slower rate of population growth, other things being equal, because the length of a generation is greater.

Cultural norms controlling premarital intercourse and the age of marriage have been particularly important in reducing fertility levels in a number of pre-modern societies. Apparently, this explains the fact that fertility was only moderately high in pre-industrial Europe. Economic historians [11] have shown that property and labour arrangements in a number of West European areas encouraged celibacy or the postponement of marriage in order to maintain certain standards of what the economic unit should be, and of what a couple should have in order to marry and raise children. Together with controls on premarital intercourse such arrangements apparently kept fertility below the levels of other pre-industrial societies. The breakdown of these controls in the first stages of modern urban-industrial development apparently resulted in an increase in fertility in some places before the long-run decline in fertility set in. The fact that fertility was only moderately high in many areas of pre-industrial Europe is evidence that very high fertility is not a universal characteristic of such societies.

Davis & Blake point out that since having some children is very important in pre-industrial societies, a society with high and variable mortality often is likely to have built into its structure strong pressures for having children early in marriage before one or both of the parents die and also for having some 'extra' children as a safeguard against the catastrophic loss of the essential minimum number. If unfavourable economic conditions develop, this may result in 'too many' children. Therefore, there is likely to be a delicate balance of pressures toward higher fertility to insure at least a certain minimum number of children, and counterpressures to minimize an intolerable surplus of children under difficult subsistence conditions. Davis & Blake present the hypothesis that this necessary pressure in opposite directions accounts for the adoption in many pre-industrial societies of those control practices which insure a minimum fertility level but permit a reduction in the numbers of children late in the child-bearing process, principally abortion and infanticide. These counter-balancing pressures also may account for the failure to adopt contraception, which operates very early in the reproductive process.

It would be desirable to have a systematic classification of societies by the values of the intermediate variables. Then we could study how particular combinations of the control variables produce a particular fertility level, and how each pattern is related to social norms about family size and ultimately to the social structure. Unfortunately, the data for such systematic classifications are not available.

However, Carr-Saunders,[12] Himes,[13] Ford,[14] Devereaux[15] and others have assembled scattered evidence on the existence in many pre-industrial societies of a wide variety of fertility control measures including contraception, abstinence, abortion, infanticide and delayed marriage. In many cases the limiting practice is not perceived as having birth limitation as an objective. Most of the evidence demonstrates the existence of certain practices in a culture without specifying either the extent of use or the effect on fertility. Nevertheless, there is basis for the supposition that more or less effective methods of population control potentially were available in many pre-industrial societies and that this probably affected fertility levels in most of them. I venture the view that such practices might have had much wider use and greater effect were it not for the rewards derived from having children in such societies and the risk that these rewards would be lost because of unpredictably high mortality.

Contraception

Contraception is not one of the potential control practices widely prevalent in any large underdeveloped society. An important unresolved question is whether this has been because adequate contraceptive technology was lacking or because normative pressures for high fertility precluded either the development of new methods or the adoption and dissemination of known methods beyond a small minority of the population.

Despite evidence that various types of contraception have been known and used by small numbers in many pre-industrial societies, there are very few examples of their adoption by sufficient numbers to affect the general fertility level. Coitus interruptus, requiring no mechanical or chemical materials, has been known in many societies for a long time. Potentially this practice might have diffused to a wider group from the small minority using it in pre-industrial societies with resultant impact on fertility levels. It is difficult to dismiss coitus interruptus as unsuitable for mass adoption, since this was the principal means by which the British and French drastically reduced their birth rates in the modern period. [16] Coitus interruptus is still one of the most important methods producing the relatively low birth rate in Britain.[17]

Many hypotheses have been advanced to explain why coitus interruptus and other possible methods were not adopted or why alternate methods were not developed before the modern period. Among various explanations two emphasize the internal structure of the family. The combination of male dominance and the lack of communication between husband and wife, especially on problems of family size and family planning, is said to retard the adoption of family planning. This might be especially true if, as has been suggested by some, the wife has the stronger interest in family limitation, while the husband is indifferent. Dominance of the husband combined with the indifference on the issue might be particularly important for such a male-dominated method as coitus interruptus. Hill, Stycos & Back[18] have provided some evidence from Puerto Rico that customary barriers to husband-wife communication may be related to failure to adopt family planning in Puerto Rico now.

Whether this type of explanation is valid is an open question. There is a *prima facie* case for the interest of the father, too, in limiting fertility in a subsistence economy, since children are consumers as well as producers. Some recent studies in underdeveloped areas indicate that the father's disinterest may have been exaggerated. Studies in India, Ceylon, Taiwan, Puerto Rico and elsewhere [19] indicate roughly similar attitudes on the part of husbands and wives on many issues about reproduction. If it is true that pre-industrial couples do not discuss fertility control or family size, this may be because a long-standing consensus on high fertility leaves little to discuss.

Other explanations for lack of use of contraception in some cultures centre on the idea that modern contraceptives were not available and that coitus interruptus was not acceptable in many cultures. Whether it was simply the availability of contraceptive means which determined fertility levels historically is currently of great practical importance. If fertility levels were high in pre-industrial societies simply because of inadequate contraceptive technology, then current programmes for reducing fertility in such areas can concentrate on making modern contraceptives available. This very simple solution is no longer widely espoused, because programmes for making contraceptives available in underdeveloped areas have not been very successful to date. While it is true that no country as yet has mounted an efficient all-out campaign to disseminate contraceptive supplies and information the efforts made have been intensive enough in some places to indicate that the motivations to limit family size either are not yet very powerful or are restrained by powerful cultural counter-pressures.

While the issue is certainly very controversial, I take the position that a variety of control measures, including some forms of contraception, have been available potentially in underdeveloped areas and that past failure to use them more extensively has been a result of normative pressures for high fertility. On the individual psychological level this reduces to a simple statement that couples had many children because they wanted them, not because they were ignorant of how to avoid having them. This does not preclude the probability that ignorance about control methods was prevalent. Nor is it necessary to assume that the size of family achieved was deliberately planned. It does require an assumption that the values about family size and limiting practices, deliberate or not, were in rough correspondence.

Obviously, at the proper time and place provision of suitable contraceptive supplies and information is indispensable for fertility decline. I am questioning only whether this necessary cause is also a sufficient cause for a fertility decline.

High Fertility is Normative

Up to this point, I have been concerned mainly with indicating that control measures were available potentially in the underdeveloped areas so that their absence is not the explanation for high fertility. But to support the position that high fertility was normative, it is also necessary to consider why there have been normative pressures for large numbers of births.

I believe that most demographers and sociologists would agree on two very general explanations. From either the individual or the social point of view, high fertility has been an adjustment both to high and variable mortality and to the central importance in community life of familial and kinship ties.

In most pre-industrial societies a wide range of activities involve interdependence with kinsmen and especially with children. These include production, consumption, leisure activity, assistance in illness and old age and many other activities covered by non-familial institutions in modern societies. To simplify greatly: large numbers of children are desired if the values considered worthwhile are obtained through familial ties rather than through other social institutions. If kinship ties are very important in a society where mortality is high and variable, the number of births desired and produced will be especially high in order to insure the survival to adulthood of the essential minimum number of children. Selective experience favours the development of beliefs and practices encouraging fertility high enough to minimize the grave risks of few or no surviving children.

Because mortality is such an important consideration in under-developed areas, it is necessary to distinguish between norms for large numbers of births and norms for large numbers of children. A considerable number of studies in contemporary underdeveloped areas have found that three or four children are reported as desired by the populations studied. This is contrasted with the six or more births women actually have had by the end of the child-bearing period. A frequent interpretation of these results is that the number of children desired has sharply declined from higher earlier levels, evidence of a trend to modern small-family values. But, it is quite possible that the number of living children desired really is not much lower now than it was 100 or more years ago. With high mortality, six or more births are required if three or four children are to survive.

For example, a United Nations study[20] in Mysore, India, in 1952 found that for a sample of living women about 45 years of age, only about 66% of the children they had ever born were still alive. This figure exaggerates somewhat the percentage of children surviving, since there is evidence of underreporting of children born alive but dead at the time of the survey. In the Mysore study, the average number of children considered ideal by respondents is fairly close to the average number surviving to women living to the end of the child-bearing period, although it is much lower than the number actually born.

In India and elsewhere the finding that three or four children are considered desirable frequently is considered paradoxical, since the populations surveyed make little use of family planning information and supplies when these are available. However, wanting three or four living children in a high mortality country is quite consistent with the much higher average number of births. Even if mortality is declining, the peasant who has learned from his culture to depend on his children for labour on the farm, for old-age security, and for other essentials cannot be expected to extrapolate declining mortality with the demographer and to calculate a long-range need for fewer children. Significantly, several studies indicate that favourable attitudes to the practice of family limitation are much more common among those who already have three or four living children. This is consistent with the view that the availability of means for birth control is largely irrelevant until what is regarded as the essential minimum number of children is secure.

Fertility and Mortality

This suggests that known low mortality is one of the necessary conditions for an effective social policy for reducing fertility. Historically developed normative pressures for large numbers of births may persist for a long time after mortality has fallen, since they are closely tied to many aspects of the social structure. Housing allocation and other social arrangements in high fertility countries are developed on the implicit assumption that many of the family members, and especially many infants, will die. When mortality declines, increasing pressure is exerted on many traditional social arrangements, thus creating a ferment for change. But this takes time, and historically there has been almost always a considerable lag between the fall of mortality and the fall of fertility. It is likely to be particularly difficult to counter the traditional pressures for high fertility when the mortality decline is only prospective. This is what is being attempted in many underdeveloped areas today.

Compensation for high mortality does not account alone for the differences in fertility between developed and underdeveloped areas. After taking into account the effects of mortality, the number of children desired probably is still somewhat larger, on the average, than in the more developed societies.

Why does the social norm prescribe a relatively large number of *living* children in underdeveloped countries? In seeking an answer, I begin with the premise that the norm depends on how having a particular number of children affects the ability of the familial unit to attain socially valued goals. This, in turn, depends on the division of labour between the family and other social institutions and on how much the performance of important functions by the family depends on the number of children produced in it. The assumption is that family size norms will tend to correspond to a number which maximizes the net utility to be derived from having children in that society. Obviously, different aspects of the society may exert opposing pressures on the norms, so a balance must be struck. Therefore, we must look for important aspects of the social organization which support the norms for family size by providing explicit or implicit social rewards or penalties depending on the number of children.

Fertility and Kinship
As already noted, the familial and kinship units are so important in underdeveloped societies that we may expect relatively high fertility in order to maintain them. This kind of global explanatory hypothesis lacks the precision to explain the existing and historical diversity ranging from moderately to very high fertility. But, if the general hypothesis is valid, then specific variations in kinship structure should help to explain the observed variations in fertility. Anthropological research reveals a rich diversity of kinship organization and functions in different societies. Unfortunately, systematic study of how these variations are related to variations in fertility, normative or actual,

is not very advanced. Nevertheless, some broad speculative generalizations can be considered.

Corporate kinship systems involving an immortal clan with a patrilocal or matrilocal basis and affecting every aspect of life, even political organization and war, are seen by Lorimer[21] as greatly enhancing the valuation of children. Joint family systems combining several nuclear units but with periodic fission and reconstitution of the joint family make for somewhat lower fertility, since they encompass social relations less fully than the corporate system. Systems based on a nuclear, neolocal familial units make for still lower fertility, since fewer routine functions are carried out within the family unit.

These broad generalizations greatly oversimplify a complex subject. Both the theory and the evidence are in a rudimentary state. Lorimer has placed emphasis on kinship organization and especially on the role of corporate kinship systems in producing high fertility in African societies. But his work gives little attention to how the corporate kinship system affects the intermediate variables so as to produce the high fertility. Davis & Blake illustrate[22] how variations in the kinship structure operate through particular intermediate variables to affect fertility. For example, they analyze the probable functional significance of the joint family system in India in inhibiting widow remarriage and, thus, reducing fertility. The idea that neolocal nuclear family systems may lead to relatively lower fertility levels even in pre-industrial societies has been discussed mainly with reference to pre-industrial Europe. The discussion particularly has centred on various economic arrangements leading to late marriage or non-marriage, as already mentioned.

Studies in India about the comparative fertility of couples living in nuclear and joint family units yield contradictory results, with some studies indicating that couples living in nuclear units have fertility at least as high as the fertility of couples in joint households.[23] One possible explanation is that high fertility increases the likelihood that joint households will split up. But such comparisons within a society are unlikely to provide relevant evidence of how a dominant family system affects the society's reproduction level. For this purpose, the units of comparison must be whole societies or societies at different time periods.

Dependence on Children
Recent Japanese data provide a striking illustration of the close relation between norms about dependence on adult children and the course of fertility. Between 1950 and 1961 the Japanese birth rate fell spectacularly from 28 to 17 per 1000. In the same period the biennial sample surveys by the Mainichi press[24] posed to a representative cross-section of the population the question: 'Do you expect to depend on your children in your old age?' In 1950 a

majority, more than 55%, answered 'definitely yes'. The proportion giving this answer declined steadily in five succeeding surveys, reaching 27% by 1961. It is rare that public opinion on a matter this vital changes so steadily and rapidly and just as rare that we have statistical data with which to document the trend.

These are only illustrative of theories and data about how kinship is related to fertility. No one has yet been able to assemble more than illustrative evidence relating levels and determinants of fertility under varying kinship systems, but it is unlikely that significant general explanations will emerge which do not take into account the role of kinship in the society.

This is not to deny that social norms about family size may be affected by non-familial aspects of the social organization. For example, emphasis in the religious system on the importance of a male heir for ritual purposes probably produces pressures over time in a high mortality society for at least two sons to guarantee the survival of at least one. This means that on the average each family will want at least four children. Such values, based on long tradition and embedded in many aspects of the society, persist long after mortality has fallen.

Taiwan is an interesting case in point of the persistence of such traditional values after mortality has fallen and even after there is an apparent willingness to adopt family planning. Taiwan has a history of slowly but steadily declining mortality under Japanese rule, followed by very rapid mortality decline after the war. Average life expectancy is now more than 60 years. The probability has been high for some time that almost all children will survive to adulthood. Fertility has begun to fall according to statistics for the whole island. In several recent small-scale pilot surveys, both husbands and wives expressed strong approval of the idea of family planning; a significant minority had begun to practise it in some form and a large majority of those interviewed indicated a desire to do so in the future. But none of this seems to portend a disavowal of traditional Chinese values. True, there is a strong consensus on the desirability of three or four children and the undesirability of larger numbers. But the preference for a moderate number of children, the number formerly achieved with larger numbers of deaths, is qualified by a strong traditional preference that at least one and preferably two or more of the children should be sons. Couples seeking help under the Prepregnancy Health Program of the Taiwanese Provincial Health Department almost always are those with at least three or four children, but they also are almost always couples with at least two sons. Strong approval is expressed in the surveys for such traditional Chinese values as the joint family, the importance of a male heir, and responsibility of children for their older parents.

Under the present mortality conditions of Taiwan a single son is very likely to survive to adulthood, so having additional sons as 'insurance' is probably an anachronism, but the traditional preference for several sons persists. The family size and sex composition being sought are approximately what a traditional Chinese family might have achieved with luck under high mortality and high fertility, but fewer births are needed now to achieve this goal. The present goal of many Taiwanese appears to be to maintain traditional values in the face of the pressures of higher survival rates by using family planning.

While a preference for sons is frequently embedded in religious institutions, it may have its origin in the value of sons for agricultural labour or for other purposes. The religious sanction may sanctify and insure what has been needed traditionally for other essential purposes.

Religious or other emphases on the importance of sons is only one of a large number of values that may affect the norms for family size, either indirectly or directly in relation to the role of the familial unit in the society. All of these must be taken into account in applying the general principle that the additional children are desired if they provide rewards greater than their costs under the particular familial arrangements of that society.

In seeking explanations for high fertility in supportive institutions and values, it would be grossly incorrect to suggest that the norms about the intermediate control variables are finely contrived in every society to produce results consistent with the norms about family size. On balance and in the long run a rough consistency is probable. But discrepancies between ends and means may develop and persist when aspects of the social structure not even recognized as related to fertility affect the reproductive level by their effect on the intermediate variables. For example, many religious systems prescribe periods of abstinence which usually (though not always) will have the effect on reducing fertility.

Illustrative of another 'unintended restraint' on fertility is the possible reduction in fecundity resulting from poor nutrition and poor health in the whole society or a stratum of it. For example, several recent Indian studies find relatively low fertility for the poorest social stratum. It is plausible that this may be a result of poor health and nutrition conditions in the lower status groups, although other explanations are possible.

A variety of such unintended effects of cultural factors in pre-industrial societies contribute to keeping fertility below its maximum biological potential. We really do not know, from systematic evidence, to what extent these operate selectively to keep fertility near the normative values. It is only a reasonable assumption that, if norms about family size are very important, the intermediate control variables will tend to reach a balance consistent with these norms. But, where social change is very rapid, such a long-run balance may not be struck exactly, and for short periods a large discrepancy between means and ends is probable.

Another approach to finding the variables that supported early high fertility is to study the correlates of the declines in fertility that have already occurred in developed societies. First of all, it is clear that in almost every case a substantial decline in mortality preceded fertility decline. [25] In Japan the period of lag was much shorter than in Western Europe. The lag may grow still shorter if social policy succeeds in accelerating fertility decline in such countries as Pakistan, India, Egypt and Korea. But, in all the countries that have such policies at present, mortality already has declined for several decades, with little evidence of fertility decline.

Other Social and Economic Variables

Apart from lower mortality, what social and economic variables are associated with fertility decline? Given the preceding analysis there is no surprise in the plausible hypothesis that a shift of functions from family to other specialized institutions is important. There is illustrative evidence that this shift has decreased the value and increased the costs of more than a small number of children for attaining the goals men seek in the more developed society. But the demonstrable changes in family functions are difficult to disentangle from the larger complex of social and economic changes in the course of social development. Broadly speaking, development is associated with many variables: e.g., urbanization, industrialization, more complex technology, greater capital investment per worker, higher living standards, and greater literacy. There is an increase in the mass media of communication and in transportation facilities which go with larger markets and the linkage of local populations in larger political, social, and economic units. In these larger units, a more complex division of labour exists not only with respect to economic life but also in almost every other aspect. Thus, the tasks of an urban society are divided among a much larger number of institutions. As the economic unit ceases to be the family, recruitment of workers is less closely linked to reproduction.

Economic Development

Because the development process is so complex, I have postponed any definition of development until this late point. At least with reference to fertility decline, I suggest that what is essential in the development process is the shift from major dependence on relatively self-contained local institutions, to dependence upon larger social, economic and political units. Such a shift implies a change in the division of labour from one in which the kinship unit is necessarily central to a larger complex in which such local units as family and village give up many functions to larger, non-familial specialized units. In such a shift, greater literacy and the development of effective communication networks are essential.

I have purposely avoided proposing industrialization and urbanization as the essential developmental changes for lower fertility, although they are usually part of the change process, and I do not minimize their importance. But I think that the essential change is the expansion of the unit within which most social and economic interchange occurs.

Some evidence that urbanization and industrialization alone may not provide the explanation for fertility decline appears in some unpublished work by Knodel & Tangoantiang at the Princeton Office of Population Research.

Tracing fertility declines from earlier times to the present, the Princeton group found that in all of the countries in Europe, with the exception of Albania, there has been a decline in fertility of 50% or more than that, with the further exception of France, the decline began some time between 1860 and 1920. The timing and steepness of the decline is not conspicuously associated with proportions of the labour force engaged in agriculture or changes in these proportions, nor is it associated consistently with urbanization. The only index examined whose movement seems almost universally to parallel that of fertility measures is illiteracy. The level of illiteracy varied widely between countries at the beginning of the decline, ranging from 24% reported in England to 79% for Russia. Yet, in each case, fertility and illiteracy declined together. A striking example of the unexpected lack of association between industrialization as normally visualized and declining fertility is that the decline began in the 1880s in Italy, Hungary and Finland, as well as in England and Wales. Literacy and mass education appear to deserve special attention in relation to changing fertility, along with the more frequently stressed urbanization and industrialization.

How can literacy and broad educational gains affect fertility? One indirect way is by helping to reduce mortality which will later reduce fertility in ways already indicated. Obviously, literacy also will facilitate the dissemination of information about the idea and means of family limitation. But I think the role of education and literacy is more basic. I suggest that with increased education and literacy the population becomes involved with the ideas and institutions of a larger modern culture. If the individual is, or believes he is, part of a larger non-familial system, he begins to find rewards in social relationships for which large numbers of children may be irrelevant. If this thesis is correct, major expenditures for education in a development programme are justified not only for developing worker skills but also for their potential effect on the fertility level, if lower fertility is a social objective.

It is pertinent that in every country for which we have empirical evidence the spread of family planning practices to attain a smaller family has been associated with a literate audience influenced by the mass media and by a person-to-person communication of their message that transcends local boundaries. In no case up to now has a government or private programme designed specifically to disseminate family planning or small family values been the principal agency for information and change.

In the pilot study in Taiwan, referred to earlier, education and contacts with the mass media were more closely related to the actual practice of family planning than were occupation, income, or rural background (see Appendix IV). It is relevant that Taiwan, a high fertility country in which a significant fertility decline has begun and where just now the probability of fertility decline seems great, has a relatively high literacy rate and also has had a rapid expansion in the circulation of the mass media and in the use of the mails for personal and business correspondence. Indicative of the possible importance of wider communication, is the symbolic, if humorous, fact that long-distance calls per capita are one of the best predictors of the 1961 fertility level for the 22 local administrative units in Taiwan.

I do not believe that education about fertility and family planning alone, completely in advance of other changes in the society, can be very effective for changing fertility norms and behaviour. Such a single specialized educational programme alone does not affect the linkage of the local population to the larger units in the broad and continuing way which can lead to the essential growing dependence on non-local and non-familial institutions. General education and literacy probably are required to do this.

High fertility norms and behaviour are too deeply embedded in traditional, emotionally-supported institutions—especially the familial—to be affected much by education or informational programmes centred on fertility alone. This is not to deny the potential importance of such programmes, once development is under way. Probably, reduced mortality sets the stage, providing the minimal threshold level required before fertility will drop. But, in addition, there must be at least minimal changes in the institutions which motivate high fertility by rewarding parents of relatively large numbers of children. There must be reason to believe that those who have smaller families can meet their needs in ways differing from the traditional patterns.

As Professor Glass has aptly put this matter: [26] 'The establishment of new demographic patterns involves the development of new incentives which press upon reproductive behavior. Such incentives need to be embedded in a social framework. They can be encouraged by persuasion but can hardly be created by an apparatus of symbols. Symbols are important. . . . But in countries with low levels of living, perhaps even more than elsewhere, it is necessary to have something material to be symbolic about.'

This view does not preclude the possibility that broad gains in literacy and education can facilitate lower fertility levels in advance of some other changes in the society. The extent to which this is possible and what associated changes are required is still an open question. Significant studies with careful controls are possible in some of the countries introducing family planning to test whether particular levels of literacy or of other development indices are a necessary threshold to a fertility decline.

The existence of the mass media and of postal networks already involves, to some extent, the larger interaction system of which I am speaking. If the literate regard themselves as members of a larger and less parochial society, the adoption of behaviours appropriate to that society may be accelerated, if at least minimal threshold changes in society make their new self-image plausible.

Obviously, changes in literacy, education and communication networks are related to many other aspects of development. Changes in all of them probably are related in interaction to fertility decline. But it is unnecessary to assume that all aspects of development must move together. We know that there have been uneven rates of movement in the past. From a policy point of view it is desirable to look for some elements subject to social control which might lead the development process and decrease the time-gap between mortality and fertility decline. I have emphasized education because it might be such a leading variable and it is given less attention usually than economic variables or urbanization.

To recapitulate, I have reviewed briefly the evidence that social norms support the moderately to very high fertility found in the so-called underdeveloped societies. I have suggested that high fertility and high fertility norms are not a result of unrestrained maximum fecundity but rather are an adjustment mainly to the high mortality and to dependence on kinship-based local institutions. Variations in the kinship structure were seen as a major possible explanation of variations from moderate to very high fertility. The net effect of a large number of possible control variables determines the extent to which the social norms about fertility are approximated in behaviour. Finally, I have suggested that the complex continuum from underdeveloped to developed societies is best represented for our purpose by a continuum from major dependence on relatively small local units to increasing interdependence in larger social units in which kinship plays a decreasing part. In this shift to larger units of interdependence, education and literacy not only have an important part to play but may lead other elements in their effect on fertility.

Appendix I. Estimated Gross Reproduction Rates for Selected Populations and Periods

1. Gross Reproduction Rates in Selected High Fertility Populations

(Statistical resources are usually poor in the high-fertility areas so data are often unavailable or of questionable reliability. Those presented below are for areas where special fertility investigations, adjustment by competent investigators or unusually good official statistics makes the data appear reasonably reliable. Nevertheless, these rates are less reliable than those for the low-fertility countries. They are cited to indicate the probable diversity in reproduction levels rather than as accurate measures in each individual case.)

Africa:[27]

Centre-Oubangui (1959)	2.0
Dahomey (1961)	3.2
Guinea (1954-55)	2.9
Ivory Coast (1958)	2.4
Mali (1957-61)	3.3
Upper Volta (1960)	3.2
North Cameroons	2.3

Asia:

Ceylon[28] (1952)	2.2
Cocos Islands[29]	4.2
India[30] (1956)	2.6
Malaysian population of Malaya[31] (1946-48)	2.7
Taiwan[32]	2.7

West Indies:[33]

Jamaica (1943)	1.8
Barbados (1946)	1.9
British Guiana (1946)	2.4
Trinidad (1946)	2.4

American Hutterites[34] (1952)	4.0

2. Gross Reproduction Rates in Selected Low Fertility Areas[35]

England and Wales:

1861	2.4
1901	1.7
1940	0.8
1958	1.2

Austria:

1931-32	0.9
1959	1.3

Belgium:

1928-32	1.0
1959	1.3

Norway:

1932-35	0.9
1958	1.4

United States:

1930-35	1.1
1959	1.8

Appendix II. Some Illustrative Results from Sample Surveys Dealing with Number of Children Wanted or Considered Ideal in Underdeveloped Societies

1. Puerto Rico[36]

A. Answers to question 'Suppose you were to get married again for the first time, how many children would you want to have?':

number of children wanted	sample of clinic out-patients (%)	general field sample (%)
0 or 1	16	8
2	40	43
3	18	26
4 or more	10	18
all God sends	16	5
total	100	100

2. India

A. Number of children considered ideal in Mysore area:[37]

	mean no. considered ideal by	
	wife	husband
Bangalore city	3.6	4.1
rural plains sample	4.7	4.6

B. Proportion of parents who say they want no more children, by present number of children:[37]

	percentage of parents who want no more			
	Bangalore city		rural plains	
number of living children	wife	husband	wife	husband
0	5	10	2	2
1-3	25	42	14	26
4-6	56	72	48	59

C. Number of children desired (from the point of view of finances) in several districts near Poona:[38]

	Nasik		Kalaba	
number of children desired	rural (%)	urban (%)	rural (%)	urban (%)
less than 3	20	27	9	18
4-5	38	46	35	34
6 or more	17	19	11	14
until a son comes	2	2	2	3
until 2 or 3 sons come	17	4	12	10
as many as are born	5	1	19	6
could not state a number	1	1	12	15
	100	100	100	100

3. Jamaica:[39]

A. Answers to question 'If you could live your life over, how many children would you like to have?':

number of children	% of women wanting this number
3 or less	50
4	29
5 or more	18
up to God, fate	3
total	100

B. Percentage of women wanting more children, by number of children they have now:

number of living children	% wanting more children
0	92
1	64
2	44
3	32
4 or 5	20
6 or more	16

4. Taichung, Taiwan:[40]

A. Answers to question, 'How many children would you like if you could (start over) and have just the number you want?':

number of children wanted	% wanting this number	
	wife	husband
less than 2	0	0
2	9	7
3	33	32
4	56	50
5	12	12
6 or more	4	6
up to God, fate	1	*
cannot say	2	4
total	100	100

* Less than 1%

B. Number of children of each sex considered ideal for Taiwanese couples by wife:

number of children	% choosing each number for	
	sons	daughters
0	0	0
1	2	28
2	71	63
3	20	3
4	1	0
either sex satisfactory	2	2
up to God, fate	1	1
not ascertained	3	3
total	100	100

C. Percentage of wives and husbands who have more children than they want, by present number of children:

	% who would prefer fewer children than they have	
present number of children	wife	husband
1	0	0
2	0	2
3	2	4
4	12	12
5 or more	61	55

Appendix III. Classification of the 'Intermediate' Variables Affecting Fertility
Taken from K. Davis & J. Blake, 'Social structure and fertility: an analytic framework', *Economic Development and Cultural Change*, 4, No. 3 (April 1956), pp. 211-235.

I. *Factors affecting exposure to intercourse*
   A. Those governing the formulation and dissolution of unions in the reproductive period.
      1. Age of entry into sexual unions.
      2. Permanent celibacy: proportion of women never entering sexual unions.
      3. Amount of reproductive period spent after or between unions.
         (a) When unions are broken by divorce, separation or desertion.
         (b) When unions are broken by death of husband.
   B. Those governing the exposure to intercourse within unions.
      1. Voluntary abstinence.
      2. Involuntary abstinence (from impotence, illness unavoidable but temporary separations).
      3. Coital frequency (excluding period of abstinence).

II. *Factors affecting exposure to conception*
   A. Fecundity or infecundity, as affected by involuntary causes.
   B. Use or non-use of contraception.
      1. By mechanican and chemical means.
      2. By other means.
   C. Fecundity or infecundity, as affected by voluntary causes (sterilization, subincision, medical treatment, etc.).

III. *Factors affecting gestation and successful parturition*
   A. Foetal mortality from voluntary causes.
   B. Foetal mortality from involuntary causes.

Appendix IV. Selected Results of a Study of Factors Associated with Approval and Use of Family Planning in Taichung, Taiwan (Pilot Study of 241 Couples with Wife 25 to 29 Years Old)

characteristics of wife or of couple	% of couples who have practised some form of family planning	% of couples who approve of family planning unconditionally
Wife's education:		
none	18	56
some primary	20	47
primary graduate	26	79
some secondary school	60	74
secondary school graduate	71	83
Frequency of reading daily newspaper–wife:		
never	19	61
sometimes	33	92
once or twice a week	41	86
daily	58	75
Family expenditures per month (N.T.):		
less than 1000	26	64
1000-1999	34	75
2000-2999	41	67
3000 or more	37	63
Farm background–wife:		
some	31	67
none	40	73
No. of 'modern' consumer objects owned:		
less than 4	18	50
4	17	77
5	21	76
6	41	69
7	47	77
8 or 9	48	66
Type of family:		
joint	27	60
stem	27	68
nuclear	40	72

Notes and References

1. Smith, T. E., The Cocos-Keeling Islands: a demographic laboratory. *Population Studies*, 14, No. 2, November 1960, pp. 94-130.

2. For example, birth rates of sixty or more are reported for several African populations in the United Nations, *Demographic Yearbook, 1961* on the basis of sample surveys.

3. *Royal Commission on Population, Report.* London: H.M.S.O., (1949, p. 24. Women recorded as married in the fertility census of 1911 and born in the period 1841-45 reported an average of 5.71 live births.

4. For example, in the United Nations, *The Mysore population study*. New York: The United Nations, 1962; and in Sovani, N. V. & Dandekar, K., *Fertility survey of Nasik, Kolaba, and Satara Districts*. Poona: Gokhale Institute of Politics and Economics, Publication No. 31, 1955.

5. Cf. Eaton, J. & Mayer, A., *Man's capacity to reproduce*. Glencoe: The Free Press, 1954, pp. 20 ff.

6. For example, Dandekar, K., *Demographic survey of six rural communities*. Poona: Gokhale Institute of Politics and Economics, 1959;

   Hatt, P. K., *Backgrounds of human fertility in Puerto Rico: a sociological survey.* Princeton: Princeton University Press, 1952;

   Hill, R., Stycos, J. M. & Back, K. W., *The family and population control: a Puerto Rican experiment in social change*. Chapel Hill: University of North Carolina Press, 1959;

   Mukherjec, S. B., *Studies on fertility rates in Calcutta*. Calcutta: Bookland Private Ltd., 1961;

   Singh, B., *Five years of family planning in the country-side*. Lucknow: J. K. Institute of Sociology and Human Relations, 1958;

   Stycos, J. M. & Back, K., *Prospects for fertility reduction*. New York: The Conservation Foundation, 1957;

   Tabah, L. & Samuel, R., Preliminary findings of a survey on fertility and attitudes toward family formation in Santiago. In Milbank Memorial Fund, *Research in family planning*. Princeton: Princeton University Press, 1962;

   United Nations. *The Mysore population study*. New York: United Nations, 1962;

   Yaukey, D., *Fertility differences in a modernizing country*. Princeton, Princeton University Press, 1961.

   A more complete annotated bibliography of such studies appears in *The sociology of human fertility: a trend report and bibliography*, Vol. 10/11, No. 2. 1961-2 in the series *Current Sociology* published by the International Sociological Association with the support of Unesco.

7. Richards, A. J. & Reining, P., Reports on fertility surveys in Buganda and Buhaya, 1952, pp. 351-404. In Lorimer, F. et al. *Culture and human fertility*, Paris: Unesco, 1954.

8. Ford, C. S., *A comparative study of human reproduction*. New Haven: Yale University Press, 1945, Yale University Publications in Anthropology, no. 32.

9. Davis, K. & Blake, J., Social structure and fertility: an analytic framework. *Economic development and cultural change*, 4, No. 3, April 1956, pp. 211-235.

10. Coale, A. J. & Tye, C. Y., The significance of age-patterns of fertility in high fertility populations. *Milbank Memorial Fund Quarterly*, 39, No. 4, October 1961, pp. 631-646.

11. For example, Eversley, D. E. C., Population and economic growth in England before the 'takeoff'. In *Contributions and Communications to the First International Conference of Economic History*. Stockholm, 1960, pp. 457-473; Habakkuk, H. J., The economic history of modern Britain. *J. Econom. Hist.* 18, No. 4, December 1958, pp. 486-501;

Krause, J. T., Some implications of recent work in historical demography. *Comp. Stud. Soc. Hist.* 1, No. 2, January 1959, pp. 164-188.

12. Carr-Saunders, A. M., *The population problem*. Oxford: Clarendon Press, 1922. The frame of reference of this important work has influenced greatly the ideas presented in the present paper.

13. Himes, N. E., *Medical history of contraception*. Baltimore: The Williams and Wilkins Co., 1936.

14. Op. cit. (see note 8).

15. Devereux, G., *A study of abortion in primitive societies*. New York: Julian Press, 1955.

16. For relevant evidence see Bergues, H. et al. *La prevention des naissances dans la famille*. Paris: Presses Universitaries de France, 1960; and Lewis-Faning, E., *Report on an inquiry into family limitation and its influence on human fertility during the past fifty years*. Papers of the Royal Commission on Population, Vol. I London: H.M.S.O. 1949.

17. Pierce, R. M. & Rowntree, G., Birth control in Britain. Part 2, *Population Studies*, 15, No. 2, November 1961, pp. 121-160.

18. Op. cit. (see note 6).

19. For a general discussion of this issue see Stycos, J. M., A critique of the traditional planned parenthood approach in underdeveloped areas. In Kiser, C. V., ed., *Research in family planning*. Princeton: Princeton University Press, 1962. References to Taiwanese data in this paper are all drawn from unpublished work of the Taiwan Population Studies Center in which participating personnel include Dr. C. H. Yen, Dr. J. Y. Peng. Dr. Y. Takeshita, Mr. T. H. Sun and Mr. S. Y. Soong.

20. United Nations. *The Mysore population study*. Op. cit. (see note 4).

21. Lorimer, F. et al., *Culture and human fertility*. Paris: Unesco, 1954.

22. Op. cit. (see note 9).

23. For example, in the experimental study in Singur, India described by Mathen, K. K., in 'Preliminary lessons learned from the rural population control study of Singur.' In Kiser, C. V., op. cit., pp. 33-50 (see note 19).

24. The Population Problems Research Council, *Fifth public opinion survey on birth control in Japan* and *Sixth opinion survey on family planning and birth control*, Tokyo: The Mainichi Newspapers, 1959 and 1962.

25. France and Spain are among possible exceptions.

26. Glass, D. V., Population growth, fertility, and population policy. *The advancement of science*, November, 1960, pp. 1-11.

27. The African rates are based on estimates made by the Princeton African Demography Project, from Census Inquiry data. They were kindly supplied by Professor W.

Brass of the University of Aberdeen. The data supplied were in the form of total fertility rates. These were converted to gross reproduction rates for this presentation on the assumption of a uniform sex-ratio at birth of 106.

28. From Sarkar, N. K., Population trends and population policy in Ceylon. *Population Studies*, 9, No. 3, March 1956, pp. 195-216.

29. Smith, T. E., op. cit. (see note 1).

30. Cf. Coale, A. J. & Hoover, E. M., *Population growth and economic development in low-income countries*. Princeton: Princeton University Press, 1958, p. 352.

31. Estimated by Smith, T. E., in *Population growth in Malaya*. London: Royal Institute of Royal Affairs, 1952, Ch. II.

32. From unpublished calculations of the Taiwan Population Studies Center.

33. From Roberts, G. W., Some aspects of mating and fertility in the West Indies. *Population Studies*, 8, No. 3, March 1955, pp. 199-227. Mr. Roberts shows that joint reproduction rates based on both male and female rates may be more useful than the conventional female gross reproduction rates, but only the female rates are cited here, for comparability with those of other countries.

34. From Eaton, J. & Mayer, A., op. cit. (see note 5) p. 40.

35. The rates for England and Wales are from reports of the Registrar General for England and Wales. All other figures in this set are from *Population Index*, April 1961, 28, No. 2.

36. From Hill, R., Stycos, J. M. & Back, K. W., op. cit. (see note 6) 1959, p. 72.

37. United Nations, *The Mysore Population Study*. Op. cit. (see note 4) p. 142.

38. Sovani, W. V. & Dandekar, K., op. cit. (see note 4) p. 104.

39. Stycos, J. M. & Back, K., op. cit. (see note 6).

40. From unpublished data collected by Taiwan Population Studies Center, associated with the Provincial Maternal and Child Health Institute, Taiwan.

Cultural Differences in the Interpretation of Natural Resources
Alexander Spoehr

An examination of the interpretation that different peoples have placed on the natural resources on which they depend falls in the more general field of human ecology. The relation of any human population to its natural resources is only part of a more inclusive set of relationships between such a population and its total natural environment. "Human ecology," though variously and often vaguely defined as a field of specific subject matter, emphasizes relationships with the environment and, as Bates (1953) has said, achieves its greatest usefulness as a point of view. The subject of this paper, therefore, is a part of human ecology, and the following remarks will stress a point of view rather than attempt a synthesis of a body of scientific literature.

I am indebted to Carl Sauer for pointing out that the concept "natural resources" is largely derived from our own society's ceaseless attempt at finding new and more intensive uses for the raw materials of nature. It is doubtful that many other societies, most of which are less involved with technological development, think about natural resources in the same way as we do. It is probable that the term itself, with the feeling tones that it carries, is primarily a product of our own industrial civilization. For this reason it is not possible to take the body of ethnographic accounts of different peoples and obtain a clear-cut view as to exactly what interpretation has been placed on their natural resources by non-Western societies in different places and at different times. In ethnographic accounts chapters dealing with such peoples are seldom written quite that way.

In the following review it has been necessary to tie a cross-cultural comparison of the interpretation of natural resources to several rather arbitrarily selected reference points. Three have been chosen and will be examined in turn: (1) natural resources in relation to technology; (2) natural resources in relation to social structure; and (3) natural resources and the interpretation of habitat. Of these three reference points, the first is most restricted in scope. The remaining two involve a progressively wider range of subject matter.

Natural Resources and Technology

It is a truism that every society must adapt itself to its environment to survive. This adaptation is largely effected through the particular technology that a given society has developed and maintains. Viewed in world perspective and from the vantage point of man's history on earth, the variety of technical systems is very great, ranging from the simple technology of food-collectors such as the Australian aborigines or the Great Basin Indians of North America to the highly complex technology of Western industrial civilization. Various classifications of technologies have been devised, and no attempt will be made here to extend them (Forde, 1934). The point is rather that, regardless of the degree of complexity of a given technology, every technology is necessarily based on a thorough knowledge of the natural resources which are utilized through the working of the technology. A food-collecting technology may be of a very simple order, but the men who practice it must of necessity have a sound empirical knowledge of that sector of the natural environment that provides the food they seek.

This point is made merely to emphasize that so-called "primitive" peoples do not exist in a state of ignorance of the natural world about them.

It is true that the knowledge they possess is essentially empirical and that the over-all characteristics of a people's technology tend to direct their interest to those particular resources of nature on which they depend. Thus the population densities of some of the Micronesian atolls are so high in relation to their few square miles of dry-land area that these communities could not possibly survive without the fish resources of the atoll lagoons. A large sector of the technology of these atoll dwellers is comprised of skills and techniques associated with fishing, the building of canoes, and seamanship, which in turn is related to an intimate knowledge of fish species, the habits and relative abundance of various species, whether or not they are poisonous, and similar matters. A given technology, by making possible a particular kind of adaptation, tends to crystallize interest and knowledge around that segment of natural resources on which the technology depends.

Differing Use of the Same Resources
Anthropological literature abounds also in examples of different peoples inhabiting the same or very similar habitats but who have made use of different sectors of the resources of their habitat. There may be a high degree of selectivity of particular resources around which the technology is centered. An interesting example can be given from Hawaii. In the days when the Hawaiians had their islands to themselves, they were fishermen and farmers. Their agricultural economy was built particularly on the cultivation of taro, which was grown chiefly in irrigated plots in the bottom-land areas of coastal valleys, usually with very high rainfall. Such a valley, famous in local history, is that of Waipio on the island of Hawaii. It is estimated that at one time from three to four thousand people lived in Waipio. During the nineteenth and twentieth centuries the economy of Hawaii completely changed. With the influx of immigrants from America, Europe, and Asia, the economy of the island of Hawaii changed to large-scale agriculture, centered on sugar cane, coffee, and cattle-raising, for none of which Waipio is suitable. The valley's population today has dwindled to twenty-six persons, and a great part of it has been abandoned. Its soil resources are neglected, for present-day large-scale agricultural technology in use on the island is not suited to them, and they have been by-passed.

The example from Hawaii again illustrates the point that interest in specific natural resources and the uses to which they are put is greatly conditioned by the nature of the technology imposed upon such resources. Technology is in itself a part of man's culture, and the interpretation of specific resources cannot be understood except as a facet of human culture.

To a considerable degree, the interest of our own society in the availability, renewability, and exploitability of natural resources springs from our singular bent toward technological invention. It is true that technological invention has been a potent force throughout man's long history on earth. Yet, viewed against the background of human history, our industrial civilization of the twentieth century has developed in a very short time. One of its characteristics, related, of course, to the growth of science, is its concern with invention. This concern the anthropologist does not find to be shared with all societies. Among many, once an adaptation to a given environment has been made through the medium of a particular technology, the manner of thought imbedded in the culture of these societies may actually militate against the inventive process. One of the best examples is given by Raymond Firth in his outstanding study of the economy of Tikopia, a very isolated small island in the southwestern Pacific. Firth (1939) notes that the material culture and the technology of Tikopia are very closely adjusted to the resources of the island environment. He notes further that the Tikopians are in no way loath to accept trade goods in the form of useful tools. However, the Polynesian people of this small island "have formulated no particular doctrine of technical invention" (*ibid.*, p. 86). Their interest is centered on legendary origins of how they themselves came to be rather than on technological origins and on the technical processes of invention and change.

Although the variety of cultures possessed by non-literate, non-Western societies is so great that the appellation "primitive" is usually a misnomer, it is true that such societies are generally small and tied to a local habitat. Every local habitat imposes certain limitations on a purely local technology. The people of a Pacific atoll must of necessity exist within the limitations of an atoll environment. It is true that as taro-raisers the Marshall Islanders have challenged the natural limitations of their atoll environment by excavating large pits in the coral lime sands of the atoll islets and, by creating humus, through filling these pits with decaying vegetable matter, are able to raise taro. This is a small-scale example of how one society has successfully challenged environmental restrictions. Yet the contrast is great when compared with the manner in which contemporary Western industrial civilization has freed itself from local environmental bonds and through its technology is world wide in scope. Chapple and Coon (1942, p. 249) have pointed out that technologically less complex societies tend to exploit single landscapes, whereas "we . . . live in all environments, not by exploiting single landscapes, separately, but by pooling and redistributing the products of all types of environment." A marked difference in the cultural interpretation of natural resources among different peoples follows from this fact. In small-scale pre-literate societies concern with natural resources tends to be local; ours is world wide.

Natural Resources and Social Structure
So far we have touched on the relation of resources to technology, which in

the last analysis comprises the characteristics of a society's tool system for converting raw materials into finished products. The techniques available to a society, however, are but one facet of its total economy. The latter comprehends also a body of generally accepted concepts regarding the control and use of resources, goods, and productive processes—such as those concepts embodied in the terms "income," "capital," and "rent"—and, in addition, the particular manner in which human beings are organized to carry out activities generally labeled as economic. In this latter category are the particular ways in which the individuals working in a factory or on a farm are organized, or the manner in which the market of a Mexican town is organized. In each case, interpersonal relations tend to fall in definable patterns, into a system of relationships that tends to persist so long as the common end—such as the exchange of goods—is being pursued. This organization of human beings in economic activity is but part of the total social structure of a society. Economic organization is related at many points to other segments of social structure. Thus, the organization of a craft industry carried out in individual households is closely related to the prevailing characteristics of the system of relations among the kinfolk of the various households. A people's kinship system is only in part an aspect of their economy.

This point is made because the use of natural resources is controlled by the nature of social structure in addition to a body of productive techniques alone. One cannot consider the link between natural resources and man merely as a matter of converting raw materials into goods through a given technology in order to house, feed, and clothe so-and-so many people, essential as these facts are.

For purposes of illustration and contrast, the following example from a technologically less complex society may be useful.

To the atoll dwellers of the Marshall Islands the coconut palm, as well as the fish resources of the sea, is a mainstay of life. A relatively simple body of techniques employing hand labor makes possible the use of the coconut for food, for export as copra, and for a variety of other products. However, the control of the coconut palm as a natural resource, the organization of production whereby it is converted into usable goods, and the distribution of income derived from its production are all linked to Marshallese social structure. The Marshall Islanders retain a feudal-like class system of nobility and commoners. Title to all the land of the atoll nominally rests with the paramount chief. Usufruct rights are apportioned among the lesser chiefs and, in turn, among the commoners. Land is not sold, and our own concepts of ownership of real property are foreign to the system. The commoners cultivate the land, and the nobility receive tribute in the form of produce. Today, a share of cash receipts from the sale of copra is also remitted to the paramount chief as tribute. In addition, land rights are, for the most part, held by lineages of kinfolk who trace descent in the matrilineal line. Each lineage has a head who represents the lineage, and the headship as an office is also passed down in the matrilineal line. Lineages, the class organization, and land tenure are all interrelated elements of a single system. As a result, to the Marshallese, the control and use of land resources are mediated through the particular characteristics of their social structure.

Cultural Influences on Resource Use

The significance of cultural factors in relation to resources is perhaps most clearly discerned during periods of rapid change. Cultural change is a complex, but not a haphazard, phenomenon. At times it may follow a rigidly defined course that from a biologist's point of view is non-adaptive, in so far as the conservation and use of resources is concerned. An oft-quoted example is found in the cattle-raising peoples of East Africa, among whom cattle are so highly regarded and are so fundamental a basis of status within the community that the greatest resistance to a reduction of herds has been encountered among these people, despite serious depletion of resources (Read, 1938). A somewhat similar case is provided by the resistance of the Navaho to reduction of sheep on their overgrazed ranges.

The purpose of these examples is simply to emphasize that any group "interprets" its natural resources within the framework of its own social structure. The point at which this probably is most apparent is in the organization of production, for it is in production that the manner of control and the use of natural resources are most evident. The initial point in the productive process is the conversion of raw materials into goods. The raw materials are derived from resources in their natural state. If the resources are especially limited, restrictive rights to their use may exist. Our own concepts of "ownership" may be viewed as the conjunction of our own particular social system and limited resources. Yet Western ideas of ownership are by no means universal and are but one example of how an exclusive right may be culturally defined. The Pacific islands provide examples of differently conceived rights to resources, where Western concepts of ownership are not applicable. Yet, among these peoples, rights controlling how resources, particularly land, are to be used and who is entitled to exercise control can also be viewed as the conjunction of social structure and habitat. The case of the Marshallese has been noted. For more extensive analyses of other island societies the reader is referred to Firth (1929, 1939), to Hogbin (1939), and to Herskovits' recent (1952) general review of the problem of ownership and land tenure.

Natural Resources and Habitat

Natural resources are physically a part of habitat, and habitat is but one aspect of that complex of physical, chemical, and biological processes, with their resultant products, which we call "nature." Modern man has conceptually isolated natural resources as that segment of the physical world that has a present or potential use for the survival and physical well-being of man, to be developed as far as possible through the application of scientific knowledge. Yet natural resources are still a part of nature.

The title of this paper, with its emphasis on the "interpretation" of natural resources, implies a comparison of attitudes held by different peoples toward natural resources. But, to return to a point made earlier, concern for the development of "natural resources" seems largely a facet of modern civilization. What is necessary is an examination, not merely of culturally conditioned attitudes toward natural resources, but of how various peoples have come to regard their relationship with their respective habitats (of which resources are but a part) and indeed with the entire physical universe in which they exist. It is at this point that the most fundamental contrast can be discerned between the Western industrial world and small-scale, often preliterate, societies.

This subject has been explored and presented, in a much more expert fashion than that of which I am capable, by Robert Redfield in his recent book, *The Primitive World and Its Transformations*. It is a subject that anthropologists have long pondered, though few with the breadth of interest displayed by Redfield. His presentation is the point of departure for the following paragraphs.

For the purpose of this essay there are two questions that are particularly relevant: (1) How have men, in different times and places, regarded nature, and hence the habitats in which they dwell? (2) How have these attitudes affected what men feel they should do about conserving and developing their habitats for human use?

In regard to the first question, the initial point to be made is taken from Redfield and the writers that he in turn draws upon. It is that virtually every people regards the universe in some sort of structured cosmology. The degree to which this cosmology is systematized varies enormously. The points of emphasis vary enormously. But everywhere, and since ancient times, man has pondered his relation to the physical facts of the universe and has attempted to see man, nature, and the supernatural in some sort of understandable relation. In this, my feeling from reading the accounts of ethnologists is the same as Redfield's (1953, pp. 105-6)—that preliterate peoples, in regarding the universe, "think of an orderly system originally set running by divine will and thereafter exhibiting its immanent order." Whether the gods do or can interfere in the machine they have set running is either not thought about or perhaps not reported sufficiently by ethnologists. It seems more probable that preliterate peoples tend to regard the universe as operating under irreversible laws, once these are set in motion.

And how is man's place regarded in this scheme? To what degree is he subject also to an order established under supernatural sanction? Here at least most preliterate societies offer a contrast with our own. The contrast is well exemplified in the opening paragraph of Elsdon Best's monograph, *Forest Lore of the Maori*. The contrast is shown both in Best's point of view and in that of the Maori of whom he was writing:

> The outlook of the Maori, as in connection with natural phenomena and nature generally, often differed widely from our own; thus he looked upon the far spread forests of his island home as being necessary to his welfare, and also as being of allied origin. This peculiar outlook was based on the strange belief that man, birds, and trees are descended from a common source; their ultimate origin lay with the primal pair, Rangi the Sky Parent and Papa the Earth Mother, though they were actually brought into being by Tane the Fertilizer, one of the seventy offspring of the above-mentioned primal parents [Best, 1942, p. 1].

Man and Nature Together   Man, to many peoples, is not set apart from nature but is part of a single order, combining man, nature, and the gods. When man utilizes the resources of nature, it is within the framework of this system of ideas. Thus, in writing of the lack of interest in technological invention displayed by the island people of Tikopia, Firth notes (1939, p. 88) that the Tikopia are governed by their theory of natural resources, which "may be described briefly as a theory of the human utilization of resources under supernatural control, which governs not only their fertility, but also the social and economic relationships of those who handle them."

Within this essentially stable system, man and nature are not conceptually opposed but are considered as parts of the same thing. The totemic rites of the Australian Karadjeri, whereby the economically and socially important species of plants and animals were believed to be assured of normal increase, reflected a similar manner of thought (Elkin, 1933). When Gayton, writing of the integration of culture and environment effected through economic activity, ceremony, and myth among the Yokuts Indians, states (1946, p. 262) that "men and animals were peers," much the same idea is expressed.

In his consideration of the involvement of man and nature in the thought of preliterate and ancient societies, Redfield notes (1953, p. 104) that the men of these societies did not "confront" nature. For them, "being already in nature, man cannot exactly confront it." Rather, Redfield suggests, the relation is one of mutuality, existing under a moral order that binds man, nature, and the gods in one.

The modern Western world has undergone a major transformation from this orientation. Man has been conceptually separated from nature, and God from both. Speaking of the development of Western thought since classical times, Redfield (pp. 109-10) states:

> The subsequent development of a world view in which God and man are both separated from nature, and in which the exploitation of material nature comes to be a prime attitude, may be attributable to our Western world almost entirely and so might be regarded, as Sol Tax has suggested (Tax, 1944), as a particular "cultural invention." By the seventeenth century in European philosophy God was outside the system as its mere clockmaker. To the early American, nature was God's provision for man's exploitation. . . . The contemporary Western world, now imitated by the Orient, tends to regard the relation of man to nature as a relation of man to physical matter in which application of physical science to man's material comfort is man's paramount assignment on earth.

These observations may appear overdrawn to some, but they illustrate what I believe is a fundamental contrast in the thinking of the Western world, as contrasted to preliterate and ancient peoples. It is a contrast that in itself is at least a partial answer to our second question posed earlier—namely, how has this contrasting attitude affected what men feel they should do about developing their habitats for human use? Certainly the tenor of contemporary American thought holds that habitat is something apart from man and is to be manipulated to his advantage. In the world of today, with the ever growing millions of human beings to clothe, feed, and house, this attitude has a very immediate and practical import.

On the other hand, despite the long history of the growth of technology, throughout which some men as far back as the earliest periods of human history must have been concerned with improving tools to develop resources for human use, preliterate societies lack the prevading instrumental attitude toward nature generally characteristic of ourselves. The difference probably accounts for the significance of magic associated with technology, which Malinowski long ago reported for the Trobriand Islands. Among these people, although their full technological skill is called upon in an enterprise, such as gardening, fishing, or voyaging, recourse to magic is had to fill the inevitable gap between the application of human skill and the certainty of success.

Western Attitudes   The contrasting attitudes of Western and preliterate thought lead to another question. For several decades anthropologists have been attempting to observe the changes that take place in small scale, for the most preliterate, societies, when they come in contact with Western industrial civilization. In so far as the interpretation of natural resources is concerned, is not the contrast just discussed at the root of the change that takes place? I suspect it is. To review all the evidence is beyond the scope of this paper, but I quote an anthropological colleague, John Gillin, comparing the Indian and the Ladino cultures (crystallized out of contact with Spain) of Guatemala:

> The principal and fundamental goal of Indian cultures is to effect a peaceful adjustment or adaptation to the universe. In contrast, the main goal of Ladino culture is to effect control of the universe by man. The Indian wishes to come to terms with the universe, the Ladino wishes to dominate it. . . . The Indian attitude is not one of abject submission to natural and supernatural forces. The basic assumptions in Indian cultures, however, do hold that man is in a world which operates according to certain laws or rules ultimately controlled by that part of the universe which we would call the supernatural or unseen, that this general plan of things is ongoing or immutable, that man must learn certain patterns of action and attitude to bring himself into conformity with this scheme of things, and that if he does so he will receive the minimum amount of punishment or misfortune and the maximum rewards of which such a scheme is capable. . . . The Ladino, on the other hand, assumes that the universe, including its supernatural department, can be manipulated by man . . . [Gillin, 1952, p. 196].

The gradual adoption of this attitude could, I believe, be documented from other societies in contact with the West. It seems to have been, for instance, a concomitant of the extension of the copra industry to various islands of the Pacific during the nineteenth and twentieth centuries. The development of the copra industry in the Marshall Islands was almost certainly accompanied by a marked change in attitude toward land, whereby it came to be regarded as a resource to be controlled and manipulated by man to his best advantage, in a fashion comparable to the Ladino point of view described by Gillin. To what degree the extension of this attitude follows the penetration of a money economy into societies such as the Marshallese, together with the growth of trade and a widening in the range of wants, is not clear.

If these contrasting attitudes toward nature, and in consequence toward natural resources, have been correctly described in these paragraphs, I should like to turn to some ramifications in regard to the interpretation of nature by our own society.

To the degree that the Western world is composed of almost completely urbanized individuals, it not merely regards habitat, and consequently natural resources, as an entity that is to be dominated and manipulated by man but tends to relegate the whole matter to a handful of specialists and, in effect, to place nature outside its immediate sphere of concern. Urban man has become so far removed from his biological moorings and so immersed in the immediate problems of urban living that he stands as an "egocentric man in a homocentric world." Despite the millions of Americans who annually visit our national parks each year, it is to be doubted that much change is thereby effected in the basic urban attitude. The aesthetic principles underlying American conservation movements can perhaps best be viewed as a minority reaction to the prevailing urban point of view. Conservation, in the sense of the attempt by the Save-the-Redwoods League to preserve stands of California giant sequoias from extinction, is an effort to protect modern man from himself. Such efforts are not, to my knowledge, found among preliterate peoples living in small communities in close and personal relation to nature. Among most of them, though it is largely unrecorded in the reports of ethnologists, I suspect that the aesthetic appreciation of nature is a common feature of daily life. Yet I should add that most of my own field experience has been in the congenial islands of the Pacific.

If the prevailing mode of thought tends to regard nature as a physical entity apart from man, with the corollary that man's duty is to develop and dominate to the best of his ability the resources of his habitat, there are nevertheless certain countercurrents in contemporary scientific thought that cannot be ignored. These countercurrents are well exemplified by Darwin and Faraday.

Darwin opened our eyes to the functioning of organic nature, and his mode of thought led to discovery of new facts and relationships in the living world. Darwin dealt with man's place in nature and with man as a part of a huge, dynamic biocoenose, of which man was only a small part, actually not very different from the other parts, and subject to the same processes and regularities. In his point of view as to man's integration with the natural world, Darwin might be considered as close to the way in which preliterate peoples regard nature, except for the fundamental difference that the former developed his point of view on the basis of observed reality; the latter, on recourse to the sanction of man-created legend and myth. Darwin left to his successors the concept of man as a part of nature, whatever qualities man may possess that distinguish him from other forms of life.

Faraday, on the other hand, introduced us to inanimate forces which could be made to serve man's needs and wants. He stimulated the invention of new devices and the formation of a great new technology based on the use of natural forces. He also stimulated the creation of a homocentric world, a modern, mechanized, exploiting world of men whose contemplating largely centers about themselves and who attempt to plan, arrange, and administer in their own name. Whereas the heritage of Darwin has provided the fascination of biological revelation, that of Faraday has brought the excitement attending the accomplishment and application of the physical sciences.

In a modern world where men are dedicated to exploiting to the utmost the natural resources of this planet—a dedication that is stimulated by the very numbers of men on earth—the point of view exemplified by Faraday is necessarily uppermost. It could hardly be otherwise. Yet one cannot forget the bearded figure of Darwin watching quietly from the shadows.

Notes and References

Bates, Marston, 1950, *The Nature of Natural History*. New York: Charles Scribner's Sons. 309 pp.
1953, "Human Ecology," pp. 700-714 in A. L. Kroeber (Chairman), *Anthropology Today: An Encyclopedic Inventory*. Chicago: University of Chicago Press. 966 pp.

Best, Elsdon, 1925, *Maori Agriculture*. (Bulletin No. 9.) Wellington, N. Z.: Dominion Museum. 172 pp.
1942, *Forest Lore of the Maori*. (Bulletin No. 14.) Wellington, N. Z.: Dominion Museum. 503 pp.

Bews, J. W., 1935, *Human Ecology*. London: H. Milford. 312 pp.

Chapple, E. D., and Coon, C. S., 1942, *Principles of Anthropology*. New York: Henry Holt & Co. 718 pp.

Darwin, Sir Francis (ed.), 1950, *Charles Darwin's Autobiography*. New York: Henry Schuman. 266 pp.

Elkin, A. P., 1933, *Studies in Australian Totemism*. ("Oceania Monographs," No. 2.) Sydney. 131 pp.

Evans-Pritchard, E. E., 1940, *The Nuer: A Description of the Modes of Livelihood and Political Institutions of a Nilotic People*. Oxford: Clarendon Press. 271 pp.

Firth, Raymond, 1929, *Primitive Economics of the New Zealand Maori*. London: G. Routledge & Sons; New York: E. P. Dutton & Co. 505 pp.
1939, *Primitive Polynesian Economy*. London: G. Routledge & Sons. 387 pp.
1946, *Malay Fishermen: Their Peasant Economy*. London: Kegan Paul, Trench, Trubner & Co. 354 pp.

Forde, C. D., 1934, *Habitat, Economy and Society: A Geographical Introduction to Ethnology*. London: Methuen & Co.; New York: Harcourt, Brace & Co. 500 pp.

Gayton, A. H., 1946, "Culture-Environment Integration: External References in Yokuts Life," *Southwestern Journal of Anthropology*, II, 252-68.

Gillin, John, 1952, "Ethos and Cultural Aspects of Personality," pp. 193-222 in Sol Tax (ed.), *Heritage of Conquest*. Glencoe, Ill.: Free Press. 312 pp.

Herskovits, M. J., 1948, *Man and His Works*. New York: Alfred A. Knopf. 678 pp.
1952, *Economic Anthropology*. New York: Alfred A. Knopf. 547 pp.

Hogbin, H. I., 1939, *Experiments in Civilization: The Effects of European Culture on a Native Community of the Solomon Islands*. London: G. Routledge & Sons. 268 pp.

Kluckhohn, Clyde, and Leighton, Dorothea, 1946, *The Navaho*. Cambridge, Mass.: Harvard University Press. 258 pp.

Malinowski, Bronislaw, 1935, *Coral Gardens and Their Magic*. 2 vols. London: Allen & Unwin.

Mead, Margaret, 1940, *Mountain Arapesh. II. Supernaturalism*. ("Anthropological Papers," Vol. XXXIV, Part III.) New York: American Museum of Natural History.

Read, Margaret, 1938, *Native Standards of Living and African Culture Change*. (Supplement to *Africa*, Vol. XI, No. 3.) 56 pp.

Redfield, Robert, 1953, *The Primitive World and Its Transformations*. Ithaca, N. Y.: Cornell University Press. 185 pp.

Sears, P. B., 1950, *Charles Darwin: The Naturalist as a Cultural Force*. New York: Charles Scribner's Sons. 124 pp.

Spoehr, Alexander, 1949, *Majuro: A Village in the Marshall Islands*. ("Fieldiana: Anthropology," Vol. XXXIX.) Chicago: Chicago Natural History Museum. 266 pp.

Tax, Sol, 1941, "World View and Social Relations in Guatemala," *American Anthropologist*, XLIII, 27-42.
1953, *Penny Capitalism: A Guatemalan Indian Economy*. (Smithsonian Institution, Institute of Social Anthropology, Publication No. 10.) Washington, D. C.: Government Printing Office. 230 pp.

Tax, Sol (ed.), 1952, *Heritage of Conquest: The Ethnology of Middle America*. Glencoe, Ill.: Free Press. 312 pp.

Thurnwald, R., 1932, *Economics in Primitive Communities*. London: Oxford University Press. 314 pp.

Microcosm-Macrocosm Relationships in North American Agrarian Society[1]
John W. Bennett

(This article has been revised and updated by the author for inclusion in this book.)

An instance of the microcosm-macrocosm problem that merits close attention is to be found in the general structure of relationships between the North American rural community and the urban-based institutions and organizations of the national society. The system to be described here is most characteristic of highly developed rural areas where relative economic security has created a stable population as well as a society that is adapted both to agrarian life and to the urban institutions with which it must contend. In short, the description pertains to the contemporary direction of adaptive change in most sectors of North American rural society.

In the background lie several general theoretical issues. One concerns the nature of human ecology, or perhaps cultural ecology, as it has been called by anthropologists. Man, like other animals, uses natural phenomena, but only man cognitively transforms these phenomena into natural re-sources—takes Nature into his own world, so to speak. Human ecology thus includes data on how men use resources to obtain the things they need, but also, and perhaps even more importantly, the things they *want*. Human eco-logy incorporates a large component of *culture*, or the stylized patterns of wants, and also *adaptive strategies*, or the ways men manipulate Nature *and* human society itself, to achieve satisfaction. Reformation of abusive practices cannot be accomplished until the sociocultural aspects of human ecology are understood.

Another theoretical issue concerns the processes called modernization, economic development, and other terms. The variety and ambiguity of these definitions suggests that different phenomena are selected as representing the necessary or desirable directions of change. With respect to the patterns described in this paper, the issue is whether they represent a necessary outcome for rural-urban relations in other societies and regions. Linear theories of change and modernization have given way, in recent years, to recognition of the great diversity of pathways, and the conception of lawful and regular change has been modified by a recognition of the essen-tially historical nature of the process.[2] Our opinion is that anthropologists need to be more concerned with specific historical phenomena, and less with vague generalizations about culture change.

A third general issue concerns the problem of the vulnerability of the local community to influences radiating from bureaucratic institutions and the mass society. Here the linear *vs.* diversity problem is not directly involved; the issue is simply one of the degree of autonomy of the local community in the face of its necessity or its desire to accept urban culture and urban controls over its activities.[3]

Within social anthropology, these problems have been especially impor-tant in the study of what are sometimes called "complex societies,"[4] a term whose meaning is vague, for it moves between criteria of contemporaneity or antiquity on the one hand and indices of social complexity or simplicity on the other. Clearly a more analytic definition is needed, and perhaps the most appropriate one for this paper is offered by the basic problem of some of the studies of contemporary small communities made by anthropologists. In these studies, the central issue has come to be the extent of the involvement of the society with the external institutions of urban and national locus. The community is seen not as a tribal isolate, but as a population nucleus that owes much of its continuing existence to its dealings with the outside. There is the suggestion here, to be elaborated later, that a "complex society" is simply any society that is composed of segments that differ ecologically; in their internal structures, or in respective power, but that nevertheless depend on each other for resources and must regularly transact business.

In many studies of such societies, there appears to be an implicit assumption of the domination of the local community by the external system. There are a number of different versions of this viewpoint. Rural sociologists on the whole continue to extol the advantages of the "family farm", in the face of a diminishing rural population and a shift to large commercial agricultural enterprises.[5] Anthropologists interested in modern rural communities have tended to view the community as an isolate, subject to acculturation by the larger national society and culture.[6] Agrarian radicals have seen the farmer and rural townsman as a victim of exploitative external interests; in fact, this view eventually lead populist and populist-socialist parties—like the Cooperative Commonwealth Federation (now New Democratic Party) of Saskatchewan—into electoral victories and a measure of control of these "exploitative" urban institutions.

Another older tradition of analysis, that represented by Redfield's distinctions between the tribal, peasant, and farming societies, perceived the problem in somewhat different terms. Here the differences were viewed as typological: tribalists were isolated, autonomous societies; peasantries were partly autonomous; farmers were nonautonomous, being wholly involved in a national socioeconomic and cultural system.[7] The idea of "impact" was not stressed, since the differences were viewed not as part of change processes, but rather as the consequences of historical differences; that is, the end-points of change were accepted as types. Redfield did concern himself, however, with the problem of the relationships of the local community to the outside in his own research and in his appreciations of the work of others on India, Norway, and other world areas.

In arriving at a description of the North American situation, we have attempted to rethink these propositions concerning community autonomy and linearity of change processes. With respect to the first, we have observed that many of the "impact" theorists have failed to consider the fact that members of rural communities have *desired* closer contact with the urban-national society and culture, and that their institutions were formed with this contact in view from the beginning; that is, the "loss" of autonomy was not necessarily a loss from their viewpoint, but simply the continuation of desired trends. Here, the "impact" model gives way to a model of developmental change. Second, we have observed that even granting a certain loss of autonomy, this is not total but partial; that is, the local social system retains many of its "traditional" institutions and utilizes these to manipulate and control the external forces. This suggests that the evolving structure of North American rural society is describable not by any one theory of change, but by parts of many. In the most general sense, the concept of adaptive behavior would appear the most useful: it is neutral with respect to preferred or assumed directions of change, and it thrusts the responsibility for determining the direction of change, in part at least, upon the members of the society under study. That is, the observer is required to analyze the local institutions not only from his own or some external theoretical viewpoint, but from the standpoint of the goals and strategies of the local people. We believe that the processes called "modernization," with respect to the "underdeveloped countries," should likewise be viewed in this context.[8]

Source of Data Presented

The generalizations in this paper are illustrated with examples from the writer's research on the social and economic development of the 4,700-square-mile "Jasper" region of the province of Saskatchewan, Canada, a study having as its most generalized objective that of testing certain cultural-ecological propositions in a contemporary agrarian setting.[9] The particular facts that prompted the investigation of microcosm-macrocosm relationships became evident in the first field season, during work on a preliminary classification of the modes of production, social communities, and cultural styles of the regional population. In this work, it became evident that the autonomy of the various subcommunities varied greatly in terms of cultural styles and preferences, modes of production, transportation and communication facilities, and geographical location. In the region studied, there are two major modes of production: cattle-grain farming on relatively small land areas and straight cattle ranching on relatively large tracts. The populations pursuing these modes of production are, in several districts, contiguous or intermixed; they use the same roads and service centers; both are broadly attuned to the processes of market economy. However, the farmers are urbanized in the sense of enthusiastically involving themselves in politics and in the political struggle for natural resources, and stress literacy and higher education for their children; whereas many of the ranchers avoid all of these, enter politics out of necessity rather than love, and deal with external agencies at arm's length, preferring to manage their own enterprises in traditional ways.

The region also contains several colonies of Hutterian Brethren (Bennett 1967), and these people completely withdraw from politics—local and national—and are alien to local cultural styles. However, they are at the same time at home in the market economy of agriculture, owing to the large and profitable scale of their operations. All three of these groups—farmers, ranchers, and Hutterites—are "farmers" in the typological sense, yet they fall along a continuum of involvement and noninvolvement in the external institutional system (Bennett 1969, Fig. 10.1, p. 310).

Of course farmers, like peasants, must deal with the outside world in order to obtain the resources they need. We have just mentioned their entrance into politics in order to influence the allocation of resources. Such activity has several functions: it serves to attract favors to the local community; it wards off undesirable consequences of legislation; and it also opens up new arenas of choice for local people. Thus, the local community is not simply vulnerable to outside forces, and indices of urban *cultural* dominance are often irrelevant with respect to the distribution of power and the ability of the local community to handle its own affairs. A local society can accept its taste standards from the outside, yet keep its internal system of social relations; it can seem to accept the regulations of government bureaus, yet quietly modify these in application and circumvent their effects. Growing prosperity, brought about by increasing adherence to modern economic procedures, can finance the revival of local tradition and forms of social interaction. This process is actively under way in many districts of the Great Plains, where, for example, country people are purchasing the old schoolhouses, abandoned in the school centralization program, and making them the focus of revived country neighborhood social networks. The flight of young people from the farm is not necessarily a symptom of the breakdown of rural culture, but can be viewed as an orderly out-migration from a rural society with an adapted population-resources ratio. E. H. Bell (1942) observed these reconstructive social tendencies in a Kansas community over two decades ago.

The point can be made in another way *via* a critique of the familiar terms "urban" and "rural." These terms reflect 19th- and early 20th-century ecological patterns, based upon poorly developed transportation and communication and upon the incomplete absorption of the agricultural economy into the national framework. By the mid-20th century, the incorporation of rural society, at least in terms of its traditional definitions, is close to completion. Hence the terms are misleading. However, it is our view that the incorporative tendencies in styles of life and economy do not necessarily mean that developed agrarian society is merely a suburb. Its agrarian basis means that it must continue to deal with agencies that are geographically and culturally distant, and that operate by rules differing considerably from those that may characterize the local social system. In spite of the cultural and economic synthesis of rural and urban, there remains a pattern of interaction between microcosm and macrocosm, between developed agrarian world and industrial-bureaucratic world. It is this pattern of interaction that concerns us here.

As we noted earlier, this has implications for the definition of the term "complex society." The complex society is one in which relationships between local units and urban-based organizations are subject to constant readjustments; this process of readjustment is what makes the society "complex." In more concrete terms, it describes a system in which the local person cannot make decisions on local terms exclusively, but must consider the wishes and demands of people outside of his local system. In this sense, "complex societies" are not new, but have existed since the Bronze Age, and anthropologists have studied them all along without knowing it. One can visualize the irrigation farmer in a Mesopotamian community, or a British farmer in the 18th century, alike coping with water masters, tax collectors, grain agents, landlords, and the politicians—and much as their descendants in 20th-century North America cope with similar functionaries and agents.

The Interaction of Local and External Frames in Resources Allocation

The survival of agriculture in almost any region of North America, but most especially in the specialized areas like the Great Plains, has depended upon the willingness of government and private sources to supply needed resources. Among these resources are credit, crop deficiency payments, marketing facilities, irrigation, grazing land, emergency livestock feeding, grants and allowances of all kinds for enterprise build-up, and many others. In the Jasper region, a Canadian government agency (the Prairie Farm Rehabilitation Act— now retitled Office for Regional Economic Development) in the late 1930s, toward the close of a devastating decade of drought and depression, began to appropriate land abandoned by homesteaders or ranchers and finance the development of community pastures. This helped local farmers to buttress their failing grain economy with livestock production. The PFRA later established a large community irrigation scheme and innumerable small private water-development projects. The provincial government in the 1940s supplied the means to permit farmers to obtain a grazing lease and to establish grazing cooperatives, in effect cooperative ranches. In the late 1930s the federal government also established the Prairie Farm Assistance Act, which provides bonuses for crop yields—grain and forage—when they fall below certain minima because of drought. In the years preceding all these developments, federal and provincial governments had encouraged and facilitated the growth of cooperatives, including the massive Wheat Pool and the Federal Wheat Board. Improved credit facilities, made available both by the local branch offices of the big eastern banks and by the federal and provincial governments, have greatly assisted the younger farmers and ranchers in their effort to establish a new enterprise or to refinance their fathers'.

One general result of all these developments, and others not mentioned, has been the movement of certain blocks of land out of private and individual tenure and into government ownership, with allocation to producers in the form of lease, use-tenure, or collective-use management. This process has been necessary in the West because of the maldistribution of scarce and variable resources: only by reserving certain areas for special use, which permits people to use them regardless of their actual place of residence, or by bringing the fluid resource, water, to the site of a man's operation, can these resources be distributed at all equitably.

Another result of the intervention of government and of general economic pressures has been a more rational distribution of modes of production in accordance with the location of particular resources. This has been accompanied by great changes in the density and distribution of population and by a generally reduced population, better adapted to the land's ability to support it under changing economic parameters. The country neighborhood has disappeared or else has become greatly enlarged, as country school districts disappear and as better roads and cars permit people to maintain social contacts over wider areas.

These are all major changes, and they have required adjustments on the part of the local people. At the same time, the entire program, with only a few exceptions, was advocated by a majority of the rural population of Saskatchewan, and the great majority of Jasper people views the changes as desirable. The acquirement of a particular program from the government agencies always required local pressure on legislative representatives and other "cultural brokers" [10] who intervened on behalf of the localities—these favors are not distributed without such local action anywhere in North America, or in the world, since funds are always less than the amount required to meet all possible needs. Thus Jasper's social and economic improvements required an entrance into politics on the part of its residents, a new series of problems, and a new set of changes to accommodate. Clearly the reconstruction of the local institutional system involved the community in a far more intimate engagement with the national society and with government agencies than it may have dreamed of in pioneer days, only one generation before the beginning of the program in the 1930s.

The Allocation of Resources

The process of resource allocation and acquirement always has two facets: (1) rules governing access to resources of all kinds laid down by external agencies, public and private; and (2) mechanisms for controlling the distribution of resources inside the community, once acquired. These two aspects of the process are found in all agrarian communities, regardless of their level of social and economic development. In peasant societies, the agencies are usually represented by landlords, tax collectors, and kindred figures, often with exploitative motives. In North American communities, government bureaus and private banks are generally more important, although in areas where tenancy is common the landlord also appears on the scene. Tenancy was insignificant in the Jasper region, but substantial portions of land—nearly all grazing land—are held in government tenure and leased to the agricultural operators on a use-right basis. Irrigation water and plots developed by the government were also leased or sold to users. Forests were similarly controlled, and credit was obtainable either from private sources or from government agencies. In our research, it was found necessary to spend considerable time with these various agencies in order to determine the methods of allocation.

The bureaucratic rules and local mechanisms of resource allocation in North America are given a uniform basis by the institution of private entrepreneurship. The agricultural enterprise is a *private place*: its resources, at least for the duration of the operator's tenure, are considered to be his property; or, even if they are given to him on a use-right basis, as in the case of leased grazing land and irrigation plots, he is relatively secure in his possessory rights for an indefinite period. It is the entrepreneur's right—and also his responsibility—to manage them in such a way as to provide both a living and profits. The "responsibility" element is relatively recent: it reflects a movement toward a conservationist doctrine, which emerged in the later generations of enterprise control when it became apparent that the exploitative policies of frontier years were wasteful of resources. [11] The responsibilities of private operators to husband resources are spelled out in most of the documents concerning the shared use of land and water, usually in the form of sanctions in the event that a man is known to be abusive or wasteful. These sanctions can cause serious resentment of government regulations by local persons who adhere to the earlier individualistic "rights" facet of the value system.

In any event, the local community will exercise a certain amount of control of its own over the allocation of resources, and also over the bureaus that regulate their availability and use. Locally, this control is characteristically distributed by status and power differentials, or in cabals and combinations that exert pressure on local magnates for favors. Control over the bureaus is exerted through consultations with legislative representatives, who then intercede on behalf of their constituents with the appropriate agencies. Another element of control over the bureaus, and one that fuses with external local aspects of allocation, is found in the frequent attempts to provoke the bureaus into investigating and punishing local people who have violated regulations in an effort to acquire these resources. Competition for resources in the local community is thus deeply bound up with the community's relations with government agencies, and some of the hostility generated in local competition can be focused outside of the community, onto the bureau.

Instrumental Relations in the Local Community
In most North American agrarian communities, the institution of private property and entrepreneurship is both cause and effect of the following series of characteristic values. [12]

(1) To help oneself is the best thing; but if you are down and out, others should give you a hand.

(2) A man should be a good neighbor—he should help his friend when it is needed.

(3) A man should get all he can—that is his right—but at the same time he should not trample on his neighbor's rights to the same things.

(4) Competition is good, but one should not be too ruthless. Some people lose out in competition, and then the winners have some kind of obligation to give them a hand.

(5) Independence is a good thing, but people can be a little *too* independent.

(6) The government should help people, but those who take too much are simply lazy.

(7) Everyone is equal, but some get ahead faster.

In these ambivalent or qualified values, there is recognition of inequality, even though strong emphasis is placed on equality; the consequences of individualism are softened by the emphasis on the obligation of the "haves" to help the "have nots." Cooperation is upheld; but so is competition, although its possible evil effects are recognized. The government is a source of benefits, but it is felt that this can also sap vital entrepreneurial fiber.

This type of value system is associated with a particular type of social system. We shall select three catchwords—individualism, egalitarianism, and particularism—and refer to the instrumental social system they define by their initial letters: IEP. The first two properties—individualism and egalitarianism—are explicit or public aspects of the system, while the third—particularism—is an implicit or covert aspect. We may describe these three characteristics in detail.[13]

Individualism refers to the tendency in these North American societies to regard the individual as responsible for his acts and achievements. It also emphasizes the acquisition of property by the individual and his right to control that property. Natural resources are considered to be "owned" by individuals, or at least under their control once assigned. As already noted, there is often resistance to or only partial acceptance of the idea that such ownership and control entail conservationist responsibility.

"Individualism" also can be used to describe the behavior of people with strong cooperative leanings who act in concert when the individual can benefit from such action. However, in North American agrarian societies, such cooperation can diminish when a level of prosperity is reached that permits the individual to satisfy his wants without joint action. This is a classic process and has been the despair of liberal politicians in both Canada and the United States for many years. The farmer can be counted upon to espouse cooperative-collective principles when he is in trouble, but he votes individualist-conservative when he is out of it.[14]

Egalitarianism refers to the tendency to conceive of the ultimate outcome of social and economic evolution as a society of equals. In this ideal state, everyone would have the same resources. In expectation of this outcome, people today should be treated as equals, with at least the potential of success. Because this view is less applicable today than it was in the pioneer period, elaborate rationalizations of existing or growing inequality have come to characterize these IEP societies. Individualistic striving has brought about inequality: a society that tries to have both experiences considerable stress.

Particularism refers to the tendency for individuals to conduct private arrangements with each other, for the acquiring or the sharing of scarce resources. The individualistic element in the instrumental social system opens the way to private deals and manipulations; and because the eventual outcome of these is inequality, particularistic behavior becomes a covert aspect of the IEP social system.

At the same time, particularistic patterns serve the ameliorative end of helping the losers, or the less fortunate individuals, to obtain a share of the rewards. Consequently, these "ruggedly individualistic" societies also develop various forms of paternalism: the big farmer or rancher giving his less fortunate neighbors a job, or a piece of land, or a loan, often expecting loyalty and docility in return.

The net effect of this system of instrumental relations is to distribute resources unevenly, but to make up for part of this inequality by ameliorative actions or by built-in checks against overly aggressive competition. The system has contradictions between values and actuality, but generally these conflicts either are not very serious or are continuously resolved to such an extent that serious protest does not develop. In the history of agrarian protest movements in North America,[15] the major action has been taken against *external* institutions and organizations that control access to markets and resources. Deprivation has been felt more acutely in this sphere than in the purely local one of socioeconomic differentiation or exploitation. There are, of course, instances of expropriation and outrageous perpetuation of privilege, but these tend to be the exceptions. In most of the Great Plains regions, the effects of drought and economic depression were far greater than the consequences of local rapacity.

The Regulations of Government Bureaus

The external agencies that regulate resource availability and use are bureaucratic organizations of a standard type: their procedures may be described as universalistic (equally applicable to everyone) and lawful (formulated by legislatures or accredited administrations and sanctioned in law). Such rules are written down and circulated in printed form. If the rules are violated, sanctions are applied. Action will be taken on individual requests and applications only if the correct procedures are followed. Presumably impartial inspectors will be used to discover if affairs in the community are going according to regulation, and information received from members of the community is not ignored. Impartial hearings are held to determine the facts in cases of violation or on petitions for redress or modification of regulations.

The ideal of universalism is, of course, not always followed in practice. Exceptions are made to the rules; and as exceptions accumulate, within the bureaus various covert or informal policies develop that often differ from the printed regulations. This does not mean that the bureaus are necessarily "corrupt"; the development of exceptional policies can proceed in an entirely rational manner, in the interests of the local people and not necessarily in tune with particularistic privilege. It is simply that in the course of interaction between community and bureau, adjustments are constantly being made to accommodate local needs, or are being extracted from the bureau by local combinations and manipulations.

Now, as we have already implied, the system of instrumental relations in most North American agrarian communities differs from the ideal bureaucratic principles just described. Particularistic connections and aims are taken into account in distributing rewards and in dealing with the bureaus. The individual's position in his community and his kin group play important roles in his successes and failures, and it is often precisely these features that the bureaus, in their impersonal, universalistic regulations, are usually supposed to ignore in their assignment of resources.

Some examples will be helpful at this point. We will cite cases from our data on the Jasper region in which the universalistic rules of the bureaus and the characteristics of an IEP system of instrumental relations interact with varying consequences.

(1) *Conflict between universalistic rules and individualistic patterns.* This can occur when an individual believes his water right entitles him to take as much as he wants at any time of the year, whereas the right specifies only so much during the spring flood season. Regulatory agencies are empowered to penalize him if he continues to assert his "right" to water, since his indiscriminate use deprives others.

(2) *Conflict between universalistic rules and particularistic patterns.* When a man pastures cattle that do not belong to him on his own lease, in order to repay an obligation, he violates regulations that permit him to pasture only his own cattle. He will be penalized unless special permission is negotiated, *in which case we also have* (2a) *a case of modification of the universalistic rules to accommodate local particularistic practices.*

(3) *Recognition of particularism by incorporation in the universalistic*

rules. A case in point would be a procedural regulation in the process of grazing lease assignment requiring the bureau, when investigating the suitability of an operator for assignment, to "take into account his reputation as an operator in the community"—along with other factors, of course.

(4) *Reinforcement of individualistic patterns by the universalistic rules.* Tax laws permit assembling a "basic herd" of cattle, which are tax free and are treated as capital, not income. This strengthens the individual entrepreneurship system of stock farming or ranching. Another example would include the insistence, noted in (2), on the use of lease land by the lessee only, and the rule forbidding him to let others use his land, except on special dispensation. This example also illustrates *the characteristic conflict or contradiction that often develops between individualistic and particularistic patterns.*

(5) *Reinforcement of egalitarian patterns by universalistic rules.* A case is found in systems of resource utilization in which every individual obtains equal shares: e.g., a watershed with irrigation plots allocated equally among applicants; or the settlement by the government of disputes by individuals over resources in such a way that everyone gets equal shares, as in an over-developed watershed in which individual water rights are abrogated and new irrigation schemes developed by this every user gets an equal or fair share.

Aside from these patterns of interaction, which differ by issue, there are more general tendencies. It is important to recognize that local people do not necessarily accept the bureaucratic regulations passively, but actively seek to modify or reinterpret them in order to extract personal and group benefit. This general procedure is conceived of as legitimate by most of the bureaus, although at the same time it borders on behavior defined in North American culture as illegal or unethical. To take a single example from our Jasper data, the regulations governing the assignment of grazing leases by the government specify that anyone who has certain qualifications is entitled to a lease. Somewhat similarly, the local society holds, publicly, that every man is entitled to a lease. However, local competition and particularistic advantage may work so as to deny the less clever, aggressive, or efficient the lease they seek. Therefore the local people can utilize the regulations to justify their own courses of action. If a lease is assigned to someone who is regarded as already having his share of this particular resource, the local people can say that the bureau is violating the local egalitarian norm—even though the local system, in its use of political influence on the bureau, will also violate this norm.

Over time, this type of interaction means that the universalistic regulations of the bureaus tend to be modified, usually in an informal context, in the direction of local particularism. We diagram the process below. Actually the process may occur in cycles: during a particular governmental regime, the system tends to become increasingly complex or "corrupt"; this is followed by a reform, usually introduced by a new government, and a new set of regulations are formulated that then begin to undergo the same process.

In the Jasper region, the process with respect to grazing land was studied over a period of two generations. The earlier Liberal government of Saskatchewan tended to favor the larger ranchers, who held what was viewed by the smaller ranchers and farmers as a disproportionate share of the land. When the Cooperative Commonwealth Federation (CCF) government took office, a new leasing system was inaugurated, with tighter rules; and parts of the large leases were detached from the ranches and given over to farmers, usually as grazing cooperatives. Ranchers who did not maintain their leases or live up to regulations were deprived of their land, when it became possible to do so, or warned. Thus the initial CCF policies led to a somewhat more equitable distribution of resources. This was aided by intense local action on the part of the farmers, who used all available political means and pressure to obtain what they felt was their share.

As time passed, the larger ranchers and a few farmers (some of them the

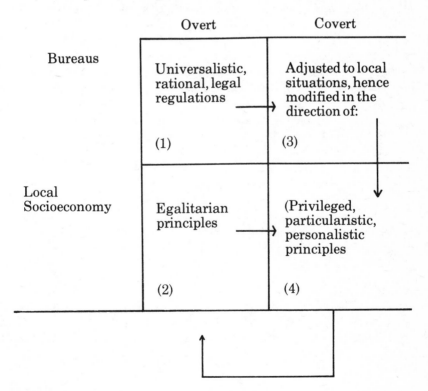

earlier beneficiaries of the new regime) began to exert pressure on the government to leave the land situation alone and not to press for further redistribution. This was reinforced by the government's recognition, in its increasing tendency to honor economic efficiency and productivity, that the larger operations were more efficient. Thus tolerance developed toward the larger or at least more productive operators. This also meant that the larger operators could resume some of their local practices of paternalism and favor-granting to the smaller.

In the early years of the new regulations, acquiring a lease open for application was simply a matter of writing an application and sending this to the bureau, where it was considered strictly on merit. Later, as complex personal and political relations developed between the government and the local people, obtaining a lease was not so simple, but required considerable interaction. The right people had to be notified; some persons were not viewed as qualified for a lease, and pressure would be exerted to have the government disqualify their applications; the bureau would informally consult local people as to the suitability of certain candidates; criteria of efficient operation could be weighed more heavily than the regulations suggested; and so on. "Deserving" young ranchers or farmers, apprenticed or paternalized by important local people, would have considerable pressure exerted in their favor in order to supply them with a lease (or with credit, water, etc.).

In only one or two cases was there evidence of outright finagling, with definitely unqualified persons acquiring the needed resources. Most of the instances in which local criteria were imposed on the bureau were "honest," insofar as the people receiving the benefit were in a position to use it. The point is not corruption or dishonesty, but the gradual substitution of particularistic frames for universalistic.

Strategic Response to External Factors

We may turn now to a more analytic approach to the strategies employed by local people in their dealings with the external agencies that regulate their access to resources. From the standpoint of local people, the external factors are divided into three major categories:

(1)   *Regulations* or rules that control resources, and social, economic, and political action within the local community. Examples are the laws governing: inheritance or the taxing of inheritances, the leasing of government land, or the conditions under which petitions can be directed toward government agencies.

(2)   *External resources* that the local community can utilize for its own benefit. Examples are agricultural credit, annuities purchasable from government or private companies, assistance in the development of water resources.

(3)   *Forces* or patterns of change in prices and costs or in national

political climates that may influence the local scene, in the sense of providing basic conditions of action or outcome.

It is important to note that these external factors do not always work together. For example, the resources in (2) include things that are offered to the community by the government in order to make up for losses or paradoxes imposed on the community by some of the "forces" in (3). An example is the extension of credit to young farmers to enable them to start out with adequate capitalization, this necessity being forced upon them by generally rising economic values. The regulations in (1) are sometimes in conflict with the forces in (3), and there is often a characteristic lag in the revision procedure. These phasic maladjustments are seen by the local people as part of the environment in which they must make their living and acquire their resources; hence their strategies of adjustment involve attempts to influence change.

All agrarian societies are of course vulnerable to economic change, for they require relatively stable conditions in order to accumulate capital. This is the principal reason why the agricultural sectors of North American societies experience recurrent crises. The rising needs for increased education, capital, machinery, and general productivity impose a severe burden upon families who mainly seek security and economic continuity at relatively low levels of savings and investment. Agricultural economy is vulnerable to variability because it has difficulty accumulating sufficient capital to finance the next level of production. Great Plains agriculture has experienced these contradictions in acute form, and it is therefore no surprise that the most vigorous agrarian protest movements emerged in that geographical region. It is also in these regions that the most complex interactions between the local rural society and the government bureaus have developed, for a general shortage of resources introduces exceptional needs for government financing of resource development.

Games-Playing

Therefore the local society must develop a system of strategies for acquiring its needed resources, and also for controlling the external agencies that provide them. In very general terms, we can consider these strategies from the standpoint of two "models." The first of these is that of a game of skill or chance. The agricultural operator can behave as if he were involved in a game, with the external factors as players or as cards in the hands of an opponent. Such a game would be full of opportunities, but would also have traps and penalties for the unwary and uninformed. Some operators would be highly skilled at the game, would consider it to be a necessary and normal part of existence; others would regard it as an unfortunate imposition from the outside.[16]

In the Jasper study, this was the principal difference between farming and ranching cultures: farmers saw the game with the government and the market as a condition of doing agriculture in a modern world. Ranchers were more inclined to externalize and resent the factors and forces—these were *impositions*, not simply conditions. Whereas the farmer has been trained in the world of marketing pools and political action, the rancher tends to avoid such interlinked systems. He adheres to views that stress the isolation of the local community: he insists on dealing with private cattle buyers who come directly to his ranch and inspect the cattle; he resists methods of sale where the animals are shipped out and impersonally evaluated, as they would be in a pooled marketing system or in "rail grading" and other existing systems. The farmer is willing to play the game by making the required moves in a known sequence; the rancher resists being "told" how to do things—he prefers his own rules. The farmer writes letters and arranges appointments with government officials in order to get what he wants; the rancher may do likewise, but not as often and usually with reluctance—he prefers to remain aloof, to play the game at a distance or with minimal investment. He wants all he can get, but he will sometimes take less in order to maintain what he defines as autonomy.

These differences are related also to the nature of the representation of the external agencies in the local community. For the farmer, the "players" in the game are usually on hand: the local agricultural extension agent, the soil conservation man, and others. These "brokers" of course have limited powers; they are often little more than channels of information and administrators of application forms—but they do constitute an element of authority that can be used to obtain resources. The rancher has less business to discuss with these people than the farmer because the operation of ranching does not involve the same things. He does not "bank" his soil; he may need to do relatively little in the way of specialized conservation and development; and his principal contacts with the external world are with meat packers and stockyards, always located at a distance from his ranch. The cattle buyer, who comes to the rancher directly, a mark of pride on the part of the independent cattleman, is therefore the principal agent of the external system. All of these things mean that the rancher is more inclined than the farmer to dichotomize internal and external. The external factors are, in a sense, "built into" farming culture in a way they are not in ranching.

On the other hand, in the case of the Hutterian colonies, the institutionalized features of the market economy are not built in at all. They are simply learned as behavioral strategies, and they are not permitted to modify the general culture. Hutterites rarely pull strings or exert pressure, partly because they do not have to, owing to their relative prosperity. However, they do require information, and they are indefatigable information-seekers, hanging around the government agencies and places of business, picking up the latest word on policy, bargains, or available resources. They seek to compete with local operators and to "get there first," but they are barred by their beliefs from entering into "deals" and local interactional networks that influence resource allocation. They are also uninvolved in the complex influence-channeling from the local community to the government bureaus in the capital, partly because as corporative entities they are legally barred from sharing in many of the benefits, and partly because this type of action involves them in politics, which is barred by their religious beliefs. As noted, their relative success is due in the main to their efficient and large-scale economic operation, which makes them excellent credit risks and can cushion losses they might sustain owing to their inability to "get in on the ground floor."

To return to the "games-playing" model, we may now list the functions of the external system of factors and some possible responses by the local agricultural operators:

The external system:

(1) *Sets limits or establishes conditions under which things can or must be done.* For example: income tax deduction and depreciation rules.

(2) *Establishes specific penalties for not doing things according to rule.* For example: taxing a "tax-free" gift of land if the giver dies within three years after the gift has been made. (Even more specific would be legal penalties for falsifying information, as on income tax.)

(3) *Takes action, or settles issues, when the local system is inactive.* For example: automatically applying estate laws when a man dies intestate.

(4) *Provides opportunities of which the local agriculturalist can take advantage.* For example: loans, tax deductions, reducing liability by incorporation of the family farm.

The local operator:

(1) *Accepts limits, conditions and penalties set by the external system, and follows them.* Example: accepting the partnership laws and settling up a family farm operation.

(2) *Takes the external rules and penalties and manipulates them to the best local advantage.* Example: combining legal features of a corporation and a partnership in creating an ideal family-farm operation.

(3) *Changes local customs to conform with the external system.* Example: ceasing to pasture a relative's cattle on one's own lease land, because regulations forbid it; hence modifying kinship obligations.

(4) *Exerts pressure on the external system to change it in accordance*

with local customs. Example: exertion of political influence, such as local pressure to secure an irrigation scheme from the government.

From the standpoint of the local agricultural operators, the external system takes on some of the characteristics of a powerful card-player, who has the stakes but who is not always attentive to the game, nor even particularly concerned about winning—only about following the rules. Hence if one knows the rules, the big player can be manipulated into losing, that is, into providing resources. Moreover, the big player even permits this to be done, if he is in one of his tolerant or benevolent moods (administrations). In any case, whether the local player is "for" or "against" government and bureaucracy, it is in his own interest to learn the rules and play the game.

This latter fact may be the point on which change differentials in many North American agrarian communities turn. Many Jasper people feared that if they adopted the point of view of the external agencies they would lose their own values. The ranchers took this position most emphatically: their political conservatism was basically a resistance to external frames of reference and a desire to retain individual autonomy, not resistance to the idea of government aid and benefits—which they always accepted when no strings were attached. Farmers, on the other hand, were generally less fearful of culture change and intervention because they forged their own economy in the context of interaction with government, hence could adopt the point of view characteristic of this world with little strain. It is true, of course, that ranchers are business-oriented in the sense that they produce for the market, are sharp traders, and are favorably impressed by the meat industry. But they reject the distant urban world, the impersonal bureau and regulations; hence they tend also to generalize about external influences as potentially disruptive.

Adaptation

While the games-playing model has some applicability to the situation, its assumptions of motivations are overly specific, since it implies that the operator behaves in a cool, detached fashion, figuring out his own moves and the moves of the opponent. A more generalized frame of reference is needed, and this can be furnished, we believe, by the concept of *adaptation* (Bennett 1969; 1970).

The inherent vagueness of this term, when applied to human behavior, must be acknowledged at the outset. The phrase, "man adapts" can mean: (a) tolerance of existing conditions; (b) adjustments to changed conditions; (c) long-term evolutionary change. Thus, the same term can refer to conformity or to innovation; to minor adjustments or to maximal alterations; to purposive action or unconscious drift. A concept with such breadth of meaning seems of little use; it is necessary to define it for specific purposes.

For ours, the term refers to the changes men make to accommodate their wants; their changing awareness of environmental resources (including human society as a resource); and the changes in these resources and the total milieu (including those changes resulting from past "adaptive" actions). That is, our conception is focused on action behavior: doing things, allocating and obtaining resources; making arrangements to use resources and to change their productivity; satisfying wants by changes in resource use and allocations. All such actions can be conscious or unconscious, and they always take place through time, which in itself becomes an important variable in the outcome. Such actions also take place in an environment which is typically complex, consisting both of natural phenomena and human intentions, behavior, and institutions.

We have found it convenient to distinguish between adaptive strategies and adaptive processes. The former represent those courses of action selected by people in order to satisfy their wants and obtain the resources to do so; such strategies exist at many levels of consciousness and over varying periods of time, and require careful definition for particular situations. Adaptive processes refer, in the main, to the long-term consequences of following particular strategies, and are generally conceptualized by the observer—a "scientific" conclusion. In this paper, the techniques used by agriculturalists to find resources and to allocate them in the community are all examples of strategies. The way these actions and interactions with government bureaus work out over time to produce certain repetitive trends in allocative measures and manipulations are examples of processes.

Why is this ecology, and not simply social organization? We believe it is human ecology because it contains implications for the natural environment —and, in larger terms, for the entire milieu which includes man himself. Returning to our earlier comments: we believe that the study of human ecology must be concerned with human behavior and social, economic, and political phenomena, since it is through these various systems that man relates to environment. Turning this around, we seriously propose that the only relevant social science is an ecological social science.

There is, of course, an analogy between manipulations of external resource-giving agencies and responses to the natural environment. This analogy is not a simply literary one, as it has often been handled by social scientists unattuned to ecological viewpoints, but has genuine analytical power. Like the natural habitat, the external agencies can be considered as "givens" that the individual confronts in his instrumental actions. Like the natural environment, they can be modified to a degree, but always in the context of certain limited possibilities. Market prices and demand offer the most cogent examples: like the weather in a semiarid-variable habitat, the market fluctuates and is largely out of control of the agricultural operator, but by varying one's strategy of production, its variability can be turned to the advantage of the operator. The analogy can be pushed a bit further: farmers have been successful in bringing the market under a degree of control by organizing marketing schemes and holdout operations and by pushing for national price control and subsidy legislation. Likewise, water resources are brought under a degree of control by building dams, reservoirs, and irrigation schemes. However, in spite of the elaborate structure of market control, and in spite of all the efforts at controlling water resources, there remains uncertainty in both: international market fluctuations elude control of the farmer and his representatives; rainfall continues to defy all efforts to control it.

The point is that an adaptive process does not imply complete control —only partial control and also a change of some kind in order to accommodate to that portion of the system that remains out of control. Thus, agriculturalists also develop cultural patterns to accommodate the degrees of uncertainty and risk that continue to characterize the system. They cannot count upon bureaucrats completely, or on legislatures, or on markets, but must adapt to the possibility of failure in their efforts to manipulate all of these, and this can take the form of a withdrawal into local cultural patterns or an intensification of tradition, or the reverse of both.

All processes can be seen in contemporary North American rural communities, sometimes simultaneously, and in the same community. Population reduction in many rural communities may simply mean a reduction down to the adapted fraction, and this fraction often consists precisely of people who are urbanized in their tastes, "rural" in social organization, and, at the same time, impressively skillful at manipulating the external agencies that provide the resources. The Hutterites have a different combination: rural in tastes and communal-democratic in social organization; but they substitute efficiency and a clever use of information for manipulation.

The environmental analogy is useful, but like the games-playing model, has its limitations. While it is true that to some degree the natural environment can be manipulated and remolded to human purposes, it cannot really be *communicated* with. The external governmental and private agencies supplying scarce resources may be like the weather in some respects, but in others they are very different, since they can be talked to, persuaded, dealt with. Transactions within the cultural medium can be conducted with them; transactions with Nature are often "outside" culture; or rather, the natural factors must be transformed into cultural factors before "meaningful" interaction takes place;—which means that the natural factors are supplied with human agents who "speak" for them. Hence the process devolves back into the adaptive action system.

The adaptational frame of reference is obviously ideally suited to the agrarian scene; its relevance for other contexts of human action is a problem we shall not deal with in this paper. The important issue is that in agrarian problems the natural environment—"natural resources"—is an inescapable ingredient, and it is the ingredient which requires an adaptational frame. In dealing with human actions concerned with want-satisfaction in purely intra-cultural contexts the point of view is perhaps not so immediately relevant. However, the growing awareness of the extensive implications for the natural environment of all human affairs argues for the general utility and applicability of this scheme. Men are constantly engaged in molding the environment—natural and social—in order to achieve their ends, and this is, in fact, the broadest generalization one can make of human history in its entirety. The fact that the use of natural resources has been governed by intra-social concerns, and not by the condition of nature itself, is one more reason for incorporating an ecological frame in social science.

Conclusion

In the beginning we raised the question of the autonomy of the agrarian community in an increasingly interconnected world. We recognized the pervasive influence of the mass culture and the market economy, but proposed that this is only part of the story. We have generalized about the actions of the agriculturalists in controlling access to the resources they need for their enterprises, and have suggested that this process of allocation and distribution constitutes a meaningful frame of existence. The picture that emerges is more complex than the simplified one regretting the loss of "autonomy" or "independence." A more accurate understanding of the situation will recognize the existence of a process of adaptation in which the rural community is not necessarily at the mercy of the national bureaucracy, but in many instances manipulates it or evades its undesirable features.

In this situation, the ruralite retains considerable scope for movement, and there remain various alternatives of action. In one sense, these alternatives are increasingly of an instrumental character, as agricultural economy becomes more closely tied to the national system. At the same time, it should be remembered that the farmer has wanted it this way: the objective of profitable commercialization was a goal from the beginning of settlement in North America, and this has been the basic evolving frame of agricultural production in Western society since the 18th century. Not all agriculturalists are in agreement as to the extent and desirability of the adaptive changes necessary to accommodate this goal, but there is general agreement that one must find one's way within its context.

The "complex society," then, in the North American context, is one in which there is interplay between local and external, microcosm and macrocosm—not one in which a single center of power dominates the entire society. North American agrarian society retains this characteristic interplay, a combination of autonomy and cultural distinctiveness, with varying degrees of acceptance of externally derived frames. In the long run, it is not profitable to think of these external frames exclusively in terms of powerful cultural forces that sweep over the defenseless farmer and destroy his bucolic existence, or reduce village life to an endless round of television viewing with long-distance aerials. The process is not this simple; the agriculturalist continues, in varying degrees, to play the game in his own best interest. His tastes and interests are becoming increasingly urbanized, but these are not the only index of his cultural status. Also to be considered are his own strategies of response to the external system and his ability to extract from it the resources he needs and wants. His ability to exercise such strategies is one measure of his independence.

Postscript: 1971-72

Our work in Jasper lasted a decade: the original version of this article was based on the first two years (1962-63), and its republication coincided with our terminal activities (1971-72). In the early sixties, Jasperites had access to fewer financial resources than the people across the line—about half as much cash from government sources than for a comparable region in Montana. By the early seventies, the picture had changed: Federal government agricultural policies paralleled (though still not equalled) those of the U.S.: more credit, bonuses, and, for the first time, payments for *not* producing. All the resources and benefits described in the article were continued, and Jasperites continued to refine their skills at obtaining and allocating them. A new round of manipulation commenced, as the Liberal government of the Province lost once again to the NDP (former CCF). During the decade, a majority of Jasper enterprises passed into the hands of third and fourth generation successors: better educated, more cosmopolitan, and more inclined to exploit opportunities. In our period of observation, Jasper moved from the partly-developed post-frontier society to the accessible rural community—or nearly so. As it did, its nostalgia for the past increased, and there was no letup in the rodeos and pageants. Ranchers moved closer to the "farmer" style of politics; farmers moved closer to the "ranching" life style, as their cattle herds increased.

   Population continued to fall, since the cost of increased rural prosperity is fewer people. The number of agricultural enterprises dropped one-fourth, but an improvement in roads meant more travel and socializing. The Province was more urbanized, more affluent, due to industrial development and big grain sales, and the NDP government was struggling to revive "agrarian socialism" in a more prosperous and even more entrepreneurially-minded

farming population. But the old uncertainties remain, and one hopes, perhaps, that Jasper's old folkways will not wither, lest it loses the coping skills
needed in this high-risk environment.

Notes

1. The original version of this paper was presented to the Washington University Conference on the Anthropology of Complex Societies, held at Bromwoods Center, Washington University, February 1966. In revising it for its latest publication, I have concentrated on the text, and have modified the notes and references, in only two or three
cases.

2. See Moore 1963, also Hoselitz 1961, for general statements about theories of change
that stress alternative possibilities in processes of urbanization and industrialization.
Moore summarizes current thinking: "With regard to theories of the direction of change,
leaving aside the evaluation of change in terms of progress or decay, it is possible, as we
have seen, to view many or most of them not as competing generalizations but as
appropriate to different aspects of social systems."

3. In another context, this is analogous to the intellectual's concern with his own
autonomy in a mass society. See Stein 1960.

4. See Casagrande 1959 and, more recently, Gluckman and Eggan 1966 for the results
of conferences that deal with this issue. Eisenstadt's (1961) survey of "Studies of Complex Societies" and Frankenberg's (1966) review and analysis of British community
studies focus on the dilemmas that arise out of a desire to continue to study relatively
stable and closed societies, on the one hand, and also to study processes of change, on
the other. Eisenstadt emphasizes the social anthropological concern with social relations
and the mechanisms by which social behavior is regulated and social institutions maintained as items of analysis or models for use in "complex society." However, the issue of
what is "complex" is not discussed by him, as is noted by several discussants of his paper
(primarily Leach and Schneider). Leach notes that the inclusion of some societies as
complex and the exclusion or dismissal of others leave one in doubt of what is meant by
"complex."
    Frankenberg is explicit here: he is concerned with the social anthropologist as a
researcher in urban industrial society. The history and development of acculturation
studies in the United States provide still different implications for the meaning of "complex." The redefinition and modifications of the term "acculturation" have entailed the
increasing inclusion of all aspects of change. The movement has been one from concern
with trait-listing to concern with processes of change (Beals 1953, Keesing 1953) and
with networks of relationships and their transactional character (Wolf 1956, 1957;
Murphy 1964). As such, it involves increasing concern for the larger system in which the
society under analysis is found, a position that involves issues of "complexity" and
methodology (cf. Manners 1965).

5. Such nostalgia and assumptions about the family farm as a basic democratic institution formed the basis for the definitive study on rural life in Saskatchewan. See the
Royal Commission Reports on Agriculture and Rural Life (1956), particularly *Report
#10*, "The Home and Family in Rural Saskatchewan."
    J. C. Gilson (1962) makes the point that the continuation of the family farm is a
goal of public policy, supported by federal and provincial government policies in market-

ing and price supports. He quotes from two sources that illustrate the value-laden concept of "family farm":

> *The Family Farm*, a report of the subcommittee on family farms to the Committee on Agriculture, House of Representatives, 84th Congress, U.S.A. Government Printing Office, Washington, 1956. After issuing the following warning: "It is recognized that any discussion of the family-type farm is easily associated with affection and sentiment, and, perhaps, emotion, because of the long identity of this rural order with the fundamental values," the subcommittee goes on to observe that, "All students of the growth of the American civilization seem in agreement that the family farm established the economic foundation for the liberties and the enterprise, and the national conscience, that are the heritage of the United States," and further that "beyond all other notice and regard, the agricultural order in the family unit pattern [family farm] must be considered especially for the spiritual, social and political vitality it has contributed to our civilization." N. F. Keiser, in an article "An Analysis of the First Interim Report of the New House Subcommittee on family-size farms," *Journal of Farm Economics*, Vol. XXXVIII, Nov., 1956, page 1005, observes, "This emphasis on the importance of the family farm to the 'American heritage' is no doubt an attempt to rationalize the social and economic perpetuation of the family farm."

Also, see the research reported in Taylor and Jones 1964.

6. For examples with varying degrees of adherence to "impact" theory, see West 1945, Goldschmidt 1947, Vidich and Bensman 1958, Gallaher 1961. The methodological issues are discussed in Arensberg 1965.

7. Redfield (1956:27-31). See Dewey 1960 for a critique of the application of folk-urban ideas to modern rural society. It is possible that at one point in North American history the folk-urban continuum was applicable, for the rural communities were just beginning to emerge from a condition of relative isolation. The writer studied such a community in the early 1940s and used the folk-urban approach to analyze its changes (Bennett 1944).

8. On this point, see Dore 1965.

9. The region was named for its major service-center, the town of Jasper, a community of 2,500 and the largest settlement in the area. Two books on the study have been published to date (1971): Bennett 1967, on the Hutterian Brethren of the region; and Bennett 1969, a general survey of the entire study. A third and final volume, on social and economic adaptations of the ranch-farm population, is in preparation (1972).

10. For comparative studies of the "cultural broker" phenomenon, see Wolf 1956; also Barnes 1954, Mintz 1959, Kenny 1960.

11. Cf. the earlier definition of "complexity": a situation in which the individual acquires increasing need to consider the interests of other people who are not part of his own social world. The exploitative frontier was not part of the national society; in its third generation in the West it has become so. (For a critique of our concept of complex society, see Adams 1970, Chapter 2.)

12. Data on values were acquired from several sources: structured interview schedules, special interviews, participant research. Comparisons of the Jasper data were made with available materials from other rural studies. A specific comparative source of importance to the study, since so many of our informants were actually derived from the background he describes, is John K. Galbraith 1964.

13. The terms "particularism" and "universalism" are, of course, owed to Talcott Parsons.

14. See Lipset 1951 for the classic study of Great Plains progressivism in its most successful phase: the Cooperative Commonwealth Federation party of Saskatchewan. This party governed the province for 20 years under the banner of "socialism." Once in office, however, most of its economic policies followed those of its farmer constituents, who were pro-cooperative but anti-collectivist. By 1964, when the party lost to the Liberals, it has become an established bureaucracy about as left-wing as the New Deal. In June 1971, while this paper was being revised for reprint publication, the old CCF, now a nation-wide Canadian left-liberal "New Democratic Party", recaptured Saskatchewan from the Liberals in a landslide victory. While the rural population had much to do with this, the growing urban population of Saskatchewan, with its labor and consumer interests, also played a large role.

15. See Hicks 1931, Sharp 1948.

16. Discussions of strategies developed for such high-risk and high-uncertainty situations can be found in Bennett 1969 and 1963. The topic has received considerable attention from experimental social psychologists, but this type of research has little relevance to the practical situations confronted by agriculturalists. Economists also devote considerable effort to the analysis of risk (see, e.g., Schwartz 1959; "Research Conference on Risk . . . " etc. 1953), but their work is rather abstract, using as a model the maximizing enterprise. Few farmers are full-fledged maximizers; nearly all of them moderate the approach on the basis of the personal and cultural assessments of risk and consumption desires. (After this was written, some studies of risk in agrarian contexts by anthropologists have appeared e.g., Caucian 1967; Johnson 1971).

References

Adams, R. N. 1970. *Crucifixion by Power*. Austin, University of Texas Press.

Arensberg, C. 1965. The community as object as a sample. *Culture and community.* C. M. Arensberg and S. T. Kimball, New York, Harcourt, Brace.

Barnes, J. A. 1954. Class and committees in a Norwegian island parish. *Human Relations* 7:39-58.

Beals, R. 1953. Acculturation. *Anthropology today.* A. L. Kroeber, ed. Chicago, University of Chicago Press.

Bell, E. H. 1942. The culture of a contemporary rural community: Sublette, Kansas. Bureau of Agricultural Economics, *U.S.D.A., Rural Life Studies No. 2.* Washington, D.C.

Bennett, J. W. 1944. Cultural change and personality in a rural society. *Social Forces* 23:123-132.

———1963. Risk and rationality: aspects of behavioral adaptation in an arid-variable habitat. *Plains Anthropologist* 8-21.
———1967. *Hutterian Brethren: the agricultural economy and social organization of a communal people.* Stanford, Stanford University Press.
———1969. *Northern Plainsmen: Adaptive Strategy and Agrarian Life*. Chicago, Aldine Publ. Co.
———1970. *The significance of the concept of adaptation for contemporary sociocultural anthropology.* Tokyo, VIII Congress of Anthropological and Ethnological Sciences. Symposium VII: 237-241.

Caucian, F. 1967. *Stratification and Risk-Taking: A Theory Tested on Agricultural Innovation. American Sociological Review* 32:912-926.

Casagrande, J. B. 1959. Some observations on the study of intermediate societies. *Intermediate societies.* V. F. Ray, ed. American Ethnological Society, Proceedings.

Dewey, R. 1960. The rural-urban continuum: real but relatively unimportant. *American Journal of Sociology* 66:60-66.

Dore, R. P. 1965. On the possibility and desirability of a theory of modernization. *International Conference on the Problems of Modernization in Asia.* Asiatic Research Center, Korea University, Seoul, Korea.

Eisenstadt, S. N. 1961. Anthropological studies of complex societies. *Current Anthropology* 2:201-222.

Frankenberg, Ronald 1966. British community studies: problems of synthesis. *The social anthropology of complex societies.* Michael Banton, ed. New York, Frederick A. Praeger.

Galbraith, J. K. 1964. *The Scotch.* Boston, Houghton Mifflin.

Gallaher, A. 1961. *Plainville: fifteen years later.* New York, Columbia University Press.

Gilson, J. C. 1962. Strengthening the farm firm. *Agricultural Economics Bulletin No. 6 (April).* Winnipeg, University of Manitoba.

Gluckman, Max, and Fred Eggan 1966. Introduction. *The social anthropology of complex societies.* M. Banton, ed. New York, Praeger.

Goldschmidt, W. 1947. *As you sow.* New York, Harcourt, Brace.

Hicks, J. D. 1931. *The Populist revolt.* Minneapolis, University of Minnesota Press.

Hoselitz, Bert 1961. Tradition and economic growth. *Tradition, values and economic development.* Braibanti and Spengler, eds. Durham, Duke University Press.

Johnson, A. W. 1971. Security and Risk-Taking among Poor Peasants: A Brazilian case in G. Dalton (ed.) *Studies in Economic Anthropology.* Washington, D.C., American Anthropological Association.

Keesing, F. M. 1953. Culture change: an analysis and bibliography of anthropological sources to 1952. *Stanford Anthropological Series, No. 1.* Stanford, Stanford University Press.

Kenny, M. 1960. Patterns of patronage in Spain. *Anthropological Quarterly* 33:14-23.

Lipset, S. M. 1951. *Agrarian socialism.* Berkeley, University of California Press.

Manners, Robert A. 1965. Remittances and the unit of analysis in anthropological research. *Southwestern Journal of Anthropology* 21:179-195.

Mintz, S. W. 1959. Internal market systems as mechanisms of social articulation. *Intermediate societies.* V. F. Ray, ed. American Ethnological Society, Proceedings.

Moore, Wilbert E. 1963. *Social change.* Englewood Cliffs, N.J., Prentice-Hall.

Murphy, R. F. 1964. Social change and acculturation. *Transactions of the New York Academy of Sciences* 26:845-854.

Redfield, R. 1956. *The peasant society and culture.* Chicago, University of Chicago Press.

Research Conference on Risk and Uncertainty in Agriculture 1953. Sponsored by Agricultural Research Service, U.S.D.A., and Farm Foundation. Held at Bozeman, Montana. Issued in mimeographed report form.

Schwartz, C. 1959. *The search for stability*. (Contemporary Saskatchewan: I.) Toronto, McClelland & Stewart.

Sharp, P. F. 1948. *The agrarian revolt in western Canada*. Minneapolis, University of Minnesota Press.

Stein, Maurice R. 1960. *The eclipse of community*. New York, Harper and Row (Harper Torchbooks).

Taylor, L., and A. R. Jones 1964. *Rural life and urbanized society*. New York, Oxford University Press.

Vidich, A. J., and J. Bensman 1958. *Small town in a mass society*. Princeton, Princeton University Press.

West, J. 1945. *Plainville, USA*. New York, Columbia University Press.

Wolf, E. R. 1956. Aspects of group relations in a complex society: Mexico. *American Anthropologist* 58:1065-1078.
———1957. Closed corporate peasant communities in Mesoamerica and Central Java. *Southwestern Journal of Anthropology* 13:1-18.

Selected References for Chapter 4

Firey, Walter 1947. *Land Use in Central Boston*. Cambridge, Mass.: Harvard University Press. An empirical study of symbolic determinants of spatial arrangements in an urban setting.

Goodman, Daniel 1970. "Ideology and Ecological Irrationality," *Bioscience*, Vo. 20, no. 23, pp. 1247-52. Argues that public ideology in contemporary America works against ecological adaptation.

Mauldin, W. Parker 1965. "Fertility Studies: Knowledge, Attitude, and Practice," *Studies in Family Planning*, no. 7 (June), pp. 1-10. [A Publication of the Population Council.] Reviews and synthesizes a variety of studies regarding fertility norms from many countries of the world.

Michelson, William H. 1970. *Man and His Urban Environment: A Sociological Approach*. Reading, Mass.: Addison-Wesley Publishing Co. Focuses on the role of collective values in determining and altering urban ecological organization.

Spengler, Joseph J. 1966. "Values and Fertility Analysis," *Demography*, Vol. 3, no. 1, pp. 109-30. An insightful discussion of the role of institutionalized goals and values in the analysis of demographic phenomena, particularly fertility.

The present chapter has presented several views on the role of the symbolic elements of culture in ecological adaptation. Underlying these arguments is the proposition that collective perceptions regarding population and the natural environment systematically affect the ways in which a population will deal with these phenomena. We have seen how, in developing areas, norms regarding family size are responsive to mortality conditions and to the role the family plays in the organization of human activities. On the environmental side of the picture, pre-industrial orientations toward natural resources were contrasted with those characterizing modern societies. And finally, we saw how cultural values affect ecological relationships in an agrarian sector of North America.

In assessing the preceding arguments the reader should remember that positions reflecting cultural determinism have been specifically avoided; adaptive strategies with respect to population and environmental phenomena cannot easily be predicted from a knowledge of related cultural norms. Rather, we have suggested that this is but one of several organizational mechanisms through which collectivities can change the ecological balance, and thus affect changes for survival. Even so, the role of culture in ecological adaptation deserves our careful attention, perhaps more so than alternative aspects of social organization. One reason is because human ecologists have in recent years largely neglected symbolic mechanisms in favor of technological, political and locational phenomena. But, more importantly, the very essence of human society is its normative order. Human activities, aside from those of a purely personal nature, are guided, or at least influenced, by socially constructed conceptions of desirable, permissible and/or expected conduct. Why should behavior affecting demographic or environmental relationships be an exception? When one recognizes their role as "raw materials" in the quest for collective survival, this omission becomes patently absurd.

Nevertheless, we still have much to learn about the effects of culture on ecological systems. Though it is quite evident that all societies manifest normative views on population growth, family size, mortality and morbidity, uses and allocation of natural resources, etc., we are relatively ignorant of why we find variations in these norms from one society to another. Furthermore, little information is available regarding the conditions underlying changes in these collective orientations and ensuing consequences. For example, one of the persistent puzzles confronting demographers today is the fact that, while norms regarding desired family size in many developing countries appear to have significantly declined, reproductive performance has not followed suit. Why not? Answers to these and similar questions are at the same time obvious and elusive. Clearly, factors other than cultural norms are at work, but their identification and comprehension await further analytical developments in human ecology.

5 Regulatory Mechanisms: The Role of Power, Policy, and Social Control

To begin our consideration of man's efforts to regulate demographic and environmental phenomena, Dudley Kirk and Dorothy Nortman review recent (as of 1966) developments in population policy in a number of industrializing nations. From their discussion it is apparent that an increasing number of governments recognize the legitimacy of political intervention in the area of family planning. In their search for effective organizational and technical means for achieving fertility control, these nations are seeking and receiving assistance from the more industrialized and economically affluent nations as well as from international bodies such as the United Nations and the World Health Organization. Thus it appears there is a generally shared recognition among the world's governments that excessive population growth is economically and socially undesirable, that it is a world problem rather than merely the concern of the more rapidly growing nations, and that political solutions can be effective.

Though examination of particular national policies is brief, some general features are evident. First, in no case is coercion an instrument for achieving compliance. Permissible ranges of family size are not legislated, couples are not forced to use contraceptives, and abortions, where they are permitted at all, are the exception rather than the rule. In short, family-planning policies have thus far been dependent upon voluntary cooperation from the public. Second, as a consequence of the preceding point, emphasis has been placed upon making family-planning services—e.g., descriptive literature, clinics and personnel, and contraceptive devices—available to those who want them, with minimum use of propaganda techniques to mold public opinion. Third, as yet there is little evidence that these policy programs have been effective, i.e., that rates of growth have declined significantly. Nevertheless the authors suggest that the objective of such strategies is to check runaway growth and at a minimum to induce declines in the birth rate comparable to those occurring in the death rate. But is this goal reasonable or even feasible? One must remember how rapidly mortality was reduced in developing areas; can we, for example, anticipate a drop in fertility rates among the less developed Latin American nations comparable to the mortality decline they experienced between 1930 and 1960?[1] Even the most optimistic observer must doubt this possibility, and the chances for comparable changes in other developing countries are not much better. Finally, Kirk and Nortman suggest that the major problems experienced by governments in implementing population policies is in the area of administration and internal organization, though they do not detail this important observation. Indeed, the crux of any successful policy formation is the ability to maximize the probability of compliance through organized action. Where policies are new or contrary to traditional practices, as in the present case,

incentives, whether in the form of material or psychological rewards, or negative sanctions, become important. What seems to be lacking in governmental
attempts to influence population growth is such an incentive system, and this
deficit is reflected in the inefficient administration and/or internal organization of these programs.

The latter two articles in this chapter deal with the relationship between regulatory mechanisms and the environment. More specifically, they
illustrate the potential role of power, policy and social control as instrumen-
talities for affecting collective action with regard to man's material surroundings. Amos Hawley's study concisely, yet convincingly, demonstrates that
communities with greater concentrations of power are more successful in
executing urban-renewal programs. This finding is one slightly affected when
a variety of alternative explanatory variables are controlled, including city
size, quality of existing buildings, relative budgetary expenditures for planning, central-city suburb and manufacturing local-service distinctions, scale of
functional activities, type of city government, socioeconomic level, and region of the country. It also persists when the unit of power concentration,
the proportion of managers in the labor force, is differentiated into industry
sub-classes.

More interesting, though, is the reasoning underlying the explanation of
this relationship. Hawley views social systems, in general, and communities, in
particular, as reservoirs of energy (cf. his article included in Chapter One of
this volume). As such, they have the capacity to act on the environment, and
to influence their social and physical surroundings in varying ways and degrees. Sources of influence (or power) are institutionalized in various sub-
systems (offices), but vary in the degree to which they are distributed among
these sub-units. Where power is concentrated on one or a few sub-systems,
". . . the community should be able to act coherently only with great difficulty, if at all, when confronted with a novel problem." Thus we arrive at
Hawley's primary proposition: the greater the concentration of power in a
community the greater the probability of success in collective action affecting
the welfare of the whole.

While this argument is highly plausible, if not convincing, it may omit
an important consideration affecting the course collective action takes. Here I
refer to the differentiation of interests within the community.[2] This is to say
that the sub-systems of a collectivity may be oriented toward varying (perhaps conflicting) goals, and this factor is not necessarily associated with the
distribution of power. Consider urban renewal: though power may be concentrated in a relatively large managerial class, it may be that the interests of
industrialists and public administrators will not be served equally by renewal
programs.[3] The former group may see blighted areas as future factory loca-

tions, while the latter may view them, once renovated, as homes for satisfied voters. In this not so hypothetical case, one would expect the two power groups to exert their influence toward conflicting ends, with the result that urban-renewal policy would not be easily arrived at. One can imagine how other environmental issues—e.g., air and water pollution, agrarian reform, and highway construction—would be evaluated differently by competing power groups. The point is, then, that the uses of power, and resulting social policy, may be contingent upon the distribution of collective interests *as well as* the distribution of power. While in no way negating Hawley's argument, these considerations add another dimension to our understanding of the adaptive functions of power relationships.

Further insight into the role of regulatory mechanisms in environmental relationships may be gained by examining the final selection in this chapter in which Jack Oppenheimer and Leonard Miller discuss recent legislative action regarding the U.S. environment. The authors suggest that within the past twenty years environmental concerns have changed, and are now manifested in a new public awareness that current conditions in both the man-made and natural environments are threatening human health and welfare. Legislative response, however, has lagged behind this shift in public sentiments, and only recently is there evidence of governmental policy for dealing with our deteriorating environment.

An examination of the form these reactions have taken shows a number of legislative acts introduced into the Congress as well as the appearance of a number of congressional committees and executive agencies specifically created for dealing with environmental issues. As might be expected, a wide variety of overlapping and at times conflicting policies have resulted from these efforts. As Oppenheimer and Miller indicate, these developments raise the familiar question of whether it is possible to deal effectively with environmental problems against the background of the varied and conflicting interests of the constituencies of the congressional legislative and appropriation committees and their executive agency counterparts.

It seems that the major barrier preventing the creation of an affective and viable policy regarding the environment is the lack of coordinated action among federal, state and local governments, as well as public-and private-interest groups. This remains true even though it is increasingly recognized that environmental deterioration is at least a national and more likely an international problem. If the social control of man's ecosystem in the public interest is to become a reality rather than a topic of public concern and political debate, coordinated collective action must be forthcoming soon. As yet the progress of adaptive response to the environmental crisis through the regulatory mechanisms of social organization has been dangerously slow.

Notes and References

1. See Eduardo Arriaga and Kingsley Davis, "The Pattern of Mortality Change in Latin America," *Demography*, Vol. 6 (August 1969), pp. 223-42.

2. On the concept of "interests" see Ralf Dahrendorf, *Class and Class Conflict in Industrial Society*. London: Routledge and Kegan Paul, 1959, pp. 157-205, H. V. Wiseman, *Political Systems: Some Sociological Approaches*. New York: Frederick A. Praeger, 1966, pp. 138-42, and Henry W. Ehrmann, "Interest Groups," in *International Encyclopedia of the Social Sciences*, ed. David Sills. Vol. 7 New York: Crowell, Collier, and MacMillan, 1968, pp. 486-92.

3. That the public administration category deviates from other managerial groups regarding its relationship to urban renewal status is apparent from Hawley's Table 5. This might be explained by the fact that public administrators are subject to conflicting demands from many public and private groups, while the others are not. Thus the greater the number of public administrators in a community, the less likely that consensus will be reached regarding public policy.

Population Policies in Developing Countries
Dudley Kirk
Dorothy Nortman

Population policy is rapidly becoming an accepted part of development programs. This is very recent, and its origin can readily be traced to the thwarting of development plans by high rates of population growth. Those of us who have followed this subject closely over the last decade are not surprised at this interest among economic planners, but like the rest of the world, we are astounded at the rapidity with which the climate of world opinion has changed on the subject of population control. Indeed, it may be that the people have been ahead of their leaders, and that the change in attitude toward limiting family size is more apparent than real. At any rate, a decade ago, only one country—India—had a "population policy," in the sense of promoting family planning. Today the roster of nations with such programs is rapidly growing. If we include Mainland China, some five-eights of the 2.3 billion people in the developing regions live in countries that now have policies favoring population control or, more specifically, the adoption of family planning.

This outburst of interest and action in the field of population is related to growing recognition of: (1) the fact that rates of population growth in the developing countries are generally high, generally rising, and generally higher than those experienced by the industrial countries at a comparable stage of economic development; (2) the extent to which high birth rates and rapid population growth are handicaps to social and economic development; and (3) the legitimacy of government action in this field—that governments both can and should do something about family planning. This paper will assume the first proposition, summarize the arguments relating to the second, and give principal attention to the third.

The whole problem of population is increasingly being viewed as a question of dynamic relationships between population growth and economic development, rather than in terms of static man-land ratios. The impact of rapid population growth is most obvious in densely populated agricultural countries such as India, but even where potential resources seem plentiful in relation to population, as in Latin America and Africa, we are coming to see that high rates of population growth impede the accumulation of sufficient capital for the exploitation of those resources.

At the most elementary level, it is of course necessary that socio-economic progress at least keep up with population growth; i.e., if population is growing at 2.5 percent per year (the present average in the developing countries), the economy must grow by at least this pace just to stand still insofar as per capita income is concerned. Or viewed the other way, population growth is a major drag on raising per capita income. Equally important, rapid population growth forces a hard choice in the allocation of resources. Planners are pulled between meeting the immediate consumption needs of the growing population and the demands for investment to raise the economic potential and future productive capacity of the country.

For the developing countries, this question of priorities is at the heart of their problems in mapping plans. Affluent nations living well beyond the subsistence level have relatively wide latitude in allocating their resources. In the countries of Asia, Africa, and Latin America, where 80 percent of family income goes for food alone—and at that the people are undernourished—to divert even 10 percent of the national income from consumption to investment involves mass suffering.

Yet investment is imperative, if these nations are to modernize. Even assuming that the capital/output ratio, i.e., the number of investment units needed to produce an additional income unit, is as low as three in agrarian economies undergoing development,[1] it would still take an investment of 9 percent of the national income to add 3 percent to aggregate income. In the absence of population growth, an annual investment of 9 percent of the national income would represent a considerable achievement, for it would result in doubling per capita income in 23 years. If, however, population is growing at 3 percent per year, a figure already surpassed in several developing countries and rapidly being approached in others, an annual investment of 9 percent represents no per capita gain whatsoever.

Population Growth Related to Economic Development

In their comprehensive analysis of the relationship between population growth and economic development in low income countries, Coale and Hoover arrived at the startling conclusion that in India "*total* output would grow faster with reduced fertility than with continued high fertility."[2] In other words, a slower rate of population growth would produce a greater total product. The explanation for this seeming anomaly is that a decline in the birth rate does not immediately affect the size of the labor force, but it does immediately reduce the number of dependents to be provided for. With fewer dependents, there is less pressure to consume; therefore more funds are immediately available for investment purposes, and a greater output results.[3] Here, then, is the dilemma. If developing countries could modernize, birth rates would presumably fall; but if birth rates would fall, developing countries could more readily modernize.

Confronted with high rates of population growth that are thus a major drag on economic development, the governments of developing countries are now endorsing population control policies at a rate and in a climate of world approval unimaginable even a few years ago. As evidenced at international conferences, it is not a case of the West pushing the rest of the world toward population control. Rather, the situation is one in which the developing countries are turning for knowledge and means to the nations with long experience in the control of family size.[4]

Developed nations can offer technical experts, supplies and equipment, and financial assistance, but their own experience in reducing rates of population growth presents no historical precedent upon which to draw. This is so because fertility decline in the West resulted from the individual decisions of married couples to limit the size of their families, which they did by resorting to abortion and to folk methods of contraception that had been known for centuries. Organized society frowned on these practices and often strongly denounced birth control movements and jailed their leaders.[5] Nevertheless, as economies industrialized, as people moved from village to town to city, and as the traditionally subordinate status of women was modified, the small family became the norm in spite of public exhortations and laws against the sale and distribution of contraceptive information and supplies.[6] Even Japan is no model for direct emulation, for despite the fact that she is an Asian country with one of the lowest birth rates in the world, in terms of industrialization, urbanization, literacy, and the like, Japan is more at an occidental than oriental level. Moreover, Japanese advocates of family planning prefer contraception to abortion, which still plays a prominent role in Japan's control of births. Clearly, each developing country must cope with its high rate of population growth in its own way, consistent with its own particular values and circumstances.

Although countries are now proceeding by declarations of policy at high governmental levels, formal policy statements are neither necessary nor sufficient to achieve a reduction in birth rates. Contraceptive practices are widespread in countries without policies, notably in the Western world. In some rapidly developing areas of Asia, such as Singapore, Hong Kong, and Taiwan, widespread practice pre-dates policy. The adoption of a formal policy does not insure a reduction of the birth rate. Even success in specific programs thus far has made little impact on the national birth rate. Examples of this can be found among some of the largest countries in the world, notably India and Pakistan and possibly Mainland China.

By contrast there are countries which have no official family planning policies, but whose governments provide or support birth control services in the interests of health and welfare. Many nations will find this the easiest route to take, whether they are developing countries concerned with high rates of population growth or advanced nations concerned with high fertility among low income groups. In some emerging nations without formal policies, family planning services are becoming available in the proliferation of experimental and pilot family planning programs which have tended to be forerunners of larger national programs and formal policies.

Among the countries that have officially decided to foster family planning, besides India, Pakistan, and Mainland China, are South Korea, Ceylon, Singapore, Hong Kong, Malaysia, Turkey, Egypt, Tunisia, Morocco, and Honduras. Taiwan has no formal policy, but the government has given full cooperation to an island-wide program that has already reached a substantial part of the population. In many other countries, at least the beginning of governmental interest is visible—The Philippines, Thailand, Nepal, Afghanistan, Iran, Kenya, Mauritius, Chile, Colombia, Peru, and Venezuela.[7]

How does a country implement a population control policy? With the desensitization of the subject, a growing group of institutions stands ready to help. The major bottlenecks, however, are less a matter of finances and supplies than of internal organization and administration. A review of some specific programs and developments is instructive, not only as a narrative of their achievements to date, but also for an understanding of their difficulties. We begin with Asia, partly because in numerical terms this is the chief home of mankind, and partly because this is the region where the new national population policies first appeared.

Asian Countries

India, the second largest country in the world next to Mainland China, was the first to declare a national program to control population growth. A modest allocation of funds for family planning was included in the First Five Year Plan (1951-56), but the program was not implemented on a large scale before the Second Plan (1956-61). The increase in tempo of activity is suggested by the following information on expenditures:

| | *Rupees* |
Five Year Plan	*(millions)*
First (1951-56)	1.5
Second (1956-61)	21.6
Third (1961-66)	261.0
Fourth (1966-71)	950.0 (tentative allocation)

Note: In June 1966, the rupee was devaluated from $.21 to $.1335.

A memorandum[8] dated 21 May 1966 from Secretary S. R. Sen of the Government of India Planning Commission (Health Division), to the Planning Secretaries of all state governments, advises that states will be reimbursed with 90 percent instead of the previous 75 percent of their expenditures. The memorandum states further: "In view of the national importance of the family planning programme, the State Governments, it is hoped, will make every effort to utilize fully the funds allocated for Family Planning and ensure that there is no diversion of these funds to any other programmes."

Thus far, the establishment of family planning clinics has been the main channel for providing contraceptive supplies and services to the people. This has been supplemented by sterilization "camps," in which this simple but definitive method of family planning was offered to men who desired it. The voluntary response has been surprisingly large; since 1963, over 100,000 men and women have sought sterilization each year, and the total is approaching one million. Some contraceptive supplies are now manufactured in India, and distribution is through private as well as public channels.

Despite difficulties the program is gaining momentum, and a great increase of activity is planned for the Fourth Five Year Plan (1966-71). The first year's goal is to insert one million of the new intra-uterine devices (IUD's), with 20 million planned for the five-year period. The "camp" technique which proved successful for sterilization procedures is contemplated for IUD service and training. The plan also anticipates five million vasectomies and ten million effective users of traditional contraceptives. If these goals are attained, the yearly number of births prevented is expected to be nine million by 1975. The emphasis on newer methods of contraception may well accelerate the progress of the program.

While provision of services and supplies is the heart of the family planning program, effective education, publicity, record-keeping, research, and evaluation are integral aspects. Training in demography, biomedical research, and communications is given in Indian medical schools and the universities and in five Demographic Training and Research Centers. The need to improve the collection of vital statistics and to develop more sensitive indicators of fertility trends is urgent. Finally, the Indian program hopes to get down to the local level, to use village doctors and midwives, as well as more specialized personnel, to advocate and provide family planning services. It is also expected that other social changes such as marrying at a later age will be encouraged to help establish a norm of small families.[9]

The objective of the program is to achieve as rapidly as possible a decline in the annual birth rate from 42 per thousand population, as currently estimated from national sample surveys, to 25 per thousand.[10] While the achievements of India's family planning program have been important, they have probably not yet had an appreciable effect on the national birth rate, although the means of measuring changes in the birth rate are too defective to detect year-to-year trends.

The urgency of the population problem in India is suggested by the current crisis in food. In January 1966, the Indian government reported it will need ten to fourteen million tons of imported food grains to meet the famine caused by the worse drought of the century. Because of the severe drought, India's crop is expected to be 80 million tons this past year, compared with 88 million the year before.[11] The famine is a catastrophe, but the food crisis is chronic. For several years now the U.S. has been sending 20 percent of its total wheat crop to India, providing 7 percent of that nation's food grain consumption.

Pakistan's efforts to implement a national family planning program have encountered many of the problems noted in India. Expenditures on family planning (chiefly for the establishment of clinical service) have averaged only about one cent per person each year. But as in India, the problems have centered on organization and administration, rather than on lack of funds.

As of July 1, 1965, Pakistan adopted a plan for upgrading and reorganizing the Family Planning Directorate with a five-year budget of 300 million rupees. The new plan as implemented would raise annual per capita expenses on family planning to twelve cents.

A major innovation is to be the insertion of intra-uterine devices by midwives under general medical supervision.[12] The local midwives will receive incentive payments for referrals and insertions, presumably to compensate them for loss of income in the prevention of births.[13] No less than 50,000 village midwives are to be recruited and given a five-week training course by 1970.[14]

The target is to make family planning available to everyone. In drawing up the present plan, weaknesses revealed in the program under the Second Five Year Plan (1960-65) were carefully studied. That plan reached 100 percent of its target in the establishment of clinics, but only 31 percent in patients attending clinics and 42 percent in personnel projected for training. Failure to reach goals was attributed, among other reasons, to the clinic orientation of the program, emphasis on the urban population (who constitute only 13 percent of the total), and the addition of family planning to existing health and medical services already concerned with other responsibilities.

Korea is seeking to reduce the annual growth rate from a current estimate of about 2.9 percent to 1.82 percent by 1971.[15] The Economic Planning Board estimates that by 1980, implementation of its population policy will result in a growth rate of 1.16 percent per annum, compared with 3.15 percent under a *laissez-faire* situation, and will produce a per capita income 36 percent above the level that would otherwise prevail.

The 1966 level of expenditures on family planning in Korea, at 6.8 cents per capita in the last budget, is at this time the highest in the world. Some 2,200 full-time field workers have been trained and equipped, or an average of one for each 2,500 women in the childbearing ages. The new plastic intra-uterine devices figure largely in the Korean program and the annual rate of insertions is reaching something on the order of 15 percent of the "target" women, i.e., those exposed to risk of unwanted pregnancy. Because of poor vital statistics, the effects of the program on the birth rate cannot be determined at the present time with any high degree of certainty, but the impact of the program is surely being felt.

In *Taiwan*, an island-wide network of family planning services has been established through the Provincial Health Ministry. The cost of educating the children and providing other services if there were no family planning in part motivated the Economic Planning Board to authorize funds for a ten-year omnibus health program, including family planning services.[16]

The feasibility of a national program was demonstrated by a mass action research project in family planning in the city of Taichung, which has become rather a classic study.[17] The principal feature of the program in Taiwan is to insert 600,000 IUD's within five years, with the object of reducing the birth rate to 19.7 by 1968. This would mean a loop for about one-third of the married women of childbearing age, including those who would marry in the period. Insertions for 1965 fell just short of the initial target of 100,000.[18]

An outstanding feature of the Taiwan program is the excellent statistical evaluation. Performance against targets can be compared at the level of the individual worker, and there is detailed evaluation of the program in relation to different areas, the acceptability of different contraceptive methods, the age and other characteristics of women accepting the IUD, etc.

Compared with India and Pakistan, Korea and Taiwan are small countries. In addition, they are relatively advanced, particularly Taiwan, when measured by such indices as literacy and education. Nevertheless, the rapid development of family planning in these countries from pilot projects into national action programs is of great importance. In neither country has the program been in effect on a sufficient scale long enough to say *how* successful it has been, but each effort is clearly moving forward rapidly.

Elsewhere in Asia, there are formal programs in Ceylon, Singapore, Hong Kong, and Malaysia. In *Singapore*, which has one of the most successful private family planning associations in the world, "An Act [No. 32 of 1965] to create a statutory authority to be the sole agency for promoting and disseminating information pertaining to family planning" was signed by President Yusof Bin Ishak in January 1966. The widespread services provided by the hitherto private association in Singapore may well have been a factor in the rapid fall of the crude birth rate from 45.4 per thousand in 1952 to 29.9 per thousand in 1965. [19] The birth rate in *Hong Kong*, 26.9 per thousand in 1965, is also relatively low for Asia, but this is in major part attributable to distortion of the age structure of the population associated with the influx of refugees from Mainland China.

In *Malaysia* also, the birth rate is falling, especially among people of Chinese background. According to the *First Malaysia Plan 1966-1970* (adopted in 1965), "The main objectives . . . are to lay the groundwork for less rapid population growth by instituting an effective programme of family planning. . . ." *Ceylon* has received technical assistance from the Swedish government in pilot projects implementing family planning in several communities. The program is now to be extended to the country as a whole by stages over a period of years. [20] The results, limited to project locations thus far, have been encouraging. In *Thailand*, a major action experiment has been conducted under the sponsorship of the National Research Council, and others are under consideration. The first, in the rural district Pho-tharam, has been in operation little more than a year, but the results already suggest a wide acceptance in Thailand of contraceptive services if they are made readily available by the government. [21]

In *Mainland China*, family planning information and materials are supplied as a part of the public health services. Directives have been issued for instruction in birth control to many of the 17 million Communist Party members and 25 million Young Communists, and they in turn are expected to become models and teachers. One son and one daughter are now considered ideal. [22]

As early as 1956 and 1957, Premier Chou En-lai and President Mao Tse-tung were quoted as making statements favorable to the adoption of family planning, and subsequently it was reported that a birth control campaign was initiated and services provided in government health centers. In 1958, however, political winds shifted, and the birth control campaign was brought to a halt, although contraceptives continued to be available. In 1962, there was a resumption of the birth control campaign, and in January of that year the state council revised import duties to permit contraceptive supplies to enter China duty-free. At the same time, the government began to advocate later age at marriage. Japanese doctors who visited China in March and April 1964 and in July 1965 reported that family planning was promoted as part of the maternal and child health program, and that all methods of contraception, including sterilization and induced abortion, were available. Oral contraceptives were used, as well as various forms of the intra-uterine device, which had become quite a popular method.

The official attitude was presumably stated by Premier Chou En-lai during his African tour in 1964. In Conakry, Guinea, where he was interviewed by Edgar Snow, he was quoted as follows:

> ... Our present target is to reduce population growth to below 2 percent; for the future we aim at even lower rate. ... However, I do not believe it will be possible to equal the Japanese rate [of about one percent] as early as 1970. ... For example, with improved living conditions over the past two years, our rate of increase again rose to 2.5 percent. ... We do believe in planned parenthood, but it is not easy to introduce all at once in China. ... The first thing is to encourage late marriages. ... [23]

An annual rate of increase at 2.5 percent would mean some 17 million additional population each year. Birth control practice is now common in the cities and in the last three years has gradually moved into the countryside. As Director Madame Huang Ching-wan of the Health Ministry said to Edgar Snow, "We plan production of material things and we must plan to avoid chaos in human reproduction." [24] This may be a revision of traditional Marxist doctrine, but it is compatible with the concept of central planning.

The Middle East and North Africa

Four governments of this region have initiated mass action programs to implement their national policies, and more seem likely to do so in the near future.

In *Turkey*, a new law providing the legal framework for financing and implementing a nation-wide family planning program was signed by the president in April 1965. The goal is a 10 percent decline in fertility in each five-year period during the next 15 years. Operationally the program will utilize the existing facilities of the Health Ministry, but full-time family planning personnel will be added, including mobile family planning teams to take the program to the people. Supplies will be offered free or at cost. Although supplies are now imported, local manufacture is contemplated. An interesting feature of the Turkish program is an education campaign among the armed forces, not merely for their personal edification, but for the "ripple" effect among the population at large, as the conscripted men return to civilian life.

Turkey has several advantages. It is homogeneous in nationality and language, which suggests a rapid cultural diffusion once family planning practice begins to take hold. In a national survey conducted in 1964, women were found to support the idea of family planning 3 to 1. Moreover, 70 percent of the men and 79 percent of the women answered affirmatively the question, 'Should the government have a program to give information to those people who want to keep from having too many children?" The Turkish program thus will have the support of the people.[25]

In *Tunisia*, an experimental program designed to develop a practical family planning service was initiated in 1964. Clinical trials with the IUD were established in the city of Tunis in three maternal and child health centers. The success of this program has led to the formulation of a national campaign with a goal of 120,000 women using the IUD within a two-year period. A unique feature of the Tunisian program is the use of workers in the major political party as a major source of information and publicity.

In the *United Arab Republic*, the government's interest in family planning goes back at least a decade, to the time when the National Population Commission, formed in 1953, opened four planned parenthood clinics. Policy, however, dates from the May 1962 draft of the National Charter, in which President Nasser declared: "Population increase constitutes the most dangerous obstacle that faces the Egyptian people in their drive towards raising the standard of production.... Attempts at family planning deserve the most sincere efforts supported by modern scientific methods."[26]

Until now there has not been a substantial governmental program, but on February 1, 1966, a widespread campaign utilizing the oral contraceptives was launched. The government has also requested foreign assistance in obtaining 50,000 IUD's and the molds for their manufacture. There is a resurgence of interest in governmental and private circles, and it is believed that these new contraceptives may make a full-scale government program more feasible and acceptable.

At the opening of the Seminar on Family Planning in Rabat, *Morocco*, on October 11, 1966, the Minister of Development and Planning declared, "We must settle down to this problem of birth control all the more because, according to the economists and statisticians, we have to fear a serious reduction of our per capita material investments."

Other countries in the region have been following these programs and developments with interest. Iran, for example, is considering expanding the family planning services in its maternity and child health centers into a national program. The Middle East area is of particular interest because of all cultural and religious groups Moslems characteristically have the highest fertility.

Africa South of the Sahara
No formal population policies or national family planning programs yet exist in Africa below the Sahara, but there is considerably greater official readiness for such programs than had been suspected. *Kenya* requested an advisory mission from the Population Council which prepared a report to the government in 1965. Its *1966-1970 Development Plan* includes "measures to promote family planning education," such as the establishment of a Family Planning Council, and to provide services in family planning clinics in government hospitals and health centers. [27] In *Mauritius*, at the opening of the Legislative Assembly on 15 March 1966, the governor called attention to the problems of unemployment and the high rate of population growth and asked the Legislature to vote funds in the capital budget for a sustained campaign for education in family planning. According to Premier Ramgoolam, programs are now under way "with the assistance of Government and the International Planned Parenthood Federation . . . both in the urban and rural areas." [28] Additional assistance is expected from the Swedish Government.

African countries firmly believe in economic and health planning by government. It is quite possible that they entertain fewer doubts about government guidance in development than do the new nations of any other continent. With the growing awareness that the reduction of infant and other deaths produces rapid population growth, there is increasing appreciation of the key importance of population growth, as opposed to population density, as a factor affecting the dynamics of economic development. Considerable interest in population problems and policies was expressed at the First African Population Conference, held at the University of Ibadan, Nigeria, In January 1966.

Latin America
This region has the most rapid rate of population growth of any major part of the world. Until quite recently this has not been a cause of much public concern, partly because of the predominancy of Catholicism, and partly because these countries have a traditional image of themselves as underpopulated, with a large area capable of new settlement.

Two developments seem to be bringing an important change in the attitudes of governments in the region. The first of these is a realization that in Latin America, as in many other parts of the world, population growth is eating up a large share, in some cases all, of the economic growth being achieved. A second factor is the growing consciousness of the problem of abortion. The reaction of the medical profession has been an important stimulus toward more liberal attitudes on contraception. Comparable fertility surveys, conducted in eight Latin American capitals and coordinated by the UN Latin American Demographic Centre in Santiago, Chile, have revealed favorable attitudes toward family planning in a large segment of the population concerned.

Until recently it was thought unlikely that governments of the region would adopt national population policies because of the opposition of the Church. However, it now seems that a number of countries will institute family planning as a regular public health service. This has already occurred in *Chile*, is to be instituted in *Jamaica* and *Honduras*, and is under serious consideration in *Colombia*. The Jamaica Five-Year Independence Plan 1962-68 calls attention to both the rapid population growth and population pressure in the island and the effects of excessive childbearing on the lives and prospects of individuals. Most recently, *Haiti* has also expressed interest in population control. In *Peru* a recent presidential statement decreed that population development "should be systematically studied in order to formulate programs of action with which to face the problems of population and socio-economic development."[29]

International Action and Reaction

These policies and programs designed to reduce rates of population growth are novel, not only for the recency of their origin, but because they seem to fly in the face of historical experience. In the presently developed nations, economic growth was accompanied in almost all cases by a sustained and substantial increase in population. To meet the challenge of development under today's circumstances of rapidly declining death rates, the official world has therefore had to reverse its historic attitude toward population growth.

If one considers the newness of the problem, reversal in attitude is occurring swiftly; but because of their multi-national character, the international agencies have moved less rapidly than many of the developing nations in taking action. Up to now, private agencies-foundations and the International Planned Parenthood Federation—have provided most of the foreign aid and technical assistance in population programs. But with the rapidly growing awareness that the dimensions of the problem are beyond the capacity of private groups, official agencies are showing increasing willingness to meet the need for technical assistance.

The UN and Its Affiliates

The UN has long had a program to stimulate demographic research and training and to improve the registration, collection, and analysis of vital data. With its recent mission to India (1965),[30] sent in response to that government's request to advise on steps to accelerate the impact of the national program on the country's birth rate, the UN moved from an investigatory phase to readiness to give technical assistance in the matter of population control. The stage for this development was set in July 1965 when the Economic and Social Council endorsed the recommendations of the Population Commissions to increase "the amount of technical assistance in population fields available to Governments of developing countries upon their request." The Council also called to the attention of the General Assembly "the need to provide the necessary resources . . . to carry out the intensified and expanded programme of activities in the field of population. . . ."

Perhaps the UN position is best exemplified by the statement of Philippe de Seynes, the Undersecretary for Economic and Social Affairs, to the 1965 Belgrade World Population Conference, that the UN is ready "to respond to all requests for assistance from any country" interested in a birth control policy, although it would maintain its traditionally neutral attitude in deference to "respect for all beliefs."

Other notable events by UN-related agencies include the World Health Organization's resolution approved unanimously last year (1965) on the occasion of its 18th annual assembly empowering the organization to give assistance to its members on birth control programs, short of actually engaging in "operational activities." A recent request by the UNICEF governing council to its director to prepare a statement on possible UNICEF activities in the area of population control also indicates the direction in which international agencies are now moving.

The impetus to move is stimulated to no small extent by the recent finding of the UN Food and Agriculture Organization that "In the six years since [1958/59] production [of food] has barely kept up with population growth. . . . "[31] In his address to the 1965 World Population Conference, FAO Director-General B. R. Sen stated "if . . . large-scale breakdowns are to be brought within a measure of control, then, side by side with a concerted effort to increase productivity of agriculture in the developing countries, population stabilization must be undertaken simultaneously as a social policy of urgent priority without further delay."

The U.S. and Other Developed Countries

The timidity and caution of the international agencies in this field was until very recently paralleled in the bilateral programs of most countries giving foreign aid. But that too is changing rapidly. In the United States the official attitude has within the past year or so turned from non-involvement in family planning programs to one of approbation and assistance. The administration is now contemplating an increase in outlay for technical assistance to foreign countries for population matters from about $2 million expended in the fiscal year ending June 1965 to $5.5 million in the fiscal year 1966, and up to $20 million in the next few years.

Funds expended thus far have been used mainly for maternal and child health programs, demographic research and surveys, and improvement of census procedures and analyses. Now, however, the Agency for International Development has advised its missions that, in line with President Johnson's decision [32] "to seek new ways to use our knowledge to help deal with the explosion of world population and the growing scarcity of world resources . . . we are ready to entertain requests for technical assistance." [33] The memorandum states that "A.I.D. does not advocate any particular method of family regulation." Korea and Taiwan are already drawing on counterpart funds to support health and family planning clinics. Turkey, Honduras, Pakistan, and Tunisia are reported to be seeking direct aid for population control programs. Assistance may take any form short of providing contraceptives or the equipment for their manufacture.

On the domestic scene, the Supreme Court's ruling on June 7, 1965, that Connecticut's anti-birth-control law was unconstitutional, on the ground that it denied the right to privacy, has been followed by widespread action to make birth control services available through tax-supported as well as private channels. Other notable recent developments affecting both the national and international scene include: (1) reversal by the American Medical Association of its former policy with a new declaration, the first since 1938, that "child-spacing measures should be made available to all patients who require them . . . whether they obtain their medical care through private physicians or tax or community supported health services;" (2) reinforcement by the National Academy of Sciences and the American Public Health Association of their earlier proposals that governmental and private organizations take effective measures to make the benefits of family planning available to all; (3) inclusion of birth control services in the U.S. anti-poverty program; and (4) recommendation by the Committee on Population of the White House Conference on International Cooperation Year in November (1965) that the U.S. government give greater support to other governments requesting help in family planning programs.

The U.S. is, of course, the chief source of foreign aid funds, but other countries have also announced interest in assisting population programs. The Ministry of Overseas Development, Great Britain's counterpart of the U.S.'s AID, is ready to participate in such programs and has offered Mauritius, for example, "financial assistance . . . on a substantial scale." [34] The Swedish International Development Authority has long been active, notably in Ceylon and Pakistan.

The Church

While the deliberations of the Roman Catholic Church have captured much of the attention of the world on religious attitude toward contraception, it should be noted that among the more than two billion people in the under-developed areas, the Buddhist, Hindu, and Moslem religions predominate. In these religions, interpretations are conveyed to the people by numerous priests and scholars, the force of the ruling depending upon the personal following of its conveyor. Attitudes toward family planning derive from custom and tradition, rather than from formal religious doctrine. Among Buddhists, Hindus, and Moslems, there appears to be no doctrinal prohibition against the use of mechanical or chemical methods to limit births.

The Roman Catholic Church, subject to growing pressure to reverse its traditional ban on the use of methods other than periodic or total abstinence, has been re-examining its position. This fact along has been interpreted by some as a weakening of its traditional proscription of modern methods. A special commission of experts appointed by the Pope during the Ecumenical Council Vatican II failed to make a specific recommendation, and the Council ended with this question still unsettled. Final authority on this matter rests with the Pope, who can be expected to come to some decision after reviewing the report recently submitted by the papal commission reorganized in March 1966.

Conclusions

It must be evident from the foregoing discussion that with developments so rapid, any review of population policies will be out of date almost by the time it is written. It is also clear that measurable progress so far relates more to attitude and policy than to action and achievement. But in most cases, government-sponsored family planning programs are so new that it would be unreasonable to expect them to have yet had a major and measurable impact on birth rates, and hence on rates of population growth. Except in Korea and in Taiwan, the programs have not yet taken hold in the rural areas, where most of the people in the developing countries live. Not unnaturally, the first successes in such programs are most likely in the more advanced of the developing countries (e.g., Taiwan and Korea) and among urban and better educated groups. Nevertheless, new reasons give important grounds for optimism.

(1) *Improvement in contraceptive technology.* The discovery and rapidly expanding use of oral contraceptives (the "pill") and of the new plastic intra-uterine devices (IUD's) have revolutionized the practice of birth control. Both have the great advantage of being dissociated from the sex act, and the latter has the additional advantage of often requiring only sufficient motivation to obtain the initial insertion. These make family planning much

more practicable for the populations of the developing countries. Ongoing research promises to improve these methods (e.g., in reducing the cost and side effects of the oral contraceptives; in reducing expulsions and increasing the efficiency of IUD's). It is also likely that even better methods will be developed in the next few years. Private foundations (e.g., the Ford Foundation and the Population Council), drug companies, and now the U.S. government are investing large sums in these endeavors.

(2) *Evidence of widespread interest and willingness to practice family planning.* Field surveys on knowledge of, attitudes towards, and practices of family planning in general populations have now been conducted in nine Asian countries, three African countries, and nine Latin American countries. The "KAP Studies," as they have come to be called, all reveal a substantial proportion of couples who would like to limit the size of their families and who are prepared to practice contraception, but who do not do so now because of ignorance and unavailability of methods suitable for their way of life. These studies show that governments have usually been more conservative on this subject than the people. The proportion of potential users of contraception of course varies from country to country, and one must recognize the gap between an expression of attitude and a willingness to take action. Nevertheless, the studies reveal a tremendous potential "market" for birth control, if suitable methods and services can be provided.[35]

(3) *Growing success of pilot projects and experiments in providing family planning services.* Historically these have met with varying success in developing countries, the results being closely related to the socio-economic level of the population concerned. With the new contraceptives, several such projects have shown striking success in obtaining acceptance among populations not previously practicing contraception.[36]

It would be quixotic to expect population policies to eliminate population growth quickly, and indeed this is not usually the objective. National targets are much more likely to be set at reducing population growth to an annual rate of, say, one percent fifteen years hence. The objective is to check runaway growth and at a mimimum to induce declines in the birth rate comparable to those occurring in the death rate. The effectiveness of population policies to achieve even these more limited objectives is still to be tested. But they are swimming with the tide of socio-economic progress and awareness on many fronts.

Until the present, the monetary investments in family planning programs have been small, and this may in part be responsible for their modest effects. Even with gathering momentum, the costs of such programs will be a minor part of development budgets. We do not yet know the minimal mix of social and economic ingredients for a take-off in reductions of the birth rate, but thus far problems of organization and administration have proved as difficult as the question of finance. It is most unlikely that the needs of family planning programs will seriously compete with other forms of socioeconomic investment. By the same token, it is probable that modest investments in such programs will bring future returns disproportionately large in relation to the size of the investment.

With two-thirds of the world's people living in underdeveloped economies, the problem engendered by their high birth rates is a global one. Birth control, hitherto a topic not fit for public discussion, let alone as a proper function of government, is now increasingly an aspect of anti-poverty programs everywhere in the world. Birth rates can no longer be regarded as a "given" factor not subject to change. It is apparent that the great majority of the world's families would like to control their size, given the proper information, the services, and methods appropriate to their ways and conditions of life. There is increasing evidence that the "population dilemma" of the modern world is at least partly amenable to solution by government action in providing voluntary family planning services and in otherwise facilitating the adoption of family planning.

Notes and References

1. This ratio is the subject of great speculation among economists. See, for example, Simon Kuznets, "Toward a Theory of Economic Growth," in *Economic Growth and Structure* (New York: W. W. Norton, 1965), p. 33.

2. Ansley J. Coale and Edgar M. Hoover, *Population Growth and Economic Development in Low-Income Countries* (Princeton University Press, 1958), p. 285.

3. It is true, as pointed out by Kuznets, *op. cit.*, p. 124, that "the empirical evidence, at least in its present state, is insufficient for a detailed analysis of the impact of population growth on the growth of aggregate output." The above argument relating to *total* output is of course more controversial than the proposition that a lower rate of growth would contribute to higher *per capita* income.

4. The subject of population control first reached the floor of the United Nations General Assembly in December 1962. In debating Resolution 1838 (XVII), it was clear that with the exception of some Latin American countries, developing nations strongly supported the clause that the UN "give technical assistance, as requested by Governments, for national projects and programmes dealing with the problems of population." UN General Assembly 7-17 December 1962, *Provisional Summary Record.*

At the UN Asian Population Conference, to which the participating countries sent official representatives, the delegates approved the recommendation that "the U.N. and its specialized agencies should expand the scope of the technical assistance which they are prepared to give at the request of governments in the development of statistics, research, experimentation and action programmes relating to population problems." ECAFE, *The Asian Population Conference 1963* (New York, 1964), p. 50.

At the UN World Population Conference in Belgrade in September 1965, although there was neither vote nor resolution on any issue, the general conviction was that rapid population growth is now a major impediment to fulfillment of the economic goals of the UN Development Decade. A growing roster of developed countries supported this view, which was voiced strongly by the demographic, economic, and other experts from most of the developing nations.

Finally, it may be noted that in response to its "Inquiry among Governments on Problems Resulting from the Interaction of Economic Development and Population Changes," the UN Secretary-General reports that "Many of the responses received from Governments of developing countries manifest more or less serious concern with the high rate at which the population of their countries is increasing, considering this as an important handicap to economic and social development." UNESCO, E/3895/Rev. 1 (24 November 1964), p. 19.

5. For a recent concise discussion of birth control movements in the West, see D. V. Glass, "Fertility and Birth Control in Developed Societies, and Some Questions of Policy for Less Developed Societies" in *Proceedings of the Seventh Conference of the International Planned Parenthood Federation*, Singapore, 1963, Excerpta Medical Foundation, International Congress Series No. 72, pp. 38-46.

6. In the U.S., for example, it was only in May 1966 that the Massachusetts Legislature repealed its 1847 law according to which the sale, distribution, and advertising of contraceptives were criminal offenses. The new law legalizes birth control information and supplies for married, but not unmarried, persons.

7. See Population Council, *Studies in Family Planning*, No. 16 (December 1966), for formal governmental policy statements.

8. No. HLH 4 (14)/65.

9. Government of India, *Third Five Year Plan*, p. 678, paragraph 68.

10. Col. B. L. Raina, Past Director of Family Planning, *Annual Report, 1962-1963*.

11. *The New York Times*, December 10, 1965.

12. *Family Planning Scheme for Pakistan during the Third Five Year Plan Period 1965-1970*, p. 3, paragraph 8.

13. *Ibid.*, p. 10, paragraph 12.

14. *Ibid.*,p. 3, paragraph 8.

15. *Korea, Summary of First Five-Year Economic Plan 1962-1966*, p. 30.

16. Taiwan, *Ten Year Health Plan 1966-1975*, p. 15.

17. It is described by Bernard Betelson and Ronald Freedman in "A Study in Fertility Control," *Scientific American*, CCX No. 5 (May 1964), pp. 3-11.

18. The total of monthly insertions for the twelve months of 1965 came to 99,253. There is now developing a considerable body of empirical data on retention, expulsion, removal, and pregnancy rates.

19. UN Statistical Office, *Population and Vital Statistics Report*, Series A, XVIII, No. 2 (1 April 1966).

20. Ceylon, *Provisional Scheme for a Nationwide Family Planning Programme in Ceylon, 1966-1976*.

21. Amos H. Hawley and Visid Prachuabmoh, "Family Growth and Family Planning in a Rural District of Thailand," in *Family Planning and Population Programs: A Review of World Developments*, Proceedings of the International Conference on Family Planning Programs, Geneva, 1965 (Chicago: University of Chicago Press, 1966), pp. 523-44.

22. *The Sunday Times* (London), January 23, 1966.

23. *The New York Times*, February 3, 1964.

24. *The Sunday Times* (London), January 23, 1966.

25. "Turkey: National Survey on Population" in *Studies in Family Planning*, No. 5 (Population Council, December 1964).

26. United Arab Republic Information Department, *The Charter*, draft presented by President Gamal Abdel Nassar on 21st May 1962, p. 53.

27. Kenya, *1966-1970 Development Plan*, p. 324.

28. Sir Seewoosagur Ramgoolam, "Mauritius and Its Problems," *Commonwealth Journal, IX*, No. 4 (August 1966), p. 144.

29. December 5, 1964, No. 244/64-DSG.

30. See UN Department of Economic and Social Affairs, *Report on the Family Planning Programme in India*, TAO/IND/48 (20 February 1966).

31. FAO, *The State of Food and Agriculture 1965*, p. 7.

32. Stated in his January 1965 State of the Union Message.

33. U.S. Department of State Circular 280, subject "Population Programs," 2/25/65, signed by Secretary of State Rusk.

34. Speech by His Excellency the Governor at the opening session of the First Legislative Assembly of Mauritius on the 15th of March 1966.

35. A review of these studies is given by W. Parker Mauldin, "Fertility Studies: Knowledge, Attitude and Practice," in *Studies in Family Planning*, No. 7 (June 1963).

36. The results of such projects are reviewed in various issues of *Studies in Family Planning*, Nos. 1-10 (July 1963-February 1966).

Community Power and Urban-Renewal Success
Amos H. Hawley

Power, in most sociological studies, is conceived as the ability to exercise influence in a decision-making process. It is viewed as a personal attribute that distinguishes leaders from followers. Working with that conception investigators normally proceed by inquiring into the reputations of members of a community, establishing juries to winnow the great from the small, constructing sociograms to determine who interacts with whom, and so on. No matter what the methodological apparatus, investigators are uniformly led to the discovery that managerial and proprietary personnel, with occasional exceptions, constitute the power figures.[1] Some of the more sophisticated start with the assumption that managers and proprietors are the principal power figures and use their sociometric tools to discover how members of an elite are grouped about various kinds of issues to form power centers. Both procedures, as Wolfinger has recently pointed out, often rest on certain unspoken and unwarranted assumptions.[2] They appear to assume, for example, that lines of influence are clearly perceptible to respondents. They also assume a static distribution of power among certain personalities. But the chief difficulty with the usual approach is that it is only applicable in a case study; it offers no facility for quantitative and comparative studies of the phenomenon. And that, it seems to me, is a disability inherent in a social-psychological approach to the study of community structure.

Before turning to an alternative way of treating the matter, a prefatory comment on the nature of that which is in question seems to be appropriate. It should be obvious that power in the social sphere, as with energy in the physical world, is ubiquitous. It is like energy, too, in that it appears in many forms. Every social act is an exercise of power, every social relationship is a power equation, and every social group or system is an organization of power. Accordingly, it is possible to transpose any system of social relationships into terms of potential or active power. Perhaps such a transposition is nothing more than the substitution of one terminology for another. At the very least, however, it focuses attention on the instruments of control and causes a social system to be viewed as a control mechanism.

The Community as an Energy System

The community, for example, may be conceived as an energy system. That is, as a system of relationships among functionally differentiated units the community constitutes a mobilization of power—the capacity to produce results —for dealing with the environment, whether physical or social. Each unit or subsystem—family, church, store, industry—is also an organization of power for the conduct of a function. Both the system and its subsystems tend to approximate a single organization model. Moreover, since the performance of its function by any one part affects in greater or lesser degree the conditions under which other parts carry out their functions, the parent system and each subsystem is an arena in which a more or less continuous interplay of influence occurs. Power, then, is expressed in two ways: (1) as functional power— that required to execute a function; and (2) as derivative power—that which spills over into external relationships and regulates the interaction between parts. The two modes of manifestation are necessarily connected. The type of function performed determines the kind of derivative influence transmitted to other parts or subsystems. There might also be a quantitative association, though the magnitude of the derivative influence is a consequence not only of the scale to which a function has developed but also of its position in the system. Those subsystems that are most instrumental in relating the system to the environment doubtlessly exert a greater derivative effect than do subsystems one or more steps removed from the key position. Space does not permit a full exposition of a system conception of power. Perhaps enough has been said to indicate that power is a product of a system having developed, that it is lodged only in a system, and that it is most appropriately treated, therefore, as a system property.[3] Whatever power an individual might appear to possess is in effect attached to the office he occupies in a system. He acquires power by attaining to an office and he loses it when he is separated from the office. But the acquiring and losing of power is illusory; the property belongs rather with the office or, better still, to the system in which the office is a specialized function.[4]

In the conduct of its routine activities the system exercises its power through established and well-worn channels; the interplay of influence is institutionalized. But the structure of relationships through which power is communicated may leave various areas of interest or activity unattended, for example, private charity, religious digression and reform, the supervision of adolescents. When crises occur in such matters or when non-routine issues affecting the whole system arise, the existing structure is put to a test. It may or may not be effective in dealing with the exceptional circumstance. Whether it is effective would appear to be contingent on the way in which derivative power is distributed in the system. Where it is highly concentrated the community should be able to act as a unit in almost any emergency. On the other hand, where power is widely distributed a community may be able to act coherently only with great difficulty, if at all, when confronted with a novel problem.

This suggests a way of dealing with the variable quantitatively. A frustrating feature of studies of power has been the understandable failure to find a way to measure its amount. If, however, we can assume that an enduring system has sufficient force to regularly perform its normal functions, we can conclude that all systems of the same kind generate equivalent amounts of power. There remains a variable, namely, the way in which power is distributed. Any given amount may be in some instances concentrated in a small sector of the system or in other instances distributed more or less uniformly over all sectors or subsystems. The measurement of distribution appears to present fewer difficulties than does the measurement of the amount of power.

Power Concentration Leads to Social Action

Now let me propose that the greater the concentration of power in a community the greater the probability of success in any collective action affecting the welfare of the whole. This follows, if it be granted that (1) success in a collective action requires the ability to mobilize the personnel and resources of the community and (2) that ability is greatest where power is most highly concentrated. The proposition does not say that a concentration of power assures success in any community venture. Various factors might intervene to defeat a collective project. Moreover, a concentration of power might be used to block a course of action. Power concentration, however, is not needed to defeat an action on the part of a community. That might occur as a result of power being so diffusely held that mobilization of the community cannot be accomplished.

Proceeding from the notion that system power resides in the sub-systems or functional units of a community, we can infer that it must be exercised through the managerial functions of the subsystems. For it is those functions that co-ordinate the several other functions in their respective sub-systems and articulate the latter with the larger system. In the absence of data on the number of managerial functions, I shall use the number of managerial personnel, that is, the number of people who reported occupations as mana-ger, proprietor, or official in the Population Census, to measure concentration of power. Personnel, it should be stressed, is used only as a substitute for, and as an index of, functions.[5] Since the significance of the number of functions varies with the number of all other functions (i.e., the size of the employed labor force), it should be expressed as a ratio to the latter. Hence the lower the ratio of managers, proprietors, and officials[6] to the employed labor force the greater is the concentration of power. (This measure will hereafter be called the MPO ratio.)

Urban-Renewal Studies

As the dependent variable, that is, an example of collective action, I shall use success in urban renewal. Urban renewal, programmed and administered by the Housing and Home Finance Agency, has the advantage of involving a standard procedure to which all participating communities must submit in like manner. Participation in the program by a municipality involves passage through a series of stages, differentiated by the extent to which the planning and other local arrangements required for federal financial support have been fulfilled. The stages are *planning, execution,* and *completion.* Arrival at the completion stage is unquestionably the best measure of success. Unfortunately only eigh-teen cities in the continental United States had by the end of 1959 advanced so far—hardly enough for statistical purposes. The next best indication of success in urban renewal is arrival at the execution stage. At that stage a city has completed its planning and has satisfied all administrative requirements for the receipt of a capital grant from the Housing and Home Finance Agency. The city is then either at the point of, or has embarked upon, the acquisition of land, the relocation of current occupants, and clearing and improving the land. At the end of 1959, ninety-five cities with population of 50,000 or more (in 1950) had advanced to the execution stage.[7]

For control purposes data on two other classes of cities of 50,000 or more population are employed. One class includes cities that entered the urban renewal program but for one reason or another abandoned their efforts sometime between 1950 and 1960. The thirty-eight cities that had that experience are called "dropouts." The second control class is made up of all cities, in states where urban renewal is legally permissible, that have not attempted urban renewal at any time. There are sixty-one such cities. All the members of this class, it is to be noted, are eligible for urban renewal assistance from the federal agency. There remains a sizable group of cities that are still in the planning stage. Eventually they will either pass into the execution stage or terminate their efforts; but at present their status is indeterminate. For that reason they are not included in the present study.

Whether urban renewal is a form of collective action that would call into operation the organization of the entire community may be debatable. The general scale of urban renewal projects is clearly relevant to the question. The average acreage involved in urban renewal projects in the 253 cities that were in the program in mid-1959 was 78.6 per city, or about one-eighth of a square mile. But one-fourth of all urban renewal acreage was contained in five cities; half the total was in nineteen cities. In the remaining cities the average acreage per city was 42.5, or a little over one-sixteenth of a square mile. That urban renewal, in the light of these magnitudes, represents a significant challenge to a community must be left as an unanswered question for the present. If it is regarded as a major undertaking in a community, it should certainly involve the local power structure. If it is considered to be a rather insignificant form of collective action, then as a dependent variable it provides a fairly severe test of the hypothesis.[8]

It seems advisable to restate the hypothesis in the operational terms set forth. The hypothesis is: MPO ratios are lowest in urban renewal cities that have reached the execution stage and highest in cities that have never attempted urban renewal. Dropout cities are expected to occupy an intermediate position between the polar classes.

The hypothesis is to be examined with reference to cities of 50,000 population or more. The abundance of data available for cities in that size range offers considerable latitude for refining the measure of power concentration and for the development of controls. In the following, however, the analysis of power concentration as an independent variable is confined primarily to ratios for the entire class of MPO's. Differentials within that class will be investigated in a later report.

As a preliminary test of the representativeness of cities of 50,000 population or more, their MPO ratios, for each urban renewal status class, are compared with those for all cities of 15,000-50,000 population, in Table 1.

Table 1
Number and MPO Ratios, Cities by Size Class
and by Urban Renewal Status

Urban Renewal Status	All Cities of 15,000 Population and Over		Cities of 50,000 Population and Over		Cities of 15,000-50,000 Population	
	No.	MPO Ratio	No.	MPO Ratio	No.	MPO Ratio
Execution stage	136	9.0	95	9.0	41	9.1
Dropout	79	10.0	38	10.1	41	9.8
Never in program	402	11.0	61	10.8	341	11.1
Total	617	10.4	194	9.5	423	10.7

Observe that the two series of ratios are very similar. Thus it seems possible that findings for large cities might apply to all cities regardless of size. Further, though somewhat tangential, support of that conclusion is found in the fact that the number of years spent in the planning stage before reaching the execution stage is unrelated to size of city. No further attempt to ascertain the representativeness of large cities has been made.

It is also to be noted in Table 1 that the ratios conform to the hypothesis. Power is most highly concentrated in the execution-stage cities and most diffusely distributed in the never-in-program cities. That the concentration of power, as represented by the ration of all MPO's to the employed labor force, is significantly greater in cities that have reached the execution stage in urban renewal than in the other classes of cities is apparent in Table 2. The probability that the association shown there is due to chance is less than 1 in a 100.

The quintile distribution of cities shown in Table 2 displays a considerable spread over the ratio range in each urban renewal status class. That raises

Table 2
Quintile Distribution of Cities (MPO Ratios),
by Urban Renewal Status

Urban Renewal Status	1st (Under 7.7)	2nd (7.8-8.9)	3rd (9.0-9.9)	4th 10.0-11.7)	5th (11.8 and Over)
Execution stage	27	22	21	17	9
Dropout	3	9	8	8	7
Never in program	9	9	8	13	22

$\chi^2 = 23.516$, $C = .330$, $P < .01$.

a question of how some cities manage to get to the execution stage without a concentration of power. The complementary question of how other cities with marked concentrations of power escape urban renewal may be given a tentative a priori answer: that is, they are susceptible and may yet enter the program. In any event, it is doubtlessly true that factors other than the distribution of power operate on urban renewal experience or the lack of it.

Factors Influencing Urban Renewal

For example, the probability that urban renewal might recommend itself to a community as a course of action should be somewhat contingent on the state of its physical equipment. If the equipment, in this instance its buildings, is fairly new and in good condition, urban renewal would make little sense. But where buildings are old or dilapidated a proposal to renew or rehabilitate would appear to be appropriate. Two measures of the condition of buildings are used here: (1) the percentage of all residential units constructed before 1920, and (2) the percentage of all residential units reported as dilapidated. Cities are classified relative to the median for each characteristic, providing two dichotomies. "Young" cities have less than 65 percent of their houses built before 1920, and "old" cities 65 percent or more of their houses built prior to that date. Cities with less than 4.7 percent of their houses dilapidated are described as "low" on that variable while those with 4.7 percent and over are classified as "high."

It is conceivable, too, that some cities might have anticipated the problems that invite urban renewal by having established a well-financed and strongly supported planning agency. Cities that have done so might not have to seek federal assistance for improvements. A contrary argument can also be advanced. Perhaps cities with substantial commitments to planning are more prepared to enter into a renewal project than are cities in which planning has not been developed to any appreciable extent. Notwithstanding my inability to resolve this question, the size of the planning budget might prove to be a factor of some consequence. For the purpose of control, planning expenditures are expressed as a ratio to total government operating costs in 1955. Ratios of less than .4 are below the median and thus identify their respective cities as "low" with respect to planning budgets, while ratios of .4 and over indicate cities with ' high" planning budgets.

There is a strong likelihood, too, that central cities of metropolitan areas might be more favorably disposed toward urban renewal than suburban cities. That should follow from the fact that central cities are generally older than are suburbs. But it should also derive from the deconcentration trend through which central cities have been losing population and industry to outlying areas. Many large suburban cities have also begun to experience declining growth rates, though in only a few cases has the trend reached a critical stage. Where substantial losses, real or threatened, have been encountered urban renewal might appear to offer a means by which to reverse the trend. There is a second factor that calls attention to the central city-suburb distinction. That is the peculiar residential distribution of managers, proprietors, and officials. Since members of those groups tend to live in suburbs while working in central cities their numbers as reported in the Census fail to reflect accurately the number of such positions in each place. The only practicable solution to this difficulty is to control for metropolitan status, that is, central city and suburb.

My operationalization of the concentration of power represents but one facet of a complex phenomenon. Other dimensions of that phenomenon should at least be admitted as control variables. For example, power may lie mainly in either the manufacturing or in the local service sector of a community's economy, whichever is most important. Relative importance is here measured by the ratio of manufacturing payroll to the combined payrolls in retailing, wholesaling, and service enterprises. Service cities have ratios of 1.5 or less and manufacturing cities have ratios of over 1.5.

The average size of manufacturing plant is another possible dimension of the distribution of power, especially if it may be construed as an indicator of the general scale of functional activities in the community. Size of plant is measured by the average number of employees per plant. Small-plant cities have averages of less than 70 employees; large-plant cities have over 70 employees per plant.

Influence of City Government

Still another expression of power distribution is found in the type of city government. In cities having a commission form of government, administrative responsibility is spread over a large number of non-elective officials. Such cities probably are unable to mobilize for action unless there is a fairly high concentration of power of the kind under study here. Administrative authority is more centralized where a mayor-council government exists. And in a city manager, government administrative authority reaches its highest degree of centralization and articulation. Hence, contrary to the findings of another study that type of city government is not important in determining urban renewal success,[9] I shall employ it as a control.

Two other controls having to do with the socioeconomic level of the resident population are used. Both assume that where the socioeconomic level is high the community may be prepared to act in a matter such as urban renewal independently of a concentration of power. The first, education, is represented by the proportion of the population with four or more years of college completed. The second, income, is measured by median income. Cities are dichotomized on the median for each variable. Cities with less than 6.0

percent of their residents with four years or more of college education are "low," and those with over that proportion are "high." The median position for the median income array falls at $3,450; cities below and above that figure are "low" and "high," respectively.

Finally, region is included among the controls. To some extent regional differences combine differences in age of cities, dilapidation, income, education, and possibly other of the control variables discussed above. Thus it is reasonable to expect that the association of power distribution with urban renewal success might vary by region. Four regions are recognized for control purposes; northeast, north central, south, and west.[10]

Further MPO Ratios

MPO ratios for each urban renewal status class and with each of the ten controls applied successively are shown in Table 3. In no instance does the introduction of a control vitiate the association of power concentration with urban renewal success, though in a number of instances the dropout cities fail to hold an intermediate position between execution stage and never-in-program cities. Although the averages for dropout cities are affected by small numbers of cities in many cases, it is also possible that power concentration has been employed to defeat urban renewal in those cities. It is worth noting that even where the concentration of power is relatively great, as in old cities, mayor-council cities, manufacturing cities, large-plant cities, low-education cities, and cities in the northeast, the concentration varies with urban renewal success. There is no indication, in short, that the importance attached to the concentration of power is peculiar to any one type or class of city. Despite the fact that suburban cities are the preferred places of residence for a large proportion of the holders of administrative positions, urban renewal success seems to require as great a concentration of power in suburbs as it does in central cities. Also of interest is the evidence that manager cities appear to be able to achieve urban renewal with less power concentration than do cities of other government classes.

To better assess the closeness of the association of power concentration with urban renewal success I have employed rank correlation analysis, using Kendall's tau-c. For this purpose the three urban renewal status classes are assumed to constitute a scale. Evidence that such an assumption is reasonable is present in Tables 1 and 3. The independent variable is treated in a quintile distribution of cities by MPO ratios, as in Table 2. The results are shown in Table 4, for which data a one-tailed test of significance was used.

It is clear from the findings in Table 4 that the concentration of power is positively and significantly associated with urban renewal success under virtually all conditions of control. Several exceptions occur, however. The relationship is not dependable for cities with mayor-council governments,

Table 3
**Mean MPO Ratios in Cities, by Urban Renewal Status,
with Selected Variables Controlled**

Control Variable	Urban Renewal Status		
	Execution Stage	Dropout	Never in Program
Age of housing:			
Young	10.1	10.7	12.2
Old	8.2	9.5	9.5
Extent of dilapidation:			
Low	9.1	9.2	11.0
High	9.1	10.9	10.2
Planning budget:			
Small	8.8	9.3*	11.0
Large	9.6	11.3	11.6
Metropolitan status:			
Central city	9.0	10.8	10.1
Suburban city	8.9	8.5	11.9
Government:			
Manager	9.5	9.7	12.3
Mayor-council	8.8	9.4	9.7
Commission	8.7	12.1	10.2†
Industry:			
Service	10.0	10.9	12.6
Manufacturing	8.1	9.2	9.7
Size of manufacturing plant:			
Small	9.5	11.0	12.0
Large	8.1	8.8	9.5
Median income:			
Low	8.8	10.7	9.6
High	9.2	9.7	11.4
Education:			
Low	8.2	9.8	8.6
High	9.8	10.5	12.4
Region:			
Northeast	8.5	8.1	9.8
North central	8.5	10.6	10.4
South	9.4	11.0	12.2†
West	11.9†	12.8*	12.6

*N is 5 or less.   †N is less than 10.

Table 4
Measures of Association of MPO Ratios with Urban Renewal Status,
with Selected Variables Controlled

Control Variable	TAU	χ/σ	P
All cities	.267	4.112	.00003
Age of housing:			
Young	.239	2.568	.00510
Old	.236	2.689	.00360
Extent of dilapidation:			
Low	.258	2.801	.00260
High	.267	2.951	.00160
Planning budget			
Small	.243	2.159	.01540
Large	.305	2.430	.00750
Metropolitan status:			
Central city	.214	2.874	.00200
Suburban city	.402	3.337	.00048
Government:			
Manager	.429	3.711	.00011
Mayor-council	.134	1.387	.08230
Commission	.302	3.337	.00048
Industry:			
Service	.169	.998	.15870
Manufacturing	.220	3.175	.00068
Size of manufacturing plant:			
Small	.301	3.292	.00048
Large	.186	2.065	.01960
Median income:			
Low	.219	2.533	.00570
High	.266	2.833	.00230
Education:			
Low	.122	1.382	.08380
High	.363	3.995	.00003
Region:			
Northeast	.108	1.096	.13350
North central	.233	2.062	.01970
South	.388	2.805	.00260
West	.105	.649	.25780

with a predominance of service industry, with small proportions of college graduates among their residents, and with locations in the northeast and the west. Some of these exceptions appear to be contrary to the positive findings involving variables known to be closely associated with them (education and income, northeastern location, and manufacturing industry). Had it been possible to refine the controls, some of the inconsistencies doubtlessly would have disappeared.

The category of all managers, proprietors, and officials is quite heterogeneous; it embraces the full range of both size and type of unit in which such positions occur. Thus it is not unlikely that one or another subclass or industry group of managers, proprietors, and officials might be primarily responsible for the observed association. But the measures reported in Table 5 indicate that that is not the case. The correlation is statistically significant for every industrial class of managers, proprietors, and official but one. The one, public administration, not only falls short of significance, it is negative. Why the prospects for urban renewal success should tend to increase with increases in the relative numbers of managers and officials in public administration poses an interesting problem. But that is not a question that can be pursued here. Nor is it possible to press the analysis of industry class of managers, proprietors, and officials further at present, though the fact that the relationship for each industry class taken separately responds differently to the application of controls clearly points to a need for a more intensive investigation.

Table 5
Measures of Association of MPO Ratios with Urban Renewal Status by Class of Industry, with Selected Variables Controlled

Industry Class	TAU	χ/σ	P
All industries	.267	4.112	.00003
Manufacturing:			
Salaried MPO's	.170	2.622	.00440
Self-employed MPO's	.209	3.229	.00137
Retail and wholesale trade	.214	3.300	.00097
Banking and finance	.209	3.229	.00137
Public administration	−.105	−1.162	.10740

Conclusion
While the findings reported in this paper should be regarded as exploratory, they clearly support the hypothesis that the lower the MPO ratio the greater

the chance of success in an action program such as urban renewal. They also demonstrate the facility and the economy in research of a conception of power as a system property. Much remains to be done, however, to develop knowledge about that property. A factor of some importance is the composition of managerial positions in a city. The relative numbers in the key industry should prove decisive, if my initial argument is correct. What constitutes a key industry, of course, is contingent upon the function the city performs for the regional and national society. The pursuit of that question will doubtlessly suggest further lines of investigation.

Notes and References

1. Representative studies include Floyd Hunter, *Community Power Structure* (Chapel Hill: University of North Carolina Press, 1953); Robert O. Schultz and Leonard U. Blumberg, "The [Determination] of Local Power Elites," *American Journal of Sociology*, 63 (1957), 290-96; Delbert C. Miller, "Decision-making Cliques in Community Power Structure," *American Journal of Sociology*, 64 (1958), 299-309; Paul Miller, "The Process of Decision-making within the Context of Community Organization," *Rural Sociology*, 17 (1952), 153-61.

2. Raymond E. Wolfinger, "The Study of Community Power," *American Sociological Review*, 25 (1960), 636-44.

3. This position has been stated recently by Richard M. Emerson, though he objects to the assumption of generalized power that is adopted, at least for present purposes, in this study ("Power-Dependence Relations," *American Sociological Review*, 27 (1962), 31-32.

4. The conception of power developed here is interchangeable with the ecological concept of dominance. Ecologists, however, have been content to treat dominance as an attribute of location or type of place, though the concept has always carried overtones of organizational properties. They have neglected to exploit the concept as an entree into the general problem of organization.

5. A similar notion appears in the introductory remarks of C. Wright Mills in his book on *The Power Elite* (New York: Oxford University Press, 1956). Nevertheless it soon becomes apparent that Mills is mainly concerned with the personal characteristics of the occupants of such positions.

6. For present purposes only managers, proprietors, and officials "not elsewhere classified" are used, [thus] eliminating technical positions that have no management or policy-determining functions. The category, it should be noted, is not limited to management positions in pecuniary establishments. It includes managers of art galleries, libraries, community funds, welfare agencies, and others.

7. Data on cities that have had urban renewal experience have been obtained from the *Annual Report of the Housing and Home Finance Agency*, 1951 through 1960 (Washington, D.C.).

8. *Urban Renewal Project Characteristics* (Washington, D.C.: Housing and Home Finance Agency, Urban Renewal Administration, June 30, 1959).

9. George S. Duggar, "The Relation of Local Government Structure to Urban Renewal," *Law and Contemporary Problems*, 26 (1961), 42-69.

10. Two other controls were used with similar results: population size and income as represented by the proportion of families with incomes of $10,000 or more per year.

Environmental Problems and Legislative Response
Jack C. Oppenheimer
Leonard A. Miller

At the beginning of 1970, there was as yet no national legislative, administrative, or judicial policy on environmental problems. Congress has been well aware of the need for an environmental policy. "Over the years, many legislative committees and individual Members (of Congress) have become aware of the difficulty of reconciling conflicting uses of the environment in the absence of any comprehensive policy guidance."[1] The legislature has responded to environmental problems as the specific biological, physical, or societal effect of the particular environmental insult was perceived, often long after the problem had reached dangerous proportions. Legislative responses have often been reactions to crisis situations, and, to a great degree, have been a function of the public's quickened and heightened awareness of all our problems resulting from the mass media.

Moreover, control of pollution has not in the past received high legislative priority. "There is a need to raise the priority of the whole pollution abatement effort within the structure of national objectives."[2]

Increasingly, legislators have come to understand that the insults to the environment are to a great extent created by modern technology. The same technology which results in the creation of pollution could, if properly harnessed to agreed-upon environmental-quality goals, help to solve environmental problems.

The traditional legislative responses to issues of conservation, and to all those problems which have now been recognized as environmental problems, have begun to change. The legislative pace is quickening. Public interest is growing. Indeed, as the paper is being written, the President is indicating that he intends to give greater attention to the details of solving environmental problems.

The current legislative responses to environmental problems are similar to previous conservation movements, but yet different in their degree of activity and the character of their concern. The men whom we may call "environmentalists" share many concerns with the traditional "conservationists." But their interest is not limited to conserving, developing, and utilizing natural resources, and preserving nature and wildlife in the original state. Their concern is with the accelerating man-made environment and the interrelationships among man, the environment that he has produced, and the natural environment. The environmentalists encompass many of the same attitudes as the conservationists, but their major interest is to create a "livable environment" in the modern urban society.[3] They may have been yesteryear's conservationists, but they are today's social engineers, epidemiologists, systems analysts, and environmental lawyers.

This paper seeks to look at the approach of the Congress toward the creation of a national environmental policy and to enumerate some of the legislative responses to the problems posed by environmental pollution. We look at these matters at the close of 1969, keeping well in mind that the months ahead may see major developments in the policies and organization with respect to the effort to combat pollution.

Conservation and Other Traditional Responses

Conservation policies arose out of the desire to preserve and protect the natural habitat from man's savagely civilizing force. Early conservation measures were concerned with such matters as the establishment of national parks; the preservation of forest lands; the regulation of the mining of minerals underlying the national public lands; the reclamation and irrigation of the public domain; the protecting and dredging of navigable rivers; the control of floods; the preservation and licensing of hydroelectric-power sites on navigable rivers; and the preservation of fish and wildlife. The stated objective of the conservation movement for some time before the turn of the century, and through the 1930s to the World War II period, was to preserve national resources. The conservation movement attempted to keep the industrialists from overexploiting the public lands, the related natural resources, and the navigable waters. As a Report of the House of Representatives Subcommittee on Science, Research, and Development stated:

> As agriculture became a technology and markets developed over a growing transportation system, the latter 1800s were characterized by an attitude of exploitation and harvest. Timber, minerals, and produce were fed into the industrial revolution. There was always another frontier, a new field, river, mine meadow, or forest.
>
> About 1900, the conservation movement began to exert its logic on American politics. The concept was crystallized that the present generation had an obligation to posterity to hand down the natural environment with adequate resources for the future.[4]

The next wave of conservation was born of the necessity to deal productively with the problems of vast unemployment during the depression of the 1930s: reforest the land, build a dam or bridge or other public work, and maintain the dignity of labor. Hard on the heels of this approach came the agricultural -soil conservationists and the social and economic developers. They were concerned with projects like the Tennessee Valley Authority and river projects which attempted to conserve, develop, and use such rivers as the Columbia, the Colorado, and the Missouri. They were attempting to develop and protect the land; to prove that government can aid industrialization, preserve natural and human resources, and provide power at lower rates.

But the legislature still did not perceive the harm that was being done to the environment. Cities were accepted as being dirty places. "[D]ust and smoke were billowing signs of progress and industrial growth, the pride of towns and cities. [Only now] . . . have [we] come to realize that contamination with wastes is an unwanted [and unnecessary] consequence of a highly technical society."[5] Indeed, as late as the 1950s, a Pennsylvania court quoted an earlier opinion by Mr. Justice Musmanno of the Pennsylvania Supreme Court, then a county judge, whose words are a classic statement of the early view of economics and pollution:

> One's bread is more important than landscape or clear skies.
> Without smoke, Pittsburgh would have remained a very pretty *village*.[6]

The modern approach to the problem of the environment began with the experimental Water Pollution Control Act of 1948.[7] In July 1955, Congress authorized a federal program of research on air pollution and technical assistance to state and local governments.[8] In 1956 Congress enacted the first comprehensive Federal Water Pollution Control Act, providing for grants to both states and localities and for municipal sewage-treatment works and providing a procedure for federal abatement efforts.[9] In 1963 and 1965 came the enactment of basic legislation of the Clean Air Act, which authorized the regulation of both mobile and stationary sources of air pollution.[10] In 1965 the Solid Waste Disposal Act authorized a small program of grants to states and localities for the planning of solid-waste disposal.[11] More amendments were to be added to these basic legislative Acts, but the federal government was, at last, involved in environmental management.

These acts signaled the new perception of the scope of the environmental problem—the increasing urbanization of the United States. The traditional conservationist's emphasis upon the esthetics of Yellowstone National Park and the natural resources of the Western public domain, to the exclusion of the problems of life in New York City, would no longer be accepted. Ironically, and as testimony to the complexities of the problem, the growth and affluence of the mobile American population is now polluting even our national parks with traffic congestion, automotive exhaust fumes, and trash of all kinds. But the new legislative crusaders, who first began to come forward in the late 1940s and during the 1950s, rightfully saw their task as that of creating livable environments in the midst of the urban sprawl of the megalopolis.

The New Environmentalists

Increasingly, the nation has come to realize that the physical environment is of immediate importance. People have learned that the environment affects their very lives. Even those problems, like noise, which have long been considered "an inevitable by-product of our modernizing society,"[12] are now the subject of concern to environmentalists and legislators. That is not to say that methods now exist to combat all pollution problems. As a Report of the Research Management Advisory Panel of the House of Representatives Subcommittee on Science, Research, and Development observed:

> It is often stated that the necessary technology for successful abatement of pollution is at hand; that it simply has not been applied, due to lack of money or because of institutional barriers. Close examination shows that this common belief (1) is not true in many instances (no present technology for gross treatment of mine drainage or nitrogen oxide emissions); (2) is true only at very high cost in other situations (sulfur dioxide removal from stack gases); and (3) is true only for partial alleviation in a third set of pollutants (automotive exhaust or municipal sewage).[13]

But it often seems as if the creation of technological breakthroughs depends upon institutional commitment and finances. A statement made several years ago by a Vice President of Ford Motor Company attests:

> Invention can be predicted with a fair degree of accuracy and it can be scheduled. In the automotive industry, our technology has advanced to the stage that our engineers can invent practically on demand. Almost any device we can dream up, the engineers can make.[14]

Although we have not reached the stage of corporate or societal commitment to manage the abatement or adequate control of automotive pollution or of other sources of pollution, we have come to a period of increasing activity in the environmental areas. This activity takes the form of citizen concern, public and private court action, and governmental regulation.

Although it is agreed that the environment can be only as clean as the citizens demand, the demand must be focused and channeled to be effective. Lawsuits are a method of effectuating citizen demands, but, with notable exceptions,[15] the suits have not been frequent enough, or successful enough, to ameliorate the larger pollution problems substantially. State and local authorities have the legal power to protect health, and a few leading states (New Jersey in airplanes and sulfur dioxide; Minnesota in atomic power; California in autos) have acted most vigorously.

The problems themselves are often not susceptible to traditional local solutions. Water pollution must be dealt with on at least a watershed basis, comprehending the drainage basin of a river system, and air pollutants which are transported by common air masses from sources to receptors must be dealt with on a regional basis. It is axiomatic that neither water nor air pollution is a respector of city, county, or state boundaries. It is no longer reasonable to suggest a complete solution to air pollution through dispersion of pollutants by high smoke stacks, since the pollutants must go somewhere. We now laugh at town officials who think that the total solution to solid-waste disposal is simply to cart its garbage across the city line, or float it downstream. Pollution is a multijurisdictional problem requiring co-operative action among federal, state, and local governments.

Current legislation, while preserving the traditional role of state and local governments to deal with what have been considered local matters, that is, health and sanitation and the use of land, recognizes the role of the federal government. The 1967 Amendments to the Clean Air Act state:

> ". . . that the prevention and control of air pollution at its source is the primary responsibility of States and local governments; and . . . that Federal financial assistance and leadership is essential for the development of cooperative Federal, State, regional, and local programs to prevent and control air pollution."[16]

The Water Quality Act of 1965, recognized the need for federal legislation when it stated: "The purpose of this Act is to enhance the quality and value of our water resources and to establish a national policy for the prevention, control, and abatement of water pollution."[17] Now it is recognized that a national policy for water must include air and solid-waste disposal, for industry has three choices in removing its waste matter—burn it, bury it, or barge it. Indeed, a national policy to solve the problems of any type of pollution must be a national policy for the environment.[18]

The Current Legislative and Executive Scene

Congressional proposals affecting the environment are numerous. Moreover, and perhaps more important, industry is now cognizant of the extent of federal interest. A spokesman for Standard Oil Company of Indiana recently stated:

> "In analyzing the hundreds of other proposed bills and amendments

dealing with pollution control and abatement, we find a consistent and determined effort to extend federal jurisdiction into the many areas traditionally reserved to the states, to increase penalties, and to advance abatement timetables."[19]

The *Congressional White Paper on a National Policy for the Environment*, reporting on "selected issues and representative legislation introduced in the 90th Congress," listed thirty-seven Senate bills and fifty-eight House bills. "Nineteen committees and over 120 members are represented." [20] In only the first session of the Ninety-first Congress, a look at representative legislation showed at least nineteen bills introduced in the Senate and at least another fifty-six House bills. The Table illustrates the magnitude of congressional concern.

The number of committees in Congress concerned with environmental pollution have their counterparts in the pollution research, development, and control activities spread throughout the executive branch. "Different aspects of the environment are treated separately by many organizations whose purposes are often in conflict." [21] Drinking-water standards are a function of the Department of Health, Education, and Welfare (HEW), while water quality in general is within the jurisdiction of the Department of the Interior. HEW also has the federal air pollution program, the major solid-waste management program, and numerous programs on urban-related environmental problems. The Departments of Agriculture, Commerce, Housing and Urban Development, Interior, and Transportation all have important research and operational missions and activities bearing upon many aspects of environmental quality, as do the Atomic Energy Commission, the Federal Power Commission, and the Tennessee Valley Authority. The Office of Science and Technology in the President's Executive Office in 1968 prepared a list for the Congress of four federal councils, twelve interagency committees which operated under the Federal Council for Science and Technology, and fourteen interagency agreements. [22] A later congressional report charted the activity of over twenty major agencies involved with problems of environmental management.[23]

In addition, there is Executive Order 11,472, issued on June 3, 1969 [24] which established the President's Environmental Quality Council and the Citizens' Advisory Committee on Environmental Quality. There is the recently enacted National Environmental Policy Act, signed by the President on January 1, 1970, which established a Council on Environmental Quality, with a long-range policy and research function similar to that of the Council of Economic Advisers.[25]

These developments raise the familiar question of whether it is possible to deal effectively with environmental problems against the background of

Table 1
Representative Legislation on Environmental Problems
Introduced in the Ninety-First Congress, First Session (1969)*

Senate	Bill No.	Introduced by
Committee on Agriculture and Forestry		
Establish a national commission on pesticides	S.1799	Mr. Nelson
Study of effects of use of certain poisons	S.2747	Mr. Tydings
Joint Committee on Atomic Energy		
Amend Atomic Energy Act of 1954 for environmental quality	S.2768	Mr. Tydings
Commerce Committee		
Amend Marine Resources Act of 1966 for environmental quality	S.2841	Mr. Hollings
Committee on Finance		
Tax incentives of water- and air-pollution abatement	S.702	Mr. Byrd (W. Va.)
Suspend investment credit	S.2648	Mr. Hartke
Committee on Foreign Relations		
U.S. as host of U.N. Conference on Environment	S.Res.179	Mr. Muskie
Interagency commission to plan for U.N. conference	S.J.Res.156	Mr. Yarborough
Committee on Government Operations		
Establish Department of Conservation and the Environment	S.2312	Messrs. Case, Gravel, Moss
Committee on Interior and Insular Affairs		
Declare a national policy on conservation	S.237	Mr. McGovern
Establish a Council on Environmental Quality	S.1075	Messrs. Jackson, Allott, Anderson, Bellmon, Bible, Burdick, Church, Fannin, Gravel, Hansen, Hatfield, Jordan (Idaho), McGovern, Metcalf, Moss, Nelson, Stevens
Establish a Council on Environmental Quality	S.1752	Mr. Nelson
Committee on the Judiciary		
Interstate Compact on Air Pollution (Ohio-West Virginia)	S.2707	Mr. Randolph
Committee on Labor and Public Works		
Support of Congress for international biological program	S.J.Res.89	Mr. Muskie
Committee on Public Works		
Water Quality Improvement Act of 1969 and Environmental Quality Improvement Act	S.7	Messrs. Muskie, Baker, Boggs, Burdick, Byrd (W.Va.) Case, Cooper, Dodd, Erwin, Fong, Hart, Inouye, Kennedy, Magnuson, Mansfield, Metcalf, Mondale, Montoya, Moss, Mur-

Table 1 Cont.

Senate	Bill No.	Introduced by
		phy, Nelson, Packwood, Prouty, Randolph, Ribicoff, Scott, Spong, Tydings, Williams (N.J.) Yarborough, Young (Ohio)
National policy for the environment	S.1085	Mr. Nelson
Inclusion of environmental quality considerations in decision-making	S.1818	Mr. Tydings
Resource Recovery Act of 1969	S.2005	Messrs. Muskie, Bayh, Boggs, Cooper, Eagleton, Metcalf, Montoya, Randolph, Spong, Yarborough, Young (Ohio)
National Material Policy Act of 1969	Amend. S.2005	Messrs. Boggs, Baker, Bayh, Cooper, Eagleton, Inouye, Montoya, Muskie, Pearson, Randolph, Spong
Provide for co-ordination of federal air, water, solid-waste programs	S.2391	Mr. Muskie *et al.* (40)
Underground uses of atomic energy and environment	S.3042	Messrs. Gravel, Muskie, Randolph

House	Bill No.	Introduced by
Committee on Agriculture		
Establish a National Commission on Pesticides	H.R.11809	Mr. Ashley
Committee on Foreign Affairs		
Plan international conference on environment	H.Res.341	Mr. Brown (Calif.)
Support for international biological program	H.J.Res.589	Messrs. Miller (Calif.), Daddario
Committee on Government Operations		
Establish a Commission on Population and Environment	H.R.10515	Mr. Udall
Environmental Quality Council	H.R.11952	Messrs. Reuss, Blatnik, Gude, Hicks, McCloskey, Moss, Vander Jagt, Wright
Establish a National Commission for Environmental Protection	H.R.12285	Mr. Ottinger
Redesignate Department of Interior as Department of Resources, Environment and Population	H.R.14308	Messrs. Bush, Carter, Frey, Gubser, Horton, Lukens, McCloskey, Pettis, Reid (N.Y.), Wold

Table 1 Cont.

House	Bill No.	Introduced by
Committee on Interior and Insular Affairs		
Study by Secretary of Interior on environmental quality	H.R.952	Mr. Bennett
	H.R.7923	Mr. Howard
	H.R.8006	Mr. Podell
Establish national policy for, and a study of, environment	H.R.11937	Mr. Foley
Establish a Council on Environmental Quality, and a study	H.R.12900	Mr. Saylor
Committee on Interstate and Foreign Commerce		
Electric Power Co-ordination Act of 1969	H.R.12585	Mr. McDonald (Mass.)
Formulation of a national policy for environment	H.R.13826	Mr. Monagan
Committee on Merchant Marine and Fisheries		
To amend the Fish and Wildlife Co-ordination Act to provide for Council on Environmental Quality	H.R.6750	Mr. Dingell
	H.R.11886	Mr. Tunney
	H.R.11942	Mr. Griffiths
	H.R.12077	Mr. Ottinger
	H.R.12180	Mr. Adams
	H.R.12228	Mr. Sisk
	H.R.12409	Mr. Moss
	H.R.12503	Mr. Diggs
	H.R.12506	Mr. Fulton (Tenn.)
	H.R.12507	Mr. Gray
	H.R.12511	Mr. Karth
	H.R.12525	Mr. Blatnik
	H.R.12527	Mr. Conte
	H.R.12573	Mr. Cohelan
	H.R.12603	Mr. Fascell
	H.R.12877	Messrs. Ruppe, McDonald (Mich.), Vander Jagt Esch
	H.R.12928	Mr. Obey
	H.R.12932	Mr. Riegle
	H.R.13042	Mr. Waggonner
Amend Fish and Wildlife Co-ordination Act to provide more protection from federal pollution	H.R.13579	Mr. Karth
Amend Marine Resources Act to provide for the environment	H.R.13247	Messrs. Lennon, Garmatz, Mosher, Rogers (Fla.), Pelly, Ashley, Keith, Downing, Schadeberg, Karth,

Table 1 Cont.

House	Bill No.	Introduced by
		Dellenback, Hathaway, Pollock, Clark, Ruppe, St. Onge, Goodling, Jones (N.C.), Bray, Hanna
Provide for research and development concerning environment	H.R.14418	Mr. Tunney
Committee on Public Works		
Amend Federal Water Pollution Act	H.R.4148	Mr. Fallon *et al.*
Pollution Disaster Fund	H.R.9895	Messrs, Vanik, Dent, Dulski, Edwards (Calif.), Vigorito
Federal Pollution Control Commission	H.R.13492	Mr. Lujan
Committee on Rules		
Establish a Select Committee on Environment	H.Res.157	Mr. Brown (Calif.)
Establish Committee on Environment	H.Res.419	Mr. Taft
	H.R.433	Messrs. Teague (Calif.), Horton, Mikva, Cahill, Blackburn, Pike, Mollohan, McCloskey, Lujan, Lloyd, Halpern, Mann, Steiger (Ariz.)
	H.Res.434	Burton (Utah)
	H.Res.435	Mr. Fish
Establish Council of Conservation Advisers	H.R.3114	Mr. Reuss
	H.R.12372	Mr. Reid (N.Y.)
Establish Joint Committee on Environmental Quality	H.R.11816	Mr. Dingell
	H.R.12265	Mr. Farbstein
	H.R.12700	Mr. Kuykendall
	H.R.12761	Mr. Charles H. Wilson
Establish national policy for environment	H.R.13764	Mr. Brown (Calif.)
Committee on Science and Astronautics		
Council on Environmental Quality	H.R.25	Messrs. Dingell, Karth
	H.R.12373	Mr. Reid (N.Y.)
Expressing support of Congress for international biological program	H.J.Res.625	Mr. Podell
	H.J.Res.674	Mr. Fulton (Pa.)
Establish Council of Ecological Advisers	H.R.3329	Mr. Tunney
Establish Citizens' Advisory Committee on Environmental Quality	H.R.13272	Messrs. Daddario, Mosher

*The bills are grouped according to committee of referral. A total of nineteen Senate and House committees are listed.

the varied and conflicting interests of the constituencies of the congressional legislative and appropriation committees and their executive-agency counterparts. Indeed, the real question may be: Can man manage the totality of the human eco-system?

Notes and References

1. U.S., Senate, Committee on Interior and Insular Affairs, and U.S., House of Representatives, Committee on Science and Astronautics, *Congressional White Paper on a National Policy for the Environment*, 90th Cong., 2nd sess. (Washington, D.C.: Government Printing Office, 1968), p. iii.

2. U.S., House of Representatives, Committee on Science and Astronautics, *The Adequacy of Technology for Pollution Abatement: Report of the Research Management Advisory Panel*, 89th Cong., 2nd sess. (Washington, D.C.: Government Printing Office, 1966) p. 2.

3. For a general statement of concern for urban environment, see U.S., Task Force on Environmental Health and Related Problems, *A Strategy for a Livable Environment: A Report to the Secretary of Health, Education, and Welfare* (Washington, D.C.: Government Printing Office, 1967).

4. U.S., House of Representatives, Committee on Science and Astronautics, *Managing the Environment: Report of the Subcommittee on Science, Research and Development* (Washington, D.C.: Government Printing Office, 1968), p. 12.

5. U.S., House of Representatives, Committee on Science and Astronautics, *Environmental Pollution: A Challenge to Science and Technology: Report of the Subcommittee on Science, Research, and Development*, 89th Cong., 2nd sess. (Washington, D.C.: Government Printing Office, 1966), p. 9.

6. *Waschak v. Moffat*, 379 Pa. 441, 109 A.2d 310, 316 (1954), *citing* Mr. Justice Musmanno, then a county judge, in *Versailles Borough v. McKeesport Coal & Coke Co., Pittsburgh Legal Journal* 83, p. 379.

7. For a discussion of legislative background in water-pollution control, see U.S., House of Representatives, *Water Pollution Control: Report of the Committee on Public Works*, 89th Cong., 2nd sess. (Washington, D.C.: Government Printing Office, 1966), pp. 9-10.

8. See U.S., Secretary of Health, Education, and Welfare, *Progress in the Prevention and Control of Air Pollution: First Report to the United States Congress*, 90th Cong., 2nd sess. (Washington, D.C.: Government Printing Office, 1968), p. 1.

9. U.S., House of Representatives, *Water Pollution Control*.

10. U.S., Secretary of Health, Education, and Welfare, *Progress in the Prevention and Control of Air Pollution*.

11. *Solid Waste Disposal Act* of 1965, 42 United States Code 3251 et seq., 79 Stat. 997, Public Law 89-272.

12. U.S., Federal Council for Science and Technology, Committee on Environmental Quality, *Noise—Sound Without Value* (Washington, D.C.: Government Printing Office, 1968), p. 1.

13. U.S., House of Representatives, *The Adequacy of Technology for Pollution Abatement*, p. 7.

14. Donald Frey (Vice President, Ford Motor Company), Address to the National Industrial Research Conference, Purdue University, January 2, 1966, quoted in Ralph Nader and Joseph A. Page, "Automobile Design and Judicial Process," *California Law Review*, vol. 55, no. 3 (August 1967), p. 652.

15. The law suits of Victor J. Yannacone, Jr., may have precipitated government action on the chemical biocide DDT. There is presently pending a thirty billion dollar law suit by Carol A. Yannacone against eight chemical companies in the United States District Court for the Southern District of New York. On another aspect of private law suits, see Leonard A. Miller and Doyle J. Borchers, "The Role of Private Lawsuits in Air Pollution Control: Speculations on Court Usage of Government Materials," Paper presented at the Annual Meeting of the Air Pollution Control Association, New York City, June 26, 1969.

16. *Clean Air Act*, 42 United States Code, *1857-1857*1, Section 101(a) (3) and (4).

17. *Federal Water Pollution Control Act*, 33 United States Code, 466.

18. *See Congressional White Paper on a National Policy for the Environment* for some attempts to create a broad national policy.

19. Richard J. Farrell, "Let the Polluter Beware!," Address to Association of General Counsel, Washington, D.C., October 6, 1969, p. 4.

20. *Congressional White Paper on a National Policy for the Environment*, pp. 17-19.

21. U.S., House of Representatives, *Managing the Environment*, p. 28.

22. *Ibid.*, pp. 33-35, citing U.S., House of Representatives, *Environmental Quality: Hearings before the Subcommittee on Science, Research, and Development of the Committee on Science and Astronautics*, 90th Cong., 2nd sess. (Washington, D.C.: Government Printing Office, 1968), pp. 26-29.

23. U.S., House of Representatives, *Managing the Environment*, p. 33.

24. Executive Order 11,472, *Federal Register*, vol. 34, no. 105, p. 8693, June 3, 1969.

25. See "National Environmental Policy Act of 1969—Conference Report," *Congressional Record—Senate*, December 20, 1969, pp. S17,450-S17,462 and "National Environmental Policy Act of 1969," Public Law 91-190, 83 Stat. 852.

Selected References for Chapter 5

Anderson, Walt, ed. 1970. *Politics and Environment: A Reader in Ecological Crisis*. Pacific Palisades, California: Goodyear Publishing Co., Inc. Contains a variety of articles dealing with political dimensions of population and environment.

Chasteen, Edgar R. 1972. *The Case for Compulsory Birth Control*. Englewood Cliffs, N.J.: Prentice-Hall, Inc. An argument for political regulation of human reproduction.

Dyck, Arthur J. 1971. "Population Policies and Ethical Responsibility." Pp. 618-38 of *Rapid Population Growth*. Baltimore: The Johns Hopkins Press. Raises questions regarding the goals and consequences of alternative population policies.

Henkin, Harmon, Martin Merta, and James Staples 1971. *The Environment, the Establishment, and the Law*. Boston: Houghton Mifflin Co. A case study of political and legal problems in affecting environmental control based upon hearings regarding the contaminating effects of DDT.

Murphy, Earl Finbar 1967. *Governing Nature*. Chicago: Quadrangle Books. General discussion of political issues in environmental control.

This chapter has been focused on some examples of organizational attempts to regulate and control selected demographic and environmental variables. Three articles dealt with social policy as a regulatory mechanism, the other with social power. Perhaps the outstanding conclusion to be drawn regarding regulation through policy is that it appears to be a rather ineffective strategy. Foremost among the reasons underlying this failure is that, with few exceptions, social policies are formulated as responses to critical problems rather than anticipating them. In other words, the need for policy regarding a particular condition is recognized only after the situation reaches the crisis stage. Such is clearly the case with regard to world population growth and environmental quality in most of the industrialized nations. Another factor is that most of the policies that have been developed are neither well formulated nor adequately coordinated. This stems from the fact that policy makers and administrators alike are often lacking sufficient power to enforce their programs, or being reluctant to utilize the power they do have available. Thus far policies regarding control of both population and environment have depended largely upon the voluntary cooperation of the persons and groups affected. An additional reason for policy failure may be that inadequate attention has been paid to the role of motivational factors. Policy makers have failed to create sufficient incentives, material or ideological, to ensure compliance. For example, perhaps too often parents are told they should limit the number of children they have for the good of the nation, or because they already have three children, and other similarly abstract justifications, rather than in terms of more personal and immediate advantages. Additional factors associated with policy failure could be given, but those mentioned above are sufficient to suggest the need for critical evaluation of existing strategies for policy formation and administration.

The brief consideration given to power suggests its effectiveness in regulating individual and collective action. What seems to be problematic is the identification of the conditions under which power can and will be exerted. Certainly governments *could*, with appropriate sanctions, coerce families to limit births, and industrialists to refrain from polluting the environment, to give just two examples. But one must remember that the most basic use of power in social organizations is for ensuring internal order. Short of complete totalitariansim, governments must take into consideration the interests of public and private sectors, and thus are in varying degrees constrained in their use of coercion. Thus the use of power for achieving compliance with social policies is contingent upon additional considerations, few of which are fully understood at present. This may explain the conservative nature of present attempts to deal with problems of population and environmental policy in most nations today.

6

**Distributional Mechanisms:
The Role of Mobility of
People and Resources**

In this final chapter of Part II we consider some specific issues regarding mobility as a solution to problems of collective survival. Historically, migration streams have developed as responses to structural imbalances between sending and receiving areas.[1] The resulting movement of people has obvious consequences for the size and composition of both populations, not all of which can be considered as contributing to ecological adaptation. In recent years considerable attention has been devoted to problems created for recipient areas due to the heavy influx of migrants. However, inadequate attention has been given to problems resulting in areas of outmigration.[2] Some important considerations in this regard, pertaining particularly to the economy, are presented in the contribution by John B. Parr.

This article is focused on outmigration as a potential means of easing difficulties in areas with high rates of unemployment and/or underemployment. The question is whether or not emigration from such an area is adaptive in the sense of providing a better fit between numbers of potential workers and the demand for labor, which would be a reduction of one variety of population pressure. Parr suggests that outmigration is perhaps the only feasible solution in certain types of depressed areas; specifically, rural settings and those industrial areas that have lost their economic base. The smaller the total population, the more likely that emigration will improve conditions for those who remain behind.

But migratory movements are rarely planned with the welfare of the collectivity as the guiding criterion. Thus almost any large-scale migration presents difficulties for communities at both ends of the journey. With respect to the depressed-area problem, Parr identifies a number of emergent problems. Perhaps the most consequential of these is that migration is always selective.[3] Typically those persons who would most likely be assets to their communities—the better workers, the young, the more achievement-oriented and imaginative—are the first to leave. More often it is the already employed, rather than the unemployed, who have the necessary skills to obtain work in other areas. The loss of economically desirable components of the population has further ramifications, including a decreased tax base, thus resulting in less support for public services, and a decrease in the attractiveness of the community as a site for new industry. In addition, the pattern of movement may have regional implications, disturbing area relationships in existing markets and services. The point to be stressed here is that, due to the selective character of migration, any evaluation of its consequences in a given instance must pay attention to the entire system of social and economic relationships within which the population is embedded.

The author also points out that, regardless of the advisability of emigration for community welfare, people are highly reluctant to move away from familiar surroundings and, again, those who *will* move are not typical of the general population. Furthermore, other factors being equal, many emigrants are likely to return to the community of origin, especially if conditions there improve. Given their generally superior employment capabilities, these return migrants are likely to hinder the unemployed in their quest for work.

Parr concludes his argument with six generalizations regarding the relationship between outmigration and the condition of depressed areas. These suggest that, due to the selectivity of migration, more problems may be created than resolved. However, it is also implied that prior consideration of potential difficulties by policymakers may reduce the disruptive features of emigration. Such a policy would need to ensure a new and improved population balance, leaving a sufficient number of skilled workers and entrepreneurs to support a growing economy, yet transferring balanced proportions of employed and unemployed to areas that could absorb them into their economies through currently vacant positions or retraining for future ones. Specific parameters for policy of this nature will not be easy to determine. In addition, even if an adaptive migration policy could be conceptualized, there is certainly little evidence that people would accept the idea of being selectively moved from one area to another in the interests of an abstract condition like that of population balance. It is much more likely that, where permitted, individuals and families alike will continue to migrate in response to perceived personal opportunities or the lack of them, often on the basis of incomplete or erroneous information.

It would be a mistake to consider the mechanism of population mobility only in terms of relatively permanent movements. A moment's thought will bring to mind the fact that all levels of social organization—household, community, region, nation, systems of nations—are characterized by recurrent movements back and forth between particular locations. Men and women travel from home to market and workplace and back again, and goods and services are regularly exchanged through the medium of human mobility. This process represents an additional means by which the exigencies of collective survival are satisfied, yet requiring only minimal disruption of established social orders.[4] A perspective on this mode of ecological adaptation is presented in Leo Schnore's discussion of the separation of home and work.

This essay is aimed at refuting the notion that workers will *always* seek to minimize the distance between residence and work location. While accepting the fact that the proportion of employees at a given site is inversely related to the distance they must travel from home, Schnore argues that one must still account for that degree of scatter away from the site that does exist. In other words, if desire to minimize distance is a constant factor affecting choice of residential and/or work location, some variable conditions must be affecting the choices of those who do not conform to the modal pattern.

Findings from this analysis suggest that variations in distance between home and place of work are a function of the ratio of cost of maintaining the home to those of transportation to work. Generally, greater distance implies greater costs, though in particular cases(e.g., marginal workers) factors such as ride-sharing and opportunities for part-time agricultural work may result in a reversal of the typical pattern.

Schnore suggests that his hypothesis might be utilized in accounting for changes observed in the patterns of population distribution, and that the study of the location of industrial activities and other work sites might also be approached in this manner. Though not cited in this essay, the earlier work of James A. Quinn clearly expresses this position.[5] Thus the hypothesis of minimum costs states: Ecological units tend to distribute themselves throughout an area so that the total costs of gaining maximum satisfaction in adjusting population to environment (including other men) are reduced to the minimum;[6] while the hypothesis of median location proposes: "Within a free competitive system, social and aesthetic factors being equal, a mobile ecological unit tends to occupy a median location with respect to (1) the environmental resources it utilizes, (2) the other units on which it depends, and (3) the other units that it serves.[7]

The generalizations suggested by Schnore and by Quinn indicate further the adaptive significance of man's ability to distribute himself and his activities in accord with the conditions that maximize survival potential (in its broadest sense). Nevertheless, it is important to note that these locational decisions are not made at will, but rather depend upon certain limiting factors. It is the systematic interaction of the parameters of optimum location with operant contingencies that give structure to the spatial dimension of man's ecological organization.

With the final article in this chapter, we turn to an examination of distributive mechanisms and the non-human environment. This contribution by Jack P. Gibbs and Walter T. Martin deals with the relationship between urbanization and collective efforts to provide resources necessary for sustaining human populations. The authors develop two propositions, namely (1) The degree of urbanization in a country varies directly with the extent of the dispersion of its objects of consumption, and (2) The magnitude of the relationship by countries between a measure of the dispersion of objects of consumption and the proportion of the population living in cities increases directly with the size of the cities considered. Both propositions are supported by the statistical evidence presented.

More important than the results of these tests, which the authors admit are quite tentative due to inadequacies in the data utilized, is the underlying theoretical argument. Gibbs and Martin view human ecology as the study of sustenance organization (see their article included in Chapter One of this volume). Cities, they say, constitute a form of social organization designed to facilitate activities associated with the exploitation of natural resources, and thus contribute directly to the survival of the unit of which they are a part. They do this primarily through their functioning as transport and control centers, thereby contributing to the conversion of widely dispersed natural resources into objects of consumption for the country as a whole.[8] Thus these authors argue that there is an interactive relationship between the dispersion of the objects of consumption of a country and its degree of urbanization. In short, they see neither of these variables as a direct cause of the other. But in taking such care not to go out on a limb regarding the question of causation, Gibbs and Martin miss an important insight.[9] While urbanization is clearly one solution to the need for organizing the concentration, processing and redistribution of widely dispersed resources and their byproducts, it can hardly be said that these materials are dispersed to permit or foster urbanization. Rather, the connecting link is in the potential mobility and redistribution of *both* people and resources which, as Gibbs and Martin clearly recognize, are organizational phenomena. Stated otherwise, it is the concomitant and complementary movement of people and resources in response to sustenance pressures that constitutes the ecological adaptation, and it is this phenomenon that is of central significance for understanding problems of collective survival.

Notes and References

1. See Donald J. Bogue, *Principles of Demography*. New York: John Wiley & Sons, 1968, pp. 753-54.

2. For example, see Calvin L. Beale, "Rural Depopulation in the United States: Some Demographic Consequences of Agricultural Adjustments," *Demography*, Vol. 1 (1964), pp. 264-72.

3. c.f. William Peterson, "Migration: Social Aspects," *International Encyclopedia of the Social Sciences*, ed. David L. Sills, Vol. 10. New York: Crowell, Collier, and MacMillan, 1968, pp. 286-92.

4. See Amos H. Hawley, *Human Ecology: A Theory of Community Structure*. New York: The Ronald Press, 1950, pp. 324-47.

5. See his *Human Ecology*. New York: Prentice-Hall, Inc. 1950, pp. 279-91 and "The Hypothesis of Median Location," *American Sociological Review*, Vol. 8 (April 1943), pp. 148-56.

6. *Human Ecology*, op. cit., p. 282.

7. Ibid, p. 286.

8. Of course cities serve additional functions as well. For examples, see Leonard Reissman, *The Urban Process: Cities in Industrial Societies*. New York: The Free Press, 1964, pp. 195-238.

9. In part this may be due to their wording of the problem: "It is not meaningful to speak of the dispersion of objects of consumption as *causing* urbanization or vice versa." But it is the "vice versa" that makes no sense, while the statement presented is at least plausible.

Outmigration and the Depressed-Area Problem
John B. Parr

The post-war emergence of full-employment and the attendant rise in prosperity levels in most Western countries have highlighted the existence of the less fortunate regions, the so-called *depressed areas*. These depressed areas are characterized by persistently high rates of unemployment or, in the case of many rural depressed areas, high rates of under-employment. Furthermore, such areas commonly possess, in varying degrees, one or more of the following characteristics: a narrow range of economic activities, declining basic industries, unskilled or unadaptable labor-forces and decayed or inefficient infrastructures. Depressed areas owe their origins generally to downward structural and/or cyclical trends in the national economy as well as to problems associated with their location *vis-à-vis* centers of population and growth areas within the country concerned. In the absence of any public policy it can be expected that, with increasing national economic development, the condition of depressed areas will become relatively worse, according to various criteria which may be applied: growth rates, per capita income, unemployment differentials.[1] The founders of the European Economic Community recognized this tendency and tried to make provision for it through various supra-national agencies, among them the European Social Fund.

Given this trend toward polarization in levels of economic development *between areas, two broad approaches* to the solution of the problems of the depressed area are possible. The first involves the encouragement of new economic activity, i.e., the policy of "bringing work to the workers." The second approach, which can be described as a market adjustment, involves the movement of workers out of labor-surplus areas. This latter policy does not, of necessity, preclude government participation or intervention. It is possible that a public agency may wish to facilitate such a market adjustment by making grants or loans to those groups of the population willing to move. Also, under certain conditions outmigration may be a valuable complement to a policy of industrial relocation.

It is not the purpose of this paper to debate the merits of the two approaches, but rather to examine the implications of outmigration as a means for easing the difficulties facing depressed areas, particularly the unemployment difficulties. The importance and the role of industrial relocation in aiding depressed areas is fully realized, but limitations of space demand this partial treatment of solutions to the depressed area problem. It will be therefore assumed throughout the paper that no government authority is trying to encourage the relocation of industrial activities in the depressed area.

Two distinctions can be made as to the nature of depressed areas for the purposes of analysis. The first pertains to the environment. Depressed conditions may be present in an urban-industrial setting but they also frequently exist within a rural milieu. A second distinction concerns the scale of the depressed area. The *depressed community* consists of an individual city, a county or a state economic area, the latter division being a creation of the United States Bureau of Census. Such communities may be black spots in an otherwise fairly prosperous area or they may form part of a larger depressed area that could be labeled a *depressed region*. This larger entity might comprise, for example, an economic sub-region (another division being used for a unit breakdown of the nation by the United States Bureau of Census), a large metropolitan area, or a river basin. This distinction is arbitrary and in several other respects unsatisfactory. It is essential nonetheless because the outmigration will affect the two types of area in differing ways: what may be relevant and important in the case of a community may have less applicability and significance at the regional level.

The Effect of Labor-Migration on the Size of the Labor-Force
Whether or not outmigration will help depressed areas will depend on the extent to which it is able to reduce the divergence between the levels of supply and demand for labor. The demand for labor in a depressed area is dependent upon the demand for the products and services of the industries in the area, upon the prevailing local wage levels and, in the long-run, upon the potentialities of the area as location for economic activity. The level of labor supply in a depressed area is influenced largely by demographic considerations: persons entering the labor force, withdrawals from the labor force, and net outmigration from the area—the latter in its turn being partly influenced by the level of wages, relative to levels outside the depressed area. Outmigration of labor can affect both the supply of and the demand for labor. The effect on the demand for labor is less obvious and will be discussed later. This section is devoted to a consideration of the effect of labor outmigration on the supply of labor or the size of the labor force. The following equation shows the various demographic components which determine the level of labor-supply in any given time period:

$$A_{(t)} = A_{(t-1)} + N_{(t-1)} + M_{(t-1)}$$

Where:

$A_{(t)}$ = Size of the area's labor-force at the beginning of the time period t.

$A_{(t-1)}$ = Size of area's labor-force at the beginning of time period t-1.

$N_{(t-1)}$ = Net local additions to the labor-force (new entrants to the labor-force *minus* withdrawals from the labor-force) during time period t-1.[2]

$M_{(t-1)}$ = Net migration of labor during time period t-1.

Since the net local additions to the labor force are generally positive and since, in the case of a depressed area, the net migration of labor is most likely to be negative, it is possible that the labor-force will grow annually, remain stationary or decline depending on the level of labor outmigration— but a decline in the labor-force being the usual case.

In order to demonstrate the effect of outmigration on the supply of labor and hence on the level of unemployment, it is possible to conceive of a depressed community with a high level of unemployment and one in which the demand for labor has become constant through time. If the level of net labor outmigration over a period of time is greater than the net local additions to the labor force, then movement of labor out of the community may ease the unemployment difficulties by reducing the size of the labor force. There are three possible paths by which this may be achieved: (1) if all the labor that moves out is unemployed; (2) if all the new entrants onto the community labor-force such as school-leavers move from the community immediately, the vacancies created by retirements from the employed labor-force can be filled from the ranks of the unemployed; or (3) similarly, if the labor that moves was formerly employed. (Very frequently in depressed areas it is the employed labor, being wage-conscious and mobile, that is most likely to move.)

Paths 2 and 3 make the rather brave assumption that the unemployed have sufficient education and skills to fill the employment vacancies as they arise. Labor is by no means an homogeneous factor of production and substitution of the employed workers who retire or migrate by unemployed labor may not be feasible. In reality, it seems that the labor outmigration, if successful, would ease the unemployment problem by some combination of the three paths. It would be indeed unusual if outmigration consisted solely of one type.

So far the demand for labor has been assumed to be constant. If demands for labor are decreasing, which is frequently the case for depressed areas, then the rate of labor outmigration will need to be stepped up to a higher level if the unemployment level is to continue to decline. In such a situation, annual outmigration of labor would have to be greater than the sum of the annual net local additions to the labor force *plus* the annual reduction in employment if the level of unemployment is to decline, the above assumptions still holding.

Outmigration Can Sometimes Help

One situation where outmigration of labor can favorably affect unemployment is the rural depressed area. In such cases outmigration of labor, specifically the redundant agricultural workers, may permit a downward adjustment of the labor-force nearer to levels of current labor demand. Even in the *high income nations*, however, this movement from the land does not seem to be taking place at a sufficiently high rate, with the result that rural areas appear relatively poor in comparison with the rest of the nation. In the case of the United States, movement out of agriculture, while it may have forestalled chronic rural unemployment in some areas, has been unable to prevent the emergence of a widening gap between per capita incomes of the farming and non-farming sectors of the national economy.[3] In those areas where, due to inefficient farming techniques, the necessity of outmigration has become very great and where the subsequent response has been relatively poor, as in parts of the South East, the South West and Appalachia, high levels of agricultural unemployment and underemployment have become major problems. The existing lack of alternative employment possibilities and the general unsuitability of most rural areas as locations for industry tend to limit the range of possible adjustments to high unemployment to outmigration. The present-day outflow from rural areas, though at inadequate levels, can be regarded as a continuation of the historic movement from country to city that has always accompanied increased agricultural efficiency resulting from technical change.

A second case where outmigration may ease a depressed area's unemployment is that of the industrial community with a narrow economic base whose principal industry has experienced a major structural decline. Examples would include a textile center whose plants are no longer competitive or a coal mining town where the operations have become increasingly high-cost and inefficient. If no new employment possibilities are forthcoming, then labor migration out of the community would ease the unemployment problem considerably. Thus the post-1920 movement of workers from distressed towns in North-East Lancashire that were heavily specialized in the manufacture of textiles had the effect of reducing high unemployment levels in these areas. In this case, the relatively poor locations of these towns had the effect of precluding large influxes of alternative employment possibilities, although some new manufacturing activity did contribute to an improvement of the unemployment situation.

The smaller the population of the area, the more likely it is that outmigration will be of help in solving the problem. For the larger area outmigration seems less suitable because of certain longer-term, adverse influences which it brings to bear on the regional economy. In the case of the smaller depressed community, however, with little prospect of being the seat of new industry, outmigration of labor appears to be one of the few workable solutions since the disadvantages caused by outmigration are minimized. These disadvantages will be considered in the following section.

Labor outmigration from a community may be judged successful because it lowers the level of unemployment there. As far as the community is concerned this will be true. However, from the national point of view, it is necessary to know whether the outmigrants find employment when they reach their destination before such a judgment can be made. If, by outmigration, the unemployment is merely transferred elsewhere, then, from the national standpoint, little has been achieved by an areal redistribution of unemployment. It might be argued that a policy of spreading unemployment evenly is preferable on social grounds to a pattern of spatially concentrated unemployment. Yet, from the point of view of overall economic efficiency and national growth considerations, there may be serious objections to this. These might include the possibility of production bottlenecks in growth sectors which could hamper the relatively smooth and rapid structural adjustments that characterize the western economies.

Difficulties Created by Outmigration
Although, under certain circumstances, outmigration may have a generally favorable effect on unemployment, there are serious problems associated with outmigration, the most important being the effect on the demand for labor. One adverse feature of outmigration is its selective character. Generally the migrants represent the best workers (who may not even be unemployed), the younger elements (good trainee material) and would-be local administrators and entrepreneurs: in other words, the area is sapped of its vital and most needed elements. Also, the age distribution of the population may well become skewed in favor of the older groups.

In the case of Scotland, two important authorities draw attention to the loss of skilled labor. Cairncross notes "While there are many factors at work to promote emigration from Scotland, and it is indeed an ancient tradition of the country, it is difficult not to associate the current rate of outflow with the slower rate of industrial expansion."[4] The recent *Report on the Scottish Economy* states "there is little doubt that there is a net loss of men in the engineering scarcity trades from Scotland each year."[5] Such losses tend to make an area less attractive for prospective, incoming industry in addition to creating obstacles to the expansion of existing industries. These losses may even cause firms to cease production completely. Owen noted an interesting case concerning the pre-war depressed area of South Wales. In certain areas, when national market conditions improved, coal mines remained closed due to a shortage of skilled miners, most of whom had left the area earlier.[6]

If the firms that cease production are in the export sector of an area's economy and if the employment loss is not replaced, serious additional unemployment difficulties may be encountered.[7] Aside from the initial employment reduction and the consequent increase in unemployment, there may be downward local multiplier effects which adversely influence employment in trade and services, thereby extending unemployment to other sectors of the local economy. Thus outmigration of certain key factors can indirectly cause employment to fall off so rapidly that the local unemployment level will have risen. Under such circumstances only outmigration at a level greater than the net annual additions to the labor-force can reduce the level of unemployment to its former level, even though this may have been already high.

If the outmigration of workers and their families leads to an actual decline in population within the area concerned, then other problems emerge. The tax base will be decreased and this is likely to mean higher average levels of taxation because of the need to maintain certain social overhead services requiring the same expenditure regardless of population levels. Alternatively, with a decreased tax income in the community, there might be a deterioration in the standard of services that can be provided. Increased taxation or a poor quality of public services are additional factors likely to diminish the area's locational attractiveness to new industry. They might also cause an increase in costs to existing industry and cause firms, particularly marginal ones, to leave the area, causing unemployment problems similar to those referred to in the preceding paragraph.

With depopulation the value of real estate is likely to decline. Because of this, banks and other lending institutions can be expected to be more stringent in advancing credit.[8] This may cause firms that rely on local capital to encounter financial difficulties. Furthermore, such general credit restrictions are likely to dampen the little local enterprise that is remaining in the area.

A further influence of depopulation is its effect on market-oriented activities. If outmigration is of such magnitude as to lead to a shrinking of the regional market, a number of firms producing for this regional market may be compelled to cease production. Phrased another way, if outmigration causes the level of population or purchasing-power to fall below certain minimum thresholds necessary for production to take place in an area, some producers can be expected to curtail or to cease production and, in so doing, create fresh unemployment. Naturally the size of these thresholds will vary from industry to industry, depending upon the nature and operation of internal economies of scale. A similar adverse influence of outmigration will apply to trade and service functions both at regional and community levels since employment in these sectors is also closely tied to population and income levels. It may well be that depopulation through outmigration is necessary but any benefits accruing to the area, such as a reduction of the labor-force nearer to levels of labor demand, will tend to be offset to some extent by declining employment in residentiary activities.[9]

In this connection it is possible that a 'local *versus* regional' conflict of interests could arise. Outmigration from a depressed community within a depressed region may well be the most sensible adjustment from the point of view of the community. It is possible, however, that such a movement could have adverse effects upon other communities and hence upon the region as a whole. For example, outmigration on a large scale might be desirable from a number of small industrial communities. Yet if this movement is out of the region, it is likely to have unfavorable effects on employment in those cities that are performing essentially trade or service functions for the region.

The Mobility from Depressed Areas

In spite of the desirability of migration from certain depressed areas, studies have shown a pronounced reluctance on the part of people to move. The social attachment to the area, in terms of association with churches and clubs, the strong family ties, the distinctive local way of life and the difficulties of adjustment to a metropolitan environment, all tend to reduce potential outmigration.[10] In Western Europe this resistance to movement from depressed areas has been particularly strong. Thus in 1954 the High Authority of the European Coal & Steel Community devised a scheme for resettling 5,000 miners from the Centre-Midi Coalfield to the more prosperous Lorraine area. There was intense local opposition and from 1954 to 1956 applications for transfer amounted to only ten percent of the proposed figure.[11]

A recent series of studies in the United States by the Area Redevelopment Administration concerned with the geographic mobility of labor revealed an above-average preference for living in depressed areas on the part of their residents. It was found that " . . . when respondents were asked whether they wanted to stay or move, it turned out that fewer of the families living in Redevelopment Areas than in other areas wanted to move. About 80 percent of the Redevelopment Area families want to stay where they are, compared to 76 percent of the rest of the population. It thus appears that there is no great desire for mobility on the part of people now living in

Redevelopment Areas. Presumably the people most willing to move are the ones who already have departed." [12] On the basis of the number of different labor-market areas lived in since 1950, [13] mobility during the year 1962-63, [14] and fulfilled plans to move [15] people living in Redevelopment Areas appear to have significantly lower levels of mobility than their counterparts living outside these areas. Part of this difference can, of course, be accounted for by the composition of the populations of Redevelopment Areas. Areal mobility tends to be highest in the younger and in the more educated groups and it it these segments of the population that are generally under-represented in Redevelopment Areas.

Role of Unemployment
Although outmigration of labor may affect the level of unemployment, it is often the unemployment level which influences, in large measure, the level of outmigration from an area, though this is by no means the sole determinant of movement. As already mentioned, cultural, social and other economic factors may be of crucial importance in explaining the level and magnitude of the movement. Unemployment, however, remains a meaningful and quantifiable indicator of economic well-being and a determinant of migration levels. Writing on the experience of the United Kingdom, Owen came to the conclusion that, given the differential economic development (differential unemployment rates) which is basically responsible for migration, the volume of migration tends to vary inversely with the general level of unemployment in the country as a whole. In times of general depression most people tend to stay at home even though they may be living in particularly depressed conditions. In times of returning general prosperity many people living in areas which are still relatively depressed tend to seek their fortunes elsewhere, especially if they are encouraged by government inducements. [16] Professor Joan Robinson maintained that so long as there was general unemployment, migration would be small but would be increased when, due to a policy of full-employment, there were too few workers in the more prosperous areas to meet their growing demands for labor. [17]

The rate of change in employment levels is also likely to be an important factor influencing the level of labor outmigration from depressed areas. It may well be that workers, on becoming unemployed, tend to wait in the area in order to ascertain the likely trends in the job market. If the unemployment rates worsen they may move out of the area but if there is a decline in the level of unemployment then the workers are likely to stay where they are. The major difficulty in testing this hypothesis is that the relevant statistics may only be published annually, yet this may not be the period of the lag. The actual determination of the lag period is likely to be a problem in itself.

An interesting behavioral pattern which has been observed is the return of migrants to the depressed areas. Goodrich drew attention to the return of workers to the depressed regions in the United States when economic conditions were generally depressed throughout. However, a further outmigration could be expected when conditions nationally improved.[18] A similar back-flow to the depressed area of Northern Ireland has been noted whenever conditions were bad throughout the United Kingdom.[19]

There is evidence to suppose that a return movement to the depressed areas also takes place when employment opportunities become available there. In the case of Morgantown, West Virginia, the location of a chemical plant in this depressed area caused substantial numbers of workers who had previously taken jobs in distant areas to return to Morgantown.[20] It even appears that much outmigration occurs in the hope that the depressed conditions are temporary. In some of the anthracite-producing communities of Pennsylvania workers leave to take jobs in New York and New Jersey. They return to their families at weekends and leave their names on the books of the local employment office. It is thought by the managers of these offices that the men would return permanently if employment opportunities became available.[21] A very similar commuting pattern and a preference for work in the depressed area, should this work become available, was seen to exist in the Mount Vernon area of Illinois.[22]

In view of this reverse mobility, outmigration from depressed areas may not be a once and for all solution to the unemployment problem. This tendency to return on the part of the better workers whenever employment becomes available in depressed areas is likely to endanger the possibility of solving an area's unemployment problem. When work becomes available it is to be expected that the returning outmigrants will be among the first to be hired, since it is frequently they who are the most highly skilled. The hard core of unemployed that remains in the area may be largely by-passed. Only if the new employment arising in a depressed area is particularly large, and this is rare, may the immobile, unemployed groups have the opportunity of employment.

Determination of the Effect of Outmigration on Unemployment Levels

It has already been demonstrated that migration out of an area not only affects the size of the labor-force but can, under certain circumstances, simultaneously affect the level of employment opportunities, i.e., the demand for labor. The overall influence of outmigration on the level of unemployment consists therefore of the combined effect of these two forces. The effect of outmigration on the size of the labor-force can be readily determined from statistics relating to the labor-force and to migration of labor. The effect of outmigration on the demand for labor is harder to determine. This is the neglected side of the outmigration question and little can be inferred from published data. One sometimes hears statements like: 'If outmigration had not taken place from this area, the unemployment difficulties would be worse than they already are.' [23] 'Outmigration from this area was on an insufficiently large scale to have reduced the unemployment level.' These statements may or may not be valid. Before either one can be confirmed or refuted, it is necessary to know the extent to which outmigration has caused or, in the second statement, might have caused a reduction in the demand for labor in the areas concerned. If outmigration has taken place from an area and the level of employment has also declined, it is necessary to know how much of this employment decline is attributable to outmigration and how much would have occurred independently of outmigration. One can trace fairly well the effects of outmigration on locally-oriented or residentiary activities. For firms in the basic or export sector of the local economy however, it is no simple matter to determine the reasons for a decline in employment, should this take place. The decline may be due to increases in the overhead costs, such as increased tax burdens, or to shortages of skilled labor, both reflecting unfavorable effects of outmigration. Naturally reductions in the level of employment can arise from such factors as plant relocations out of the area, local industries in secular decline and business failures, none of which need to be due to the debilitating effects of outmigration. To evaluate the precise effects of outmigration on the demand for labor is therefore a difficult problem that tends to be complicated by extraneous factors which obscure the relationships being sought.

The effects of outmigration on the supply and the demand for labor will vary according to the size and to the precise local conditions within each depressed area. Areas must be studied on an individual basis over time with particular attention being given to the effects of outmigration on the demand for labor. This is likely to be a difficult assignment and may help to explain why most migration studies tend to concentrate on the supply side of the problem, namely, on the extent to which the labor-force can be reduced to meet the existing local demands for labor.

Conclusions

Because of the great diversity among depressed areas, any generalization concerning the relationship between outmigration and the condition of depressed areas must be open to close scrutiny. Labor outmigration and unemployment are closely inter-related and the fact that high levels of unemployment and outmigration can occur together within a region indicates that they are dual reactions to an imbalance in the local supply and demand of labor. Bearing in mind the dangers of generalization some tentative conclusions are advanced.

One: It should not be overlooked that outmigration of labor and of the population generally is one of the most common adjustments to social and economic change: often it is the most desirable one. On the other hand, in the case of depressed areas there exists a great resistance to movement. Whilst the origins of this immobility are not fully known, it remains a reality that those concerned with the implementation of policies toward depressed areas can scarcely afford to ignore.

Two: To say that outmigration of labor might solve the unemployment problems of a depressed area is a dangerous oversimplification. It is necessary to specify the type of labor that needs to move away from a depressed area. Outmigration of certain types of labor may prevent some firms from maintaining production in a particular area because of a shortage of skilled labor. This reduction in demand for labor, if large, would be likely to aggravate the unemployment situation. Thus, whenever outmigration of labor appears desirable or necessary it refers to those elements of the labor-force whose absence will not provide a liability to the area.

Three: Where outmigration leads to a reduction of the total population, the employment in market-oriented activities is likely to be unfavorably affected. Total population reduction is also likely to lead to an increase in taxes or to a decrease in the quality of public services that may cause firms in the export sector of the local economy not to continue production at that location. This would exaggerate the unemployment problem and make further outmigration necessary.

Four: Outmigration may be able to reduce unemployment but it can also be the indirect cause of unemployment. The overall success or otherwise of outmigration in the reduction of unemployment is therefore a combination of the positive and negative effects. If the overall effect is significantly positive in the long-run, then outmigration can be judged successful. This has been the case in areas of heavy rural unemployment and in the case of depressed industrial communities, the ghost town being the extreme case. Frequently, however, the general effect of outmigration is to leave the depressed area in a position of being less able to revive itself than before the movement took place. Increased taxation, a top-heavy age structure of the population, a loss of the skilled and enterprising elements of the labor-force and a shortage of local capital all tend to militate against the indigenous growth of new economic activity and against the likelihood of these areas attracting new employment.

Five: It seems unlikely that outmigration will take place from a depressed area unless there is some given differential margin in unemployment rates between the depressed areas and the rest of the nation, particularly the receiving areas. Because of this, it would be unreasonable to assume that the movement of labor could remove these areal variations in unemployment levels completely. Experience demonstrates that labor migration does not solve the problems of a general depression, although the role of labor out-migration as a possible solution to the problems of depressed areas during periods of national prosperity should not be understated.

Six: In those situations where outmigration may be of benefit to depressed areas public agencies can perform a valuable service in selecting, planning and facilitating the movement away from depressed areas. This appears to be a neglected feature of depressed area policy in most countries faced with the problem. Outmigration as a means for the amelioration of unemployment difficulties is a delicate instrument of policy that demands prudent application. Inasmuch as outmigration can correct only some of the unfavorable aspects of depressed areas, it would probably be a mistake not to combine and integrate a policy of outmigration with other redevelopment programs in so far as these are complementary or additive.

Notes and References

1. A convincing account of this trend toward this divergence in levels of economic development is contained in chapters 3 and 5 of Gunnar Myrdal's *Economic Theory and Underdeveloped Regions* (London, England: Methuen, 1957).

2. This expression is somewhat broader than the natural increase of the labor force (school-leavers *minus* retirements). In addition to the natural increase this expression includes such changes as people (particularly women) entering and leaving the labor force for reasons not associated with leaving school, reaching retirement age or migration into or out of the area.

3. Dale Hathaway, "Migration from Agriculture: The Historical Record and its Meaning." *American Economic Review*, May 1960. p. 384.

4. A. K. Cairncross, "Production and Employment in Scotland," *Scottish Journal of Political Economy*, October 1958, p. 250.

5. *Report on the Scottish Economy*, The Scottish Council (Development and Industry), November 1961, pp. 112-113.

6. A. D. K. Owen, "The Social Consequences of Industrial Transference," *Sociological Review*, October 1937, p. 343.

7. A discussion of the export sector of a local economy is contained in Charles M. Tiebout, *The Community Economic Base Study* (New York, New York: Committee for Economic Development, Supplementary Paper Number 16, 1962), pp. 40-42.

8. *The Measurement and Behavior of Unemployment* (Princeton, New Jersey: National Bureau for Economic Research, 1957), p. 351.

9. Even if a high percentage of the outmigrants are unemployed there may be a substantial reduction in expenditure that was based on welfare payments, accumulated savings and loans.

10. B. H. Luebke and John Fraser Hart, "Migration from a Southern Appalachian Community,"

11. *Regional Development in the European Economic Community*, (London, England: Political and Economic Planning, 1962), p. 60.

12. United States Department of Commerce, Area Redevelopment Administration, *The Geographic Mobility of Labor*, September 1964, p. 26.

13. *Ibid.*, p. 26.

14. United States Department of Commerce, Area Redevelopment Administration, *The Propensity to Move*, July 1964, p. 6.

15. *Ibid.*, pp. 14-16.

16. *Op. cit.*, p. 336.

17. Joan Robinson, *Essays in the Theory of Employment* (Oxford, England: Blackwell, 1947), p. 39.

18. Carter Goodrich et al., *Migration and Economic Opportunity*, (Philadelphia, Pennsylvania: University of Pennsylvania Press, 1936).

19. K. S. Isles and Norman Cuthbert, *An Economic Survey of Northern Ireland*, (Belfast, Ireland: Her Majesty's Stationery Office, 1957), p. 225.

20. G. G. Somers, "Labor Supply for Manufacturing in a Coal Area," *Monthly Labor Review*, December 1954, p. 130.

21. Information supplied in correspondence by Professor Paul D. Simkins, Department of Geography, Pennsylvania State University.

22. R. C. Wilcock, "Employment Effects of a Plant Shutdown in a Depressed Area," *Monthly Labor Review*, September 1957, p. 1951.

23. For example, Laurence C. Hunter, "Employment and Unemployment in Great Britain: Some Regional Considerations," *Manchester School of Economics and Social Studies*, January 1963, pp. 32-33.

The Separation of Home and Work: A Problem for Human Ecology
Leo F. Schnore

The daily journey to work is receiving increased attention in discussions of the urban community. Seen in historical perspective, the separation of place of work from place of residence is a relatively recent phenomenon and has been closely associated with the course of industrialization. Liepmann has suggested that these recurrent daily movements between home and work *supplement* migration and enhance the stability of community structure by contributing to the flexibility of industrial-economic organization. This contribution is most important in effecting adjustments to the changes that occur with the expansion and decline of particular industries, the short-distance relocation of factories, and seasonal fluctuations.[1] It has even been suggested that the daily journey to work might be tending to *supersede* migration as a means of adjustment to change, since the lengthening commuting radius of the automobile has reduced the amount of migration necessary within local areas.[2]

The separation of home and work, however, is not without its dysfunctional features. Some attention has been directed toward the possibility of severe physiological and psychological strain upon individual employees who must travel long distances to work. In addition, there have been numerous discussions of the problems of cities themselves, increasingly threatened with a drastic shrinkage of their tax bases. The problems of financing municipal services may be expected to multiply with a continuation of the trend toward decentralization. In addition to the costs of daily movement to the family budgets of modern workers, the costs of elaborate transportation systems to the municipality must be considered. In particular, the initial capital costs of underground and overhead systems in the largest cities are enormous. Added to these, however, are operating expenses, many of which elude exact calculation. Still another increasing cost to the city is that represented by the loss of revenue, arising out of traffic congestion for component business units. A significant proportion of this congestion is brought about by the work trips of persons finding employment within the local area.

The traffic problem has persuaded planners and other interested officials to participate in such efforts as the federal program of origin-and-destination traffic studies. These surveys, jointly supported by federal, state, and municipal funds, have been carried out in a large number of cities, and represent a valuable new source of urban data.[3] With the inception of such studies a large body of by-product material has become available for analysis by social scientists and a fund of research knowledge is being rapidly accumulated.[4]

The Principle of Least Effort

In the course of two examinations of the residential locations of industrial employees, it has been asserted that their distribution is the consequence of the operation of an underlying "Principle of least effort."[5] An application of this hypothesis to account for the residential distribution of industrial workers was first attempted by Carroll, whose principal argument is "that employees of industrial plants seek to minimize the distance between home and work, and that the aggregate choices of large numbers of employees will tend to produce the observed pattern."[6] More recently, the staff of the Industrial Areas Study, University of North Carolina, has subscribed to this explanatory device.[7]

The weight of Carroll's argument rests upon the observation of a gradient pattern of worker residences by distance from the workplace. "The central thesis of this paper," he says, "is that industrial workers will seek to minimize distance from home to work. This generalization was based on data showing that the number of employees resident in each successive mile zone from the plant site beyond the first few miles diminished as distance was increased."[8] Some attention is given by Carroll to factors other than the possible motives of the industrial employees studied. Some interesting hypotheses pertaining to the possible influence upon residential distribution patterns of such variables as type of industry, wage level, and size of city are presented. In the main, however, these are conceived only as limiting conditions to the operation of the "fundamental principle" of least effort. In Carroll's words:

> It will be sufficient to indicate that, while many factors are involved in the selection of homes and places of work, the persistence of the desire to minimize the distance separating workplace from home acting through each individual worker may be the single element which can create pattern out of the aggregate choices of large numbers of workers. It is, of course, obvious that these choices are differentially limited for each individual worker so that only in large aggregates can patterns begin to appear.[9]

Thus, the cause of the observed gradient distribution is to be found in a single dominating desire experienced by individual workers. It might be argued, however, that should an individual have at his disposal time and money in quantities sufficient to relieve him, to some extent, from the ordinary restrictions imposed by transport costs, he might locate his residence almost anywhere, and for any of a variety of motives. The latter might include, in fact, a desire to maximize the distance between home and work. The least-effort hypothesis appears to confuse motivation with its external limiting conditions.

Even if the foregoing consideration is omitted, however, the least-effort hypothesis remains subject to serious question on logical grounds. If the tendency to minimize effort is assumed to be *constant* throughout the population, it appears that the hypothesis offers a plausible explanation of the *concentration* of residences near work sites, but fails to account for the equally obvious *scatter* away from those sites. This assumption of a constant desire to minimize effort meets still another difficulty if an explanation of change over time is attempted. Given this constant, the antecedent factors responsible for any change must be sought in the external conditions which limit the "basic desire" to minimize effort, for this desire is not conceived as a variable. Thus an explanation, in these terms, of the decentralization movement would appear to require an assumption to the effect that the desire to minimize effort has been on the wane in recent years.

These observations suggest that the factors considered by Carroll as comprising only limitations upon the operation of the least-effort principle may be those worthy of more serious study in their own right. Toward this end, certain findings taken from a study of Flint, Michigan will be presented here.[10]

Findings

The Distance Between Home and Work

The fact that the distribution of worker residences assumes a gradient pattern with respect to distance might have been anticipated on the basis of Carroll's research. The upper panel of Table 1 shows that, in the case of all six plants, the great majority of workers live within six miles of their place of employment. The computation of ratios of workers to resident population,[11] however, shows that *each plant draws workers from each of the five distance zones in accordance with the number of persons it employs*. The gradient

Table 1

Per Cent Distribution and Ratio of Workers to
Resident Population of Employees of Principal Industrial
Installations in Flint, Michigan, by Distance, 1950

| Distance Zones (in miles) | Industrial Installation | | | | | | |
	A	B	C	D	E	F	Total
Per Cent Distribution							
0-6	80.4	85.2	85.9	84.4	77.5	97.2	83.4
6-12	7.6	5.3	6.0	6.6	9.9	1.3	6.6
12-18	4.6	4.7	5.8	7.0	5.0	0.9	4.9
18-30	5.4	4.2	1.9	1.6	3.8	0.6	3.8
30+	2.0	0.6	0.4	0.4	3.8	...	1.3
Total	100.0	100.0	100.0	100.0	100.0	100.0	100.0
Number of Workers per 1,000 Resident Population							
0-6	90.2	62.2	36.5	27.3	21.8	13.1	251.1
6-12	63.7	29.1	19.0	16.1	10.8	1.3	140.0
12-18	35.2	23.8	17.2	15.6	10.4	0.9	103.1
18-30	2.7	1.4	0.4	0.2	0.5	a	5.2
30+	0.1	a	a	a	0.1	a	1.9
N	24,700	16,100	9,360	7,130	5,710	2,970	65,970

a Less than 0.05.

pattern of these ratios in strict accordance with size of plant employment could not be readily deduced from prior suggestions to the effect that the average distance between home and work varies directly with the size of plant employment.[12]

The ratio for the largest plant (A) is seen to decline steadily with distance, reaching a plateau at approximately 18 miles and beyond. The ratios for the remaining plants, however, begin to level off at the second zone, with the decline remaining in strict accordance with the size of plant employment. It is interesting to note that the only one of the smaller plants exerting any pulling power over the area in the last distance zone (plant E) is the newest of the major industrial sites in the Flint area. The tendency for newer and more rapidly expanding industrial installations to draw workers from a wider area has been noted by other investigators.[13]

Thus the size of the plant employment and the length of time that it has been located at a given site appear to be variables of more than passing interest to one would explain the residential distribution of industrial employees. Even if viewed as conditions to the operation of some more basic tendency, their importance should not be overlooked.

The Distribution of Workers by Workshift
The fact that the origin-and-destination data used here contain information on the time of arrival at work allows an examination of the spatial distribution of employees working on different shifts. Table 2 summarizes the results of this study. As may be seen, *the proportions of workers on the first (day) shift decline regularly with distance, while the proportions of those employed on the two remaining shifts increase as distance increases.*[14] Again, the least-

Table 2
Per Cent Distribution of Employees of Principal
Industrial Installations in Flint, Michigan,
by Shift, by Distance, 1950

| Workshift | Distance Zone (in miles) | | | | | |
	0-6	6-12	12-18	18-30	30+	Total
First	57.3	50.7	46.3	37.8	22.9	54.5
Second	38.4	45.1	49.4	56.5	68.5	41.1
Third	4.3	4.2	4.3	5.7	8.6	4.4
Total	100.0	100.0	100.0	100.0	100.0	100.0
N	38,530	4,276	3,466	2,457	722	49,451[a]

a The total number of cases is less than the total in Table 1 because no data were available regarding the workshift of employees who must be assumed to walk to work.

effort hypothesis suggests nothing in the way of an explanation, for it assumes that the desire to minimize effort is a constant, that is, an attribute of all workers. Certain other possibilities, given no recognition in the development of the least-effort hypothesis, might be considered here.

First of all, it should be remembered that more recently employed workers, those with the least accumulated seniority, are most often assigned to the afternoon and evening shifts. These are the employees hired periodically in response to fluctuations in demand, and represent "marginal workers," a concept widely used in labor force analysis. The relationship found here between workshift and distance suggests the hypothesis that *the "marginal labor force" may also be physically marginal to a given industrial community.*[15]

From the standpoint of the individual worker, residential location some distance from a center might be advantageous in two ways. For one thing, alternative sources of employment in nearby cities are more accessible. Secondly, a mode of adjustment to fluctuation in labor demand is made possible—a way of life promising more security than can be gained through industrial employment alone. Here we refer to the pattern of part-time agriculture discussed in detail by Firey.[16]

Firey identifies a trend toward what can be described as an urbanization of the originally rural population and a ruralization of the urbanites participating in the outward drift from the city. It is his judgment that Genesee County (of which Flint is the center) is one of those counties in Michigan within which the farm population has most fully taken to urban wage employment, while at the same time its decentralizing urban population has begun the practice of extensive gardening and part-time farming in the area surrounding the city. "Thus gardening or part-time farming," he concludes, "has in a certain sense become a way of life for a large proportion of the people in Genesee County. This is particularly true of the zone which immediately surrounds Flint and the radial bands which extend along the paved highways leading outward from the city . . . [for] within this star-like area part-time farming or gardening is the predominant pattern."[17] Whether or not for the same reasons, this pattern has long been established in the continental countries, where great numbers of workers alternate between agricultural and industrial employment during the course of the year.[18] Its emergence in this country is not surprising, since our urban communities have tended to become increasingly market-oriented and, thus, increasingly subject to fluctuations in supply, demand and employment opportunities.

Prospects of Other Employment
Proportionately greater difficulty in securing off-season employment is encountered where the units of production are highly specialized or where

the occupational specialization of the workers is great. An increase in the size of the production unit may also be expected to result in further difficulties should a temporary shutdown become necessary, since great numbers of workers are released at one time and in one place. The automobile industry, which forms the basis of Flint's economy, serves as an excellent example of this situation. The industry as a whole employs thousands and is, moreover, highly concentrated geographically. "The results," according to one observer, "are aggravated by the sensitive inter-linkages among units, which necessitate that the closing of one unit be followed by the closing of others. Thus, a cessation of activities in the automobile industry throws such large numbers out of work that it is impossible for the community to absorb them in other types of employment. . . ."[19]

Perhaps it is this difficulty of finding other full-time employment in nearby industries that encourages the widespread part-time farming by shop workers observed by Firey. Given a location on one of the major arteries leading to the city, a factory worker is within relatively easy access of industrial employment, yet has ample land on which to raise garden crops in sufficient quantity to supplement purchased foodstuffs. Such a practice would be encouraged if he should be employed on either the late afternoon or evening workshift in the plant, for he would then be able to utilize the daylight hours in work on the land. It is even conceivable that great numbers of these workers prefer work on the later shifts, especially during the planting and harvesting seasons when the daylight hours can be used to greater advantage. It should also be remembered that the factories represent a significant source of extra income to persons whose principal occupation is farming and who maintain their rural residence. At any rate, the observed relationship between distance from workplace and the time of work may have as one consequence the stimulation of the pattern of part-time agriculturism discussed here, and it is within this broader community context that the findings might be interpreted.

Ride Sharing and the Ability to Pay Costs of Transportation
Still another matter we might consider is the ability of workers to pay the costs of transportation to and from work. Table 3 shows that *as distance increases up to approximately 30 miles, the proportion of cars in which only one person is travelling to work declines, while the proportions in which there are two, three, and four or more persons increase. The mean number of passengers per car also increases with distance up to this "breaking point."*[20] One possible explanation for the reversal of the observed tendency in the last distance zone may be found in the widely scattered distribution, at this extreme distance, of those who must regularly travel to the city for employment. Since the area surrounding the central city increases as the square of

the radial distance from it, workers are presumably more scattered at this extreme distance, and thus find it more difficult to make ride-sharing arrangements with others.

When considered in an *a priori* manner, ride-sharing might be expected to increase with distance, for such a practice is an effective method of distributing the high costs of automobile transportation.[21] The significance of this practice may be realized when it is remembered that the ability to pay transport costs to and from centers of activity appears to be one of the most critical selective factors in the centrifugal shift of our decentralizing urban population. It might be suggested here that *many family units which otherwise could not participate in the decentralization movement may be able to do so by virtue of such arrangements as ride-sharing. Such a minimization of transport costs, together with the added security obtained by part-time agricultural activities, may account for the presence in these peripheral areas of large numbers of families whose general economic status would otherwise not permit such location.* These are the persons whose scattered residential distribution remains inexplicable when the least-effort hypothesis is utilized.

Conclusions and Implications

We have indicated in the foregoing sections certain apparent limitations upon the use of the least-effort hypothesis in this problem area. These limitations, for the most part, appear to be a consequence of the form in which that hypothesis is stated. The postulation of a constant attribute as a fundamental

Table 3
Per Cent Distribution of Cars Travelling to Principal
Industrial Installations on Work Trips in Flint, Michigan,
by Number of Persons in Car, by Distance, 1950

Number of Persons in Car	Distance Zone (in miles)					
	0-6	*6-12*	*12-18*	*18-30*	*30+*	*Total*
One	79.6	62.8	55.3	44.9	61.7	75.0
Two	15.2	24.4	24.7	23.9	16.4	17.0
Three	3.1	7.8	10.2	11.0	6.6	4.3
Four+	2.1	5.0	9.8	20.2	15.3	3.7
Total	100.0	100.0	100.0	100.0	100.0	100.0
Mean	1.29	1.58	1.79	2.24	1.90	1.35
N	18,315	2,038	1,505	812	274	22,944

causal factor meets resistance when variation is encountered. The remaining space will be devoted to the consideration of an alternative hypothesis of an intentionally different form.

From one theoretical point of view, the daily journey to work may serve as one of the most easily perceived data in the observation of community organization. As treated by one student of human ecology, the regular ebb and flow of community activity is viewed as itself expressive of community structure. According to Hawley:

> Recurrent movements, as the name indicates, comprise all those movements that are routine and repetitive. They might also be called functional, for it is by this type of movement that the functioning of the community is carried on. . . . Each [of these movements] is an integral part in an established organization and is therefore essential to the maintenance of that organization. Recurrent movements involve no break with the past, no disruption of an established order. They are the means by which an existing equilibrium is maintained.[22]

The increasing *spatial* differentiation of the modern community, of which the separation of home and work is one aspect, might also be considered as reflecting an increasing *functional* differentiation. Such an interpretation assumes, of course, that space presents at least one measurable dimension of community structure. This assumption is, in fact, given formal expression by Hawley when he suggests that "the distribution of the elements of [the physical] structure [of the city] form a pattern of land uses which presumably is expressive of the interdependence among the various activities comprised by the city."[23]

In this spatial pattern, the functional units [24] occupying different sites may be thought of as possessing different locational requirements. One requirement common to all units, of course, is *space itself*, or room in which to operate. But units may differ in the amount of space required. Because space is limited, particularly at the center of an area, those requiring the greatest amounts of space might be expected to locate away from that center. At the same time, any location involves cost to the occupant by virtue of his occupancy. Costs being highest at the center, the units least able to maintain occupancy of sites at the center may be expected to be found at or near the periphery. [25] This cost, however, is not the only one exacted from a unit.

One other key characteristic of any site is the degree of *accessibility* to other units it may have. Units may have quite specifically defined needs for accessibility to other units, and this may be taken as another locational requirement. Just as with space, moreover, this need is fulfilled only at a cost to the unit involved. [26] The cost, in this case, is experienced as the cost of transportation, for either the movement of the members of the unit from the site to another place or for the movement of goods and services to the site occupied.

Effect of Distance on Rent and Transportation Costs

Two assumptions regarding these costs underlie this discussion. The first is that rent, or the cost of occupancy of a site, *declines with distance* from an activity center. The most frequently observed decline is at a somewhat greater than proportional rate. Secondly, transport costs are assumed to *increase with distance*, at an approximately proportional rate, although significantly modified by the method of transport utilized. If it is then assumed that costs of location represent the sum of these costs, the following hypothesis suggests itself: *The maximum distance from significant centers of activity at which a unit tends to locate is fixed at that point beyond which further savings in rent are insufficient to cover the added costs of transportation to these centers.*

It is, perhaps, in the interaction of these two broadly conceived "cost" factors that an explanation of the residential distributions of employees may be found. Units obviously differ in their ability to pay both of these costs, and the family unit is no exception. First of all, the work site may be taken to represent one of the most significant "centers of activity" for the family unit of the employee. Exchanges between the family unit and the production unit at the work site—in the form of the physical movement of the worker—are frequent, so that a certain degree of access is an important requirement. Within this broad range, then, it might be expected that the cost-paying ability of the family unit becomes significant. The area in which any given unit may be able to afford location may also be fairly broad. In the aggregate, however, the area open to families of a given cost-paying ability may be distributed about the relevant centers of activity in such a manner that the gradient pattern of residential distribution becomes readily observable. Since the ability to pay costs of transport and occupancy are conceived as *variables* in this formulation, no difficulty is encountered in the fact of scatter. Indeed, such a gradient distribution would be expected to follow.

It is in the light of this hypothesis that the characteristics of the population participating in the outward drift from the city may be reasonably interpreted. Available census data indicate that the ability to pay transport costs may well be a selective factor in residential decentralization, for peripheral areas of metropolitan districts are found to be occupied by families of higher than average socioeconomic status. [27] In addition to costs of transport, of course, other financial considerations are involved in peripheral location. The entire range of family purchases may be expected to be somewhat more costly in the outlying areas, at least until sufficient densities of population make possible greater economies in the provision of goods and services. These remarks are not intended to imply that the economic aspect of location is the only one that can be identified, or that these costs are somehow the only factors operative. Nor are space and time granted some kind of deterministic role with reference to the location of units of the community. Emphasis is placed upon spatial and temporal relations in this approach for the simple reason that the patterns and processes in which we are interested occur in a space-time context.

In addition to static descriptions of community structure, ecological theory attempts to provide some information upon the processes of change in that structure. The general approach sketched here might also prove useful in an attack upon the problem of change in community organization. The hypothesis suggested above might be utilized in accounting for changes observed in the patterns of population distribution. That important changes have occurred is well known. Although changes in costs of occupancy should not be overlooked, the long-range trend toward residential decentralization can be viewed, in this context, as a consequence of a long-range decline in transportation costs. As such, this interpretation represents a formal statement of the frequent impressionistic observation to the effect that the automobile has "released" population from the immediate confines of the city. At any rate, some attention should be directed toward the development of hypotheses suitable to the description of change, in addition to those which offer only plausible accounts for observations relating to a given point in time, as in the case of the least-effort hypothesis.

With respect to the distribution of other centers of activity significant to the functioning of the family, it has been found that many are located at a lesser average distance than that between home and workplace.[28] The location of these units could also be approached through the use of hypotheses of this general order. Retail shopping centers, for example, might tend to locate at a relatively low average distance from their supporting populations (made up of family units, in the main) by virtue of the necessity for frequent contacts with those populations. The latter need may well be one of the key locational requirements of such units, and the concomitant costs could be treated from the point of view outlined here as those deriving from the necessity for a high degree of accessibility to other units. The study of the location of industrial activities and other work sites might also be approached in this manner. Treatment of the location of *all* units comprising the community would be necessary in a complete description of communal land uses.

In any event, the approach outlined here—although far from entirely satisfactory—might be productive of more general information than would one in which a single observed relationship is given priority out of proportion to its apparent significance. This discussion is intended primarily to indicate that another approach of apparently equal feasibility is possible. The fact that the least-effort hypothesis has happened to dominate the little research already carried out in this problem area should not deter the presentation of alternative modes of explanation.

Notes and References

1. Kate K. Liepmann, *The Journey to Work* (New York: Oxford University Press, 1944), pp. 10-19.

2. Amos H. Hawley, *Human Ecology* (New York: The Ronald Press, 1950), p. 337.

3. The survey method is described in some detail in J. F. Harbes, "Urban Origin-and-Destination Traffic Surveys," *Traffic Engineering*, 15 (1945), pp. 296-299; and J. T Lynch, "Traffic Planning Studies in American Cities," *Public Roads*, 24 (1945), pp. 161-78.

4. A review of available studies using these and other data has been carried out by Donald L. Foley; see his "Urban Daytime Population: A Field for Demographic--Ecological Analysis," *Social Forces*, 32 (1954), pp. 323-30.

5. This hypothesis is given its most detailed elaboration in George K. Zipf, *Human Behavior and the Principle of Least Effort* (Cambridge: Addison-Wesley Press, 1949). A summary exposition may be found in "The Hypothesis of the 'Minimum Equation' as a Unifying Social Principle," *American Sociological Review*, 12 (1947), pp. 627-50.

6. J. Douglas Carroll, Jr., *Home-Work Relationships of Industrial Employees* (unpublished doctoral dissertation, Harvard University, 1950), p. 21. Certain of Carroll's research findings are summarized in "Some Aspects of Home-Work Relations of Industrial Workers," *Land Economics*, 25 (1949), pp. 414-22, and in "The Relation of Homes to Work Places and the Spatial Pattern of Cities," *Social Forces*, 30 (1952), pp. 271-82.

7. Residential Distribution Patterns of the Workers of Manufacturing Installations and Daytime-Nighttime Differentials in Proportional Distribution of the Total Population of Selected Domestic Urban Areas: Flint, Michigan (unpublished pilot study, Industrial Areas Study, Institute for Research in Social Science, University of North Carolina, 1952), pp. 501-502.

8. *Home-Work Relationships of Industrial Employees*, p. 130.

9. *Ibid.*, p. 24.

10. The data presented below were gathered in the origin-and-destination traffic study carried out in Flint. The author is indebted to the Michigan State Highway Department for the use of these materials. The time of the traffic survey, the summer of 1950, permitted some use of these data in combination with statistics from the decennial census. Flint, a single-industry city, had a population just in excess of 163,000 in 1950. The study reported here was confined to the 66,000 employees of the six Flint plants of the General Motors Corporation: (A) Buick Motor, (B) Chevrolet Motor, (C) Fisher Body, (D) A. C. Sparkplug-Dort Highway, (E) Chevrolet Assembly, and (F) A. C. Sparkplug-Industrial Avenue. Reference will be made to these plants by these letter designations.

11. This ratio, shown in the lower panel of Table 1, is a rough measure of the "pulling power" of each of the plants. A more adequate measure would be one expressing the ratio of workers to the resident population 15-65 years of age. Such a ratio would contain a denominator more closely representative of the actual numbers of potential

workers. Unfortunately, the data necessary for the computation of such a ratio for the areal units treated here were not available.

12. Liepmann, *op. cit.*

13. "It is in fact," according to Liepmann, "a common experience that new and expanding works have high proportions of their employees coming from considerable distances, as against more local recruitment by old-established firms," *Ibid.*, p. 15.

14. This same relationship between distance and workshift was found for each of the six individual plants studied, although data for the latter are not presented in this report.

15. Estimates of manufacturing employment in Flint have been made for 1950, which has been identified as an extremely stable year when the magnitude of fluctuation in employment from month to month was at a minimum. These figures approximate the employment of the six General Motors plants under study. Manufacturing employment rose from 63,300 in May to a high of 67,400 in September, and then fell off to 66,400 by November. The difference of 4,100 between the high (September) and low (May) figures provides an estimate of the size of Flint's marginal labor force during this period. (These estimates were abstracted from the Monthly Estimate of the Labor Force prepared by the Flint Office of the Michigan Unemployment Compensation Commission, and appear in the appropriate issues of the *Labor Market Letter* published by that office.)

16. Walter Firey, *Social Aspects to Land Use Planning in the Country-City Fringe: The Case of Flint, Michigan* (East Lansing: Michigan State Agricultural Experiment Station, Special Bulletin 339, 1946). Although Firey's study was also limited to Flint, a similar pattern has been found in many other areas. See, for example, Nathan L. Whetten and R. F. Field, *Studies of Suburbanization in Connecticut, 2, Norwich: An Industrial Part-time Farming Area* (Storrs: Connecticut State Agricultural Experiment Station Bulletin 226, 1938).

17. *Op. cit.*, pp. 16-17. Statistics revealing the number and size of farm units within the county offer a measure of corroboratory evidence. As farms have increased in number there has occurred a concomitant decrease in their size.

18. Liepmann, *op. cit.*, p. 17.

19. Hawley, *op. cit.*, p. 312.

20. Although not shown in Table 3, the same relationship between distance and the number of persons in the car was found for each of the six individual plants studied.

21. It has been estimated that each mile added to the daily journey to work adds an additional $25.00 to the annual cost of work transportation alone. Richard Dewey, "Peripheral Expansion in Milwaukee County," *American Journal of Sociology*, 54 (1948), p. 121.

22. *Op. cit.*, pp. 326-27. The material upon which the following discussion is based was drawn from a seminar at the University of Michigan conducted by Hawley.

23. *Ibid.*, p. 382.

24. "Functional unit" is used here in a very general sense. It may be tentatively defined as "an organization of activities dependent upon still other activities." In other words, it is the unit referent of which the interdependent community is composed.

25. The usual explanation of this pattern attributes these cost differentials to competi-

tive bidding for sites. The limited quantity of space at the center plays a large role in such an interpretation. See, for example, Edgar M. Hoover, *The Location of Economic Activity* (New York: McGraw-Hill Book Co., Inc., 1948), p. 92.

26. Here, especially, "cost" must not be taken solely in a monetary sense, for costs in time and energy are equally relevant. The term is here conceived in a generic sense, subsuming all of these conceptions.

27. Outlying areas of metropolitan districts have been found to contain significantly greater proportions of persons with the following characteristics: one or more years of college education; self-employed; females not in the labor force; professionals and proprietors, managers and officials. Census of Housing data provide interesting supplementary evidence. Among other differences, the outlying areas have been found to contain higher proportions of one-family, owner-occupied homes, of larger and more recent construction.

28. Trips to 20 other activities have been found to be shorter than work trips. See Donald L. Foley, "The Use of Local Facilities in a Metropolis," *American Journal of Sociology*, 56 (1950), pp. 238-46. See also Carroll, *Home-Work Relationships of Industrial Employees*, pp. 71-4 and 86, where it is noted that "trips to work are short, but shopping, school, and church trips are shorter."

Urbanization and Natural Resources: A Study in Organizational Ecology
Jack P. Gibbs
Walter T. Martin

This paper describes an attempt to formulate and test a theory designed to explain differences among countries with respect to two related phenomena —*urbanization* and *metropolitanization*. In the former case the theory seeks to account for differences in the proportion of the population residing in cities as such, while in the case of metropolitanization the concern is with differences in the proportion of the population residing in large cities. No attempt at a formal definition of "city" is made, but, as later sections will show, the term as used here conforms to generally accepted practice.[1]

Organization for Sustenance
A matter that has received insufficient attention from sociologists is social organization designed to obtain material sustenance, i.e., *objects of consumption*, for the population.[2] This relative neglect of organization for sustenance probably results from the dominance of economics and geography in this area, and a tendency on the part of sociologists, in their reaction to economic and geographic determinism, to throw the baby out with the bath. Furthermore, emphasis on psychology and anthropology rather than economics and

geography in the academic training of sociologists encourages a social-psychological orientation for each new crop of fledgling sociologists.

Whatever the reasons, sociological literature frequently gives the impression that society exists more or less without contact with the world seen by economists and geographers. Characteristically such matters as soil fertility, the location of coal deposits, and trade between nations appear to exist somewhere off stage and to have little relevance for the community as a configuration of visiting patterns, the family as a small group, the church as a voluntary association, or the factory as a status hierarchy. Certainly "family image sets," "dyadic interaction," and the "upper-upper class" are legitimate sociological concerns while soil fertility and coal deposits *per se* are not. It would be most unfortunate, however, if emphasis on the social-psychological, interactional aspects of the social system discouraged the study of man's increasingly efficient organization for providing himself with the material things of life. While ore deposits, water resources, and other objects of potential consumption are not of sociological interest in and of themselves, the intensive and extensive organization of effort to convert natural resources into objects of consumption is a critically important part of organized human effort, and, as such, is a legitimate and important area of sociological analysis.

The Fathers of sociology established a precedent for sociological inquiry into all aspects of society. In more recent times the most notable attempt by sociologists to develop an analytical framework encompassing man's organized efforts in relation to his natural environment is human ecology.[3] It is unfortunate for sociology that the human ecology that developed in America has been almost entirely a micro-ecology oriented around the city block and census tract, and increasingly a "social geography" concerned with the spatial distribution of churches, foreign born, and juvenile delinquents. As Hawley has rightly pointed out, many statements on human ecology " . . . seem to indicate a subordination of interests in functional relations to a concern with the spatial patterns in which such relations are expressed."[4] From the point of view developed here the spatial factor may be of vital importance in some respects, but is of interest to human ecology only if it influences organization for sustenance. That is, space as such is relevant to human ecology only as it confronts human beings in their attempts to obtain objects of consumption, just as it is of importance to other forms of organization only as it generates, restricts, or otherwise affects the formation, operation, and duration of groups, institutions, and other social forms. Thus both the logic and desirability of designating mapping activities as the major content of human ecology are questionable. This explicit rejection of spatial analysis as the major concern of human ecology is essential to the revitalization and further development of a once promising discipline. The conception of human ecology as the study of sustenance organization[5] appears to be more consistent with the nature of ecology in other fields and to be potentially more fruitful than spatial ecology for the development of useful theory and meaningful empirical propositions.[6] This paper explores one of the implications of an organizational ecology.[7]

Human Ecology and Urbanization

Urbanization is included within the scope of human ecology, it follows, not because cities have spatial dimensions but because cities represent one way in which populations organize to obtain a greater quantity and variety of objects of consumption.[8] The theory to be advanced here holds that it is only when cities are regarded as organizations for sustenance that differences among countries with respect to urbanization can be explained and predicted.

There is considerable agreement that most cities come into being and grow as a consequence of activities associated with the exploitation of natural resources.[9] In this connection it is helpful to view the relationship between the dispersion of these objects of consumption and the growth of urbanization. Given a land area with a dispersion of natural resources, such as the hypothetical country depicted in Figure 1, there are two alternatives open to a population in its attempt to exploit natural resources and convert them into objects of consumption for the country as a whole.

Figure 1

Alternative Transportation Connections between Areas with Different Natural Resources in a Hypothetical Country

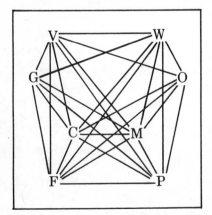 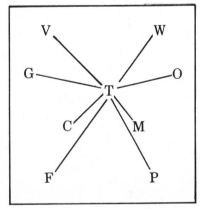

C, coal deposits; F, land suited for growing fibrous products such as cotton; G, land suited for growing grains; M, location of metallic substances such as iron; O, oil deposits; P, grazing lands producing animal products; T, transport center; V, land suited for growing vegetables and fruits; W, land areas covered with forests suited for producing wood products.

While the hypothetical country shown in Figure 1 is grossly over-simplified, it serves to illustrate the basic alternatives. Faced by the necessity of exchanging dispersed natural resources or bringing them together for combination into new objects of consumption, the population can attempt to link all areas possessing needed resources with individual transportation routes, as shown in Figure 1A. The alternative is to link all resource areas through the creation of a center and system of transportation lines, as indicated in Figure 1B. It is widely recognized that the transportation routes which evolve in countries never resemble the network of possible routes shown in 1A. [10] Inevitably, through foresight or survival, a center such as "T" in Figure 1B develops and functions as a transportation hub, a place of trade, a center of control over extractive industries, and as a locale for processing and combining raw materials. Actually, of course, several such centers may develop rather than one. [11]

As suggested earlier, the conception of the city as functioning primarily as a center of control of production and processing raw materials gained through the exploitation of natural resources is not a new idea in human ecology. If the conception is accepted as a valid one, however, there are certain consequences that have not been fully realized in ecological theory.

Transport and control centers (designated "T" in Figure 1B) arise as part of an organized effort to convert widely dispersed natural resources into objects of consumption for the country as a whole. In Figure 1B, if area G is suitable only for growing grain, the resident population of G will be dependent upon T for all other objects of consumption other than grain products, and as a consequence of G's dependence, T requires a larger population in order to control and process the raw materials that become the objects of consumption for the people in area G. On the other hand, suppose G is surrounded in the immediate area by all the natural resources shown in Figure 1 so that the raw materials needed to produce G's objects of consumption are not dispersed throughout the country. If this were the case, G would be independent of T for most practical purposes and T's population would not need to be as large. Clearly, from this point of view, the existence of T as an urban center and the size of its population at any given time result from the fact that the objects of consumption in the hypothetical country are widely dispersed. If all possible objects of consumption were equally available at all points in the country the development of T would no longer be a necessity. [12]

A decrease in T's population could also be brought about by a drop in consumption in one or more of the natural resource areas. If wood products ceased to be in demand as an object of consumption in the hypothetical country, the stimulus determining the size of the population of T would be reduced in proportion to the persons in T who were occupied in controlling or processing wood products that move from W to all other areas through

T. [13] This assumes, of course, that consumption of some substitute for wood does not stimulate a similar population in T.

The Link between Urbanization and Dispersion of Objects

This line of reasoning leads to the first theoretical proposition: *The degree of urbanization in a country varies directly with the extent of the dispersion of its objects of consumption.*

The proposition anticipates that those countries with a limited number of different types of objects of consumption evenly distributed over its territory will have a small proportion of population living in cities. In contrast, those countries consuming a diversity of objects that are widely dispersed will have a large proportion of population living in cities.

Before testing the first proposition it is necessary to consider the nature of the relationship between the dispersion of objects of consumption and urbanization beyond the *de facto* generalization contained in the first proposition. It is not meaningful to speak of the dispersion of objects of consumption as *causing* urbanization or vice versa. The acquisition of widely dispersed consumption items would not be possible without a sustenance organization such as urbanization. On the other hand, urban centers of an appreciable number and size cannot exist in a country without a wide area of raw materials upon which to draw so as to support the urban population, which means a wide dispersion of objects of consumption. Thus, in causal terms, there is an interactive relationship between the dispersion of the objects of consumption of a country and its degree of urbanization. In final analysis, both are products of people organizing themselves in such a way as to obtain more sustenance and a greater diversity in consumers goods. To obtain these goals people must draw raw materials from greater distances, which requires urbanization as a means to control the requisitioning and processing of raw materials.

A Test of the First Proposition

Given the necessary data a precise measure could be made of the degree to which objects consumed are dispersed. For any country it would be possible to determine the distance each object of consumption has been carried from its point of origin as a raw material to its point of acceptance by a consumer. The average distance that all consumption items have been carried would thus be a measure of the extent to which the country's consumption objects are dispersed. [14] Since the data necessary for such a precise measure are not available and could not be obtained without enormous expenditure, the writers have employed alternative and available types of data.

For purposes of measurement, a country's objects of consumption can be divided into two types. First, are those objects that have their origin within the borders of the country; the degree of their dispersion can be designated as the degree of internal dispersion. Second, are consumption objects that are obtained by international trade or conquest, and the degree of their dispersion can be designated as the degree of external dispersion.[15] Although a measure of dispersion should incorporate both internal and external types, existing data make it possible to take into account only the degree of external dispersion.[16]

Data suitable for a rough measure of the degree of external dispersion have been provided by the Statistical Office of the United Nations.[17] In this publication the amount of trade in millions of U.S. dollars among most of the countries and colonial territories of the world is given by exports and imports for a number of years.

The pre-war year of 1938 was selected since it avoids the disruption of World War II and corresponds roughly with the period covered in Davis' comprehensive measures of the degree of urbanization in selected countries, as shown in Table 1.

A crude component measure of the external dispersion of a country's objects of consumption can be obtained by multiplying the number of millions of dollars of imports of the country by the distance in miles between it and each exporting country. The product obtained expresses the imports in terms of "million dollar miles." The composite measure for a country is the sum of the component measures (there being as many component measures as there are countries from which imports were received), and is designated as the "total million dollar miles." Since this value is influenced to a considerable degree by population size, it must be reduced to a per capita basis.

A simplified measure of the degree of external dispersion was developed that eliminated measuring the distance of trade routes between each country and other countries or territories from which it received imports, an operation that would require some 130 separate measures in certain cases. Instead, the amount of imports in millions of dollars and the distance the imports traveled were measured by the distance between the geographic centers of the importing countries and those of the *regions* of which the exporting countries are a part.[18] Furthermore, this distance was measured as the shortest between the two points rather than along trade routes. For example, in the case of United States imports from Brazil the straight line distance was calculated between the approximate geographic centers of the United States and South America. Following this procedure, a component measure was obtained for each country from which imports were received. The sum of these values for each country, when divided by the population and multiplied by 10,000, is expressed as total million dollar miles of imports per 10,000 population.[19] The resulting measures shown in column 1 of Table 2 are designated for the sake of simplicity as measures of relative external dispersion (RED).

Table 1
Per Cent of Population in Cities
by Size Class for Selected Countries[1]

Region and Country	Year	In Cities 5,000+ Per Cent	In Cities 10,000+ Per Cent	In Cities 25,000+ Per Cent	In Cities 100,000+ Per Cent	Index[a]	Per Cent in the Largest City
Africa							
Egypt	1939	b	27.0	19.7	13.2	b	8.2
Asia and Oceania							
Australia[2]	1939	71.2	67.9	62.1	47.3	62.1	18.4
New Zealand	1941	52.5	49.4	41.5	31.8	43.8	13.7
Japan	1935	64.5	45.8	36.8	25.3	43.1	8.5
India	1941	12.3	10.5	8.1[c]	4.2	8.8	0.5
European Countries							
Great Britain[3]	1931	81.7[c]	73.6	63.1	45.2	65.9	20.5
Germany[3]	1939	57.4[c]	51.7	43.5	31.8	46.1	6.3
France[3]	1936	41.7[c]	37.5	29.8	16.0	31.2	6.8
Sweden	1940	35.9	32.1	25.6	16.1	27.4	9.3
Greece[3]	1937	33.1[c]	29.8	23.1	14.8	25.2	7.0
Poland[3]	1931	22.8[c]	20.5	15.8	10.7	17.4	3.6
Latin America							
Argentina[4, d]	1943[c]	48.9	46.8	42.7	34.0	43.1	18.5
Chile[4]	1940	44.8	41.1	34.3	23.1	35.8	19.0
Cuba	1943	38.8	35.5	28.8	18.8	30.5	13.8
Venezuela	1941	36.2	31.3	23.3	14.8	26.4	10.4
Panama	1940	26.2	24.7	24.7	17.7	23.4	17.7
Mexico	1940	27.5	21.9	16.8	10.2	19.1	7.4
Brazil[4]	1940	21.3	18.4	14.6	11.0	16.3	3.8
Colombia	1938	19.0	15.2	12.1	7.1	13.3	3.7
Guatemala	1940	13.2	8.4	6.0	5.0	8.2	5.0
North America							
United States	1940	52.7	47.6	40.1	28.8	42.3	5.7
Canada	1941	43.0	38.5	32.7	23.0	34.3	7.8

[a] The index of urbanization was computed by adding the percentages in the previous four columns and dividing by four.

[b] Figures not available to the authors.

[c] Percentages based on estimated population figures.

[d] Data on cities incomplete.

[1] Except where otherwise indicated, the percentages were computed from census data.

[2] *Hammond's New World Atlas*, 1947, p. 82. The figures for cities of 100,000+ include suburbs. The date of the figures is not certain, but it appears to be 1939.

[3] These figures were taken from United States Department of State, Division of Geography and Cartography, *Europe (without U.S.S.R.): Cities of 10,000 Population and Over by Size Categories, circa 1930*, No. 108, April 5, 1944. The percentage for 5,000+ in each case was estimated by assuming that the ratio between the percentage in cities 5,000+ and the percentage in cities 10,000+ was the same as the average ratio in the United States and Canada.

[4] The population figures on which the percentages rest were taken from the *Handbook of Latin American Population Data* (Washington, D.C.: Office of Inter-American Affairs, 1945).

Source: Kingsley Davis, *The Population of India and Pakistan* (Princeton, New Jersey: Princeton University Press, 1951), Table 45, p. 129. Used by permission.

Table 2
Total Million Dollar Miles of Imports per 10,000 Population, 1938, and Ranks of Measures of Urbanization, circa 1940, for 22 Countries

Country	(1) Million Dollar Miles of Imports*	(2) Rank of Col. 1	Rank of Per Cent Urbanization†						
			(3) Rank of Col. 1 Without Egypt	(4) In Cities 5,000+	(5) In Cities 10,000+	(6) In Cities 25,000+	(7) In Cities 100,000+	(8) By Davis Index	(9) In Largest City
New Zealand	12,961.6	1	1	6	4	5	4.5	4	7
Australia	6,564.5	2	2	2	2	2	1	2	4
Great Britain	4,408.4	3	3	1	1	1	2	1	1
Sweden	2,137.2	4	4	13	12	12	12	12	9
Argentina	2,057.0	5	5	7	6	4	3	5.5	3
Chile	1,371.5	6	6	8	8	8	8	8	2
Canada	1,353.7	7	7	9	9	9	9	9	12
Panama	1,239.3	8	8	16	16	13	11	15	5
Venezuela	1,205.2	9	9	12	13	14	14.5	13	8
France	1,063.4	10	10	10	10	10	13	10	15
Germany	999.8	11	11	4	3	3	4.5	3	16
United States	965.7	12	12	5	5	6	6	7	17
Cuba	808.7	13	13	11	11	11	10	11	6
Japan	511.4	14	14	3	7	7	7	5.5	10
Greece	459.4	15	15	14	14	15	14.5	14	14
Colombia	451.2	16	16	19	20	20	20	19	20
Brazil	390.4	17	17	18	19	19	17	18	19
Egypt	327.0	18	–	–	15	16	16	–	11
Guatemala	240.0	19	18	20	22	22	21	21	18
Poland	180.5	20	19	17	18	18	18	17	21
Mexico	174.2	21	20	15	17	17	19	16	13
India	61.9	22	21	21	21	21	22	20	22

* Total million dollar miles of imports per 10,000 population.
† Ranks of the per cents given in Table 1.

It should be obvious that this measure of the external disperson of a country's objects of consumption is extremely crude.[20] Ideally, distance should be measured by trade routes between the population centers of individual countries rather than as the shortest distance between the geographical centers of a country and its region. The practice of using "shortest distance" rather than "trade route distance" does not affect all countries equally.[21] In Japan, for example, it produces the unrealistic picture of imports from Europe moving across Siberia rather than via the Panama Canal or Singapore, resulting in a far lower total million dollar miles of Japanese imports than is, in fact, the case.

Measures of Urbanization

In recognition of the fact that a standard and definitive measure of the degree of urbanization in a country has yet to be produced,[22] we have tested the first proposition of the theory with six different measures of urbanization. These six measures are shown in Table 1 and the rank of each measure within the column is shown in Table 2.

The first proposition was tested in terms of six hypotheses, each of which involves a different measure of urbanization. The hypotheses and the results of the tests are given below. In all six tests the column designation refers to Table 2.

Hypothesis No. 1:   There will be a direct relationship by countries between the ranks of the percent of the population living in cities of 5,000 population and over (col. 4) and the ranks of the RED measures (col. 3).[23] The rank difference coefficient of correlation (*rho*) for these two variables is +.70.[24]

Hypothesis No. 2:   There will be a direct relationship by countries between the ranks of the percent of the population living in cities of 10,000 population and over (col. 5) and the ranks of the RED measures (col.2). *Rho* is +.78.

Hypothesis No. 3:   There will be a direct relationship by countries between the ranks of the percent of the population living in cities of 25,000 population and over (col. 6) and the ranks of the RED measures (col. 2). The value of *rho* is +.80.

Hypothesis No. 4:   There will be a direct relationship by countries between the ranks of the percent of the population living in cities of 100,000 population and over (col. 7) and the ranks of the RED measures (col. 2). *Rho* is + .83.

Hypothesis No. 5:   There will be a direct relationship by countries between the ranks of the percent of the population living in the largest city (col. 9) and the ranks of the RED measures (col. 2). *Rho* is +.77.

Hypothesis No. 6:   There will be a direct relationship by countries between the ranks of the Davis index of urbanization [25] (col. 8) and the ranks of the RED measures (col. 3). [26] The computed value of the *rho* is +.77.

Considering the crudeness of the measure of the external dispersion of a country's objects of consumption and the failure to take into account internal dispersion, the results of the tests of the above six hypotheses lend considerable support to the validity of the first proposition of the theory.

The results of these tests should not be interpreted to mean that the dispersion of objects of consumption is a variable isolated from and independent of certain sociological variables that have long been known to be in some way related to the degree of urbanization. It would doubtless be impossible, for example, to obtain widely dispersed objects of consumption without a highly developed economic organization and technological system. While the degree of dispersion of consumption goods is in all probability tied up with a large number of economic and technological variables, the physical fact of dispersion remains a crucial variable. Thus it may be assumed that neither Australia nor New Zealand is more economically and technologically advanced than the United States; yet with only one exception both of these countries rank higher than the United States on the six measures of urbanization shown in Table 1, and significantly, they also show much higher measures of dispersion of objects of consumption. While a highly developed economic and technological system is probably a necessary condition for a high degree of dispersion of objects of consumption, the physical fact of the distance separating consumers and the items they consume is of considerable importance. The probable linkage of the dispersion of consumption objects and economic and technological variables would appear to add to the significance of the dispersion of these objects an an ecological variable. Needless to say, however, the nature of the connection between such dispersion and economic-technological variables should be studied carefully in future ecological analysis. In the meantime, a comment is in order concerning the view that it is actually high income rather than high urbanization that makes it possible to bring together widely dispersed objects of consumption. Per capita income and urbanization are indeed positively related. This relationship points up an important aspect of the theory: urbanization is an efficient organization for obtaining sustenance whether measured by income per capita or the dispersion of objects of consumption.

The findings reported in the test of the six hypotheses will not be unexpected to many researchers since a connection between foreign trade and urbanization has been noted in other studies. The present theory, however, provides a rationale for explaining the connection between the two variables. It remains to be seen whether sheer per capita volume of foreign trade correlates more highly with urbanization than does a weighted measure (such a comparison should be made with a refined measure of dispersion of objects of consumption). It also remains to be seen what the results will be when various economic and technological variables are held constant in testing the theory.

A Second Proposition

As suggested above, countries may differ with respect to the proportion of the population residing in cities (urbanization), and with respect to the proportion of the population living in "large" cities (metropolitanization). These two dimensions of urbanization have a peculiar relationship in that a high degree of metropolitanization assures a high degree of urbanization but the reverse is not true. In theory at least it would be possible for a country to have a high degree of urbanization and a low degree of metropolitanization.

The theory of dispersion of objects of consumption points to the possibility that countries with a high RED measure are strongly urbanized because they have a high degree of metropolitanization. Where there are large metropolises the country's inhabitants must organize themselves in such a way that the metropolitan centers can draw consumers goods from a wide area, which means a wide dispersion of objects of consumption. Such is not the case for countries with a large proportion of their population living in small cities, since small cities have only to draw materials from their immediate environs. In short, whether or not a large proportion of the population lives in small cities depends upon conditions other than the external dispersion of objects of consumption, but the presence of a large proportion of the population in metropolises is completely dependent upon a large amount of consumption objects being brought from a considerable distance.

If this line of reasoning is sound, we should expect to find that the strength of the relationship between a measure of the dispersion of objects of consumption and the proportion of the population living in cities varies with the population size range of the cities. That is, if metropolitanization is defined as "large cities" the relationship by countries between the dispersion of consumption objects and metropolitanization will vary with the definition of large city. For example, if the proportion of the population living in cities between 5,000 and 10,000 is accepted as a measure of metropolitanization (which, of course, is not usually the case), the relationship between the dispersion of consumers items and metropolitanization will be less than is the case where the proportion of the population living in cities between 10,000 and 25,000 is the measure of metropolitanization. Stated in abstract form, this line of reasoning becomes the second proposition of the theory: *The magnitude of the relationship by countries between a measure of the dispersion of objects of consumption and the proportion of the population living in cities increases directly with the size of the cities considered.*

A Test of the Second Proposition

In order to test this proposition it is necessary to establish the proportion of

Table 3
Total Million Dollar Miles of Imports per 10,000 Population, 1938, and Per Cent of Population Living in Four Types of Cities, circa 1940, for 21 Countries

Country	(1) Total Million Dollar Miles of Imports*	(2) Rank of Col. 1	Percent of Population Living in†							
			(3) Cities of 5,000-10,000	(4) Rank of Col. 3	(5) Cities of 10,000-25,000	(6) Rank of Col. 5	(7) Cities of 25,000-100,000	(8) Rank of Col. 7	(9) Cities of over 100,000	(10) Rank of Col. 9
New Zealand	12,961.6	1	3.1	16	7.9	5	9.7	9.5	31.8	4.5
Australia	6,564.5	2	3.3	14	5.8	12.5	14.8	2	47.3	1
Great Britain	4,408.4	3	8.1	2	10.5	1	17.9	1	45.2	2
Sweden	2,137.2	4	3.8	10.5	6.5	11	9.5	11	16.1	12
Argentina	2,057.0	5	2.1	19	4.1	16	8.7	12	34.0	3
Chile	1,371.5	6	3.7	12	6.8	8	11.2	7	23.1	8
Canada	1,353.7	7	4.5	8	5.8	12.5	9.7	9.5	23.0	9
Panama	1,239.3	8	1.5	21	0.0	21	7.0	15	17.7	11
Venezuela	1,205.2	9	4.9	6	8.0	4	8.5	13	14.8	14.5
France	1,063.4	10	4.2	9	7.7	6	13.8	3	16.0	13
Germany	999.8	11	5.7	3	8.2	3	11.7	4	31.8	4.5
United States	965.7	12	5.1	5	7.5	7	11.3	6	28.8	6
Cuba	808.7	13	3.3	14	6.7	9.5	10.0	8	18.8	10
Japan	511.4	14	18.7	1	9.0	2	11.5	5	25.3	7
Greece	459.4	15	3.3	14	6.7	9.5	8.3	14	14.8	14.5
Colombia	451.2	16	3.8	10.5	3.1	18	5.0	18	7.1	19
Brazil	390.4	17	2.9	17	3.8	17	3.6	20	11.0	16
Guatemala	240.0	18	4.8	7	2.4	19.5	1.0	21	5.0	20
Poland	180.5	19	2.3	18	4.7	15	5.1	17	10.7	17
Mexico	174.2	20	5.6	4	5.1	14	6.6	16	10.2	18
India	61.9	21	1.8	20	2.4	19.5	3.9	19	4.2	21

* Total million dollar miles of imports per 10,000 population.
† Per cents deduced from data shown in Table 1.

the population in each country that resides in cities of different population ranges. The data in Table 1 permit the deduction of the percent of the population living in cities of 5,000 to 10,000, 10,000 to 25,000, 25,000 to 100,000, and over 100,000. These percentages and their corresponding ranks are shown in Table 3.[27]

The second proposition was tested in the form of three hypotheses. These three hypotheses stated in operational terms and the results of their tests are as follows (all column designations refer to Table 3):

Hypothesis No. 1:   The rank-difference correlation between the RED measures (col. 2) and the percent of the population in cities of 5,000 to 10,000 inhabitants will be lower than that between the RED measures and the percent of the population in cities of 10,000 to 25,000 inhabitants (col. 6). The computed values of *rho* are +.01 and +.43 respectively.

Hypothesis No. 2:   The rank-difference correlation between the RED measures (col. 2) and the percent of the population in cities of 10,000 to 25,000 inhabitants (col. 6) will be lower than that between the RED measures and the percent of the population in cities of 25,000 to 100,000 (col. 8). In this case, the computed values of *rho* are +.43 and +.65 respectively.

Hypothesis No. 3:   The rank-difference correlation between the RED measures (col. 2) and the percent of the population in cities of 25,000 to 100,000 (col. 8) will be lower than that between the RED measures and the percent of the population in cities of 100,000 inhabitants or more (col. 10). The computed *rho* values are +.65 and +.81 respectively.

As the results of these tests show, with increasing size of the cities there is a uniform increase in the magnitude of the relationship between a measure of the external dispersion of objects of consumption (RED) and the proportion of the population living in cities of a given size range. Only when metropolitanization is defined in terms of population living in cities of 100,000 and over (the usual definition), do we find an impressively high correlation.

Conclusion

It has been shown that the conception of cities as a particular type of organization for sustenance leads to a theory of the dispersion of objects of consumption as a possible explanation of differences between countries in the extent of urbanization and metropolitanization. A measure of resource dispersion—million dollar miles of imports per 10,000 population—was developed. This measure was used to test two propositions derived from the theory: (1) the degree of urbanization of a country varies directly with the extent of the dispersion of its objects of consumption; (2) the magnitude of the relationship by countries between a measure of the dispersion of objects of consumption and the proportion of the population living in cities increases directly with the size of the cities.

Table 4
The Relationships by Countries between the Measure of the Dispersions of Objects of Consumption and the Variables Stipulated in Two Theoretical Propositions

Proposition 1		*Proposition 2*	
Measure of Urbanization	*Rho*	*Per Cent in City Size Category*	*Rho*
Davis index	+.77[a]	5-10,000	+.01
Per cent in cities:		10-25,000	+.43[b]
5,000+	+.70[a]	25-100,000	+.65[a]
10,000+	+.76[a]	100,000+	+.81[a]
25,000+	+.80[a]		
100,000	+.83[a]		
Largest city	+.77[a]		

[a] Significant at .01 per cent level or beyond for one-tail test.
[b] Significant at .05 per cent level or beyond for one-tail test.

As Table 4 shows, regardless of the specific measure of urbanization, fairly strong support is provided for the first proposition. Similarly, the second proposition is supported—with the values of *rho* varying from +.01 for small cities (5,000 to 10,000 population) to +.81 for metropolises of 100,000 or more. According to our theory, urbanization is closely related to external dispersion of objects of consumption but this relationship varies from nil in the case of small towns to a high correlation in the case of metropolises. This is interpreted as meaning that the metropolitan type of organization, on one hand, is faced with the necessity of bringing together widely dispersed consumption objects and, on the other hand, is capable of getting this job done.

Both the general position regarding human ecology and the specific findings presented here have implications which cannot be treated in a single paper. The tests were presented as simple demonstrations of the ability of organizational ecology to generate meaningful empirical propositions.[28] The results, while providing support for the theory, are suggestive rather than conclusive; they are not viewed as a basis for either accepting or rejecting the conception of human ecology discussed here. Nevertheless, we hope that this presentation will stimulate interest in a reconsideration of human ecology.

Notes and References

1. It is recognized that in any international comparison of urbanization or metropoli-

tanization the investigator inevitably faces the technical and theoretical problems revolving around the lack of a common technical definition of "city," but the writers prefer at this stage to concentrate on elaboration of the theory itself.

2. By "objects of consumption" is meant material things, raw or processed, that are consumed by a population. Thus the "natural resources" of an area may or may not be objects of consumption at any given time.

3. From a large literature on human ecology two recent items are selected as examples of quite different orientations: Amos H. Hawley, *Human Ecology, a Theory of Community Structure*, New York: Ronald Press, 1950; and James A. Quinn, *Human Ecology*, New York: Prentice Hall, 1950. Also of interest concerning different conceptions of ecology is Fred Cottrell, *Energy and Society*, New York: McGraw-Hill, 1955.

4. Hawley, *op. cit.*, p. 69.

5. While the details of this conception of human ecology cannot be spelled out in a single paper it should be stipulated that the unit of observation is a population, not the individual. The units examined in this paper are large national populations, but smaller populations, such as those of cities, villages, or neighborhoods, are also appropriate units if they involve organization for sustenance.

6. The writers lay no claims to novelty in presenting a conception of ecology that over the years has been advanced or rejected by persons too numerous to cite. The co-author of this paper, Martin, notes that positions he has taken in the past on this matter are inconsistent with the one taken here. At the same time he wishes to express his appreciation to Jesse F. Steiner, whose seminar discussions of "functional ecology" have stimulated his thought along these lines. Steiner is in no sense responsible, however, for the details of the present paper.

7. The writers use "organizational ecology" with reluctance since from their point of view this designation (like "functional ecology") represents a redundancy. However, the term does make more explicit the differentiation between the conception of human ecology presented here and the idea of human ecology as the study of spatial distribution.

8. In this connection it should be noted that organization in an ecological sense need not be the result of conscious action or purposive planning; neither is purposive organization omitted from human ecology.

9. See e.g., N. P. Gist and L. A. Halbert, *Urban Society*, 4th Edition, New York: Crowell, 1956, Chapter 4; and Chauncey D. Harris and Edward L. Ullman, "The Nature of Cities," *The Annals*, 242 (November 1945), pp. 7-17.

10. For detailed treatment of this phenomenon in terms of the "principle of least effort" see George Kingsley Zipf, *Human Behavior and the Principle of Least Effort*, Cambridge: Addison-Wesley, 1949, esp. pp. 348-364.

11. While the theory advanced here is not presented as an explanation of city location, it is not unrelated to this matter. Implicit in the present theory is the suggestion that the location and development of concentrations of populations are tied in closely with the pattern of dispersion of objects of consumption. While detailed discussion of the implications of this view for city location theory must await a later paper, we see no major conflict between the present theory and prevailing theories of location. For example, the former does not contradict the "break in transportation" theory but rather clarifies it by

showing that a break in transportation can be a determinant in the location of a city only when the source of a population's objects of consumption lie beyond the break. For a review of "locational" theories see Harris and Ullman, *op. cit.* More elaborate presentations are given in August Lösch, *The Economics of Location* (translated from the Second Revised Edition by William H. Woglom with the assistance of Wolfgang F. Stolper) New Haven: Yale University Press, 1954; and Walter Isard, *Location and Space-Economy*, New Haven: Yale University Press, 1954.

12. Even though objects of consumption are evenly dispersed throughout a society (i.e., there is an undifferentiated natural environment) the development of regional specialization in the production of objects of consumption results in a special case of dispersion of objects of consumption (Region A produces coal, Region B produces wheat, etc.). The effects of this organizational differentiation for urbanization would appear to be identical with those of geographic differentiation. The presence of a critical factor, surplus production, is assumed here as in the rest of the paper but left implicit.

13. Here can be seen a problematical relationship between the existence of urban centers and the diversity of objects of consumption. As a general rule, the greater the diversity of types of objects of consumption the more dispersed are the raw materials and the greater the necessity for urban centers to control and process the widely dispersed raw materials.

14. A more exact measure would of course take into account the weight of objects of consumption as well as the distance carried.

15. The fact that the degree of a country's internal dispersion of objects of consumption is not taken into account here in the test of the propositions derived from the theory may mean that only moderately high relationships will be found to hold.

16. For simplicity, the factor of external dispersion of objects of consumption was not taken into account in Figure 1. We are assuming that the consequences of internal and external dispersion of objects of consumption are identical as far as the degree of urbanization is concerned; subsequent study may prove this assumption unwarranted.

17. Statistical Office of the United Nations, "Direction of International Trade," in *Statistical Papers*, Series T, Vo. 6, No. 10.

18. Except that in the case of countries within the same region the distance was calculated between the approximate geographic centers of both the importing and exporting countries. The ten regions used by the United Nations in reporting imports are: North America, Central America, South America, Northwest Europe, Southern Europe, Eastern Europe, Middle East, other Asia, Oceania, and other Africa.

19. Estimates of midyear populations for 1937 were obtained from *Demographic Yearbook, 1948*, New York: United Nations, 1949, pp. 75-85.

20. The objection to a measure of total million dollar miles per 10,000 population as a sociological variable can be anticipated on the ground that it is abstract to the point of being meaningless as far as common sense experience is concerned. The utility of a variable is not, of course, determined by common sense experience. A sociological variable need not be in accord with common sense experience any more than is the "square of the distance" in physics.

21. The same point probably holds for the internal dispersion of the countries' objects of consumption.

22. For a discussion of problems faced in measuring urbanization, see E. E. Bergel, *Urban Sociology*, New York: McGraw-Hill, 1955, pp. 3-14.

23. Egypt was excluded from this test because the percent of Egypt's population residing in cities of over 5,000 for the year of 1939 is not known.

24. If the assumption of a random sample from a hypothetical universe is made, this and all other *rho*'s reported for the six hypotheses are significant at the .01 level of significance or beyond.

25. See footnotes to Table 1 for a description of this index.

26. Egypt does not have an index of urbanization because the percent of Egypt's population living in cities of over 5,000 in 1939 is not known, and it has consequently been excluded from this test.

27. Egypt is excluded from Table 3 because the proportion of its population living in cities of between 5,000 and 10,000 cannot be deduced from the data in Table 1.

28. Hawley's *Human Ecology, op. cit.*, though empirically oriented, on close inspection appears to be more concerned with conceptual analysis than specific empirical propositions.

Selected References for Chapter 6
Beale, Calvin L. 1964. "Rural Depopulation in the United States: Some Demographic Consequences of Agricultural Readjustment," *Demography*, Vol. 1, no. 1. pp. 264-72. Discusses problems in rural areas stemming from selective out-migration.

Bogue, Donald J. 1959. "Population Distribution.: Pp. 383-99 of *The Study of Population*, ed. P. M. Hauser and O. D. Duncan, Chicago: University of Chicago Press. Basic principles and problems in the study of population distribution.

Carroll, Thomas F. 1964. "Land Reform as an Explosive Force in Latin America," Pp. 81-125 of *Explosive Forces in Latin America*, ed. J. J. TePaske and S. N. Fisher. Columbus, Ohio: Ohio State University Press. Reviews problems resulting from inequitable man-land ratios characteristic of most Latin American countries.

Hauser, Philip M. 1969. "The Chaotic Society: Product of the Social Morpological Revolution," *American Sociological Review*, Vol. 34 (February), pp. 1-19. Focuses on problematic implications of changing spatial organization of modern societies.

Keyfitz, Nathan 1971. "Migration as a Means of Population Control," *Population Studies*, Vol. 25 (March), pp. 63-72. An analysis of the limitation of migration as a mechanism for coping with excessive population growth.

This chapter has examined the adaptive significance of the fact that the basic components of ecological systems, people and resources, are mobile. Thus one means of improving the balance between populations and the environments upon which they depend for survival ought to be the spatial redistribution of one or both. We have considered several aspects of this problem, though by no means have we dealt with all the relevant issues.

Migration was examined as a means of alleviating the problems of depressed areas. A major problem inherent in this solution appears to be the selective character of migratory movements. Paradoxically, the sectors of the populations of depressed areas most likely to migrate are those which are most needed for economic progress to take place. In addition, migration policy has been lacking with the result that inadequate attention has been given to the total system of relationships between depressed populations and surrounding areas. For migration to be a viable solution to population imbalance, possibly detrimental consequences must be anticipated and resolved. Recurrent movements of population were considered in that they involve less disruptive adjustments of existing social relationships. It was suggested that the distance people will regularly travel from home to work is contingent upon balanced "costs". If this is true, then population balance might be achieved through manipulation of the factors affecting these costs. But, once again, this would involve the development of a much more detailed and restrictive policy regarding population movements than presently exists.

The second set of considerations dealt with in this chapter revolved primarily around the movement of resources. It was shown that dependence upon widely dispersed objects of consumption is associated with a greater degree of urbanization. In other words, urban concentration is a necessary condition for a population to effectively transport and process needed resources which are not available locally. This is an example of the complementary and coordinated movement of both people and resources in the interests of greater ecological adaptation.

From the discussions presented in this chapter it should be evident that movement constitutes an important mechanism for dealing with ecological problems. Other things being equal, redistribution of population and/or resources should be a viable solution to at least some of the problems of collective survival. But, unfortunately, as is usually the case, other things are *not* equal. Human beings resist being moved unless the choice is theirs, and more often than not patterns of geographic mobility work against the interests of the collectivity. On the other hand, environmental redistribution appears to be increasingly feasible, though considerations of national interest, public policy, and resource conservation, among others, are complicating factors. A final consideration of the interrelationships among the four adaptive mechanisms discussed in these chapters is contained in the Epilogue.

Part III, which follows, is focused on various unresolved issues regarding population and environment. It will be seen that inadequate attention to adaptive mechanisms and their interrelationships accounts for much that is problematic about these topics.

Part III
Critical Issues in Ecological Adaptation: Evaluations and Forecasts

7

Population Control:
Fact or Fiction?

This chapter is focused entirely on the problematic aspects of population control, omitting other relevant but less critical demographic issues for the study of human ecology. At the most inclusive level this discussion will be concerned with questions of excessive population growth, but it soon becomes apparent that major attention has been directed toward fertility control as the key to population control.

The dilemma surrounding contemporary concerns with population control is this: On the one hand techniques sufficient for curbing fertility rates now exist and, indeed, have proven successful in a few cases; on the other, dangerously high fertility still characterizes the vast majority of the less-developed nations.[1] One result of this situation is considerable disagreement in evaluating the accomplishments and needed emphases of population-control programs. The next two essays, which should be considered together, represent widely divergent positions on this question. For purposes of comparison we can view Donald J. Bogue's argument as optimistic, and that presented by Kingsley Davis as pessimistic regarding progress in population control.

Bogue's optimism is patently clear from his statement that it is quite reasonable to assume that *the world population crisis is a phenomenon of the 20th century, and will be largely if not entirely a matter of history when humanity moves into the 21st century.*[2] With some exceptions, the author feels that by the year 2000 (a scant thirty years hence!) most regions of the world will have achieved a balance between fertility and mortality.[3]

What are the factors underlying Bogue's optimism? Essentially these are results of various international fertility-control programs that have been achieved during the past decade. The year 1960, according to this argument, marks a drastic turning point in the world population growth, making trends prior to that point largely irrelevant for projecting future patterns.[4] More specifically, Bogue lists (1) grass-roots approval of program goals, (2) increased support from political leaders, (3) accelerated professional and research concentration on fertility control, (4) slackening programs in death control, (5) a variety of social and psychological stimulants to family planning, and (6) rapid improvements in contraceptive technology as positive features contributing to overall program success. The experience of the Republic of Korea is summarized to illustrate the argument. It is even suggested that *instead of a 'population explosion' the world is on the threshold of a 'contraception adoption explosion'.*[5]

In concluding, Bogue emphasizes that to assert that pre-1960 conditions will characterize future world population is to misrepresent the facts. He sees the vital revolution as having already begun, and strongly suggests that the ultimate outcome, world-wide fertility control, is inevitable given the progress made thus far. One must recognize that Bogue is *not* depreciating the importance of the population crisis, but rather is convinced that the problem can and will be alleviated.

On the other extreme Davis presents a most critical analysis of current efforts at population control, arriving at the general conclusion that they are limited to family planning and are therefore ineffective. In developing support for his argument the author thoroughly reviews the nature and goals of current policies and programs. He finds an almost exclusive emphasis on the widespread dispersion of modern contraceptive technology as the key to resolving the world's population crisis. His concern is not that there is anything inherently wrong with such a strategy, but rather that it simply doesn't yield the results promised.

An examination of the goals of family-planning programs shows that they are based on a naive conception of the determinants of reproductive behavior. Little attention is given to influencing any factors other than the decision to accept contraception, and alternative means of controlling fertility are either ignored or rejected. In addition, the goals proposed—e.g., fertility rates comparable to those existing in present industrialized societies— would result in sizeable population increases for already over-populated areas. One of the most problematic features of current family planning programs is the emphasis on enabling couples to have the number of children they want. As Davis points out, these fertility ideals invariably indicate a general preference for relatively large families, thus the result of leaving this matter up to the parents would be a perpetuation of excessive fertility. The net evaluation of the goals of family-planning programs, then, leads to the conclusion that a family-planning orientation limits the aims of current population policy.

The second major criticism levied by Davis involves the treatment of motivation in the family-planning approach. In particular, the problem stems from a failure to recognize that reproductive ideals and behavior are conditioned by various aspects of social and economic organization—e.g., the structure of power and family systems, the status of women, and the functional utility of children. The effectiveness of family-planning propaganda and technology is thus dependent upon the creation of an organizational environment which will instill motivation for smaller families. The necessary changes in social organization are rarely considered in family-planning strategies.

As further evidence for his argument, Davis introduces a consideration of the recent demographic experience of underdeveloped countries. He is generally skeptical regarding any signs of decreased fertility clearly due to family-planning programs. A detailed analysis is provided for Taiwan, generally considered to be the "showpiece" for proponents of the family-planning approach. Of primary significance is the author's contention that the decline in fertility registered for the island's population between 1950 and 1965 was largely a consequence of modernizing trends in social and economic organization set in motion long before the introduction of a family-planning program. Though he does not deny that *some* of the reduction was due to organized family-planning efforts, the larger portion is attributed to individual initiative. Additional criticisms are aimed at the program's apparent acceptance of existing (relatively high) fertility norms and the exclusive focus on married women. In short, Davis presents a compelling argument to the effect that the Taiwanese program falls short as a model of effective population control.

Finally, Davis suggests that family-planning programs cannot at present be considered even first steps to population control since they merely postpone the adoption of truly effective measures. Several alternative approaches are outlined, all of which involve the alteration of societal norms for family formation and organization. For example, Davis proposes later marriage (somewhat beyond the age of twenty) and a variety of incentives and sanctions for discouraging reproduction within marriage. Particular emphasis is placed upon maximizing the attractiveness of non-familial roles for women.

In summarizing his argument the author stresses an all too often neglected fact: the things that make family planning acceptable are the very things that make it ineffective for population control. It is the survival of societies rather than the family as an institution which is at stake, and to offer only the means for couples to control fertility is to invite eventual disaster. The dilemma of population policy, then, is how to arrive at rates of population growth that are optimum for the needs and limitations of whole societies, yet to avoid dictatorial methods which result in personal hardships and the loss of individual freedoms. Davis' answer is the variety of "attractive substitutes" for family interests proposed in this essay.

The discrepancy between the views of Davis and Bogue regarding the effectiveness of current family planning programs requires little elaboration. What is needed, assuming one attributes at least *some* significance to Davis' argument, is further consideration of the next steps. The final contribution to this chapter, prepared by Bernard Berelson, contains a detailed examination of this problem. In agreement with Davis, Berelson assumes that reliance upon family-planning programs alone will not be adequate to counter the trend of rapid growth among most of the nations of the world. At the same time he suggests, in accord with Bogue, that significant advances have resulted from national family-planning effects. The major contribution of this essay, though, lies in the author's systematic evaluation of supplementary and alternative proposals to current fertility-control measures. Unfortunately few definitive solutions emerge.

Berelson examines a wide variety of proposals. Some involve minimal variation from existing practices, such as the institutionalization of maternal care in rural areas of developing countries and the call for more research, while others appear to be radical or reactionary in light of current norms—

e.g., payment for periods of non-pregnancy or non-birth and the sale of licenses for having children. Most fall between these extremes, though, in that they have been seriously considered by more than a few advocates of population policy, perhaps even tried, but widespread adoption has not resulted. Another source of variation among proposals is the extent of purposive action required of participants. On the one extreme are the various involuntary control measures that would presumably be dictated by national or international organizations, on the other the so-called incentive systems, largely dependent upon individual or couple motivation. An intermediate group includes those proposals involving a combination of external agency and participant action, such as the proposals for intensified educational campaigns. The common thread linking this diverse set of alternatives to family planning is that all have at some time been seriously presented as potential solutions to the problem of excessive population growth.

In evaluating these proposals Berelson employs six criteria: (1) scientific/medical/technological availability, (2) political acceptance, (3) administrative capability, (4) economic feasibility, (5) moral acceptability, and (6) effectiveness. Considering the first criterion, the author concludes that the necessary technology and medical personnel are available for some but not all proposals. Generally, the closer a proposal is to traditional family-planning programs, the more likely it is that these requirements can be met. The question of political viability is much less certain for most proposals; Berelson suggests that this depends largely upon the extent to which programs promote social values other than mere population control as, for example, do health and welfare plans. But the problem of competing interests and values appears to be the major political barrier to national as well as international programs. Another major problem area has to do with the administration of population policy. Many of the proposals considered here do not specify administrative procedures, but the real issue lies in the fact that those countries most in need of increased population control also have the least developed administrative systems. The economic criterion reveals mixed results. While some proposals would not impose excessive financial burdens, others, such as the various incentive and benefits plans would. Perhaps the most difficult criterion to utilize involves moral and ethical considerations. The question, as old as human society itself, is focused on identifying an optimum balance between individual and collective interests. Do current rates of population growth threaten collective survival to such an extent that intrusion upon individual freedoms is morally justified? Though Berelson takes no concrete position on this matter, he is clearly opposed to any policy that seriously infringes upon individual choice, and concludes that most official doctrine in the emerging population programs is conservative. Finally, he suggests that a vigorous program of alternative measures *can* extend contraceptive practices by an economically worthwhile amount wherever conducted. This is not to say that all proposals are or can be equally effective, nor can they be initiated and evaluated with equal ease.

Overall, the author groups the various proposals considered into three levels of relative effectiveness based upon his evaluative criteria. Highest effectiveness is attributed to (1) extension of conventional family-planning programs, (2) intensified educational campaigns, and (3) augmented research efforts. The intermediate groups include (1) extension of voluntary control and (2) shifts in social and economic institutions. Least effective, according to this evaluation, are those proposals based upon (1) incentive programs, (2) tax and welfare benefits and penalties, (3) political channels and organizations, and (4) involuntary fertility controls.

As Berelson himself states, "The picture is not particularly encouraging." Each of the proposals considered here runs up against one or more technological, political, economic, administrative, or moral barriers. However this effort to evaluate proposals for a more comprehensive population policy is not fruitless; several useful insights emerge. For example, Berelson dispels the notion that there may be a single magic strategy that will result in rapid and efficient control of population growth. Various methods, used in combination, offer the greatest promise for eventual success. More important is the recognition that in the last analysis, what will be scientifically available, politically acceptable, administratively feasible, economically justifiable, and morally tolerated depends upon people's perceptions of consequences; greater measures to meet the problem must rely on heightened awareness of what is at stake, by leaders and masses alike. Nevertheless, the question of "beyond family planning, what?" remains problematic. All that appears certain, Professor Bogue to the contrary, is that the survival of mankind is increasingly dependent upon its resolution.

Notes and References

1. See Ansley J. Coale, "The Voluntary Control of Human Fertility," *Proceedings of the American Philosophical Society*, Vol. III (June 22, 1967), pp. 164-169.

2. Emphasis provided by the author.

3. On the consequences of a "zero growth rate" see Leslie A. Westoff and Charles F. Westoff, *From Now to Zero: Fertility, Contraception and Abortion in America.* Boston: Little, Brown and Co., 1970, pp. 335-38.

4. Recently reported data for some of the "larger" less developed areas supports the trend assumed here. See Dudley Kirk, "A New Demographic Transition?" in *Rapid Population Growth: Consequences and Policy Implications.* Baltimore and London: Johns Hopkins University Press, 1971, Table 1, p. 128.

5. Emphasis provided by the author.

The End of the Population Explosion
Donald J. Bogue

Recent developments in the worldwide movement to bring runaway birth rates under control are such that is now is possible to assert with considerable confidence that the prospects for success are excellent. In fact, it is quite reasonable to assume that *the world population crisis is a phenomenon of the 20th century, and will be largely if not entirely a matter of history when humanity moves into the 21st century*. No doubt there will still be problematic areas in the year 2000, but they will be confined to a few nations that were too prejudiced, too bureaucratic, or too disorganized to take action sooner, or will be confined to small regions within some nations where particular ethnic, economic, or religious groups will not yet have received adequate fertility control services and information. With the exception of such isolated remnants (which may be neutralized by other areas of growth-at-less-than-replacement), it is probable that by the year 2000 each of the major world regions will have a population growth rate that either is zero or is easily within the capacity of its expanding economy to support.

The implications of these assertions for the feeding of the human race are obvious. Given the present capacity of the earth for food production, and the potential for additional food production if modern technology were more fully employed, mankind clearly has within its grasp the capacity to abolish hunger—within a matter of a decade or two. Furthermore, it is doubtful whether a total net food shortage for the entire earth will ever develop. If such a deficit does develop, it will be mild and only of short duration. The really critical problem will continue to be one of maldistribution of food among the world's regions.

These optimistic assertions are not intended to detract from the seriousness of the present population situation. Some years of acute crisis lie immediately ahead for India, China, the Philippines, Indonesia, Pakistan, Mexico, Brazil, Egypt, and other nations. Severe famines quite probably will develop within local areas of some of these nations unless emergency international measures are taken. My purpose here is to emphasize that the engineers and the agricultural technicians striving to increase the output of material goods in these nations are not working alone. Paralleling their activity is a very ambitious international fertility control program which is just starting to "pay off."

These remarks are certainly not intended to cause the participants in this international fertility control program to relax their efforts and be lulled into complacency. The successful outcome anticipated above is not one that will come automatically, but only as a result of a continued all-out "crash program" to make the widest and most intensive use of the medical, sociological and psychological knowledge now available, and of the practical experience that has recently emerged from experimental family planning programs. It also anticipates a continued flow of new research findings and enriched practical experience that is promptly fed back into programs of fertility reduction.

This view is at variance with the established view of many population experts. For more than a century, demographers have terrorized themselves, each other, and the public at large with the essential hopelessness and inevitability of the "population explosion." Their prophecies have all been dependent upon one premise: "If recent trends continue. . . . " It is an ancient statistical fallacy to perform extrapolations upon this premise when in fact the premise is invalid. It is my major point that *recent trends have not continued, nor will they be likely to do so*. Instead, there have been some new and recent developments that make it plausible to expect a much more rapid pace in fertility control. These developments are so new and so novel that *population trends before 1960 are largely irrelevant in predicting what will happen in the future.*

In times of social revolution, it often is fruitless to forecast the future on the basis of past experience. Instead, it is better to abandon time series analysis and study the phenomenon of change itself, seeking to understand it and to learn in which direction and how rapidly it is moving. If enough can be learned about the social movement that is bringing about the change, there is a hope that its eventual outcome can be roughly predicted. This procedure is followed here. The result is subjective and crude, but I believe it to be nearer the future course of demographic history than the official population projections now on record.

Reasons for Optimism

Limitations of space permit only a listing of major social developments which, in my view, justify the relatively optimistic prospect I have set forth.

1. Grass Roots Approval

All over the world, wherever surveys of the attitudes of the public with respect to fertility have been taken, it has uniformly been found that a majority of couples with three living children wish to have no more. Of these, a very large proportion approve of family planning in principle and declare they would like to have more information about it. They also approve of nationwide health service that includes family planning. In other words, active objections among the masses on cultural, moral, or religious grounds are minor rather than major obstacles. This is true both in Asia and Latin America, and seems to be developing rapidly in Africa. Thus, at the "grass roots" level, the attitudinal and cultural conditions are highly favorable. Previously, it had been feared that traditionalism and religious attitudes would prove to be almost insuperable blocks to rapid fertility control. But the more sociologists study the situation, the more they accept as correct the generalization that, in most places where there is a population problem, the attitude toward family planning among the mass of the people is strongly positive.

2. Aroused Political Leadership

Whereas fertility control was regarded as a subversive, immoral, and sinful program during the 150 years of fertility decline in Europe and the United States, in the nations with a population problem today the national political leadership openly accepts family planning as a moral and rational solution. Heads of state in India, Pakistan, Korea, China, Egypt, Chile, Turkey, and Colombia, for example, have made fertility control an integral part of the national plan for economic development. In this, they have followed the lead of Japan. The national ministers of health and welfare not only are permitted but are expected to provide family planning services. National health services are adding family planning to their clinic services, financed by public tax funds. The mass media are increasingly carrying official endorsements, public encouragements, and specific information.

3. Accelerated Professional and Research Activity

Professional groups in the developing countries (as well as in the rest of the world) are rapidly losing whatever antipathy or prejudice against family planning they may have had. Everywhere, the medical profession is rapidly giving it a solid endorsement—even in nations where there have been problems of religious objection. Within religious groups where there formerly was a hard inflexible prohibition against the use of chemical or mechanical contraceptive appliances, there is now a great deal of difference of opinion. Gradually, the laity is reaching the belief that the control of natality is a matter for the individual conscience, or a medical matter to be discussed with a physician—but not with a priest. Physicians and priests alike tend to accept this interpretation without forthright challenge.

Universities, both in the United States and abroad, have undertaken large-scale and sustained research activities in the fields of family planning. Their activities cover the entire range of topics—medical, sociological, and psychological. Most of the nations with a national family planning program are sponsoring research into the problem. This includes not only projects to discover new and improved ways of promoting fertility control, but also the evaluation of present programs. These activities are not amorphous, but within a remarkably short time have been coordinated. The process of integration was greatly facilitated by the holding in Geneva in 1965 of an International Conference on Family Planning Programs.

Much of the credit for the development described above is due to the activities of not-for-profit organizations that have taken population control as a focus of their activities: the Ford Foundation, Rockefeller Foundation, Population Council, and International Planned Parenthood are the leaders. The Swedish Government, the Milbank Memorial Fund, the Planned Parenthood Association of America, and the Pathfinder Fund have also been highly important sponsors of these activities. These organizations have provided unprecedented financial and technical support.

4. The Slackening of Progress in Death Control
Immediately after World War II, the industrialized nations of the world realized that there was a series of public health and medical programs that could be accomplished quickly and cheaply to bring about a reduction in mortality. These have now been largely carried out—there have been campaigns against malaria, smallpox, cholera, yellow fever, and other diseases that can be brought under control with an injection, a semi-annual house spraying, etc. The results have been dramatic, and death rates have tumbled. However, further progress in death control will be slower, because the remaining problems are those for which a solution is more difficult or is as yet unknown. For example, the death rate in Latin America stands at about 14 per thousand now. Modern medicine could bring it, at best, only to about 8 per thousand— a fall of 6 points. But a very much greater investment must be made, and over a considerably longer span of time, to achieve these 6 points than was required to obtain the preceding six points. In Asia the death rate still stands at about 20, even after the advent of the "miracle drugs" and the mass-inoculation and mass-treatment programs. It may be expected to drift lower, but at a slower pace than before.

This slackening of death control has a most important implication—a decline in the birth rate would be more directly reflected in a decline in the rate of population growth. During the past two decades, even if birth rates were declining, death rates were declining still faster, so that the population growth rate increased. That trend now appears to be reaching the end of a cycle: the cycle appears to be on the verge of reversing itself.

5. A Variety of Sociological and Psychological Phenomena, Previously Unknown or Underappreciated, Are Promoting the Rapid Adoption of Family Planning by The Mass of The People.
Here we can only list them, without explanation:

a. Privation is itself a powerful motivating force for fertility control.
b. Private communication about family planning is far greater than had been thought, and can easily be stimulated to attain flood proportions.

c. "Opinion leaders"—indigenous men and women who are knowledgable about birth control and freely undertake to influence others to adopt it—can be mass-produced cheaply and very rapidly by means of mass media and other action programs. Thus, in this area just as in economic development, there is a "multiplier effect" which, if capitalized upon, can greatly hasten "takeoff" into rapidly declining fertility.

d. It is becoming evident that fathers are very nearly equally as interested and responsible in controlling fertility as are wives. Programs aimed at couples, instead of at females, are highly effective.

e. We are discovering that illiterate rural populations will make use of the traditional methods of family planning—condom, suppositories, etc.—very nearly as readily as urban populations, after a brief period of information and trial. They will also adopt the newer methods as—or even more—readily.

6. Improved Technology in Contraception Promotes Massive Adoption by Uneducated People at a Rapid Pace

Oral contraceptives and the intra-uterine devices have both proved to be highly acceptable after only short periods of instruction and familiarity. Even illiterate rural villagers make sustained use of these methods where they have been given unprejudiced trial. These developments are only half-a-decade old, but they already have had a profound impact upon fertility control programs and plans. As yet there is still a great deal of prejudice against the oral compounds in Asia, so that the advantages of a two-method assault have not been fully realized there. In Latin American experiments, where the "pills" and intra-uterine devices are used side-by-side as alternative methods, the results are highly impressive.

We are repeatedly being told by the physiologists, however, that our so-called "modern" methods of contraception are crude and barbarous—each with unpleasant side-effects and unsuitable for as much as one quarter of the population. They insist that much superior methods are on the horizon—that soon there will be dramatic improvements, that costs will be cheaper, and that the need for "sustained motivation" to practice contraception will be greatly reduced. Millions of dollars are being poured into experimental research on this front each year. This activity is taking place both in the public and the private sector. The giants of the drug industry know that huge markets can be gained by improving upon present contraceptive technology—and that huge markets will be lost if a competitor discovers and markets a superior product. As a result, all of the leading motives that bring about frenzied activity for progress among scientists have been harnessed and are at work in behalf of improving contraceptive technology—prestige, economic gain, anxiety, compassion.

The Example of Korea

In order to illustrate the above points, let us take as an example the recent experience of Korea. In 1962, the Republic of Korea formally adopted family planning as one of its national policies. In 1965, a National Survey of Family Planning was conducted. Following are some points from that survey.

1. Eighty-nine percent of the wives and 79 percent of the husbands approved of family planning.

2. The rate of approval was only slightly lower in the rural than in the urban areas (88 percent for rural women and 77 percent for rural men).

3. Of the minority who disapproved, only 8 percent mentioned religion or morals. Traditional resistance was as low in rural as in urban areas.

4. Inability to read was no barrier; 81 percent of those unable to read nevertheless approved of family planning.

5. On the verbal level, the population declared itself willing to practice family planning if given services. Seventy-seven percent of the urban women and 71 percent of the rural women made such a declaration. Among husbands, 71 percent of the urban and 65 percent of the rural made such a declaration.

6. Unwillingness to practice family planning was concentrated primarily among young couples who had not yet had the number of children they desired and older couples (past 40 years of age) who were approaching the end of their child-bearing. Couples in the years of prime importance for birth control, 25-40, were most positive in their attitudes. Moreover, the greater the number of living children, the greater the willingness to practice.

7. As a result of the national information program, 85 percent of the urban and 83 percent of the rural population had heard of family planning. Moreover, 67 percent of the urban and 64 percent of the rural population had knowledge of at least one contraceptive method. Even among the illiterate, 51 percent knew of one method or more. Knowledge of the more reliable methods—oral pill, IUCD, condom—was only very slightly less widespread in rural than in urban areas.

8. At the time of the interview, 21 percent of the urban and 14 percent of the rural couples were practicing family planning. Even among the illiterate population, 10 percent were currently practicing family planning. Although small, these percentages very obviously have sprung from a condition of near-zero within a span of three years. If only 2 percent are added each year, within 35 years population growth would be near zero.

9. The methods used by rural families were equal to or superior to those of the urban population in terms of reliability:

Method	Percent of those using a method	
	Rural	Urban
Condom	51.1	61.1
I.U.C.D.	18.4	27.0
Oral Pill	8.5	3.5
Foam tablet	34.5	42.2

10. In April of 1965 there were 2207 field workers in the national family planning service, stationed in the health centers or in local offices. This is only the first wave of a rapid build-up to a point where there will be one field worker for each 10,000 population. The medical and social science departments of Seoul National University are actively engaged in research, evaluation, and participation in the national program. A private organization, Planned Parenthood Federation of Korea, has a branch in each province and is providing service and information through its office. Yonsel Medical College is conducting special experiments in rural areas, with assistance from the Population Council.

11. The progress of the national program in giving family planning services is most impressive. The progress that results when a well-designed family planning program is carried out in a population of low education is illustrated by the Sungdong Gu Action-Research Project on Family Planning, Conducted by Seoul National University School of Public Health under the sponsorship of the Population Council. This program started in July, 1964. It included the use of mass media (T.V., radio, newspaper, posters, pamphlets, leaflets), group meetings, and home visiting. During the first 15 months of the program, of a total of 44,900 eligible (married women in the ages 20-44), 9,809 visited the family planning station for family planning information. About 85 percent of these visitors (19 percent of all the eligible women) accepted a method of family planning. Acceptance was divided roughly equally between condoms and other traditional methods and the IUCD's. Within a period, a total of 5,722 insertions (13 percent of the eligible women) were made. Even when allowance is made for the fact that the first year's experience would "skim off" the accumulated group of already-motivated people, the fact that one-fifth of the fertile population could be induced to adopt family planning within such short time is most impressive. It suggests the potential progress that can be made when a well-balanced program of information and service is provided, making use both of the mass media and personal contact.

The above brief notes on the progress of fertility control in Korea are not isolated instances. A recent report from the Pakistan Family Planning Programme suggests that more than one million families in that nation of 100 million (about 5 percent of the eligible population) now are currently contracepted through this program alone. In India, more than a million insertions of IUCD's are being made anually—in addition, the use of other methods of contraception is rising. In Colombia in Latin America, the oral pills and the IUCD both are being accepted at phenomenal rates; it is estimated that more than 120,000 couples in this nation of 18 million persons are using the oral pills alone; this is roughly 3 percent of the eligible population. In addition, large quantities of other methods are known to be used. In Santiago, Chile, the IUCD is so well known and widely used that it is a part of the medical service throughout the metropolitan area.

To summarize: wherever one looks in the underdeveloped segments of the world, one finds evidence of firmly established and flourishing family planning activity. By whatever crude estimates it is possible to make, it is quite clear that a sufficiently large share of the population already is making use of modern contraceptives to have a depressing effect upon the birth rate. Even conservative evaluation of the prospects suggests that *instead of a "population explosion" the world is on the threshold of a "contraception adoption explosion."* Because of lack of adequate vital statistics, the effects of this new "explosion" will not be readily measurable for a few years, but they will start to manifest themselves in the censuses of 1970 and will be most unmistakable in 1980.

Predictions for the Future

Given the situation that has just been described, what can be said concerning the future population of the world? If we insist on extrapolating past trends, we are making the unrealistic assertion that conditions have remained and will continue to remain unchanged. If we predict a slow change of the type that was typical of Europe and Northern America before 1960, we are implicitly asserting that the current programs are having zero effect: this assertion is contrary to fact. The course taken here has been to try to comprehend the nature of the change that is taking place, and to predict its probable course and speed, so that its impact may be guessed. As crude and subjective as this procedure is, it appears to offer more valid predictions than conventional population projections.

Looking at the developments listed above, realizing that they are only 5 years old or less, knowing that accomplishments in this area are cumulative and grow by exponential curves, and appreciating that new discoveries and improvements will accrue promptly along all fronts—medical, social, and psychological—both from basic research and from accumulating experience and evaluation—the following generalizations appear to be justified:

The trend of the worldwide movement toward fertility control has already reached a state where declines in death rates are being surpassed by declines in birthrates. Because progress in death control is slackening and progress in birth control is accelerating, the world has already entered a situation where the pace of population growth has begun to slacken. The exact time at which this "switch-over" took place cannot be known exactly, but we estimate it to have occurred about 1965. From 1965 onward, therefore, the rate of world population growth may be expected to decline with each passing year. The rate of growth will slacken at such a pace that it will be zero or near zero at about the year 2000, so that population growth will not be regarded as a major social problem except in isolated and small "retarded" areas.

In evaluating these conclusions, it must be kept in mind that the topic is a deadly serious one, and the penalties for misjudgment may be very great. There is one set of penalties that results from over-optimism. But there is another set of penalties that results from over-pessimism. It is quite possible that nothing has sapped the morale of family planning workers in the developing countries more than the Malthusian pessimism that has been radiated by many demographic reports. It is like assuring soldiers going into battle that they are almost certain to be defeated. If the comments made here should be so fortunate as to fall into the hands of these same family planning workers, it is hoped that those who read them will appreciate just how close they actually are to success. They have it within their grasp to improve dramatically their countries' fortunes. Coupled with the companion programs of industrialization and modernization, the effects could appear almost miraculous as they unfold in the 1970s and 1980s.

Population Policy: Will Current Programs Succeed?
Kingsley Davis

Throughout history the growth of population has been identified with prosperity and strength. If today an increasing number of nations are seeking to curb rapid population growth by reducing their birth rates, they must be driven to do so by an urgent crisis. My purpose here is not to discuss the crisis itself but rather to assess the present and prospective measures used to meet it. Most observers are surprised by the swiftness with which concern over the population problem has turned from intellectual analysis and debate to policy and action. Such action is a welcome relief from the long opposition, or timidity, which seemed to block forever any governmental attempt to restrain population growth, but relief that "at last something is being done" is no guarantee that what is being done is adequate. On the face of it, one could hardly expect such a fundamental reorientation to be quickly and successfully implemented. I therefore propose to review the nature and (as I see them) limitations of the present policies and to suggest lines of possible improvement.

The Nature of Current Policies

With more than 30 nations now trying or planning to reduce population growth and with numerous private and international organizations helping, the degree of unanimity as to the kind of measures needed is impressive. The consensus can be summed up in the phrase "family planning." President Johnson declared in 1965 that the United States will "assist family planning programs in nations which request such help." The Prime Minister of India said a year later, "We must press forward with family planning. This is a programme of the highest importance." The Republic of Singapore created in 1966 the Singapore Family Planning and Population Board "to initiate and undertake population control programmes."[1]

As is well known, "family planning" is a euphemism for contraception. The family-planning approach to population limitation, therefore, concentrates on providing new and efficient contraceptives on a national basis through mass programs under public health auspices. The nature of these programs is shown by the following enthusiastic report from the Population Council:[2]

> No single year has seen so many forward steps in population control as 1965. Effective national programs have at last emerged, international organizations have decided to become engaged, a new contraceptive has proved its value in mass application, ... and surveys have confirmed a popular desire for family limitation....
>
> An accounting of notable events must begin with Korea and Taiwan.... Taiwan's program is not yet two years old, and already it has inserted one IUD [intrauterine device] for every 4-6 target women (those who are not pregnant, lactating, already sterile, already using contraceptives effectively, or desirous of more children). Korea has done almost as well ... has put 2,200 full-time workers into the field, ... has reached operational levels for a network of IUD quotas, supply lines, local manufacture of contraceptives, training of hundreds of M.D.'s and nurses, and mass propaganda....

Here one can see the implication that "population control" is being achieved through the dissemination of new contraceptives, and the fact that the "target women" exclude those who want more children. One can also note the technological emphasis and the medical orientation.

What is wrong with such programs? The answer is, "Nothing at all, if they work." Whether or not they work depends on what they are expected to do as well as on how they try to do it. Let us discuss the goal first, then the means.

Goals

Curiously, it is hard to find in the population-policy movement any explicit discussion of long-range goals. By implication the policies seem to promise a great deal. This is shown by the use of expressions like *population control* and *population planning* (as in the passages quoted above). It is also shown by the characteristic style of reasoning. Expositions of current policy usually start off by lamenting the speed and the consequences of runaway population growth. This growth, it is then stated, must be curbed—by pursuing a vigorous family-planning program. That family planning can solve the problem of population growth seems to be taken as self-evident.

For instance, the much-heralded statement by 12 heads of state, issued by Secretary-General U Thant on 10 December 1966 (a statement initiated by John D. Rockefeller III, Chairman of the Board of the Population Council), devotes half its space to discussing the harmfulness of population growth and the other half to recommending family planning.[3] A more succinct example of the typical reasoning is given in the Provisional Scheme for a Nationwide Family Planning Programme in Ceylon:[4]

> The population of Ceylon is fast increasing. . . . [The] figures reveal that a serious situation will be created within a few years. In order to cope with it a Family Planning programme on a nationwide scale should be launched by the Government.

The promised goal—to limit population growth so as to solve population problems—is a large order. One would expect it to be carefully analyzed, but it is left imprecise and taken for granted, as is the way in which family planning will achieve it.

When the terms *population control* and *population planning* are used, as they frequently are, as synonyms for current family-planning programs, they are misleading. Technically, they would mean deliberate influence over all attributes of a population, including its age-sex structure, geographical distribution, racial composition, genetic quality, and total size. No government attempts such full control. By tacit understanding, current population policies are concerned with only the *growth* and *size* of populations. These attributes, however, result from the death rate and migration as well as from the birth rate; their control would require deliberate influence over the factors giving rise to all three determinants. Actually, current policies labeled population control do not deal with mortality and migration, but deal only with the birth input. This is why another term, *fertility control*, is frequently used to describe current policies. But, as I show below, family planning (and hence current policy) does not undertake to influence most of the determinants of human reproduction. Thus the programs should not be referred to as population control or planning, because they do not attempt to influence the factors responsible for the attributes of human populations, taken generally; nor should they be called fertility control, because they do not try to affect most of the determinants of reproductive performance.

The ambiguity does not stop here, however. When one speaks of controlling population size, any inquiring person naturally asks, What is "control"? Who is to control whom? Precisely what population size, or what rate of population growth, is to be achieved? Do the policies aim to produce a growth rate that is nil, one that is very slight, or one that is like that of the industrial nations? Unless such questions are dealt with and clarified, it is impossible to evaluate current population policies.

Reduction, not Zero Growth
The actual programs seem to be aiming simply to achieve a reduction in the birth rate. Success is therefore interpreted as the accomplishment of such a reduction, on the assumption that the reduction will lessen population growth. In those rare cases where a specific demographic aim is stated, the goal is said to be a short-run decline within a given period. The Pakistan plan adopted in 1966[5] (p. 889) aims to reduce the birth rate from 50 to 40 per thousand by 1970; the Indian plan[6] aims to reduce the rate from 40 to 25 "as soon as possible"; and the Korean aim[7] is to cut population growth from 2.9 to 1.2 percent by 1980. A significant feature of such stated aims is the rapid population growth they would permit. Under conditions of modern mortality, a crude birth rate of 25 to 30 per thousand will represent such a multiplication of people as to make use of the term *population control* ironic. A rate of increase of 1.2 percent per year would allow South Korea's already dense population to double in less than 60 years.

One can of course defend the programs by saying that the present goals and measures are merely interim ones. A start must be made somewhere. But we do not find this answer in the population-policy literature. Such a defense, if convincing, would require a presentation of the *next* steps, and these are not considered. One suspects that the entire question of goals is instinctively left vague because thorough limitation of population growth would run counter to national and group aspirations. A consideration of hypothetical goals throws further light on the matter.

Industrialized Nations as the Model
Since current policies are confined to family planning, their maximum demographic effect would be to give the underdeveloped countries the same level of reproductive performance that the industrial nations now have. The latter,

long oriented toward family planning, provide a good yardstick for determining what the availability of contraceptives can do to population growth. Indeed, they provide more than a yardstick; they are actually the model which inspired the present population policies.

What does this goal mean in practice? Among the advanced nations there is considerable diversity in the level of fertility.[8] At one extreme are countries such as New Zealand, with an average gross reproduction rate (GRR) of 1.91 during the period 1960-64; at the other extreme are countries such as Hungary, with a rate of 0.91 during the same period. To a considerable extent, however, such divergencies are matters of timing. The birth rates of most industrial nations have shown, since about 1940, a wave-like movement, with no secular trend. The average level of reproduction during this long period has been high enough to give these countries, with their low mortality, an extremely rapid population growth. If this level is maintained, their population will double in just over 50 years—a rate higher than that of world population growth at any time prior to 1950, at which time the growth in numbers of human beings was already considered fantastic. The advanced nations are suffering acutely from the effects of rapid population growth in combination with the production of ever more goods per person.[9] A rising share of their supposedly high per capita income, which itself draws increasingly upon the resources of the underdeveloped countries (who fall farther behind in relative economic position), is spent simply to meet the costs, and alleviate the nuisances, of the unrelenting production of more and more goods by more people. Such facts indicate that the industrial nations provide neither a suitable demographic model for the nonindustrial peoples to follow nor the leadership to plan and organize effective population-control policies for them.

Zero Population Growth as a Goal

Most discussions of the population crisis lead logically to zero population growth as the ultimate goal, because *any* growth rate, if continued, will eventually use up the earth. Yet hardly ever do arguments for population policy consider such a goal, and current policies do not dream of it. Why not? The answer is evidently that zero population growth is unacceptable to most nations and to most religious and ethnic communities. To argue for this goal would be to alienate possible support for action programs.

Goal Peculiarities Inherent in Family Planning

Turning to the actual measures taken, we see that the very use of family planning as the means for implementing population policy poses serious but unacknowledged limits on the intended reduction in fertility. The family-planning movement, clearly devoted to the improvement and dissemination of contraceptive devices, states again and again that its purpose is that of enabling couples to have the number of children they want. "The opportunity to decide the number and spacing of children is a basic human right," say the 12 heads of state in the United Nations declaration. The 1965 Turkish Law Concerning Population Planning declares:[10]

> *Article 1.* Population Planning means that individuals can have as many children as they wish, whenever they want to. This can be ensured through preventive measures taken against pregnancy. . . .

Logically, it does not make sense to use *family* planning to provide *national* population control or planning. The "planning" in family planning is that of each separate couple. The only control they exercise is control over the size of *their* family. Obviously, couples do not plan the size of the nation's population, any more than they plan the growth of the national income or the form of the highway network. There is no reason to expect that the millions of decisions about family size made by couples in their own interest will automatically control population for the benefit of society. On the contrary, there are good reasons to think they will not do so. At most, family planning can reduce reproduction to the extent that unwanted births exceed wanted births. In industrial countries the balance is often negative—that is, people have fewer children as a rule than they would like to have. In underdeveloped countries the reverse is normally true, but the elimination of unwanted births would still leave an extremely high rate of multiplication.

Actually, the family planning movement does not pursue even the limited goals it professes. It does not fully empower couples to have only the number of offspring they want because it either condemns or disregards certain tabooed but nevertheless effective means to this goal. One of its tenets is that "there shall be freedom of choice of method so that individuals can choose in accordance with the dictates of their consciences,"[11] but in practice this amounts to limiting the individual's choice, because the "conscience" dictating the method is usually not his but that of religious and governmental officials. Moreover, not every individual may choose: even the so-called recommended methods are ordinarily not offered to single women, or not all offered to women professing a given religious faith.

Thus, despite its emphasis on technology, current policy does not utilize all available means of contraception, much less all birth-control measures. The Indian government wasted valuable years in the early stages of its population-control program by experimenting exclusively with the "rhythm" method, long after this technique had been demonstrated to be one of the least effective. A greater limitation on means is the exclusive emphasis on contraception itself. Induced abortion, for example, is one of the surest means of controlling reproduction, and one that has been proved capable of reducing birth rates rapidly. It seems peculiarly suited to the threshold stage of a population-control program—the stage when new conditions of life first make large families disadvantageous. It was the principal factor in the halving of the Japanese birth rate, a major factor in the declines in birth rate of East-European satellite countries after legalization of abortions in the early 1950s, and an important factor in the reduction of fertility in industrializing nations from 1870 to the 1930s.[12] Today, according to *Studies in Family Planning*,[13] "abortion is probably the foremost method of birth control throughout Latin America." Yet this method is rejected in nearly all national and international population-control programs. American foreign aid is used to help *stop* abortion.[14] The United Nations excludes abortion from family planning, and in fact justifies the latter by presenting it as a means of combating abortion.[15] Studies of abortion are being made in Latin America under the presumed auspices of population-control groups, not with the intention of legalizing it and thus making it safe, cheap, available, and hence more effective for population control, but with the avowed purpose of reducing it.[16]

Although few would prefer abortion to efficient contraception (other things being equal), the fact is that both permit a woman to control the size of her family. The main drawbacks to abortion arise from its illegality. When performed, as a legal procedure, by a skilled physician, it is safer than childbirth. It does not compete with contraception but serves as a backstop when the latter fails or when contraceptive devices or information are not available. As contraception becomes customary, the incidence of abortion recedes even without its being banned. If, therefore, abortions enable women to have only the number of children they want, and if family planners do not advocate—in fact decry—legalization of abortion, they are to that extent denying the central tenet of their own movement. The irony of anti-abortionism in family-planning circles is seen particularly in hair-splitting arguments over whether or not some contraceptive agent (for example, the IUD) is in reality an abortifacient. A Mexican leader in family planning writes:[17]

> One of the chief objectives of our program in Mexico is to prevent abortions. If we could be sure that the mode of action [of the IUD] was not interference with nidation, we could easily use the method in Mexico.

The questions of sterilization and unnatural forms of sexual intercourse usually meet with similar silent treatment or disapproval, although nobody doubts the effectiveness of these measures in avoiding conception. Sterilization has proved popular in Puerto Rico and has had some vogue in India (where the new health minister hopes to make it compulsory for those with a certain number of children), but in both these areas it has been for the most part ignored or condemned by the family-planning movement.

On the side of goals, then, we see that a family-planning orientation limits the aims of current population policy. Despite reference to "population control" and "fertility control," which presumably mean determination of demographic results by and for the nation as a whole, the movement gives control only to couples, and does this only if they use "respectable" contraceptives.

The Neglect of Motivation

By sanctifying the doctrine that each woman should have the number of children she wants, and by assuming that if she has only that number this will automatically curb population growth to the necessary degree, the leaders of current policies escape the necessity of asking why women desire so many children and how this desire can be influenced.[18] (p. 41),[19] Instead, they claim that satisfactory motivation is sown by the popular desire (shown by opinion surveys in all countries) to have the means of family limitation, and that therefore the problem is one of inventing and distributing the best possible contraceptive devices. Overlooked is the fact that a desire for availability of contraceptives is compatible with *high* fertility.

Given the best of means, there remain the questions of how many children couples want and of whether this is the requisite number from the standpoint of population size. That it is not is indicated by continued rapid population growth in industrial countries, and by the very surveys showing that people want contraception—for these show, too, that people also want numerous children.

The family planners do not ignore motivation. They are forever talking about "attitudes" and "needs." But they pose the issue in terms of the "acceptance" of birth control devices. At the most naive level, they assume that lack of acceptance is a function of the contraceptive device itself. This reduces the motive problem to a technological question. The task of population control then becomes simply the invention of a device that *will* be acceptable.[20] The plastic IUD is acclaimed because, once in place, it does not depend on repeated *acceptance* by the woman, and thus it "solves" the problem of motivation.[21]

But suppose a woman does not want to use *any* contraceptive until after she has had four children. This is the type of question that is seldom raised in the family-planning literature. In that literature, wanting a specific number of children is taken as complete motivation, for it implies a wish to control the size of one's family. The problem woman, from the standpoint of family planners, is the one who wants "as many as come," or "as many as God sends." Her attitude is construed as due to ignorance and "cultural values," and the policy deemed necessary to change it is "education." No compulsion can be used, because the movement is committed to free choice, but movie strips, posters, comic books, public lectures, interviews, and discussions are in order. These supply information and supposedly change values by discounting superstitions and showing that unrestrained procreation is harmful to both mother and children. The effort is considered successful when the woman decides she wants only a certain number of children and uses an effective contraceptive.

In viewing negative attitudes toward birth control as due to ignorance, apathy, and outworn tradition, and "mass-communication" as the solution to the motivation problem, [22] family planners tend to ignore the power and complexity of social life. If it were admitted that the creation and care of new human beings is socially motivated, like other forms of behavior, by being a part of the system of rewards and punishments that is built into human relationships, and thus is bound up with the individual's economic and personal interests, it would be apparent that the social structure and economy must be changed before a deliberate reduction in the birth rate can be achieved. As it is, reliance on family planning allows people to feel that "something is being done about the population problem" without the need for painful social changes.

Designation of population control as a medical or public health task leads to a similar evasion. This categorization assures popular support because it puts population policy in the hands of respected medical personnel, but, by the same token, it gives responsibility for leadership to people who think in terms of clinics and patients, of pills and IUD's, and who bring to the handling of economic and social phenomena a self-confident naiveté. The study of social organization is a technical field; an action program based on intuition is no more apt to succeed in the control of human beings than it is in the area of bacterial or viral control. Moreover, to alter a social system, by deliberate policy, so as to regulate births in accord with the demands of the collective welfare would require political power, and this is not likely to inhere in public health officials, nurses, midwives, and social workers. To entrust population policy to them is "to take action," but not dangerous "effective action."

Similarly, the Janus-faced position on birth-control technology represents an escape from the necessity, and onus, of grappling with the social and economic determinants of reproductive behavior. On the one side, the rejection or avoidance of religiously tabooed but otherwise effective means of birth prevention enables the family-planning movement to avoid official condemnation. On the other side, an intense preoccupation with contraceptive technology (apart from the tabooed means) also helps the family planners to avoid censure. By implying that the only need is the invention and distribution of effective contraceptive devices, they allay fears, on the part of religious and governmental officials, that fundamental changes in social organization are contemplated. Changes basic enough to affect motivation for having children would be changes in the structure of the family, in the position of women, and in the sexual mores. Far from proposing such radicalism, spokesmen for family planning frequently state their purpose as "protection" of the family—that is, closer observance of family norms. In addition, by concentrating on *new* and *scientific* contraceptives, the movement escapes taboos attached to old ones (the Pope will hardly authorize the condom, but may sanction the pill) and allows family planning to be regarded as a branch of medicine: over-population becomes a disease, to be treated by a pill or a coil.

We thus see that the inadequacy of current population policies with respect to motivation is inherent in their overwhelmingly family-planning character. Since family planning is by definition private planning, it eschews any societal control over motivation. It merely furnishes the means, and, among possible means, only the most respectable. Its leaders, in avoiding social complexities and seeking official favor, are obviously activated not solely by expediency but also by their own sentiments as members of society and by their background as persons attracted to the family-planning movement. Unacquainted for the most part with technical economics, sociology, and demography, they tend honestly and instinctively to believe that something they vaguely call population control can be achieved by making better contraceptives available.

The Evidence of Ineffectiveness

If this characterization is accurate, we can conclude that current programs will not enable a government to control population size. In countries where couples have numerous offspring that they do not want, such programs may possibly accelerate a birth-rate decline that would occur anyway, but the conditions that cause births to be wanted or unwanted are beyond the control of family planning, hence beyond the control of any nation which relies on family planning alone as its population policy.

This conclusion is confirmed by demographic facts. As I have noted above, the widespread use of family planning in industrial countries has not given their governments control over the birth rate. In backward countries today, taken as a whole, birth rates are rising, not falling; in those with population policies, there is no indication that the government is controlling the rate of reproduction. The main "successes" cited in the well-publicized policy literature are cases where a large number of contraceptives have been distributed or where the program has been accompanied by some decline in the birth rate. Popular enthusiasm for family planning is found mainly in the cities, or in advanced countries such as Japan and Taiwan, where the people would adopt contraception in any case, program or no program. It is difficult to prove that present population policies have even speeded up a lowering of the birth rate (the least that could have been expected), much less that they have provided national "fertility control."

Let us next briefly review the facts concerning the level and trend of population in underdeveloped nations generally, in order to understand the magnitude of the task of genuine control.

Rising Birth Rates in Underdeveloped Countries

In ten Latin-American countries, between 1940 and 1959,[23] the average birth rates (age-standardized), as estimated by our research office at the University of California, rose as follows: 1940-44, 43.4 annual births per 1000 population; 1945-49, 44.6; 1950-54, 46.4; 1955-59, 47.7.

In another study made in our office, in which estimating methods derived from the theory of quasi-stable populations were used, the recent trend was found to be upward in 27 underdeveloped countries, downward in six, and unchanged in one.[24] Some of the rises have been substantial, and most have occurred where the birth rate was already extremely high. For instance, the gross reproduction rate rose in Jamaica from 1.8 per thousand in 1947 to 2.7 in 1960; among the natives of Fiji, from 2.0 in 1951 to 2.4 in 1964; and in Albania, from 3.0 in the period 1950-54 to 3.4 in 1960.

The general rise in fertility in backward regions is evidently not due to failure of population-control efforts, because most of the countries either have no such effort or have programs too new to show much effect. Instead, the rise is due, ironically, to the very circumstance that brought on the population crisis in the first place—to improved health and lowered mortality. Better health increases the probability that a woman will conceive and retain the fetus to term; lowered mortality raises the proportion of babies who survive to the age of reproduction and reduces the probability of widowhood during that age.[25] The significance of the general rise in fertility, in the context of this discussion, is that it is giving would-be population planners a harder task than many of them realize. Some of the upward pressure on birth rates is independent of what couples do about family planning, for it arises from the fact that, with lowered mortality, there are simply more couples.

Underdeveloped Countries with Population Policies

In discussions of population policy there is often confusion as to which cases are relevant. Japan, for instance, has been widely praised for the effectiveness of its measures, but it is a very advanced industrial nation and, besides, its government policy had little or nothing to do with the decline in the birth rate, except unintentionally. It therefore offers no test of population policy under peasant-agrarian conditions. Another case of questionable relevance is that of Taiwan, because Taiwan is sufficiently developed to be placed in the urban-industrial class of nations. However, since Taiwan is offered as the main showpiece by the sponsors of current policies in underdeveloped areas, and since the data are excellent, it merits examination.

Studies in Taiwan

Taiwan is acclaimed as a showpiece because it has responded favorably to a highly organized program for distributing up-to-date contraceptives and has also had a rapidly dropping birth rate. Some observers have carelessly attributed the decline in the birth rate—from 50.0 in 1951 to 32.7 in 1965—to the family-planning campaign, [26] but the campaign began only in 1963 and could have affected only the end of the trend. Rather, the decline represents a response to modernization similar to that made by all countries that have become industrialized. [27] By 1950 over half of Taiwan's population was urban, and by 1964 nearly two-thirds were urban, with 29 percent of the population living in cities of 100,000 or more. The pace of economic development has been extremely rapid. Between 1951 and 1963, per capita income increased by 4.05 percent per year. Yet the island is closely packed, having

Table 1
Decline in Taiwan's Fertility Rate,
1951 through 1966

Year	Registered births per 1000 women aged 15-49	Change in rate (percent)
1951	211	
1952	198	−5.6
1953	194	−2.2
1954	193	−0.5
1955	197	+2.1
1956	196	−0.4
1957	182	−7.1
1958	185	+1.3
1959	184	−0.1
1960	180	−2.5
1961	177	−1.5
1962	174	−1.5
1963	170	−2.6
1964	162	−4.9
1965	152	−6.0
1966	149	−2.1

*The percentages were calculated on unrounded figures. Source of data through 1965, *Taiwan* Demographic Fact Book (1964, 1965); for 1966, *Monthly Bulletin of Population, Registration Statistics of Taiwan* (1966, 1967).

870 persons per square mile (a population density higher than that of Belgium). The combination of fast economic growth and rapid population increase in limited space has put parents of large families at a relative disadvantage and has created a brisk demand for abortions and contraceptives. Thus the favorable response to the current campaign to encourage use of the IUD is not a good example of what birth-control technology can do for a genuinely backward country. In fact, when the program was started, one reason for expecting receptivity was that the island was already on its way to modernization and family planning.[28]

At most, the recent family-planning campaign—which reached significant proportions only in 1964, when some 46,000 IUD's were inserted (in 1965 the number was 99,253, and in 1966, 111,242);[29, 30] (p. 45)—could have caused the increase observable after 1963 in the rate of decline. Between 1951 and 1963 the average drop in the birth rate per 1000 women (see Table 1) was 1.73 percent per year; in the period 1964-66 it was 4.35 percent. But one hesitates to assign all of the acceleration in decline since 1963 to the family-planning campaign. The rapid economic development has been precisely of a type likely to accelerate a drop in reproduction. The rise in

Figure 1
Births per 1000 Women Aged 15 through 49 in Japan and Taiwan

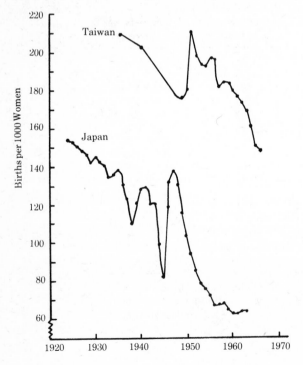

manufacturing has been much much greater than the rise in either agriculture or construction. The agricultural labor force has thus been squeezed, and migration to the cities has skyrocketed.[31] Since housing has not kept pace, urban families have had to restrict reproduction in order to take advantage of career opportunities and avoid domestic inconvenience. Such conditions have historically tended to accelerate a decline in birth rate. The most rapid decline came late in the United States (1921-33) and in Japan (1947-55). A plot of the Japanese and Taiwanese birth rates (Fig. 1) shows marked similarity of the two curves, despite a difference in level. All told, one should not attribute all of the post-1963 acceleration in the decline of Taiwan's birth rate to the family-planning campaign.

The main evidence that *some* of this acceleration is due to the campaign comes from the fact that Taichung, the city in which the family-planning effort was first concentrated, showed subsequently a much faster drop in fertility than other cities.[30] (p. 69),[32] But the campaign has not reached throughout the island. By the end of 1966, only 260,745 women had been fitted with an IUD under auspices of the campaign, whereas the women of reproductive age on the island numbered 2.86 million. Most of the reduction in fertility has therefore been a matter of individual initiative. To some extent the campaign may be simply substituting sponsored (and cheaper) services for those that would otherwise come through private and commercial channels. An island-wide survey in 1964 showed that over 150,000 women were already using the traditional Ota ring (a metallic intrauterine device popular in Japan); almost as many had been sterilized; about 40,000 were using foam tablets; some 50,000 admitted to having had at least one abortion; and many were using other methods of birth control.[30] (pp. 18, 31).

The important question, however, is not whether the present campaign is somewhat hastening the downward trend in the birth rate but whether, even if it is, it will provide population control for the nation. Actually, the campaign is not designed to provide such control and shows no sign of doing so. It takes for granted existing reproductive goals. Its aim is "to integrate, through education and information, the idea of family limitation *within the existing attitudes, values, and goals* of the people"[30] [p. 8 (italics mine)]. Its target is *married* women who do not want any more children; it ignores girls not yet married, and women married and wanting more children.

With such an approach, what is the maximum impact possible? It is the difference between the number of children women have been having and the number they want to have. A study in 1957 found a median figure of 3.75 for the number of children wanted by women aged 15 to 29 in Taipei, Taiwan's largest city; the corresponding figure for women from a satellite town was 3.93; for women from a fishing village, 4.90; and for women from a farming village, 5.03. Over 60 percent of the women in Taipei and over 90 percent of those in the farming village wanted 4 or more children.[33] In a sample of wives aged 25 to 29 in Taichung, a city of over 300,000, Freedman and his co-workers found the average number of children wanted was 4; only 9 percent wanted less than 3, 20 percent wanted 5 or more.[34] If, therefore, Taiwanese women used contraceptives that were 100-percent effective and had the number of children they desire, they would have about 4.5 each. The goal of the family-planning effort would be achieved. In the past the Taiwanese woman who married and lived through the reproductive period had, on the average, approximately 6.5 children; thus a figure of 4.5 would represent a substantial decline in fertility. Since mortality would continue to decline, the population growth rate would decline somewhat less than individual reproduction would. With 4.5 births per woman and a life expectancy of 70 years, the rate of natural increase would be close to 3 percent per year.[35]

In the future, Taiwanese views concerning reproduction will doubtless change, in response to social change and economic modernization. But how far will they change? A good indication is the number of children desired by couples in an already modernized country long oriented toward family planning. In the United States in 1966, an average of 3.4 children was considered ideal by white women aged 21 or over.[36] This average number of births would give Taiwan, with only a slight decrease in mortality, a long-run rate of natural increase of 1.7 percent per year and a doubling of population in 41 years.

Detailed data confirm the interpretation that Taiwanese women are in the process of shifting from a "peasant-agrarian" to an "industrial" level of reproduction. They are, in typical fashion, cutting off higher-order births at age 30 and beyond.[37] Among young wives, fertility has risen, not fallen. In sum, the widely acclaimed family-planning program in Taiwan may, at most, have somewhat speeded the later phase of fertility decline which would have occurred anyway because of modernization.

The Situation in Korea

Moving down the scale of modernization, to countries most in need of population control, one finds the family-planning approach even more inadequate. In South Korea, second only to Taiwan in the frequency with which it is cited as a model of current policy, a recent birth-rate decline of unknown extent is assumed by leaders to be due overwhelmingly to the government's family-planning program. However, it is just as plausible to say that the net effect of government involvement in population control has been, so far, to delay rather than hasten a decline in reproduction made inevitable by social and economic changes. Although the government is advocating vasectomies and providing IUD's and pills, it refuses to legalize abortions, despite the rapid rise in the rate of illegal abortions and despite the fact that, in a recent survey, 72 percent of the people who stated an opinion favored legalization. Also, the program is presented in the context of maternal and child health; it thus emphasizes motherhood and the family rather than alternative roles for women. Much is made of the fact that opinion surveys show an overwhelming majority of Koreans (89 percent in 1965) favoring contraception [38] (p. 27), but this means only that Koreans are like other people in wishing to have the means to get what they want. Unfortunately, they want sizable families: "The records indicate that the program appeals mainly to women in the 30-39 year age bracket who have four or more children, including at least two sons. . . ."[38] (p. 25).

In areas less developed than Korea the degree of acceptance of contraception tends to be disappointing, especially among the rural majority. Faced with this discouragement, the leaders of current policy, instead of reexamining their assumptions, tend to redouble their effort to find a contraceptive that will appeal to the most illiterate peasant, forgetting that he wants a good-sized family. In the rural Punjab, for example, "a disturbing feature . . . is that the females start to seek advice and adopt family planning techniques at the far end of their reproductive period."[39] Among 5196 women coming to rural Punjabi family-planning centers, 38 percent were over 35 years old, 67 percent over 30. These women had married early, nearly a third of them before the age of 15;[40] some 14 percent had eight or more *living* children when they reached the clinic, 51 percent six or more.

A survey in Tunisia showed that 68 percent of the married couples were willing to use birth-control measures, but the average number of children they considered ideal was 4.3.[41] The corresponding averages for a village in eastern Java, a village near New Delhi, and a village in Mysore were 4.3, 4.0, and 4.2, respectively.[42, 43] In the cities of these regions women are more ready to accept birth control and they want fewer children than village women do, but the number they consider desirable is still wholly unsatisfactory from the standpoint of population control. In an urban family-planning center in Tunisia, more than 600 of 900 women accepting contraceptives had four living children already.[44] In Bangalore, a city of nearly a million at the time (1952), the number of offspring desired by married women was 3.7 on the average; by married men, 4.1.[43] In the metropolitan area of San Salvador (350,000 inhabitants) a 1964 survey[45] showed the number desired by women of reproductive age to be 3.9, and in seven other capital cities of Latin America the number ranged from 2.7 to 4.2. If women in the cities of underdeveloped countries used birth-control measures with 100-percent efficiency, they still would have enough babies to expand city populations senselessly, quite apart from the added contribution of rural-urban migration. In many of the cities the difference between actual and ideal number of children is not great; for instance, in the seven Latin-American capitals mentioned above, the ideal was 3.4 whereas the actual births per women in the age range 35 to 39 was 3.7.[46] Bombay City has had birth-control clinics for many years, yet its birth rate (standardized for age, sex, and marital distribution) is still 34 per 1000 inhabitants and is tending to rise rather than fall. Although this rate is about 13 percent lower than that for India generally, it has been about that much lower since at least 1951.[47]

Is Family Planning the "First Step" in Population Control?

To acknowledge that family planning does not achieve population control is not to impugn its value for other purposes. Freeing women from the need to have more children than they want is of great benefit to them and their children and to society at large. My argument is therefore directed not against family-planning programs as such but against the assumption that they are an effective means of controlling population growth.

But what difference does it make? Why not go along for awhile with family planning as an initial approach to the problem of population control? The answer is that any policy on which millions of dollars are being spent should be designed to achieve the goal it purports to achieve. If it is only a first step, it should be so labeled, and its connection with the next step (and the nature of that next step) should be carefully examined. In the present case, since no "next step" seems ever to be mentioned, the question arises, Is reliance on family planning in fact a basis for dangerous postponement of effective steps? To continue to offer a remedy as a cure long after it has been shown merely to ameliorate the disease is either quackery or wishful thinking, and it thrives most where the need is greatest. Today the desire to solve the population problem is so intense that we are all ready to embrace any "action program" that promises relief. But postponement of effective measures allows the situation to worsen.

Unfortunately, the issue is confused by a matter of semantics. "Family *planning*" and "fertility *control*" suggest that reproduction is being regulated according to some rational plan. And so it is, but only from the standpoint of the individual couple, not from that of the community. What is rational in the light of a couple's situation may be totally irrational from the standpoint of society's welfare.

The need for societal regulation of individual behavior is readily recognized in other spheres—those of explosives, dangerous drugs, public property, natural resources. But in the sphere of reproduction, complete individual initiative is generally favored even by those liberal intellectuals who, in other spheres, most favor economic and social planning. Social reformers who would not hesitate to force all owners of rental property to rent to anyone who can pay, or to force all workers in an industry to join a union, balk at any suggestion that couples be permitted to have only a certain number of offspring. Invariably they interpret societal control of reproduction as meaning direct police supervision of individual behavior. Put the word *compulsory* in front of any term describing a means of limiting births—*compulsory sterilization, compulsory abortion, compulsory contraception*—and you guarantee violent opposition. Fortunately, such direct controls need not be invoked, but conservatives and radicals alike overlook this in their blind opposition to the idea of collective determination of a society's birth rate.

That the exclusive emphasis on family planning in current population policies is not a "first step" but an escape from the real issues is suggested by two facts. (i) No country has taken the "next step." The industrialized countries have had family planning for half a century without acquiring control over either the birth rate or population increase. (ii) Support and encouragement of research on population policy other than family planning is negligible. It is precisely this blocking of alternative thinking and experimentation that makes the emphasis on family planning a major obstacle to population control. The need is not to abandon family-planning programs but to put equal or greater resources into other approaches.

New Directions in Population Policy

In thinking about other approaches, one can start with known facts. In the past, all surviving societies had institutional incentives for marriage, procreation, and child care which were powerful enough to keep the birth rate equal to or in excess of a high death rate. Despite the drop in death rates during the last century and a half, the incentives tended to remain intact because the social structure (especially in regard to the family) changed little. At most, particularly in industrial societies, children became less productive and more expensive.[48] In present-day agrarian societies, where the drop in death rate has been more recent, precipitate, and independent of social change,[49] motivation for having children has changed little. Here, even more than in industrialized nations, the family has kept on producing abundant offspring, even though only a fraction of these children are now needed.

If excessive population growth is to be prevented, the obvious requirement is somehow to impose restraints on the family. However, because family roles are reinforced by society's system of rewards, punishments, sentiments, and norms, any proposal to demote the family is viewed as a threat by conservatives and liberals alike, and certainly by people with enough social responsibility to work for population control. One is charged with trying to "abolish" the family, but what is required is selective restructuring of the family in relation to the rest of society.

The lines of such restructuring are suggested by two existing limitations on fertility. (i) Nearly all societies succeed in drastically discouraging reproduction among unmarried women. (ii) Advanced societies unintentionally reduce reproduction among married women when conditions worsen in such a way as to penalize childbearing more severely than it was penalized before. In both cases the causes are motivational and economic rather than technological.

It follows that population-control policy can de-emphasize the family in two ways: (i) by keeping present controls over illegitimate childbirth yet making the most of factors that lead people to postpone or avoid marriage, and (ii) by instituting conditions that motivate those who do marry to keep their families small.

Postponement of Marriage

Since the female reproductive span is short and generally more fecund in its first than in its second half, postponement of marriage to ages beyond 20 tends biologically to reduce births. Sociologically, it gives women time to get a better education, acquire interests unrelated to the family, and develop a cautious attitude toward pregnancy. [50] Individuals who have not married by the time they are in their late twenties often do not marry at all. For these reasons, for the world as a whole, the average age at marriage for women is negatively associated with the birth rate: a rising age at marriage is a frequent cause of declining fertility during the middle phase of the demographic transition; and, in the late phase, the "baby boom" is usually associated with a return to younger marriages.

Any suggestion that age at marriage be raised as a part of population policy is usually met with the argument that "even if a law were passed, it would not be obeyed." Interestingly, this objection implies that the only way to control the age at marriage is by direct legislation, but other factors govern the actual age. Roman Catholic countries generally follow canon law in stipulating 12 years as the minimum *legal* age at which girls may marry, but the actual average age at marriage in these countries (at least in Europe) is characteristically more like 25 to 28 years. The actual age is determined, not by law, but by social and economic conditions. In agrarian societies, postponement of marriage (when postponement occurs) is apparently caused by difficulties in meeting the economic prerequisites for matrimony, as stipulated by custom and opinion. In industrial societies it is caused by housing shortages, unemployment, the requirement for overseas military service, high costs of education, and inadequacy of consumer services. Since almost no research has been devoted to the subject, it is difficult to assess the relative weight of the factors that govern the age at marriage.

Encouraging Limitation of Births within Marriage

As a means of encouraging the limitation of reproduction within marriage, as well as postponement of marriage, a greater rewarding of nonfamilial than of familial roles would probably help. A simple way of accomplishing this would be to allow economic advantages to accrue to the single as opposed to the married individual, and to the small as opposed to the large family. For instance, the government could pay people to permit themselves to be sterilized;[51] all costs of abortion could be paid by the government; a substantial fee could be charged for a marriage license; a "child-Tax" [52] could be levied; and there could be a requirement that illegitimate pregnancies be aborted. Less sensationally, governments could simply reverse some existing policies that encourage childbearing. They could, for example, cease taxing single persons more than married ones; stop giving parents special tax exemptions; abandon income-tax policy that discriminates against couples when the wife works; reduce paid maternity leaves; reduce family allowances; [53] stop awarding public housing on the basis of family size; stop granting fellowships and other educational aids (including special allowances for wives and children) to married students; cease outlawing abortions and sterilizations; and relax rules that allow use of harmless contraceptives only with medical permission. Some of these policy reversals would be beneficial in other than demographic respects and some would be harmful unless special precautions were taken. The aim would be to reduce the number, not the quality, of the next generation.

A closely related method of de-emphasizing the family would be modification of the complementarity of the roles of men and women. Men are now able to participate in the wider world yet enjoy the satisfaction of having several children because the housework and childcare fall mainly on their wives. Women are impelled to seek this role by their idealized view of marriage and motherhood and by either the scarcity of alternative roles or the difficulty of combining them with family roles. To change this situation women could be required to work outside the home, or compelled by circumstances to do so. If, at the same time, women were paid as well as men and given equal educational and occupational opportunities, and if social life were organized around the place of work rather than around the home or neighborhood, many women would develop interests that would compete with family interests. Approximately this policy is now followed in several Communist countries, and even the less developed of these currently have extremely low birth rates.[54]

That inclusion of women in the labor force has a negative effect on reproduction is indicated by regional comparisons.[18] (p. 1195).[55] But in most countries the wife's employment is subordinate, economically and emotionally, to her family role, and is readily sacrificed for the latter. No society has restructured both the occupational system and the domestic establishment to the point of permanently modifying the old division of labor by sex.

In any deliberate effort to control the birth rate along these lines, a government has two powerful instruments—its command over economic planning and its authority (real or potential) over education. The first determines (as far as policy can) the economic conditions and circumstances affecting the lives of all citizens; the second provides the knowledge and attitudes necessary to implement the plans. The economic system largely determines who shall work, what can be bought, what rearing children will cost, how much individuals can spend. The schools define family roles and develop vocational and recreational interests; they could, if it were desired, redefine the sex roles, develop interests that transcend the home, and transmit realistic (as opposed to moralistic) knowledge concerning marriage, sexual behavior, and population problems. When the problem is viewed in this light, it is clear that the ministries of economics and education, not the ministry of health, should be the source of population policy.

The Dilemma of Population Policy

It should now be apparent why, despite strong anxiety over runaway population growth, the actual programs purporting to control it are limited to family planning and are therefore ineffective. (i) The goal of zero, or even slight, population growth is one that nations and groups find difficult to accept. (ii) The measures that would be required to implement such a goal, though not so revolutionary as a Brave New World or a Communist Utopia, nevertheless tend to offend most people reared in existing societies. As a consequence, the goal of so-called population control is implicit and vague; the method is only family planning. This method, far from de-emphasizing the family, is familistic. One of its stated goals is that of helping sterile couples to *have* children. It stresses parental aspirations and responsibilities. It goes along with most aspects of conventional morality, such as condemnation of abortion, disapproval of premarital intercourse, respect for religious teachings and cultural taboos, and obeisance to medical and clerical authority. It deflects hostility by refusing to recommend any change other than the one it stands for: availability of contraceptives.

The things that make family planning acceptable are the very things that make it ineffective for population control. By stressing the right of parents to have the number of children they want, it evades the basic question of population policy, which is how to give societies the number of children they need. By offering only the means for *couples* to control fertility, it neglects the means for societies to do so.

Because of the predominantly pro-family character of existing societies, individual interest ordinarily leads to the production of enough offspring to constitute rapid population growth under conditions of low mortality. Childless or single-child homes are considered indicative of personal failure, whereas having three to five living children gives a family a sense of continuity and substantiality.[56]

Given the existing desire to have moderate-sized rather than small families, the only countries in which fertility has been reduced to match reduction in mortality are advanced ones temporarily experiencing worsened economic conditions. In Sweden, for instance, the net reproduction rate (NRR) has been below replacement for 34 years (1930-63), if the period is taken as a whole, but this is because of the economic depression. The average replacement rate was below unity (NRR = 0.81) for the period 1930-42, but from 1942 through 1963 it was above unity (NRR = 1.08). Hardships that seem particularly conducive to deliberate lowering of the birth rate are (in managed economies) scarcity of housing and other consumer goods despite full employment, and required high participation of women in the labor force, or (in freer economies) a great deal of unemployment and economic insecurity. When conditions are good, any nation tends to have a growing population.

It follows that, in countries where contraception is used, a realistic proposal for a government policy of lowering the birth rate reads like a catalogue of horrors: squeeze consumers through taxation and inflation; make housing very scarce by limiting construction; force wives and mothers to work outside the home to offset the inadequacy of male wages, yet provide few childcare facilities; encourage migration to the city by paying low wages in the country and providing few rural jobs; increase congestion in cities by starving the transit system; increase personal insecurity by encouraging conditions that produce unemployment and by haphazard political arrests. No government will institute such hardships simply for the purpose of controlling population growth. Clearly, therefore, the task of contemporary population policy is to develop attractive substitutes for family interests, so as to avoid having to turn to hardship as a corrective. The specific measures required for developing such substitutes are not easy to determine in the absence of research on the question.

In short, the world's population problem cannot be solved by pretense and wishful thinking. The unthinking identification of family planning with population control is an ostrich-like approach in that it permits people to hide from themselves the enormity and unconventionality of the task. There is no reason to abandon family-planning programs; contraception is a valuable technological instrument. But such programs must be supplemented with equal or greater investments in research and experimentation to determine the required socioeconomic measures.

Notes and References

1. *Studies in Family Planning*, No. 16, 1967.

2. *Ibid.*, No. 9, 1966, p. 1.

3. The statement is given in *Studies in Family Planning* 1, p. 1, and in *Population Bulletin*, 23, 6, 1967.

4. The statement is quoted in *Studies in Family Planning*, 1, p. 2.

5. *Hearings on S. 1676, U.S. Senate, Subcommittee on Foreign Aid Expenditures*, 89th Congress, Second Session, April 7, 8, 11, 1966, pt. 4.

6. B. L. Raina, in *Family Planning and Population Programs*, B. Berelson, R. K. Anderson, O. Harkavy, G. Maier, W. P. Mauldin, S. G. Segal, Eds., University of Chicago Press, Chicago, 1966.

7. D. Kirk, *Ann. Amer. Acad. Polit. Soc. Sci.* 369, 53, 1967.

8. As used by English-speaking demographers, the word *fertility* designates actual reproductive performance, not a theoretical capacity.

9. K. Davis, *Rotarian* 94, 10, 1959; *Health Educ. Monographs* 9, 2, 1960; L. Day and A. Day, *Too Many Americans*, Houghton Mifflin, Boston, 1964; R. A. Piddington, *Limits of Mankind*, Wright, Bristol, England, 1956.

10. *Official Gazette* 15 April 1965; quoted in *Studies in Family Planning*, 1, p. 7.

11. J. W. Gardner, Secretary of Health, Education, and Welfare, "Memorandum to Heads of Operating Agencies", January 1966, reproduced in *Hearings on S. 1676*, 5, p. 783.

12. C. Tietze, *Demography*, 1, 119, 1964; *Journal Chronic Diseases* 18, 1161, 1964; M. Muramatsu, *Milbank Mem. Fund Quarterly* 38, 153, 1960; K. Davis, *Population Index* 29, 345, 1963; R. Armijo and T. Monreal, *Journal Sex Res*, 1964, 143, 1964; Proceedings World Population Conference, Belgrade, 1965; Proceedings International Planned Parenthood Federation.

13. *Studies in Family Planning*, No. 4, 1964, p. 3.

14. D. Bell (then administrator for Agency for International Development), in *Hearings on S. 1676* (5), p. 862.

15. *Asian Population Conference*, United Nations, New York, 1964, p. 30.

16. R. Armijo and T. Monreal, in *Components of Population Change in Latin America*, Milbank Fund, New York, 1965, p. 272; E. Rice-Wray, *American Journal Public Health* 54, 313, 1964.

17. E. Rice-Wray, in "Intra-Uterine Contraceptive Devices," *Excerpta Med. Intern. Congr. Ser.* No. 54, 1962, p. 135.

18. J. Blake, in *Public Health and Population Change*, M. C. Sheps and J. C. Ridley, Eds., University of Pittsburgh Press, Pittsburgh, 1965.

19. J. Blake and K. Davis, *Amer. Behavioral Scientist*, 5, 24, 1963.

20. See "Panel discussion on comparative acceptability of different methods of contraception," in *Research in Family Planning*, C. V. Kiser, Ed., Princeton University Press, Princeton, 1962, pp. 373-86.

21. "From the point of view of the woman concerned, the whole problem of continuing motivation disappears. ... " [D. Kirk, in *Population Dynamics*, M. Muramatsu and P. A. Harper, Eds., Johns Hopkins Press, Baltimore, 1965].

22. "For influencing family size norms, certainly the examples and statements of public figures are of great significance ... also ... use of mass-communication methods which help to legitimize the small-family style, to provoke conversation, and to establish a vocabulary for discussion of family planning." [M. W. Freymann, in *Population Dynamics*, M. Muramatsu and P. A. Harper, Eds., Johns Hopkins Press, Baltimore, 1965].

23. O. A. Collver, *Birth Rates in Latin America*, International Population and Urban

Research, Berkeley, California, 1965, pp. 27-28; the ten countries were Colombia, Costa Rica, El Salvador, Ecuador, Guatemala, Honduras, Mexico, Panamá, Peru, and Venezuela.

24. J. R. Rele, *Fertility Analysis through Extension of Stable Population Concepts.* International Population and Urban Research, Berkeley, California, 1967.

25. J. C. Ridley, M. C. Sheps, J. W. Lingner, J. A. Menken, *Milbank Mem. Fund Quarterly* 45, 77, 1967; E. Arriaga, unpublished paper.

26. "South Korea and Taiwan appear successfully to have checked population growth by the use of intrauterine contraceptive devices" [U. Borell, *Hearings on S. 1676* (5), p. 556].

27. K. Davis, *Population Index* 29, 345, 1963.

28. R. Freedman, *ibid.* 31, 421, 1965.

29. Before 1964 the Family Planning Association had given advice to fewer than 60,000 wives in 10 years and a Pre-Pregnancy Health Program had reached some 10,000, and, in the current campaign, 3650 IUD's were inserted in 1965, in a total population of 2½ million women of reproductive age. See *Studies in Family Planning*, No. 19, 1967, p. 4, and R. Freedman *et al.*, *Population Studies* 16, 231, 1963.

30. R. W. Gillespie, *Family Planning on Taiwan,* Population Council, Taichung, 1965.

31. During the period 1950-60 the ratio of growth of the city to growth of the noncity population was 5:3; during the period 1960-64 the ratio was 5:2; these ratios are based on data of Shaohsing Chen, *Journal Sociol. Taiwan* 1, 74, 1963, and data in the United Nations *Demographic Yearbooks.*

32. R. Freedman, *Population Index* 31, 434, 1965. Taichung's rate of decline in 1963-64 was roughly double the average in four other cities, whereas just prior to the campaign its rate of decline had been much less than theirs.

33. S. H. Chen, *Journal Soc. Sci. Taipei* 13, 72, 1963.

34. R. Freedman *et al.*, *Population Studies* 16, 227, 1963; *ibid.*, p. 232.

35. In 1964 the life expectancy at birth was already 66 years in Taiwan, as compared to 70 for the United States.

36. J. Blake, *Eugenics Quarterly* 14, 68, 1967.

37. Women accepting IUD's in the family-planning program are typically 30 to 34 years old and have already had four children. [*Studies in Family Planning* No. 19, 1967, p. 5].

38. Y. K. Cha, in *Family Planning and Population Programs*, B. Berelson *et al.*, Eds., University of Chicago Press, Chicago, 1966.

39. H. S. Ayalvi and S. S. Johl, *Journal Family Welfare* 12, 60, 1965.

40. Sixty percent of the women had borne their first child before age 19. Early marriage is strongly supported by public opinion. Of couples polled in the Punjab, 48 percent said that girls *should* marry before age 16, and 94 percent said they should marry before age 20, (H. S. Ayalvi and S. S. Johl, *ibid.*, p. 57). A study of 2380 couples in 60 villages of Uttar Pradesh found that the women had consummated their marriage at an average age of 14.6 years, [J. R. Rele, *Population Studies* 15, 268, 1962].

41. J. Morsa, in *Family Planning and Population Programs*, B. Berelson *et al.*, Eds., University of Chicago Press, Chicago, 1966.

42. H. Gille and R. J. Pardoko, *ibid.*, p. 515; S. N. Agarwala, *Med. Dig. Bombay* 4, 653, 1961.

43. *Mysore Population Study*, United Nations, New York, 1961, p. 140.

44. A. Daly, in *Family Planning and Population Programs*, B. Berelson *et al.*, Eds., University of Chicago Press, Chicago, 1966.

45. C. J. Goméz, paper presented at the World Population Conference, Belgrade, 1965.

46. C. Miro, in *Family Planning and Population Programs*, B. Berelson *et al.*, Eds., University of Chicago Press, Chicago, 1966.

47. *Demographic Training and Research Centre (India) Newsletter* 20, 4, August 1966.

48. K. Davis, *Population Index* 29, 345, 1963. For economic and sociological theory of motivation for having children, see J. Blake [University of California (Berkeley)], in preparation.

49. K. Davis, *Amer. Economic Review* 46, 305, 1956; *Sci. Amer.* 209, 68, 1963.

50. J. Blake, *World Population Conference*, [Belgrade, 1965], United Nations, New York, 1967, vol. 2, pp. 132-36.

51. S. Enke, *Rev. Economics Statistics* 42, 175, 1960; ———, *Econ. Develop. Cult. Change* 8, 339, 1960; ———, *ibid.* 10, 427, 1962; A. O. Krueger and L. A. Sjaastad, *ibid.*, p. 423.

52. T. J. Samuel, *Journal Family Welfare India* 13, 12, 1966.

53. Sixty-two countries, including 27 in Europe, give cash payments to people for having children [U.S. Social Security Administration, *Social Security Programs Throughout the World*. 1967, Government Printing Office, Washington, D.C., 1967, pp. xxvii-xxviii].

54. Average gross reproduction rates in the early 1960s were as follows: Hungary, 0.91; Bulgaria, 1.09; Romania, 1.15; Yugoslavia, 1.32.

55. O. A. Collver and E. Langlois, *Econ. Develop. Cult. Change* 10, 367, 1962; J. Weeks, [University of California, Berkeley], unpublished paper.

56. Roman Catholic textbooks condemn the "small" family (one with fewer than four children) as being abnormal [J. Blake, *Population Studies* 20, 27, 1966].

57. Judith Blake's critical readings and discussions have greatly helped in the preparation of this article.

Beyond Family Planning
Bernard Berelson

This paper rests on these propositions: (1) among the great problems on the world agenda is the population problem; (2) that problem is most urgent in the developing countries where rapid population growth retards social and economic development; (3) there is a time penalty on the problem in the sense that, other things equal, anything not done sooner may be harder to do later, due to increased numbers; and accordingly (4) everything that can properly be done to lower population growth rates should be done, now. As has been asked on other occasions, the question is: what is to be done? There is a certain agreement on the general objective (i.e., on the desirability of lowering birth rates, though not on how far how fast), but there is disagreement as to means.

The 1960s have witnessed a substantial increase of awareness and concern with population matters throughout the world[1] and of efforts to do something about the problem, particularly in the developing countries. That something typically turns out to be the establishment of national family planning programs, or rough equivalents thereof. There are now 20 to 25 countries with efforts along this line, on all three developing continents, all of them either set up or revitalized in this decade. Thus, the first response to too high growth rates deriving from too high birth rates is to introduce voluntary contraception on a mass basis, or try to.

Why is family planning the first step taken on the road to population control? Probably because from a broad political standpoint it is the most acceptable one: since closely tied to maternal and child care it can be perceived as a health measure beyond dispute; and since voluntary it can be justified as a contribution to the effective personal freedom of individual couples. On both scores, the practice ties into accepted values and thus achieves political viability. In some situations, it is an oblique approach, seen as the politically acceptable way to start toward "population control" on the national level by promoting fertility control and smaller family size among individual couples. Moreover, it is a gradual effort and an inexpensive one, both of which contribute to its political acceptability. Though the introduction of family planning as a response to a country's population problem may be calculated to minimize opposition, even that policy has been attacked in several countries by politicians who are unconvinced and/or see an electoral advantage in the issue.

How effective have family planning programs been as a means toward population control? There is currently some controversy among qualified observers as to their efficacy,[2] and this is not the place to review that issue. But there is sufficient agreement on the magnitude and consequence of the problem that additional efforts are needed to reach a "solution," however that is responsibly defined.

For the purpose of this paper, then, let us assume that today's national family planning programs, mainly via voluntary contraception, are not "enough"—where "enough" is defined not necessarily as achieving zero growth in some extended present but simply as lowering birth rates quickly and substantially. "Enough" begs the question of the ultimate goal and only asks that a faster decline in population growth rates be brought about than is presently in process or in prospect—and, within the range of the possible, the faster the better.[3] Just to indicate the rough order of magnitude, let us say that the proximate goal is the halving of the birth rate in the developing countries in the next decade or two—from, say, over 40 births per thousand per year to 20-25.[4] For obvious reasons, both emigration and increased death rates are ruled out of consideration.

What is to be done to bring that about, beyond present programs of voluntary family planning?[5] I address that question in two ways: first, by listing the programs or policies more or less responsibly suggested to this end in recent years; and second, by reviewing the issues raised by the suggested approaches.

Proposals: Beyond Family Planning

Here is a listing of the several proposals, arranged in descriptive categories. (There may be a semantic question involved in some cases: when is a proposal a proposal? Are "suggestions" or "offers for consideration" or lists of alternatives to be considered as proposals? In general, I have included all those cases presented in a context in which they were readily perceived as providing a supplementary or alternative approach to present efforts. The list may include both proposals for consideration and proposals for action.)

A.   Extensions of Voluntary Fertility Control

1. Institutionalization of maternal care in rural areas of developing countries: a feasibility study of what would be required in order to bring some degree of modern medical or paramedical attention to every pregnant woman in the rural areas of five developing countries with professional back-up for difficult cases and with family planning education and services a central component of the program aimed particularly at women of low parity (Taylor & Berelson[6]).
2. Liberalization of induced abortion (Davis[7], Ehrlich[8], Chandrasekhar[9]).

B.   Establishment of Involuntary Fertility Control

1. Mass use of "fertility control agent" by government to regulate births at acceptable level: the "fertility control agent" designed to lower fertility in the society by five per cent to 75 percent less than the present birth rate, as needed; substance now unknown but believed to be available for field testing after 5-15 years of research work; to be included in water supply in urban areas and by "other methods" elsewhere (Ketchel[10]); "addition of temporary sterilants to water supplies or staple food" (Ehrlich[11]).
2. "Marketable licenses to have children," given to women and perhaps men in "whatever number would ensure a reproduction rate of one," say 2.2 children per couple: for example, "the unit certificate might be the 'deci-

child,' and accumulation of ten of these units by purchase, inheritance or gift, would permit a woman in maturity to have one legal child" (Boulding[12]).

3. Temporary sterilization of all girls via time-capsule contraceptives, and again after each delivery, with reversibility allowed only upon governmental approval; certificates of approval distributed according to popular vote on desired population growth for a country, and saleable on open market (Shockley[13]).

4. Compulsory sterilization of men with three or more living children (Chandrasekhar[14]); requirement of induced abortion for all illegitimate pregnancies (Davis[15]).

C. Intensified Educational Campaigns

1. Inclusion of population materials in primary and secondary schools systems. (Davis[16], Wayland[17], Visaria[18]): materials on demographic and physiological aspects, perhaps family planning and sex education as well; introduced at the secondary level in order to reach next waves of public school teachers throughout the country.

2. Promotion of national satellite television systems for direct informational effect on population and family planning as well as for indirect effect on modernization in general: satellite broadcasting probably through ground relays with village receivers (Ehrlich[19], Meier & Meier[20], UNESCO[21], Schramm & Nelson[22]).

D. Incentive Programs

This term requires clarification. As used here, it refers to payments, or their equivalent, made directly to contracepting couples and/or to couples not bearing children for specified periods. It does *not* refer to payments to field workers, medical personnel, volunteers, *et al.*, for securing acceptance of contraceptive practice; that type of payment, now utilized in many programs, is better called a fee or a stipend in order to differentiate it from an incentive as used here. Beyond that distinction, however, the term is fuzzy at the edges: is the provision of free contraceptive consultation and supplies to be considered an incentive? or free milk to the infant along with family planning information to the mother? or free transport to the family planning service, which then provides general health care? or a generous payment in lieu of time off from work for a vasectomy operation? or even a financial burden imposed for undesirable fertility behavior? In the usage here, I try to limit the term to direct payment of money (or goods or services) to members of the target population in return for the desired practice. This usage is sometimes referred to as a "positive" incentive in distinction to the "negative" incentive inherent in tax or welfare penalties for "too many" children (E below).

1. Payment for the initiation or the effective practice of contraception: pay-

ment or equivalent (e.g., transistor radio) for sterilization (Chandrasekhar[23], Pohlmann[24], Samuel[25], Davis[26]) or for contraception (Simon[27], Enke[28], Samuel[29]).

2. Payment for periods of non-pregnancy or non-birth: a bonus for child spacing or non-pregnancy (Young[30], Bhatia[31], Enke[32], Spengler[33], Leasure[34]); a savings certificate plan for twelve-month periods of non-birth (Balfour[35]); a lottery scheme for preventing illegitimate births among teen-agers in a small country (Mauldin[36]); "responsibility prizes" for each five years of childless marriage or for vasectomy before the third child, and special lotteries with tickets available to the childless (Ehrlich[37]).

E. Tax and Welfare Benefits and Penalties

i.e., an anti-natalist system of social services in place of the present pro-natalist tendencies.

1. Withdrawal of maternity benefits, perhaps after N (3?) children (Bhatia[38], Samuel[39], Davis[40]) or unless certain limiting conditions have been met, like sufficient child spacing, knowledge of family planning, or level of income (Titmuss & Abel-Smith[41]).

2. Withdrawal of children or family allowances, perhaps after N children (Bhatia[42], Titmuss & Abel-Smith[43], Davis[44]).

3. Tax on births after the Nth (Bhatia[45], Samuel[46], Spengler[47]).

4. Limitation of governmentally provided medical treatment, housing, scholarships, loans and subsidies, etc., to families with fewer than N children (Bhatia[48], Davis[49]).

5. Reversal of tax benefits, to favor the unmarried and the parents of fewer rather than more children (Bhatia[50], Titmuss & Abel-Smith[51], Samuel[52], Davis[53], Ehrlich[54], David[55]).

6. Provision by the state of N years of free schooling at all levels to each nuclear family, to be allocated by the family among the children as desired (Fawcett[56]).

7. Pensions for poor parents with fewer than N children as social security for their old age (Samuel[57], Ohlin[58] Davison[59]).

F. Shifts in Social and Economic Institutions

i.e., broad changes in fundamental institutional arrangements that could have the effect of lowering fertility.

1. Increase in minimum age of marriage: through legislation or through substantial fee for marriage licenses (David[60], Davis[61]); or through direct bonuses for delayed marriage (Young[62]); or through payment of marriage benefits only to parents of brides over 21 years of age (Titmuss & Abel-Smith[63]); or through a program of government loans for wedding ceremonies when the bride is of a sufficient age, or with the interest rate inversely related

to the bride's age (Davis [64]); or through a "governmental 'first marriage grant' . . . awarded each couple in which the age of both (*sic*) partners was 25 or more" (Ehrlich [65]); or through establishment of a domestic "national service" program for all men for the appropriate two-year period in order to develop social services, inculcate modern attitudes including family planning and population control, and at the same time delay age of marriage (Berelson, Etzioni [66]).

2. Promotion or requirement of female participation in labor force (outside the home) to provide roles and interests for women alternative or supplementary to marriage (Hauser[67], Davis[68], David[69]).

3. "Direct manipulation of family structure itself—planned efforts at deflecting the family's socializing function, reducing the noneconomic utilities of offspring, or introducing nonfamilial distractions and opportunity costs into people's lives"; specifically, through employment of women outside the home (Blake [70]); "selective restructuring of the family in relation to the rest of society" (Davis[71]).

4. Promotion of "two types of marriage, one of them childless and readily dissolved, and the other licensed for children and designed to be stable;" the former needs to be from 20-40 percent of the total in order to allow the remainder to choose family size freely (Meier & Meier[72]).

5. Encouragement of long-range social trends leading toward lower fertility, e.g., "improved and universal general education, or new roads facilitating communication, or improved agricultural methods, or a new industry that would increase productivity, or other types of innovation that may break the 'cake of custom' and produce social foment" (Hauser [73]); and improved status of women (U.N./ECOSOC[74]).

6. Efforts to lower death rates even further, particularly infant and child death rates, on the inference that birth rates will follow them down (Revelle[75], Heer & Smith[76]).

G. Approaches via Political Channels and Organizations

1. U.S. insistence on "population control as the price of food aid," with highly selective assistance based thereon, and exertion of political pressures on governments or religious groups impeding "solution" of the population problem, including shifts in sovereignty (Ehrlich[77]).

2. Re-organization of national and international agencies to deal with the population problem: within the United States, "coordination by a powerful governmental agency, A Federal Department of Population and Environment (DPE) . . . with the power to take whatever steps are necessary to establish a reasonable population size" (Ehrlich [78]); within India, creation of "a separate Ministry of Population Control" (Chandrasekhar [79]); development of an "international specialized agency larger than WHO to operate programs for

extending family limitation techniques to the world ... charged with the responsibility of effecting the transfer to population equilibrium" (Meier & Meier[80]).

3. Promotion of zero growth in population, as the ultimate goal needed to be accepted now in order to place intermediate goals of lowered fertility in proper context (Davis[81]).

H. Augmented Research Efforts

1. More research on social means for achieving necessary fertility goals (Davis[82]).

2. Focused research on practical methods of sex determination (Polgar[83]).

3. Increased research toward an improved contraceptive technology (NAS[84]).

Proposals: Review of the Issues

Here are 29 proposals beyond family planning for dealing with the problem of undue population growth in the developing world. I naturally cannot claim that these are all the proposals made more or less responsibly toward that end, but my guess is that there are not many more and that these proposals are a reasonably good sample of the total list. In any case, these are perhaps the most visible at the present time and the following analysis is limited to them.

Since several of the proposals tend in the same direction, it seems appropriate to review them illustratively against the criteria that any such proposals might be required to meet. What are such criteria? There are at least six: (1) scientific/medical/technological readiness, (2) political viability, (3) administrative feasibility, (4) economic capability, (5) moral/ethical/philosophical acceptability, and (6) presumed effectiveness. In other words, the key questions are: is the scientific/medical/technological base available or likely? will governments approve? can the proposal be administered? can the society afford the proposal? is it morally acceptable? and finally, will it work?

Such criteria and questions have to be considered against some time scale. As indicated at the outset of this paper, I suggest the next decade or two on the double grounds that the future is dim enough at that point let alone beyond and that in any case it is difficult to develop plans and programs now for a more remote future. National economic plans, for example, are typically limited to five years and then a new one made in accord with the conditions existing at that time. In any case, long-run social goals are normally approached through successive short-run efforts.

Since the population problem in the developing world is particularly serious in its implications for human welfare, such proposals deserve serious consideration indeed. What do the proposals come to, viewed against the indicated criteria? (I use India throughout as the major illustrative case since it is the key example of the problem; disregarding Mainland China, India has a much larger population than all the other countries with population programs combined.)

Scientific/Medical/Technological Readiness

Two questions are involved: (1) is the needed technology available? and (2) are the needed medical or para-medical personnel available or readily trainable to assure medical administration and safety?

With regard to temporary contraception, sterilization, and abortion, the needed technology is not only available now but is being steadily improved and expanded. The IUD (intrauterine device) and the oral pill have been major contraceptive developments of the past decade, and several promising leads are now being followed up[85]—though it cannot be said with much confidence that any of them will eventuate for mass use within the next few years.[86] Improved technologies for sterilization, both male and female, are being worked on; and there has been a recent development in abortion technique, the so-called suction device now being utilized in Eastern Europe and the U.S.S.R.[87]

However, neither Ehrlich's "temporary sterilants" nor Ketchel's "fertility control agent" (B-1) is now available or on the technological horizon—though that does not mean that the research task ought not to be pursued against a subsequent need, especially since such substances could be administered voluntarily and individually as well as involuntarily and collectively. In the latter case, if administered through the water supply or a similar source, the substance would need to be medically safe and free of side effects for men and women, young and old, well and ill, physiologically normal and physiologically marginal, as well as for animals and perhaps plants. As some people have remarked, such an involuntary addition to a water supply would face far greater difficulties of acceptance simply on medical grounds than the far milder proposals with regard to fluoridation to prevent tooth decay.

Though a substantial technology in fertility control does exist, that does not mean that it can be automatically applied where most needed, partly because of limitations of trained personnel. In general, the more the technology requires the services of medical or para-medical personnel (or, what is much the same, is perceived as requiring them), the more difficult it is to administer in the developing countries. For example, such traditional contraceptives as condoms or foams can be distributed freely through a variety of non-medical channels, including commercial ones, though that network is not without limitations in the poorer countries. Oral contraceptive pills *are* now distributed in large numbers without substantial medical intervention in a number of countries—sold by pharmacies without prescription—but not with medical sanction; and most qualified medical specialists here and abroad believe that the pills should be given only after proper medical examination and with proper medical follow-up. IUDs were first inserted only by obstetricians, then by medical doctors, and now, in a few situations where female medical personnel are unavailable in sufficient numbers, by specially trained paramedical personnel (notably, on a large scale, in Pakistan).

In the case of sterilization and abortion, the medical requirement becomes more severe. For example, when the policy of compulsory vasectomy of men with three or more children was first being considered in India (see footnote 14), an estimate was made that the policy would affect about 40 million males: "one thousand surgeons or para-surgeons each averaging 20 operations a day for five days a week would take eight years to cope with the existing candidates, and during this time of course a constant supply of new candidates would be coming along"[88]—at present birth rates, probably of the order of 3.5 million a year. Large-scale abortion practice, assuming legality and acceptability, might additionally require hospital beds, which are in particularly short supply in most developing countries. Just as an indication of order of magnitude, in India, for example, there are approximately 22 million births annually; to abort five million would require the equivalent of about 800 physicians, each doing 25 a day five days a week fifty weeks a year, which is approximately 10 percent of the obstetrical/gynecological specialists in India, or perhaps 25 percent of the female specialists; and about 10 million bed days, which is over half the estimated number of maternity bed days in the country at present.[89] However, the newer abortion technique might not require hospitalization—theoretically the abortion "camp" may be feasible, as was the vasectomy "camp," except perhaps for the greater sensitivities attaching to the status of women, though it is not medically desirable—and paramedical personnel may be acceptable as well. Reportedly, the newer technique does not involve hospitalization in some parts of Eastern Europe and Mainland China.

In short, the technology is available for some but not all current proposals, and the same may be the case for properly trained personnel.

Political Viability

As mentioned earlier, the "population problem" has been increasingly recognized by national governments and international agencies over the past decade, and favorable policies have been increasingly adopted: national family planning programs in some 20-25 countries, positive resolutions and actions within the United Nations family, large programs of support by such developed countries as United States and Sweden, the so-called World Leaders' Statement. There is no reason to think that that positive trend has run its course.

At the same time, the political picture is by no means unblemished. Some favorable policies are not strong enough to support a vigorous program even where limited to family planning on health grounds; in national politics "population control" can become a handy issue for a determined opposition; internal ethnic balances are sometimes delicately involved, with political ramifications; national size is often equated with national power, from the standpoint of international relations and regional military balances; the motives behind the support and encouragement of population control by the developed countries are sometimes perceived as politically expedient if not neocolonialist or neo-imperialist; and on the international front, as represented by the United Nations, there is still considerable reluctance based on both religio-moral and political considerations. In short, elite ambivalence and perceived political liability are not absent even in the favoring countries. That state of affairs may not be surprising looked at historically and given the sensitive religious, military, and political issues involved, but it does not provide maximum support for energetic measures directed at the "necessary" degree of population control.

The question of political acceptability of such proposals becomes in effect two questions: what is presumably acceptable within the present situation? and what might be done to enlarge the sphere of acceptability (as, for example, in proposals G-1 and G-2)?

In the nature of the political case, population measures are not taken in isolation—which is to say, they are not given overriding claim upon the nation's attention and resources even though they have been given special authority in a few countries. They must thus compete in the political arena with other claims and values, and that kind of competition accords with the political bases of an open society.

Any social policy adopted by government rests on some minimum consensus upon goals and means. They need not be the ultimate goals or the final means; as noted above, the socio-economic plans of developing countries are typically five-year plans, not 20- or 40- or 100-year plans. Indeed, an ultimate goal of population policy—that is, zero growth—need not be agreed upon or even considered by officials who can agree upon the immediate goal of lowering growth by a specified amount or by "as much as possible" within a period of years. And since there are always goals beyond goals, one does not even need to know what the ultimate goal is, only the direction in which it will be found (which is usually more likely of agreement). Would the insistence *now* on the acknowledgment of an *ultimate* goal of zero growth advance the effort or change its direction?

The means to such ends need not be final either. Indeed, at least at the outset of a somewhat controversial program, the means probably must fit within the framework of existing values, elite or mass, and preferably both—

for example, a family planning program for maternal and child health and for preventing unwanted births even though the resultant growth rate may still remain "too high" by ultimate standards.

Specifically, against this background, how politically acceptable do some of the proposals appear to be?

To start with, the proposal of involuntary controls in India in 1967 (B-4) precipitated "a storm of questions in Parliament," [90] was withdrawn, and resulted in a high-level personnel shift within the family planning organization. No other country has seriously entertained the idea. Leaving aside other considerations, political instability in many countries would make implementation virtually impossible.

Social measures designed to affect the birth rate indirectly—e.g., tax benefits, social security arrangements, etc.—have been proposed from time to time. In India, there have been several such proposals: for example, by the United Nations mission, [91] by the Small Family Norm Committee, [92] by the Central Family Planning Council (e.g., with regard to age of marriage, the education and employment of women, and various social welfare benefits), [93] and in almost every issue of such publications as *Family Planning News, Centre Calling,* and *Planned Parenthood* (illustrative recent headings: "Tax to Reduce Family Size," "Relief for Bachelors Urged," "Scholarships for Children, Family Planning for Parents"). As Samuel reports, with accompanying documentation, "the desirability of imposing a tax on births of fourth or higher order has been afloat for some time. However, time and again, the suggestion has been rejected by the Government of India." [94] In some cases, action has been taken by either the Central Government (e.g., income tax "deductions for dependent children are given for the first and second child only" [95]) or certain states (e.g., "Maharashtra and Uttar Pradesh have decided to grant educational concessions and benefits only to those children whose parents restrict the size of their families . . . " [96] and the former state is reportedly beginning to penalize families with more than three children by withholding maternity leave, educational benefits, and housing privileges, though in the nature of the case only a small proportion of the state's population is affected by these disincentives [97]). As an indication of political sensitivity, an order withdrawing maternity leave for non-industrial women employees with three or more living children—at best a tiny number of educated women—was revoked before it really went into effect. [98] There is a special political problem in many countries, in that economic constraints on fertility often turn out in practice to be selective on class, racial, or ethnic grounds, and thus exacerbate political tensions.

As another example, promoting female participation in the labor force runs up against the political problem that such employment would be competitive with men in situations of already high male un- and under-employment. One inquiry concludes: "The prospective quantitative effect of moves in this direction seems very questionable. The number of unemployed in India has been rising by approximately 50 percent every five years, and this is a well-known and very hot political issue. The government can hardly be blamed for being reluctant to promote female employment at the expense of male employment, which the great bulk of female employment almost surely would be."[99]

Acceptance of Programs

Given the present and likely political climate both within and between countries, whether programs for lowering population growth and birth rates are politically acceptable or not appears to depend largely upon whether they are perceived as positive or negative: where "positive" means that they are seen as promoting other social values as well as population limitation and where "negative" means that they are seen as limited *per se*. For example, family planning programs, as noted above, are often rationalized as contributing both to maternal and child health and to the effective freedom of the individual family; a large-scale television network would contribute to other informational goals (though it is also politically suspect as providing too much power to the government in office); promotion of female participation in the labor force would add to economic productivity at the same time that it subtracted from the birth rate; extension of MCH services to rural areas is clearly desirable in itself, with or without family planning attached; incorporation of population material in school systems can be justified on educational grounds as well as population ones; a pension for the elderly would have social welfare benefits as well as indirect impact upon the large family as a social security system; contraceptive programs in Latin America are promoted by the medical community as a medical and humanitarian answer not to the population problem but to the extensive illegal and dangerous practice of abortion. On the other hand, imposing tax liabilities or withdrawing benefits after the Nth child, not to mention involuntary measures, can be attacked as a punitive means whose only purpose is that of population limitation.

It would thus require great political courage joined to very firm demographic convictions for a national leader to move toward an unpopular and severe prescription designed to cure his country's population ills. Indeed, it is difficult to envisage such a political move in an open society where a political opposition could present a counter view and perhaps prevail. Witness the views of two strong advocates of additional measures beyond family planning:

A realistic proposal for a government policy of lowering the birth rate reads like a catalogue of horrors. . . . No government will institute such hardship simply for the purpose of controlling population growth.[100] If a perfected control agent were available now, I am certain that it would not be utilized in any democratic country, for no population would be likely to vote to have such agents used on itself. This means that the effects of overpopulation are not yet acute enough for people to accept an unpleasant alternative.[101]

The political problem of population control, like many political matters of consequence, is a matter of timing: in the 1950s nothing much could be done but in the 1960s a number of countries and international agencies moved at least as far as family planning programs. Political accommodation is typically a matter of several small steps with an occasional large one; and in this case it rests upon the seriousness with which the population problem is viewed. That is growing, hence political acceptability of added measures may also grow. Regardless of what the future may bring in this regard, several social measures like those in the list of proposals have been made from time to time and have encountered political obstacles. At least for the time being, such obstacles are real and must be taken into account in any realistic proposal.

The governmental decisions about measures taken to deal with undue population growth must be taken mainly by the countries directly involved: after all, it is their people and their nation whose prospects are most centrally affected. But in an interconnected world, with peace and human welfare at issue, others are properly concerned from both self-interested and humanitarian standpoints—other governments from the developed world, the international community, private groups. What of the political considerations in this connection?

A recommendation (G-1) that the United States exert strong political pressures to effect population control in developing countries seems more likely to generate political opposition abroad than acceptance. It is conceivable that such measures might be adopted by the Congress, though if so certainly against the advice of the executive agencies, but it is hardly conceivable that they would be agreed to by the proposed recipients. Such a policy is probably more likely to boomerang against a population effort than to advance the effort.

The proposal to create an international super-agency (G-2) seems more likely of success, but not without difficulty. WHO, UNICEF, and UNESCO have moved some distance toward family planning, if not population control, but only slowly and against considerable political restraint on the international front. [102] A new international agency would find the road easier only if restricted to the convinced countries. Certainly the present international organizations at interest would not be expected to abdicate in its favor. If it could be brought into being and given a strong charter for action, then almost by definition the international political climate would be such as to favor action by the present agencies, and then efficiency and not political acceptability would be the issue.

Administrative Feasibility

Given technical availability and political acceptability, what can actually be done in the field? This is where several "good ideas" run into difficulties in the developing world, in the translation of a theoretical probability into a practical program.

One of the underdeveloped elements of an underdeveloped country is administration: in most such countries there is not only a limited medical infrastructure but also a limited administrative apparatus to be applied to any program. Policies that look good on paper are difficult to put into practice—and that has been true in the case of family planning efforts themselves, where the simple organizational and logistic problems of delivering service and supplies have by no means been solved in several large countries after some years of trying. Again, this is one of the realities that must be dealt with in any proposals for action.

It is difficult to estimate the administrative feasibility of several of the proposals listed above, if for no other reason simply because the proponents do not put forward the necessary organizational plans or details. How are "fertility control agents" or "sterilants" to be administered on an involuntary mass basis in the absence of a central water supply or a food processing system? How are men with three or more children to be reliably identified in a peasant society and impelled to undergo sterilization against their will; and what is to be done if they decline, or if the fourth child is born? What is to be done with parents who evade the compulsory programs, or with the children born in consequence? How can an incentive system be honestly run in the absence of an organized network of offices positioned and staffed to carry out the regulatory activity? How can a system of social benefits and penalties, including marriage disincentives, be made to work under similar conditions?

Such questions are meant only to suggest the kinds of considerations that must be taken into account if proposals are to be translated into program. They are difficult but perhaps not insurmountable: somewhat similar problems have been addressed in the development of family planning programs themselves, as with the availability of medical and para-medical personnel. But it would seem desirable that every responsible proposal address itself to such administrative problems in the attempt to convert a proposal into a workable plan.

Some proposals do move in that direction. The plan to institutionalize maternal care in rural areas with family planning attached (A-1) is currently under study in several developing countries with regard to feasibility in administration, personnel, and costs. The plans for a national television system for informational purposes (C-2) have worked out some of the administrative problems, though the basic question of how to keep a television set working in a non-electrified area of a non-mechanical rural culture is not addressed and is not easy (as in the parallel case of keeping vehicles in working order under such conditions). The plan to build population into the school curriculum (C-1) has been carried forward to the preparation of materials and in a few cases beyond that.[103] The plans for incentive programs sometimes come down to only the theoretical proposition that people will do things for money, in this case refrain from having children; but in some cases the permissible payment is proposed on the basis of an economic analysis, and in a few cases an administrative means is also proposed.[104] The plan for wedding loans tied to the bride's age appreciates that a birth registration system might be needed in order to control against misreporting of age.[105]

Thus the *why* of population control is easy, the *what* is not very hard, but the *how* is difficult. We may know that the extension of popular education or the increase of women in the labor force or a later age of marriage would all contribute to population control in a significant way. But there remains the administrative question of how to bring those developments about. For example, the proposal (F-1) to organize the young men of India into a social service program, directed toward later age at marriage and general modernization of attitudes, is extremely difficult from an administrative standpoint even if it were acceptable politically and financially: consider the administrative, supervisory, and instructional problems in the United States of handling nine to ten million young men (the number affected in India), many of them unwilling participants easily "hidden" by their families and associates, in a series of camps away from home.[106] As has been observed, if a country could administer such a program it could more easily administer a family planning program, or perhaps not need one.

In short, several proposals assume administrable workability of a complicated scheme in a country that cannot now collect its own vital statistics in a reliable manner. Moreover, there is a near limit to how much administrative burden can be carried by the typical developing country at need: it cannot carry very many large-scale developmental efforts at the same time, either within the population field or overall. For population is not the only effort: agriculture, industry, education, health, communications, the military—all are important claimants. And within the field of population, a country that finds it difficult to organize and run a family planning program will find it still harder to add other programs along with that one. So difficult administrative choices must be made.

Economic Capability

From the standpoint of economic capability there are two questions: is the program worthwhile when measured against the criterion of economic return? and can it be afforded from present budgets even if worthwhile?

Most of the proposals probably pass the second screen: if scientifically available and politically and administratively acceptable, an involuntary fertility control agent would probably not be prohibitive economically; incorporation of population materials into the school curriculum is not unduly expensive, particularly when viewed as a long-term investment in population limitation; imposition of taxes or withdrawal of benefits or increased fees for marriage licenses might even return a net gain after administrative cost.

But a few proposals are costly in absolute if not relative terms. For example, the institutionalization of maternal care (A-1) might cost the order of $500,000,000 for construction and $200,000,000 for annual operation in India, or respectively $25,000,000 and $10,000,000 in a country of 25 million population [107] (although later estimates are substantially lower). The plan for a "youth corps" in India would cost upwards of $450,000,000 a year if the participants were paid only $50 annually. The plan for pensions to elderly fathers without sons could cost from $400 million to $1 billion a year, plus administrative costs. [108] The satellite television system for India would cost $50,000,000 for capital costs only on a restricted project, [109] with at least another $200,000,000 needed for receiving sets, broadcast terminals, and programming costs if national coverage is to be secured (depending largely on distribution of sets); or, by another estimate, $30-$35,000,000 a year over 20 years (or $700 million—$440 million in capital outlay and $250 million in operating costs) in order to cover 84 percent of the population by means of nearly 500,000 receiving sets. [110] All of these proposals are intended to have beneficial consequences beyond population and hence can be justified on multiple grounds, but they are still expensive in absolute amounts.

The broad social programs of popular education, rationalization of agriculture, and increased industrialization (F-4) already absorb even larger sums though they could no doubt utilize even more. Here, however, the better question is a different one. Presently less than one percent of the total funds devoted to economic development in such countries as India, Pakistan, South Korea, and Turkey are allocated to family planning programs—in most cases, much less. Would that tiny proportion make a greater contribution to population control, over some specified period, if given over to education or industrialization or road-building, for their indirect effect, rather than utilized directly for family planning purposes? [111] From what we now know, the answer is certainly No.

Incentives and Benefits
Still other proposals, particularly those concerned with incentives and bene-

fits, are more problematic, and unfortunately no clear directions are apparent. For comparative purposes, let us start with the generally accepted proposition that in the typical developing country today, one prevented birth is worth one to two times the per capita income, on economic grounds alone. In that case, the typical family planning program as currently operated is economically warranted in some substantial degree.[112] The per caput annual income of the developing countries under consideration range, say, from $75 to $500. In similar order of magnitude, the typical family planning program operates annually at about six cents per caput, and in Taiwan and South Korea, where the programs are more effective, "each initial acceptor costs about $5; each acceptor continuing effective contraception for a year costs about $7-$10; each prevented birth costs, say, $20-$30 (at three years of protection per averted birth); and each point off the birth rate at its present level costs . . . about $25,000 per million population."[113]

This order of cost is not certified in all other situations, so even the economic value of family planning programs is not yet altogether clear[114] although most indications to date are that it is strongly positive.[115] Beyond family planning, the situation is still less clear. Assuming that some level of incentive or benefit would have a demographic impact, what would the level have to be to cut the birth rate by, say, 20 percent? We simply do not know: the necessary experiments on either administration or effectiveness have not been carried out. There is, of course, the possibility that what would be needed could not be afforded and that what could be afforded would not be effective.

For guidance, let us review what has been proposed with respect to incentives. Again we take the Indian case; and for comparative purposes, the present budget of the Indian family planning program is about $60,000,000 a year, far higher than in the recent past (only about $11,000,000 in the 1961-1966 Plan) and not yet fully spent.

On the ground that incentives for vasectomy are better than incentives for contraception—easier to administer and check on a one-time basis and likely to be more effective in preventing births[116]—Pohlman proposes for India a range of money benefits depending upon parity and group acceptance: from $7 to a father of four or more children if half the villagers in that category enter the program, up to $40 to a father of three children if 75 percent accept. If the 50 percent criterion were met in both categories throughout India, the current plan would cost on the order of $260,000,000 in incentives alone, omitting administrative costs (based on these figures: 90 million couples, of whom about 40 percent are parity four and above, and 15 percent are parity three; or about 36.0 and 13.5 million respectively; half of each times $7 and $20 respectively). The decline in the birth rate would be slightly over one fourth, perhaps a third, or of the order of $35-$40 a prevented birth by a rough estimate.[117]

Simon proposes an incentive of half the per capita income "each year to each fertile woman who does not get pregnant."[118] Here a special problem arises. In a typical developing population of 1000, about 25-30 percent of the married women of reproductive age (MWRA) give birth each year: 1000 population means from 145-165 MWRA, with a birth rate of, say, 40. Thus, incentives could be paid to about three-fourths of the women with no effect on the birth rate—since they would not be having a child that year under normal circumstances—so that the cost could be three to four times larger than "needed" for any desired result. Even if the incentive were fully effective, and each one really did prevent a birth, a cut of ten points in the Indian birth rate would cost of the order of $250,000,000 (or 5,000,000 prevented births at $50 each)—and substantially larger if the anyway non-pregnant, including the non- or semi-fecund, could not be screened out efficiently. (Compare this level of incentive with Spengler's suggestion of "rewards to those who prevent births—say $5-$10 per married couple of reproductive age each year they avoid having offspring."[119] In the typical case, the couple could collect for three years and then, as before, have the child in the fourth year; or, if an incentive of this size were effective, the cost would be four times the indicated level.)

Enke addresses himself to this problem by suggesting a system of blocked accounts for Indian women who would have to remain non-pregnant for three to four years with examinations thrice yearly.[120] Here again the cost could be high: about $100 for three to four years of non-pregnancy at his proposed rates, or perhaps $500,000,000 a year to effect a similar cut in the birth rate (i.e., over 20,000,000 prevented births over four years at $100 each). And on the administrative side, the plan requires not only a substantial organization for management and recordkeeping, but also the dubious assumption that the Indian peasant is sufficiently future-oriented and trustful of governmental bureaucracy.

Finally, Balfour has suggested an ingenious scheme for providing national saving certificates to married women in the reproductive ages who remain non-pregnant for three, four, five, or more years at the rate of about $3-$4 a year.[121] He estimates that this plan in action would cost about $200 per year per thousand population, which comes to about $100,000,000 for all India.

But these are only speculations: to date we simply do not know whether incentives will lower a birth rate or rather, how large they would have to be in order to do so. These illustrations show only that an incentive program could be expensive. In any case, incentive systems would require a good amount of supervision and recordkeeping; and presumably the higher the incentive (and hence the greater the chance of impact), the greater the risk of false reporting and the greater need of supervision—which is not only expensive but difficult administratively.

Moral/Ethical/Philosophical Acceptability

Beyond political acceptability, is the proposal considered right and proper—by the target population, government officials, professional or intellectual elites, the outside agencies committed to assistance?

"One reason the policy of seeking to make voluntary fertility universal is appealing—whether adequate or not—is that it is a natural extension of traditional democratic values: of providing each individual with the information he needs to make wise choices, and allowing the greatest freedom for each to work out his own destiny. The underlying rationale is that if every individual knowledgeably pursues his self-interest, the social interest will best be served." [122] But what if "stressing the right of parents to have the number of children they want . . . evades the basic question of population policy, which is how to give societies the number of children they need?" [123] Thus the issue rests at the center of political philosophy: how best to reconcile individual and collective interests.

Today, most observers would acknowledge that having a child is theoretically a free choice of the individual couple—but only theoretical in that the freedom is principled and legal. For many couples, particularly among the poor of the world, it is not effectively free in the sense that the individual couple does not have the information, services, and supplies to implement a free wish in this regard. Such couples are restrained by ignorance, not only of contraceptive practice but of the consequences of high fertility for themselves, their children, and their country; they are restrained by religious doctrine, even though they may not accept the doctrine; they are restrained legally, as with people who would abort a pregnancy if that action were open to them; they are restrained culturally, as with women subject to the subordination that reserves for them only the child-bearing and child-rearing role. Hence effective freedom in child-bearing is by no means realized in the world today, as recent policy statements have remarked.[124]

Where does effective freedom lie? With the free provision of information and services for voluntary fertility limitation? With that plus a heavy propaganda campaign to limit births in the national interest? With that plus an incentive system of small payments? large payments? finders fees? With that plus a program of social benefits and penalties geared to the desired result? Presumably it lies somewhere short of compulsory birth limitation enforced by the state.

One's answer may depend not only on his own ethical philosophy but also upon the seriousness with which he views the population problem: the worse the problem, the more one is willing to "give up" in ethical position in order to attain "a solution." As usual, the important and hard ethical questions are those involving a conflict of values. In some countries, for example, people who are willing to provide temporary contraception as a means for population control under present circumstances are reluctant to extend the practice to sterilization and firmly opposed to abortion [125] —though again the wheel of history seems to be moving the world across that range under the pressure of population growth. But in some groups, notably religious groups, morality in this connection is absolute and no compromise with social need is to be tolerated, as for example in the case of Pope Paul's encyclical of July 1968.

How much in ethical values should a society be willing to forego for the solution of a great social problem? Suppose a program for population control resulted in many more abortions in a society where abortion is not only morally repugnant but also widely unavailable by acceptable medical standards: how much fertility decline would be "worth" the result? What of infanticide under the same conditions? How many innocent or unknowing men may be vasectomized for a fee (for themselves or the finders) before the practice calls for a moral restraint? How large an increase in the regulatory bureaucracy, or in systematic corruption through incentives, or in differential effect by social class to the disadvantage of the poor, [126] is worth how much decrease in the birth rate? How much association of child-bearing with monetary incentive is warranted before "bribing people not to have children" becomes contaminating, with adverse long-run effects on parental responsibility? [127] How much "immorality," locally defined as extramarital sex, is worth importing along with how much contraceptive practice (assuming the association)? How much withholding of food aid is ethical, judged against how much performance in fertility decline? If it were possible to legislate a later age of marriage, would it be right to do so in a society in which young women have nothing else to do, and against their will? In countries, like our own, where urbanization is a serious population problem, is it right to tell people *where* to live, or to impose heavy economic constraints that in effect "force" the desired migration? Is it right to withdraw educational benefits from the children in "too large" families?—which is not only repressive from the standpoint of free education but in the long run would be unfortunate from the standpoint of fertility control. In the balance—and this is a question of great but neglected importance—what weight should be given to the opportunities of the next generations as against the ignorance, the prejudices, or the preferences of the present one?

These are not light questions, nor easy ones to answer. And they have not been seriously analyzed and ventilated, beyond the traditional religious concern about the acceptability of contraception and abortion. Most official doctrine in the emerging population programs is conservative—as is only to be expected at the outset of a great social experiment of this character.

Guidance on such ethical questions is needed. As an offer toward further consideration, these propositions are put forward: (1) "an ideal policy would permit a maximum of individual freedom and diversity. It would not prescribe a precise number of children for each category of married couple, nor lay down a universal norm to which all couples should conform"; [128] correlatively, it would move toward compulsion only very reluctantly and as the absolutely last resort; (2) "an ideal program designed to affect the number of children people want would help promote other goals that are worth supporting on their own merits, or at least not conflict with such goals"; [129] correlatively, it would not indirectly encourage undesirable outcomes, e.g., bureaucratic corruption; (3) an ideal program would not burden the innocent in an attempt to penalize the guilty—e.g., would not burden the Nth child by denying him a free education simply because he was the Nth child of irresponsible parents; (4) an ideal program would not weigh heavily upon the already disadvantaged—e.g., by withdrawing maternal or medical benefits or free education from large families, which would tend to further deprive the poor; (5) an ideal program would be comprehensible to those directly affected—i.e., it should be capable of being understood by those involved and hence subject to their response; (6) an ideal program would respect present values in family and children, which many people may not be willing to bargain away for other values in a cost-benefit analysis; and (7) an ideal program would not rest upon the designation of population control as the final value justifying all others; "preoccupation with population growth should not serve to justify measures more dangerous or of higher social cost than population growth itself."[130]

Presumed Effectiveness
If proposals are scientifically ready, politically and morally acceptable, and administratively and financially feasible, to what extent will they actually work in bringing population growth under control? That is the final question.

Again we do not know the answer. We are not even sure in the case of family planning programs with which we now have some amount of experience. But as order of magnitude and as a kind of measuring rod for other proposals, the impact of family planning programs, when conducted with some energy at the rate of investment indicated above, ranges roughly as follows: in situations like Singapore, South Korea, and Taiwan, they have recruited 20-33 percent of the married women of reproductive age as contraceptive acceptors within 3-4 years, and in difficult situations like India and Pakistan, from 5-14 percent of the target population. [131] In other settings, like Malaysia or Ceylon or Turkey or Kenya or Tunisia or Morocco, either it is too early to tell or the program has been conducted under political or other restraints so that it is difficult to say what an energetic program could have achieved; as it is, family planning is being introduced into such situations at a pace politically acceptable and administratively feasible. Overall, it appears that a vigorous program *can* extend contraceptive practices by an economically worthwhile amount wherever conducted.[132]

What of the proposals beyond family planning? How well might they do, given administrative implementation?

To begin with, the compulsory measures would probably be quite effective in lowering fertility. Inevitably in such schemes, strongly motivated people are ingenious enough to find ways "to beat the system"; if they were numerous enough the system could not be enforced except under severe political repression.[133] Otherwise, if workable, compulsion could have its effect.

What about the proposals for the extension of voluntary contraception? Institutionalizing maternal care in the rural areas with family planning attached does promise to be effective over, say, five to ten years, particularly in its potential for reaching the younger and lower parity women. The International Postpartum Program did have that effect in the urban areas,[134] and presumably the impact would extend to the rural areas though probably not to the same degree because of the somewhat greater sophistication and modernization of the cities. The importance of the particular target is suggested in this observation: "The objective in India is to reach not the 500,000,000 people or the 200,000,000 people in the reproductive ages or the 90,000,000 married couples or even the 20-25,000,000 who had a child this year—but the 5,000,000 women who gave birth to their first child. And this may be the only institutionalized means for reaching them."[135] The total program is costly, but if it could establish family planning early in the reproductive period in a country like India, and thus encourage the spacing of children and not just stopping, it could have great demographic value in addition to the medical and humanitarian contribution.

A liberalized abortion system, again if workable, could also be effective in preventing unwanted births, but it would probably have to be associated with a contraceptive effort: otherwise there might be too many abortions for the system as well as for the individual woman (who might need three a year to remain without issue; in Mainland China, where abortion on demand is available, it is reported that a woman may have only one a year).[136] Free abortion for contraceptive failures would probably make for a fertility decline, but how large a one would depend upon the quality of the contraceptive program. With modern contraception (the IUD and the pill) the failure rates are quite small, but women who only marginally tolerate either method, or both, would be available for abortion. Free abortion on demand has certainly lowered fertility in Japan and certain Eastern European countries,[137] and where medically feasible would do so elsewhere as well; as a colleague observes, in this field one should not underestimate the attraction of a certainty as compared to a probability. Abortion for illegitimate pregnancies, whether voluntary (A-2) or required (B-4), would not have a large impact on the birth rate in most developing countries since known illegitimacy is small (assuming that the children of the numerous consensual unions and other arrangements in Latin America are not considered "illegitimate.")

The educational programs, whether in the school system or in the mass media, would almost certainly have an effect over the years though it will be difficult for technical reasons to determine the precise or even approximate degree of impact. Anything that can be done to "bring home" the consequences of undue population growth to family and nation will help reach the goal of fertility decline, but in the nature of the case education alone will have a limited effect if life circumstances remain stable.

The large question of the effect of the various incentive and benefit/liability plans (D and E) simply cannot be answered: we have too little experience to know much about the conditions under which financial factors will affect child-bearing to any substantial degree. Perhaps everyone has his price for everything; if so, we do not know what would have to be paid, directly or indirectly, to bring people not to bear children.

Such as it is, the evidence from the *pro*-natalist side is not encouraging. All the countries of Europe have family allowance programs of one kind or another,[138] most of them legislated in the 1930s and 1940s to raise the birth rate; collectively they have the lowest birth rate of any continent. The consensus among demographers appears to be that such programs cannot be shown to have effected an upward trend in the birth rate where tried. A recent review of the effect of children's allowances upon fertility concludes:

> It would be helpful to be able to state categorically that children's allowances do or do not increase the number of births among families that receive them. Unfortunately, there is no conclusive evidence one way or the other. . . . To argue that the level of births in the United States or anywhere else depends upon the existence, coverage, and adequacy of a set of family allowances is certainly simplistic. Such a conclusion can and ought to be rejected not only on logical grounds but also on the basis of the demonstrated complexity of the factors producing specific birthrates. . . . Recent fertility statistics show no relation between the existence or character of a family allowance program and the level of the birthrate. In specific low-income agricultural countries with such programs, fertility is high. In specific high-income modernized nations with such programs, fertility is low. . . . Whether the less developed countries have any form of family or children's allowances appears wholly unrelated to the level of fertility.[139]

As in the case of abortion for illegitimate pregnancies, several of the benefit/liability proposals would affect only a trivial fraction of people in much of the developing world: for example, again in India, programs for governmental employees who make up perhaps 5 percent of the labor force, tax or social security systems where the rural masses are not regularly covered, maternity benefits since so few women are covered, fees for marriage licenses, control of public housing which is insignificant, denial of education benefits to married students who are trivially few and not now covered in any case. Such measures are probably more relevant to the developed than the developing countries. However, because the impact of incentive and benefit/liability plans is uncertain and may become important, the field needs to become better informed on the possibilities and limitations, which information can only come from experimentation under realistic circumstances and at realistic levels of payment.

A higher age of marriage and a greater participation of women in the labor force are generally credited with effecting fertility declines. In India, average female age at marriage has risen from about 13 to about 16 in this century, or about half a year a decade, although the age of marital consummation has remained rather steady at 17 years (since most of the rise is due to the decrease in child marriages). In a recent Indian conference on raising age at marriage, the specialists seemed to differ only on the magnitude of the fertility decline that would result: a decline of 30 percent in the birth rate in a generation of 28 years if the minimum female age of marriage were raised to 20 [140] or a decline of not more than 15 percent in 10 years [141] —"seemed to" since these figures are not necessarily incompatible. In either case, the decline is a valuable one. But the effectiveness of increased age of marriage rests in the first instance on its being realized; here are the perhaps not unrepresentative views of knowledgeable and committed observers:

> ... In the absence of prolonged education and training, postponing the age of marriage becomes a formidable problem (Chandrasekhar)[142]
> ... Legislation regarding marriage can rarely be used as a measure of fertility control in democratic countries. The marital pattern will mostly be determined by social circumstances and philosophies of life and any measure by government clashing with them will be regarded as a restriction on freedom rather than a population policy (Dandekar)[143]

Similarly, an increase in the proportion of working women—working for payment outside the home—might have its demographic effect, [144] but could probably come about only in conjunction with other broad social trends like education and industrialization, which themselves would powerfully affect fertility (just as a fertility decline would assist importantly in bringing them about). [145] Both compulsory education and restrictions on child labor would lower the economic value of children and hence tend toward fertility decline: The question is, how are they to be brought about?

Finally, whether research would affect fertility trends depends of course upon its nature and outcome, aside from the general proposition that "more research" as a principle can hardly be argued against. Most observers believe that under the typical conditions of the developing society, any improvement in the contraceptive technology would make an important difference to the realization of present fertility goals and might make an important contribution to turning the spiral down. Indeed, several believe that this is the single most important desideratum over the short run. Easy means for sex determination should have some effect upon the "need for sons" and thus cut completed family size to some extent. Research on the social-economic side would probably have to take effect through the kinds of programs discussed above.

The picture is not particularly encouraging. The measures that would work to sharply cut fertility are politically and morally unacceptable to the societies at issue, as with coercion, and in any case unavailable; or they are difficult of attainment in any visible future, as with the broad social trends or shift in age of marriage. The measures that might possibly be tried in some settings, like some version of incentives or benefit/liability plans, are uncertain of result at the probable level of operation. Legalization of abortion, where medically available, would almost certainly have a measurable effect, but acceptability is problematic.

Conclusion

Where does this review leave us with regard to proposals beyond family planning? Here is my own summary of the situation.

(1) There is no easy way to population control. If this review has indicated nothing else, it has shown how many obstacles stand in the way of a simple solution to the population problem—or a complicated one, for that matter. By way of illustrative capitulation, let us see how the various proposals seem to fit the several criteria, in the large (Table 1).[146] That is only one observer's judgment of the present situation, but whatever appraisal is made of specific items it would appear that the overall picture is mixed. There is no easy way.

(2) Family planning programs do not compare unfavorably with specific other proposals—especially when one considers that any *actual* operating program is disadvantaged when compared with any competitive *ideal* policy. (As any practical administrator knows, when an "ideal" policy gets translated into action it develops its own set of realistic problems and loses some of the shine it had as an idea.) Indeed, on this showing, if family planning programs did not exist, they would have to be invented: it would appear that they would be among the first proposals to be made and the first programs to be tried, given their generally acceptable characteristics.

In fact, when such proposals are made, it turns out that many of them call for *more* family planning not less, but only in a somewhat different form.

Table 1
Illustrative Appraisal of Proposals by Criteria

	Scientific Readiness	Political Viability	Administrative Feasibility	Economic Capability	Ethical Acceptability	Presumed Effectiveness
A. Extension of Voluntary Fertility Control	High	High on maternal care, moderate to low on abortion	Uncertain in near future	Maternal care too costly for local budget, abortion feasible	High for maternal care, low for abortion	Moderately high
B. Establishment of Involuntary Fertility Control	Low	Low	Low	High	Low	High
C. Intensified Educational Campaigns	High	Moderate to high	High	Probably high	Generally high	Moderate
D. Incentive Programs	High	Moderately low	Low	Low to moderate	Low to high	Uncertain
E. Tax and Welfare Benefits and Penalties	High	Moderately low	Low	Low to moderate	Low to moderate	Uncertain
F. Shifts in Social and Economic Institutions	High	Generally high, but low on some specifics	Low	Generally low	Generally high, but uneven	High, over long run
G. Political Channels and Organizations	High	Low	Low	Moderate	Moderately low	Uncertain
H. Augmented Research Efforts	Moderate	High	Moderate to high	High	High	Uncertain
Family Planning Programs	Generally high, but could use improved technology	Moderate to high	Moderate to high	High	Generally high, but uneven on religious grounds	Moderately high

In the present case, of the proposals listed above, at least a third put forward in effect simply another approach to family planning, often accepting the existing motivation as to family size. In any case, family planning programs are established, have some momentum, and, importantly, would be useful as the direct instrument through which other proposals would take effect. So that, as a major critic acknowledges, "there is no reason to abandon family-planning programs."[147]

What is needed is the energetic and full implementation of present experience; this is by no means being done now. Much more could be done on the informational side, on encouragement of commercial channels of contraception, on the use of para-medical personnel, on logistics and supply, on the training and supervision of field workers, on approaches to special targets ranging from post-partum women to young men under draft into the armed forces. If the field did well what it knows how to do, that in itself would in all likelihood make a measurable difference—and one competitive in magnitude with other specific proposals—not to mention the further impetus of an improved contraceptive technology.

(3) Most of the proposed ideas are not new; they have been around for some time. So if they are not in existence, it is not because they were not known but because they were not accepted—presumably, for reasons like those reflected in the above criteria. In India, for example, several of the social measures being proposed have been, it would seem, under almost constant review by one or another committee for the past 10-15 years—withdrawal of maternity benefits, imposition of a child tax, increase in age of marriage, liberalization of legal abortion, incorporation of population and family planning in the school curriculum.[148] In Mainland China, reportedly, later age of marriage is common among party members,[149] and in Singapore a 1968 law restricts maternity privileges beyond the third child for employed women and makes public housing available to childless couples.[150] As for general social development—compulsory education, industrialization, improved medical care, etc.—that is in process everywhere, though of course more can always be done (but not very quickly). So it is not correct to imply that it is only new ideas that are needed; many ideas are there, but their political, economic, or administrative feasibility is problematic.

(4) The proposals themselves are not generally approved by this set of proposers, taken together. All of them are dissatisfied to some degree with present family planning efforts, but that does not mean that they agree with one another's schemes to do better. Thus, Ohlin believes that "the demographic significance of such measures (maternity benefits and tax deductions for children) would be limited. By and large those who now benefit from such arrangements in the developing countries are groups which are already involved in the process of social transformation" and that "changes in marital

institutions and norms are fairly slow and could not in any circumstances reduce fertility sufficiently by itself when mortality falls to the levels already attained in the developing world." [151] Ketchel opposes several "possible alternatives to fertility control agents":

> Financial pressures against large families would probably be effective only in developed countries in which there are large numbers of middle-class people. In underdeveloped countries practically no financial inducements to have children now exist to be reversed, and the imposition of further taxes upon the many poor people would depress their living standards even further. . . . In order to be effective, economic pressures would probably have to be severe enough to be quite painful, and when they reached a level of painfulness at which they were effective, they would probably seriously affect the welfare of the children who were born in spite of the pressures. . . . The same objection applies to the use of financial rewards to induce people not to have children because such programs would make the families with children the poorer families. . . . The age at which people marry is largely determined by slowly changing cultural and economic factors, and could probably be changed quickly in a population only by rather drastic measures (in which) an inordinately severe punishment for violators would be required. . . . Statutory regulations of family size would be unenforceable unless the punishment for exceeding the limit was so harsh that it would cause harm to the lives of the existing children and their parents. Such possible procedures as vasectomizing the father or implanting long-acting contraceptives in the mother would require a direct physical assault by a government agent on the body of an individual. [152]

Meier argues against the tax on children on both humanitarian and political grounds. [153] To the U.N. Advisory Mission to India, "it is realised that no major demographic effects can be expected from measures of this kind (maternity benefits), particularly as only a small proportion of families are covered . . . but they could contribute, together with the family planning programme, to a general change in the social climate relating to child-bearing." [154] Earlier, in supporting a family planning effort in India, Davis noted that "the reaction to the Sarda Act (the Child Marriage Restraint Act of 1929) prohibiting female marriage (below 14) shows the difficulty of trying to regulate the age of marriage by direct legislation." [155] Myrdal warns against cash payments to parents in this connection, as a redistributional reform, and supports social awards to the children in kind. [156] Kirk believes that "it might prove to be the height of folly to undermine the existing family structure, which continues to be a crucial institution for stability and socialization in an increasingly mobile and revolutionary society." [157] Raulet believes that "Davis' main observation . . . that alternatives to the present stress on familism will ultimately be required . . . obviously makes no sense for most less developed countries today. . . . Aside from the repressive tone of some of (the proposed) measures, the most striking thing about these proposals is the impracticality of implementing them. . . . The application of social security measures and negative economic sanctions . . . are so far beyond the present economic capacities of these countries, and would raise such difficult administrative and economic problems, that they are probably not worth serious mention." [158]   Finally, Ehrlich is contemptuous of the professors whose "idea of 'action' is to form a committee or to urge 'more research.' Both courses are actually substitutes for action. Neither will do much good in the crisis we face now. We've got lots of committees, and decades ago enough research had been done at least to outline the problem and make clear many of the steps necessary to solve it. Unless those steps are taken, research initiated today will be terminated not by success but by the problem under investigation." [159]

(5) In a rough way, there appears to be a progression in national efforts to deal with the problem of population control. The first step is the theoretical recognition that population growth may have something to do with the prospects for economic development. Then, typically, comes an expert mission from abroad to do a survey and make a report to the government, as has occurred in India, Pakistan, South Korea, Turkey, Iran, Tunisia, Morocco, and Kenya among others. The first action program is in family planning, and most of the efforts are still there. Beyond that, it apparently takes (1) some degree of discouragement over progress combined with (2) some heightened awareness of the seriousness of the problem to move the effort forward. To date those conditions have been most prominently present in India—and that is the country that has gone farthest in the use of incentives and in at least consideration of further steps along the lines mentioned above. It may be that in this respect the Indian experience is a harbinger of the international population scene. It is only natural that on matters of such sensitivity, governments try "softer" measures before "harder" ones; and only natural, too, that they move gradually from one position to the next to realize their goals. Indeed, some proposals require prior or simultaneous developments, often of a substantial nature: for example a loan system tied to age of brides may require a good system of vital registration for purpose of verification, instruction in population in the schools requires some degree of compulsory education, tying family planning to health programs requires a medical infrastructure.

Finally, it is also worth noting that more extreme or controversial proposals tend to legitimate more moderate advances, by shifting the boundaries of discourse.

(6) Proposals need to be specified—proposals both for action schemes and for further research. It is perhaps too much to ask advocates to spell out all the administrative details of how their plan is to operate in the face of the kinds of obstacles and difficulties discussed above, or even get permission to operate: the situations, settings, opportunities, and personalities are too diverse for that. But it does seem proper to ask for the fullest possible specification of actual plans, under realistic conditions, in order to test out their feasibility and likely effectiveness. The advocates of further research similarly ought to spell out not only what would be studied and how, but also how the results might be applied in action programs to affect fertility. Social research is not always readily translated into action, especially into administrative action; and the thrust of research is toward refinement, subtlety, precision, and qualification whereas the administrator must act in the large. Short of such specification, the field remains confronted with potentially good ideas like "raise the age of marriage" or "use incentives" or "substitute pension systems for male children" without being able to move very far toward implementation.

(7) Just as there is no easy way, there is no single way. Since population control will at best be difficult, it follows that every acceptable step be taken that promises some measure of impact. The most likely prospect is that population control, to the degree realized, will be the result of a combination of various efforts—economic, legal, social, medical—each of which has some effect but not an immediately overwhelming one. [160] Accordingly, it is incumbent upon the professional fields concerned to look hard at various approaches, including family planning itself, in order to screen out what is potentially useful for application. In doing so, on an anyway difficult problem, it may be the path of wisdom to move with the "natural" progression. Some important proposals seem reasonably likely of adoption—institutionalization of maternal care, population study in the schools, the TV satellite system for informational purposes, a better contraceptive technology, perhaps even liberalization of abortion in some settings—and we need to know not only how effective such efforts will be but, beyond them, how large a money incentive needs to be to effect a given amount of fertility control and how effective those indirect social measures are that are decently possible of realization. It may be that some of these measures would be both feasible and effective—many observers 15 years ago thought that family planning programs were neither—and a genuine effort needs to be made in the next years, wherever feasible, to do the needed experimentation and demonstration. The "heavy" measures—involuntary means and political pressures—may be put aside for the time being, if not forever.

(8) In the last analysis, what will be scientifically available, politically acceptable, administratively feasible, economically justifiable, and morally tolerated depends upon people's perceptions of consequences. If "the popula-

tion problem" is considered relatively unimportant or only moderately important, that judgement will not support much investment of effort. If it is considered urgent, much more can and will be done. The fact is that despite the large forward strides taken in international recognition of the problem in the 1960s, there still does not exist the informed, firm, and constant conviction in high circles that this is a matter with truly great ramifications for human welfare. [161] Such convictions must be based on sound knowledge. Here it would appear that the demographers and economists have not sufficiently made their case to the world elite—or that, if made, the case has not sufficiently been brought to their attention or credited by them. Population pressures are not sharply visible on a day-to-day or even year-to-year basis nor, short of major famine, do they lend themselves to dramatic recognition by event. Moreover, the warnings of demographers are often dismissed, albeit unfairly and wrongly, on their record of past forecasts: [162] after all, it was only a generation ago that a declining population was being warned about in the West. It is asking government leaders to take very substantial steps indeed when population control is the issue—substantial for their people as well as for their own political careers—and hence the case must be not only substantial but virtually incontrovertible. Accordingly, the scientific base must be carefully prepared (and perhaps with some sense of humility about the ease of predicting great events, on which the record is not without blemishes). Excluding social repression and mindful of maximizing human freedom, greater measures to meet the problem must rely on heightened awareness of what is at stake, by leaders and masses alike.

What is beyond family planning? Even if most of the specific plans are not particularly new, that in itself does not mean that they are to be disregarded. The questions are: which can be effected, given such criteria? how can they be implemented? what will be the outcome?

This paper is an effort to promote the discourse across the professional fields concerned with this important issue. Given the recent stress on family planning programs as the "means of choice" in dealing with the problem, it is natural and desirable that counter positions should be put forward and reviewed. But that does not in itself settle the critical questions. What can we do now to advance the matter? Beyond family planning, what?

Notes and References

1. As one example, see "Declaration on Population: The World Leaders' Statement," signed by 30 heads of state, in *Studies in Family Planning*, no. 26, January 1968.

2. For example, see Kingsley Davis, "Population Policy: Will Current Programs Succeed?", *Science*, vol. 158, 10 Novemebr 1967, p. 730-739; Robert G. Potter, Ronald Freedman, and L. P. Chow, "Taiwan's Family Planning Program," *Science*, vol. 160, 24 May 1968, p. 848-853; and Frank W. Notestein, "Population Growth and Its Control," MS prepared for American Assembly meeting on World Hunger, Fall 1968.

3. See, for example, the section on "Goals" in Davis, *op. cit.*, p. 731-733, and the 1968 presidential address to the Population Association of America, "Should the United States Start a Campaign for Fewer Births?", by Ansley J. Coale.

4. For current targets of some national family planning programs, see table 8, p. 39, and accompanying text in Bernard Berelson, "National Family Planning Programs: Where We Stand," prepared for University of Michigan Sesquicentennial Celebration, November 1967, which concludes: "By and large, developing countries are now aiming at the birth rates of Western Europe 75 years ago or the United States 50 years ago."

5. For a first effort to outline the matter, see point 12, p. 46-51, in Berelson, *op. cit.*

6. Howard C. Taylor Jr. & Bernard Berelson, "Maternity Care and Family Planning as a World Program," *American Journal of Obstetrics and Gynecology*, vol. 100, 1968, p. 885-893.

7. Davis, *op. cit.*, p. 732, 738.

8. Paul R. Ehrlich, *The Population Bomb*, Ballatine Books, 1968, p. 139.

9. S. Chandrasekhar, "Should We Legalize Abortion in India?", *Population Review*, 10, 1966, 17-22.

10. Melvin M. Ketchel, "Fertility Control Agents as a Possible Solution to the World Population Problem," *Perspectives in Biology and Medicine*, vol. 11, 1968, p. 687-703. See also his "Should Birth Control Be Mandatory?", in *Medical World News*, 18 October 1968, p. 66-71.

11. Ehrlich, *op. cit.*, p. 135-36. The author appears to dismiss the scheme as unworkable on page 136 though two pages later he advocates "ample funds" to "promote intensive investigation of new techniques of birth control, possibly leading to the development of mass sterilizing agents such as were discussed above."

12. Kenneth E. Boulding, *The Meaning of the Twentieth Century: The Great Transition*, Harper & Row, p. 135-36. For the record, I note a statement that appeared too late for consideration but does argue for "mutual coercion, mutually agreed upon by the majority of the people affected:" Garrett Hardin, "The Tragedy of the Commons," *Science*, 162, 13 December 1968, p. 1247.

13. William B. Shockley, in lecture at McMaster University, Hamilton, Ontario, reported in *New York Post*, 12 December 1967.

14. Sripati Chandrasekhar, as reported in *The New York Times*, 24 July 1967. Just as this paper was being completed, the same author "proposed that every married couple in India deny themselves sexual intercourse for a year. . . . Abstinence for a year would do enormous good to the individual and the country" (as reported in *The New York Times*, 21 October 1968). The reader may wish to consider this the 30th proposal and test it against the criteria that follow.

15. Davis, *op. cit.*, p. 738.

16. Davis, *op. cit.*, p. 738.

17. Sloan Wayland, "Family Planning and the School Curriculum," in Bernard Berelson et al., eds., *Family Planning and Population Programs*, University of Chicago Press, 1966, p. 353-62; his "Population Education, Family Planning and the School Curriculum," MS prepared for collection of readings edited by John Ross and John Friesen, *Family*

Planning Programs: Administration, Education, Evaluation, forthcoming 1969; and two manuals prepared under his direction: *Teaching Population Dynamics: An Instructional Unit for Secondary School Students and Critical Stages in Reproduction: Instruction Materials in General Science and Biology,* both Teachers College, Columbia University, 1965.

18. Pravin Visaria, "Population Assumptions and Policy," *Economic Weekly,* 8 August 1964, p. 1343.

19. Ehrlich, *op. cit.,* p. 162.

20. Richard L. Meier & Gitta Meier, "New Directions, A Population Policy for the Future," University of Michigan, revised MS, October 1967, p. 11.

21. UNESCO Expert Mission, *Preparatory Study of a Pilot Project in the Use of Satellite Communication for National Development Purposes in India,* 5 February 1968, especially the section on "The Population Problem," p. 13-14, paras. 61-66.

22. Wilbur Schramm & Lyle Nelson, *Communication Satellites for Education and Development—The Case of India.* Stanford Research Institute, July 1968: "Family Planning," p. 63-66.

23. Sripati Chandrasekhar, as reported in *The New York Times,* 19 July 1967. Here again I note for the record a very recent "Proposal for a Family Planning Bond," by Ronald J. Ridker, USAID—India, July 1968. This memorandum is a comprehensive and quite detailed review of the issues involved in providing 20-year bonds for couples sterilized after the second or third child. Along this same line, see another late suggestion of a bond linked both to age of marriage and to number of children, in *Approaches to the Human Fertility Problem,* prepared by The Carolina Population Center for the United Nations Advisory Committee on the Application of Science and Technology to Development, October 1968, p. 68.

24. Edward Pohlman, "Incentives for 'Non-Maternity' Cannot 'Compete' with Incentives for Vasectomy," Central Family Planning Institute, India, MS 1967?

25. T. J. Samuel, "The Strengthening of the Motivation for Family Limitation in India," *The Journal of Family Welfare,* vol. 13, 1966, p. 11-12.

26. Davis, *op. cit.,* p. 738.

27. Julian Simon, "Money Incentives to Reduce Birth Rates in Low-Income Countries: A Proposal to Determine the Effect Experimentally;" "The Role of Bonuses and Persuasive Propaganda in the Reduction of Birth Rates;" and "Family Planning Prospects in Less-Developed Countries, and a Cost-Benefit Analysis of Various Alternatives," University of Illinois, MSS 1966-1968?

28. Stephen Enke, "Government Bonuses for Smaller Families," *Population Review,* vol. 4, 1960, p. 47-54.

29. Samuel, *op. cit.,* p. 12.

30. Michael Young, in "The Behavioral Sciences and Family Planning Programs: Report on a Conference," *Studies in Family Planning,* no. 23, October 1967, p. 10.

31. Dipak Bhatia, "Government of India Small Family Norm Committee Questionnaire," *Indian Journal of Medical Education,* vol. 6, October 1967, p. 189. As the title indicates, this is not a proposal as such but a questionnaire soliciting opinions on various ideas put forward to promote "the small family norm."

32. Stephen Enke, "The Gains to India from Population Control," *The Review of Economics and Statistics*, May 1960, p. 179-180.

33. Joseph J. Spengler, "Agricultural Development is Not Enough," MS prepared for Conference on World Population Problems, Indiana University, May 1967, p. 29-30.

34. J. William Leasure, "Some Economic Benefits of Birth Prevention," *Milbank Memorial Fund Quarterly*, 45, 1967, p. 417-25.

35. Marshall C. Balfour, "A Scheme for Rewarding Successful Family Planners," Memorandum, The Population Council, June 1962.

36. W. Parker Mauldin, "Prevention of Illegitimate Births: A Bonus Scheme," Memorandum, The Population Council, August 1967.

37. Ehrlich, *op. cit.*, p. 138.

38. Bhatia, *op. cit.*, p. 188.

39. Samuel, *op. cit.*, p. 14.

40. Davis, *op. cit.*, p. 738.

41. Richard M. Titmuss & Brian Abel-Smith, *Social Policies and Population Growth in Mauritius*, Methuen, 1960, p. 130-31.

42. Bhatia, *op. cit.*, p. 189.

43. Titmuss & Abel-Smith, *op. cit.*, p. 131-36.

44. Davis, *op. cit.*, p. 739.

45. Bhatia, *op. cit.*, p. 189-90.

46. Samuel, *op. cit.*, p. 12-14.

47. Spengler, *op. cit.*, p. 30.

48. Bhatia, *op. cit.*, p. 190.

49. Davis, *op. cit.*, p. 738.

50. Bhatia, *op. cit.*, p. 190.

51. Titmuss & Abel-Smith, *op. cit.*, p. 137.

52. Samuel, *op. cit.*, p. 12-14.

53. Davis, *op. cit.*, p. 738.

54. Ehrlich, *op. cit.*, p. 136-37.

55. A. S. David, *National Development, Population and Family Planning in Nepal*, June-July 1968, p. 53-54.

56. James Fawcett, personal communication, September 1968.

57. Samuel, *op. cit.*, p. 12.

58. Goran Ohlin, *Population Control and Economic Development*, Development Centre of the Organization for Economic Cooperation and Development, 1967, p. 104.

59. W. Phillips Davison, personal communication, 4 October 1968. Davison suggests a good pension (perhaps $400 a year) for men aged 60, married for at least 20 years, with no sons.

60. David, *op. cit.*, p. 53.

61. Davis, *op. cit.*, p. 738.

62. Young, *op. cit.*, p. 10.

63. Titmuss & Abel-Smith, *op. cit.*, p. 130.

64. Kingsley Davis, personal communication, 7 October 1968.

65. Ehrlich, *op. cit.*, p. 138.

66. Bernard Berelson, Amitai Etzioni, brief formulations, 1962, 1967.

67. Philip M. Hauser, in "The Behavioral Sciences and Family Planning Programs: Report on a Conference," *Studies in Family Planning*, no. 23, October 1967, p. 9.

68. Davis, *op. cit.*, p. 738.

69. David, *op. cit.*, p. 54.

70. Judith Blake, "Demographic Science and the Redirection of Population Policy," in Mindel C. Sheps & Jeanne Clare Ridley, eds., *Public Health and Population Change: Current Research Issues*, University of Pittsburgh Press, 1965, p. 62.

71. Davis, *op. cit.*, p. 737.

72. Meier & Meier, *op. cit.*, p. 9. For the initial formulation of the proposal, see Richard L. Meier, *Modern Science and the Human Fertility Problem*, Wiley, 1959, chapter 7, esp. p. 171 ff.

73. Philip M. Hauser, "'Family Planning and Population Programs:' A Book Review Article," *Demography*, vol. 4, 1967, p. 412.

74. United Nations Economic and Social Council. Commission on the Status of Women. "Family Planning and the Status of Women: Interim Report of the Secretary-General," 30 January 1968, esp. p. 17 ff.

75. Roger Revelle, as quoted in "Too Many Born? Too Many Die. So Says Roger Revelle," by Milton Viorst, *Horizon*, Summer 1968, p. 35.

76. David M. Heer & Dean O. Smith, "Mortality Level and Desired Family Size," paper prepared for presentation at Population Association of America meeting, April 1967. See also David A. May and David M. Heer, "Son Survivorship Motivation and Family Size in India: A Computer Simulation," *Population Studies*, 22, 1968, p. 199-210.

77. Ehrlich, *op. cit.*, p. 161-66, *passim.* The author makes the same point in his article, "Paying the Piper," *New Scientist*, 14 December 1967, p. 655: "Refuse all foreign aid to any country with an increasing population which we believe is not making a maximum effort to limit its population. . . . The United States should use its power and prestige to bring extreme diplomatic and/or economic pressure on any country or organization [the Roman Catholic Church?] impeding a solution to the world's most pressing problem."

78. Ehrlich, *op. cit.*, p. 138. In the earlier article cited just above, he calls for a "Federal Population Commission with a large budget for propaganda," presumably limited to the United States (p. 655).

79. S. Chandrasekhar, "India's Population: Fact, Problem and Policy," in S. Chandrasekhar, ed., *Asia's Population Problems*, Allen & Unwin, 1967, p. 96, citing a Julian Huxley suggestion of 1961.

80. Meier & Meier, *op. cit.*, p. 5.

81. Davis, *op. cit.*, p. 731-33.

82. Davis, *op. cit.*, p. 738, 739.

83. Steven Polgar, in "The Behavioral Sciences and Family Planning Programs: Report on a Conference," *Studies in Family Planning*, no. 23, October 1967, p. 10. See also the recent suggestion of research on "the possibilities for artificially decreasing libido," in *Approaches to the Human Fertility Problem, op. cit* p. 73.

84. National Academy of Sciences, Committee on Science and Public Policy, *The Growth of World Population*, 1963, p. 5, 28-36. This recommendation has of course been made on several occasions by several people: "we need a better contraceptive." For an imaginative account of the impact of biological developments, see Paul C. Berry, *Origins of Positive Population Control, 1970-2000*, Working Paper, Appendix to *The Next Thirty-Four Years: A Context for Speculation*, Hudson Institute, February 1966.

85. For example, see Sheldon J. Segal, "Biological Aspects of Fertility Regulation," MS prepared for University of Michigan Sesquicentennial Celebration, November 1967.

86. In passing it is worth noting that such expectations are not particularly reliable. For example, in 1952-1953 a Working Group on Fertility Control was organized by the Conservation Foundation to review the most promising "leads to physiologic control of fertility," based on a survey conducted by Dr. Paul S. Henshaw and Kingsley Davis. The Group did identify a lead that became the oral contraceptive (already then under investigation) but did not mention the intrauterine device. The Group was specifically searching for better ways to control fertility because of the population problem in the developing world, and considered the contraceptive approach essential to that end: "It thus appears imperative that an attempt be made to bring down fertility in overpopulated regions without waiting for a remote, hoped-for transformation of the entire society. . . . It seems plausible that acceptable birth control techniques might be found, and that the application of science to developing such techniques for peasant regions might yield revolutionary results." (*The Physiological Approach to Fertility Control, Report of the Working Group on Fertility Control*, The Conservation Foundation, April 1953, p. 69.)

87. Z. Dvorak, V. Trnka, and R. Vasicek, "Termination of Pregnancy by Vacuum Aspiration," *Lancet*, vol. 2, 11 November 1967, p. 997-98; and D. Kerslake and D. Casey, "Abortion Induced by Means of the Uterine Aspirator," *Obstetrics and Gynecology*, vol. 30, July 1967, p. 35-45.

88. A. S. Parkes, "Can India Do It?", *New Scientist*, vol. 35, July 1967, p. 186.

89. These are only illustrative magnitudes. Actually, the five million does not really represent 5/22nd of the birth rate since an aborted woman could again become pregnant within a period of months, whereas a newly pregnant woman would not normally become so for over a year. Thus it may be that abortion needs to be combined with contraceptive practice and used mainly for contraceptive failures or "accidents" in order to be fully effective as a means of fertility limitation in the developing countries.

90. Report in *The New York Times*, November 17, 1967. The then-Minister had earlier suggested a substantial bonus (100 rupees) for vasectomy, the funds to be taken from U.S. counterpart, "but both Governments are extremely sensitive in this area. Yet in a problem this crucial perhaps we need more action and less sensitivity" (S. Chandrasekhar, in *Asia's Population Problem, op. cit.*, p. 96).

91. United Nations Advisory Mission, *Report on the Family Planning Programme in India*, February 1966. See Chapter XI: "Social Policies to Promote Family Planning and Small Family Norms."

92. Bhatia, *op. cit.*

93. Central Family Planning Council, Resolution No. 8, January 1967, in *Implications of Raising the Female Age at Marriage in India*, Demographic Training Research Centre, 1968, p. 109; and *Centre Calling*, May 1968, p. 4.

94. Samuel, *op. cit.*, p. 12.

95. United Nations Advisory Mission, *op. cit.*, p. 87.

96. *Planned Parenthood*, March 1968, p. 3.

97. Report in *The New York Times*, September 12, 1968.

98. *Planned Parenthood*, April 1968, p. 2.

99. Davidson R. Gwatkin, "The Use of Incentives in Family Planning Programs," Memorandum, Ford Foundation, November 1967, p. 6-7.

100. Davis, *op. cit.*, p. 739.

101. Ketchel, *op. cit.*, p. 701.

102. For a review of this development see Richard Symonds & Michael Carder, *International Organisations and Population Control (1947-1967)*, Institute of Development Studies, University of Sussex, April 1968.

103. See footnote 17. At present population materials are being included in school programs in Pakistan, Iran, Taiwan, and elsewhere.

104. As, for example, with Balfour, Mauldin, and Pohlman, *op. cit.*; and for the economic analysis, Enke and Simon, *op. cit.*

105. Davis, *op. cit.* (footnote 64).

106. In effect, Israel has a program of this general character, though not for population control purposes, but it is a highly skilled society especially from an administrative standpoint. I understand that the Ceylon Government has a program of "agricultural youth settlements," aimed jointly at youth unemployment and agricultural production but not population control. Of the 200,000 unemployed youth aged 19-25, the Government plans to settle 20-25,000 in the 1966-70 period.

107. Taylor & Berelson, *op. cit.*, p. 892.

108. Davison, *op. cit.* and revised figures.

109. UNESCO Expert Mission, *op. cit.*, p. 23.

110. Schramm & Nelson, *op. cit.*, p. 164-68, *passim.*

111. For the negative answer, see Enke and Simon, *op. cit.* Data from family planning budgets and national development budgets contained in five-year development plans.

112. Enke and Simon, *op. cit.*; see also Paul Demeny, "Investment Allocation and Population Growth," *Demography*, vol. 2, 1965, p. 203-232; and his "The Economics of Government Payments to Limit Population: A Comment," *Economic Development and Cultural Change*, vol. 9, 1961, p. 641-644.

113. Berelson, *op. cit.* (footnote 4), p. 20.

114. Warren Robinson, "Conceptual and Methodological Problems Connected with Cost-Effectiveness Studies of Family Planning Programs" and David F. Horlocher, "Measuring the Economic Benefits of Population Control: A Critical Review of the Literature," Working Papers nos. 1 & 2, Penn State-U.S. AID Population Control Project, May 1968.

115. Even in the United States, where a recent study concluded that "Altogether, the economic benefits (of family planning programs) alone would be at least 26 times greater than the program costs:" Arthur A. Campbell, "The Role of Family Planning in the Reduction of Poverty," *Journal of Marriage and the Family*, vol. 30, 1968, p. 243.

116. Pohlman, *op. cit.*

117. Mr. Pohlman has under preparation a major MS on this subject, entitled *Incentives in Birth Planning.*

118. Simon, "Family Planning Prospects. . . . ," *op. cit.* (footnote 27), p. 8.

119. Spengler, *op. cit.*, p. 29-30. The Population Council is just now completing an analysis of the possible effects and costs of incentive programs with differing assumptions as to acceptance and continuation.

120. Enke, "The Gains. . . . ," *op. cit.* (footnote 32), p. 179.

121. Balfour, *op. cit.*

122. Coale, *op. cit.*, p. 2. However, the author does point out, a few sentences later, that "it is clearly fallacious to accept as optimal a growth that continues until overcrowding makes additional births intolerably expensive."

123. Davis, *op. cit.*, p. 738.

124. For example, The World Leaders' Statement, *op. cit.*; and the Resolution of the International Conference on Human Rights on "Human Rights Aspects of Family Planning," adopted 12 May 1968, reported in *Population Newsletter* issued by the Population Division, United Nations, no. 2, July 1968, p. 21 ff.

125. The issue was sufficiently alive in classical times to prompt the great philosophers to take account of the matter in their political proposals. In Plato's *Republic*, "the number of weddings is a matter which must be left to the discretion of the rulers, whose aim will be to preserve the average of population (and) to prevent the State from becoming either too large or too small"—to which end certain marriages have "strict orders to prevent any embryo which may come into being from seeing the light; and if any force a way to the birth, the parents must understand that the offspring of such a union cannot be maintained, and arrange accordingly" (Modern Library edition, p. 412, 414). In Aristotle's *Politics*, "on the ground of an *excess* in the number of children, if the established customs of the state forbid this (for in our state population has a limit), no child is to be exposed, but when couples have children in excess, let abortion be procured before sense and life have begun. . . . " (Modern Library edition, p. 316).

126. After noting that economic constraints have not been adopted in South Asia, though often proposed, Gunnar Myrdal continues: "The reason is not difficult to understand. Since having many children is a main cause of poverty, such measures would penalize the relatively poor and subsidize the relatively well off. Such a result would not only violate rules of equity but would be detrimental to the health of the poor families, and so of the growing generation." *Asian Drama: An Inquiry into the Poverty of Nations*, Pantheon, 1968, vol. 2. p. 1502-3.

127. Frank W. Notestein, in "Closing Remarks," in Berelson *et al.*, editors, *op. cit.*: "There is a real danger that sanctions, for example through taxation, would affect adversely the welfare of the children. There is also danger that incentives through bonuses will put the whole matter of family planning in a grossly commercial light. It is quite possible that to poor and harassed people financial inducements will amount to coercion and not to an enlargement of their freedom of choice. Family planning must be, and must seem to be, an extension of personal and familial freedom of choice and thereby an enrichment of life, not coercion toward its restriction." (p. 828-29).

128. Coale, *op. cit.*, p. 7.

129. Coale, *op. cit.*, p. 7.

130. Coale, *op. cit.*, p. 6.

131. Figures based on monthly reports from national programs. Since most of the Indian achievement is in sterilization, it may have a more pronounced effect. For a sophisticated analysis of the Taiwan effort that concludes, "What we are asserting with some confidence is that the several hundred thousand participants in the Taiwan program have, since entering the program, dramatically increased their birth control practice and decreased their fertility," see Robert G. Potter, Ronald Freedman, and L. P. Chow, "Taiwan's Family Planning Program," *Science*, vol. 160, 24 May 1968, p. 852.

132. Berelson, *op. cit.*, p. 35-38.

133. In this connection, see the novel by Anthony Burgess, *The Wanting Seed*, Ballantine Books, 1963. At the same time, a long-time observer of social affairs remarks that "the South Asian countries . . . can, to begin with, have no other principle than that of voluntary parenthood. . . . State direction by compulsion in these personal matters is not effective. . . . " (Myrdal, *op. cit.*, p. 1501).

134. Gerald I. Zatuchni, "International Postpartum Family Planning Program: Report on the First Year," *Studies in Family Planning*, no. 22, August 1967, p. 14 ff.

135. Howard C. Taylor, Jr., personal communication.

136. Edgar Snow, "The Chinese Equation," *The* (London) *Sunday Times*, January 23, 1966.

137. For example, the repeal of the free abortion law in Rumania resulted in an increase in the birth rate from 14 in the third quarter of 1966 to 38 in the third quarter of 1967. For an early report, see Roland Pressat, "La suppression de l'avortement légal en Roumanie: premiers effets," *Population*, vol. 22, 1967, p. 1116-18.

138. See U.S. Department of Health, Education, and Welfare, Social Security Administration. "Social Security Programs Throughout the World, 1964."

139. Vincent H. Whitney, "Fertility Trends and Children's Allowance Programs," in Eveline M. Burns, editor, *Children's Allowances and the Economic Welfare of Children: The Report of a Conference*, Citizens' Committee for Children of New York, 1968, p. 123, 124, 131, 133.

140. S. N. Agarwala, "Raising the Marriage Age for Women: A Means to Lower the Birth Rate," in *Implications of Raising the Female Age at Marriage in India*, Demographic Training and Research Centre, 1968, p. 21.

141. V. C. Chidambaram, "Raising the Female Age at Marriage in India: A Demographer's Dilemma," in *Implications, op. cit.*, p. 47.

142. Chandrasekhar, *op. cit.* (footnote 79), p. 96.

143. Kumudini Dandekar, "Population Policies," *Proceedings of the United Nations World Population Conference*, 1965, p. 4.

144. However, see David Chaplin, "Some Institutional Determinants of Fertility in Peru," manuscript, April 1968, for some evidence that welfare and labor regulations in Peru discourage the employment of women in low-fertility occupations (factory work) by making them more expensive to employ than men. Laws thus designed to promote maternity do so only by default since the higher fertility of the disemployed women will occur outside the protection of adequate medical and welfare institutions.

145. Actually, recent research is calling into question some of the received wisdom on the prior need of such broad institutional factors for fertility decline. If further study supports the new findings, that could have important implications for present strategy in the developing countries. See Ansley J. Coale, "Factors Associated with the Development of Low Fertility: An Historic Summary," *Proceedings of the United Nations World Population Conference*, 1965, vol. 2, p. 205-209; and his paper, "The Decline of Fertility in Europe from the French Revolution to World War II," prepared for University of Michigan Sesquicentennial Celebration, November 1967.

146. As the roughest sort of summary of table 1, if one assigns values from 5 for High to 1 for Low, the various proposals rank as follows:

Family Planning Programs 25
Intensified Educational Campaigns 25
Augmented Research Efforts 24
Extension of Voluntary Fertility Control 20
Shifts in Social and Economic Institutions 20
Incentive Programs 14
Tax and Welfare Benefits and Penalties 14
Political Channels and Organizations 14
Establishment of Involuntary Fertility Control 14

147. Davis, *op. cit.*, p. 739. The same critic was a strong advocate of family planning in India, and quite optimistic about its prospects even in the pre-IUD or pill era and with a health base. See Kingsley Davis, "Fertility Control and the Demographic Transition in India," in *The Interrelations of Demographic, Economic, and Social Problems in Selected Underdeveloped Areas*, Milbank Memorial Fund, 1954, concluding:

"Although India is already well-launched in the rapid-growth phase of the demographic transition, there is no inherent reason why she should long continue in this phase. She need not necessarily wait patiently while the forces of urbanization, class mobility, and industrial development gradually build up to the point where parents are forced to limit their offspring on their own initiative and without help, perhaps even in the face of official opposition. . . . Realistically appraising her situation, India has a chance to be the first country to achieve a major revolution in human life—the planned diffusion of fertility control in a peasant population prior to, and for the benefit of, the urban-industrial trans. 87-88).

148. See, for example, Visaria, *op. cit.*, p. 1343; Bhatia, *op. cit.;* Samuel, *op. cit.*, p. 12; U.N. Advisory Mission, *op. cit.*, Chapter XI; Chandrasekhar, in *Asia's Population Problem, op. cit.;* Myrdal, *op. cit.*, p. 1502; *Implications. . . ,op. cit.;* and "Shah Committee Recommends Liberalization of Abortion Laws," *Family Planning News*, September 1967, p. 23.

149. Snow, *op. cit.*

150. K. Kanagaratnam, personal communication, August 8, 1968.

151. Ohlin, *op. cit.,* p. 104, 105.

152. Ketchel, *op. cit.,* p. 697-99.

153. Meier, *op. cit.,* p. 167.

154. United Nations Advisory Mission, *op. cit.,* p. 87.

155. Davis, *op. cit.,* p. 86.

156. Myrdal, *op. cit.,* p. 1503.

157. Dudley Kirk, "Population Research in Relation to Population Policy and National Family Planning Programs," paper presented at meetings of the American Sociological Association, August 1968.

158. Harry M. Raulet, *Family Planning and Population Control in Developing Countries,* Institute of International Agriculture, Michigan State University, November 1968, pp. 5-6, 49-50.

159. Ehrlich, *op. cit.,* p. 191.

160. It begins to appear that the prospects for fertility control may be improving over the decades. After reviewing several factors that "favor a much more rapid (demo- graphic) transition than occurred in the West"–changed climate of opinion, religious doctrine, decline of infant mortality, modernization, fertility differentials, grass roots concern, and improved contraceptive technology–Dudley Kirk shows in a remarkable tabulation that the later a country began the reduction of its birth rate from 35 to 20, the shorter time it took to do so: from 73 years (average) in 1831-1860, for example, to 21 years after 1951, and on a consistently downward trend for over a century. In his "Natality in the Developing Countries: Recent Trends and Prospects," prepared for University of Michigan Sesquicentennial Celebration, November 1967, p. 11-13.

161. Nor, often, among the general public. For example, in mid-summer 1968 the Gallup Poll asked a national sample of adults: "What do you think is the most important problem facing this country today?" Less than one per cent mentioned population. (Gallup release, 3 August 1968, and personal communication.)

162. For an old but enlightening review, see Harold Dorn, "Pitfalls in Population Fore- casts and Projections," *Journal of the American Statistical Association,* vol. 45, 1950, p. 311-34.

Selected References for Chapter 7

Grier, George 1971, *The Baby Bust*. Washington, D.C.: Center for Metropolitan Studies. An optimistic account of recent fertility trends in the United States. Deserves critical examination.

Nash, A.E. Keir 1971, "Going Beyond John Locke? Influencing American Population Growth,: *Milbank Memorial Fund Quarterly,* Vol. 69 (January), pp. 7-31. A discussion of ideological problems affecting the control of population growth in the United States.

Revelle, Roger 1971, "Summary and Recommendations". Pp. 1-99 of *Rapid Population Growth*. Baltimore: The Johns Hopkins Press. Resume of major issues surrounding rates of population growth in the world today.

Sauvy, Alfred 1961, *Fertility and Survival.* London: Chatto and Windus. A discussion of demographic and economic conditions in the world today and their implications for population control.

Westoff, Leslie A. and Charles F. Westoff 1971, *From Now to Zero: Fertility, Contraception and Abortion in America*. Boston: Little, Brown and Co. A comprehensive and readable review of population control in the contemporary United States.

The essays included in this chapter have focused on man's efforts, in word and deed, to regulate his reproduction effectively. While the authors have concentrated on diverse aspects of the problem from varying points of view, several issues are discussed in all three presentations. First, there appears to be agreement that, unless impeded, current rates of population growth will have perilous consequences for the future of mankind. Even Bogue, the most optimistic of the three authors, recognizes this fact. Indeed, few students of modern demographic history would deny the existence, if not current at least recent, of a population crisis.

Second, there is little doubt that thus far the major organized attack on the problem has been through national family-planning programs. Evaluation of the effectiveness of these programs, however, vary considerably. Donald Bogue's optimism has already been noted. Though Berelson attributes some degree of success to family-planning strategies, he also recognizes that the population crisis is by no means resolved and goes only so far as to indicate that, of the various alternative strategies thus far proposed, family planning has the highest probability of success. Only Davis seriously questions the effectiveness of these programs, though he feels they should not be abandoned.

Finally, there is the question as to whether additional strategies, in addition to conventional family-planning programs, are needed in the quest for population control. Bogue lists several social movements that he sees as contributing to the success of conventional programs—e.g., aroused political leadership, accelerated research activity, mass acceptance of contraceptive ideology—but neither author emphasizes a need for increased concentration on these factors nor recognizes any problems restricting their effectiveness. Davis stresses the *necessity* of additional approaches, focusing on a restructuring of familial norms and roles, and argues that, without the implementation of these alternative strategies, population policy cannot be effective. Berelson, of course, gives most comprehensive attention to the question of alternatives and supplements to family planning. It is perhaps his more systematic and rigorous analysis that leads him to question the viability of most of these alternatives.

Another perspective for viewing these analyses or approaches to population control is in terms of the adaptive mechanisms specified in earlier chapters of this volume. Perhaps most obvious is the role of science and technology. That degree of control that has been achieved over human fertility is largely due to scientific and technological innovations resulting in the development of contraceptive techniques such as the pill and the IUD. Furthermore, some of the alternative proposals briefly discussed by Berelson— e.g., fertility control agents and time-capsule contraceptives—are dependent upon laboratory research still in its early stages. Indirectly, the reduced rates of population growth that seem to be associated with increasing urbanization and industrialization can be partially attributed to advances in scientific and technological organization. Yet it is quite obvious that none of the authors of the preceding essays would argue that science and technology alone can resolve the current population crisis. Indeed, they would clearly reject such a contention.

Only slightly less evident is the importance attributed by these writers to symbolic mechanisms. Thus we find Berelson arguing that people's evaluations (perceptions) of consequences determine the significance of scientific, political, administrative, economic and moral criteria for population policy. Davis suggests that adequate policy must take into consideration social organizational factors that effect norms for family formation and family size. Even Bogue recognizes, at the grass roots level, the importance of attitudinal and cultural conditions favorable to family planning. Stated otherwise, there seems to be consensus that collectively held perceptions, norms, and ideologies exert a significant influence on reproductive behavior, and that effective population policy will have to deal with these factors.

The significance of regulatory mechanisms for population control is much more problematic. Certainly the formalization of any population policy reflects at least minimal effort at control, though it is quite apparent that the manner and degree of enforcement suggested has been highly variable. The increased concern of governments with population control is evident from the discussions presented by all three contributors to this chapter. Furthermore, both Davis and Berelson review proposals for population policy that emphasize not only political concern, but also direct intervention in the form of penalties, incentives, and legal regulation. With sufficient legitimation and means of enforcement, any organization can effectively enforce its policies; but the closer these regulations come to violating values regarding personal freedom, the less likely that members will voluntarily adhere to them. As is made quite clear by Berelson, the right to determine reproductive and sexual behavior is firmly rooted in the collective ideology of modern society. It follows that attempts to dictate population policy should be expected to encounter serious public resistance, and historical experience clearly supports this contention.

Finally, there appears to be agreement that population redistribution can do little to provide long-run solutions to the population crisis. No one seriously proposes that international migration offers an answer, and for most countries facing problems of excessive growth there are few frontier areas not already heavily populated. Even if there were, redistribution of population would offer only a temporary solution.

Thus it appears that only three mechanisms of ecological adaptation offer potentially viable solutions for the problem of population control: science and technology, ideology and culture, and social regulation. All three have been suggested and attempted at one point or another, and thus far none, either alone or in combination, have proved successful. Moreover, no solution seems to be forthcoming in the near future. This is not to say that the means for effectively controlling population growth are not currently available, for they are. The problem lies in their implementation. The question facing the architects of population policy is how to instill a collective recognition, among leaders and masses alike, of the perilous course inherent in recent demographic history. With such agreement may come the reality that, at least in this case, individual and collective interests are one. Only from a common orientation to the problem can effective collective action be initiated toward a viable solution to the dilemma of population control.

8

Environmental Quality:
Shaping the Habitat of Man

In the preceding chapter attention was focused on issues surrounding man's efforts to control the growth of human populations. With this final chapter we turn to the other side of the ecological coin, the environment. The three essays contained here represent a variety of views regarding the significant problems man faces in his efforts to exploit, manipulate, and control his habitat.

The first contribution, by Hans H. Landsberg, presents a broad inquiry into the question of present and future adequacy of natural resources for the United States.[1] Discussion is organized around the contrast between resource quantity and resource quality. With respect to the quantity issue the author is relatively optimistic. He suggests that the cumulative and joint impact of increased knowledge and improved technology is such that resource availability does not *appear* to be a crucial problem for the forseeable future. A brief consideration of a variety of resource commodities, including land, forests, fuel supplies, metals and water, indicates sufficient numbers to exclude any significant limitation to U. S. growth because of resources. Nevertheless, Landsberg cautions his readers against total acceptance of this picture. This is particularly important when one remembers that the U. S. is dependent upon imports for several resource supplies, and the world picture is far from clear.

More problematic is the question of resource quality.[2] Like all other components of human experience, natural resources are viewed by varying persons or groups under varying conditions as being good or bad, functional or dysfunctional, adequate or in need of change. Evaluations of resource quality frequently turn out to be evaluations of resource use, and often reflect the consequences of use for the vested interests of evaluators. Landsberg illustrates the paradox of this situation with a consideration of the effects of modern technology on resource quality. Conclusions reached regarding technological pollution of the environment seem to vary with situational demands, and frequently overlook the more beneficial results of technology. The heart of the issue, the author argues, is the extent to which a user's actions affect others. In other words, he is saying that environmental (or resource) quality should be evaluated in terms of consequences for collectivities, not individuals.

A major problem is encountered when one attempts to measure the balance of positive and negative effects where the collective welfare is in question. Landsberg suggests the concept of costs, to be measured in terms of the extent to which a producer's actions result in unpleasantness, nuisance, or other aggravation for his neighbor or environment. These side effects, however, are not readily observable, particularly when human values have been offended. Moreover, relative costs depend upon arbitrary divisions of the collectivity into self and other, we and they, though the larger the scope of consideration, the more likely public interest will be defended. These considerations notwithstanding, Landsberg opts for an economic approach to the question of costs. This approach, he argues, suggests a number of areas that call for better understanding. Essentially these involve a specification of dollar values associated with particular environmental conditions and their consequences for individual and collective life. In short: We must find ways of measuring society's demands for improving the quality of resources, the environment.

Though this essay raises and perhaps even clarifies several issues it unfortunately provides few solutions. The reader is impressed with the notion that for the present the major issues with respect to resources are qualitative rather than quantitative. For example, what constitutes optimal resource use? Who should have ultimate authority for decisions on these matters? How far should restrictive regulations be pushed? And, most importantly, what will be the human consequences of further delays in resolving these issues? These questions are yet to be resolved.

Though sometimes overlooked by critics of the ecological scene, man, far more than any other species, creates and modifies his own environment. The conditions and parameters of ecological adaptation are not completely set by the dictates of nature, even in societies with minimal technologies.[3] And as scientific and technological development progress, elements of nature become grist for the mill of civilization, and we find that the non-human backdrop of contemporary urban-industrial society is far removed from a pristine state of nature; unfortunately it is becoming readily apparent that, in his passion to transform and control nature, man is at the same time creating an environment that may one day prove to be his downfall.[4] The second contribution to this chapter, by F. S. L. Williamson, briefly examines some of the consequences of recent trends in population growth and technological control for the quality of the environment and its inhabitants.

Williamson takes the position that the combined effects of rapid population growth, increasing spatial concentration (urbanization), and undesirable side-effects of technology result in a socio-physical environment that appears to be detrimental to man's physical and psychological well-being. This condition he refers to as population pollution. In recent years a great deal of attention has been given to the impact of increasing environmental pollution on physical health.[5] Though he recognizes that severe physical manifestations can ultimately result from repeated exposure to small concentrations of environmental pollutants, Williamson is optimistic that modern technology can exercise some considerable control over environmental pollution, and that the current ecological crisis in the world makes it certain that some progress, perhaps a goodly amount, will be made.[6]

The second aspect of population pollution is reflected in social and psychological pathology associated with the increasing density of social interaction and living arrangements which accompanies urbanization.[7] Unlike the problem of environmental pollution, Williamson sees no evidence or potential for a trend that would mitigate this situation. Is urban man doomed to a future riddled with stress-producing social and physical arrangements? Perhaps not. On the one hand Williamson suggests that natural selection may operate to produce a new species of man capable of adapting to the exigencies of a densely populated and technologically complex environment. He goes so far as to suggest that we must realistically face up to the fact that our biological inheritance, in its currently recognizable form, is not going to persist. On the other hand, evidence regarding the relationship between population density and social pathology is not unequivocal.[8] We have only begun to investigate the modes and consequences of this aspect of population pollution.

It is perhaps appropriate that the final essay in this chapter is both wide-ranging in scope and critical in posture. Prepared by Lynton K. Caldwell, it is focused on identifying some of the more important factors accounting for the inability and/or unwillingness of industrial man to deal effectively with problems of environmental quality. While these comments are directed primarily at the U. S. situation, many are applicable to the more developed nations generally.

One of the characteristics most frequently associated with modernization—with the process of becoming more civilized—is the predominance of rational modes of thought in making decisions.[9] At the collective level one would expect this rationality to be formalized in terms of policy with respect to those matters most crucial to the public welfare. An examination of environmental policy in the United States, however, causes one to question the degree of rationality involved and, with Caldwell, to search for a plausible explanation.

Perhaps the basic tenet of Caldwell's argument is that, in order to improve the quality of man's environment, the quality of man himself must also be improved. The upgrading of man and his environment are aspects of a single great and complex process: advancement of the quality of civilization. One mode of evaluating the level of development of a civilization is in terms of its patterns of social organization, and a look at industrial society from this perspective is most instructive.

Caldwell argues, as have other contributors to this volume, that the driving force in industrial society is technology, but that the development of technology is always influenced and in many respects guided by political, economic and normative considerations. Stated otherwise, the effects of technology are mediated through social organization: the real power and limitation of technology lies in its combination with other things—with economic, industrial, or military activities. Technoscience enlarges choice but does not guide it.

An examination of the history of man-environment relationships in the

United States reveals an absence of environmental choices designed to maximize the public interest. Rather, those choices made reflect the preferences of private parties whose short-run goals serve, in the long-run, to destroy or impair environmental assets. How could this situation have come about? What is there about the structure of American society which makes it possible for a few "aggressive and purposive politicoeconomic advantage seekers" to threaten the ecological future of the entire nation? Why have we not been able to establish any culturally-based guidelines for environmental policy?

In Caldwell's view, the explanation for this situation may be located in our cultural heritage.[10] He identifies four common value orientations that legitimate private actions in spite of their potentially harmful consequences for the collectivity. These are: (1) our uncritical bias for growth, (2) a passive acceptance of technoeconomic determinism, (3) a belief that alternative environmental choices are relative, none more justifiable than others, and (4) a laissez-faire attitude toward the rights of individuals in relation to the environment. These values, individually and in combination, work against effective public control of the environment in that: (1) none imply or require self-restraint or control, (2) none suggest individual or collective accountability, (3) none concede the existence of criteria for evaluating the use of the environment that are independent of individual interest or preference, and (4) all suggest resistance to any general pattern of environmental development in society or to any meaningful standards of environmental quality, *per se.*

To combat this deplorable situation Caldwell urges a reformation in public education, with emphasis on developing within the collective conscience a set of attitudes toward the environment which will result in responsible environmental decisions.[11] But, as the author clearly recognizes, these changes will not come easily: The attack upon environmental abuses of our industrial society readily becomes an attack upon certain aspects of the structure of the society itself. The changes in social organization necessary to affect a redefinition of man-environment relationships will involve shifts in the structure of political power, economic exploitation, scientific-technological goals and moral norms. They will further necessitate a recognition that environmental quality affects the lives of all men, and therefore conditions the course of societal development. Caldwell succinctly summarizes the task facing industrial society when he writes: If man is to be the master of his own ingenuity, and not its victim, he will have to find better ways to relate means to ends, and to evaluate the ends that science makes available to him.

Notes and References

1. Evaluation of resource problems for the entire world is extremely difficult due to lack of adequate data. For a discussion of the problem and some tentative conclusions see Joseph L. Fisher and Neal Potter, "Natural Resources Adequacy for the United States and the World," in *The Population Dilemma,* 2nd. ed., ed. Philip M. Hauser. Englewood Cliffs, N. J.: Prentice-Hall, Inc., 1969, pp. 106-38.

2. For a comprehensive discussion of this issue under the broader scope of "environmental quality" see Lynton K. Caldwell, *Environment: A Challenge To Modern Society*. New York: The Natural History Press, 1970, pp. 27-87.

3. See, for example, Julian H. Steward, *Theory of Culture Change*. Urbana: University of Illinois Press, 1955, pp. 99-177 and Andrew P. Vayda, ed., *Environment and Cultural Behavior: Ecological Studies in Cultural Anthropology*. Garden City, N.Y.: The Natural History Press, 1969.

4. For a particularly polemic argument along these lines see Barry Weisberg, *Beyond Repair: The Ecology of Capitalism*. Boston: The Beacon Press, 1971.

5. For examples, see Edward S. Deevey, Jr., "General and Urban Ecology," in *The Urban Condition*, ed. Leonard J. Duhl. New York: Basic Books, Inc., 1963, pp. 20-32; Ian L. McHarg, "Man and Environment," in *Ibid*, pp. 44-58; Isabel M. Mountain, et al., "Health and the Urban Environment. VII. Air Pollution and Disease Symptoms in a 'Normal' Population," *Archives of Environmental Health*, Vol. 17 (September 1968), pp. 343-52; and Lester B. Lave and Eugene P. Seskin, "Air Pollution and Human Health," Science, Vol. 169, no. 3947 (August 21, 1970), pp. 723-33.

6. Other writers are less satisfied with current progress in the fight against pollution. One recent report begins "The battle against air and water pollution is going badly—where it is going at all." See A. Myrick Freeman III, *The Economics of Pollution Control and Environmental Quality*. New York: General Learning Press, 1971.

7. For recent discussion of this problem see John B. Calhoun "Population Density and Social Pathology," *Scientific American*, Vol. 32, no. 206 (1966), pp. 134-46; Nathan Keyfitz, "Population Density and the Style of Social Life," *BioScience*, Vol. 16 (December 1966), pp. 868-73; and Robert Edward Mitchell, "Some Social Implications of High Density Housing," *American Sociological Review*, Vol. 36 (February 1971), pp. 18-29.

8. See William H. Michelson, *Man and His Urban Environment: A Sociological Approach*. Reading, Mass.: Addison-Wesley Publishing Co., 1970, pp. 148-67.

9. For evidence supporting this contention see Alex Inkeles, "Making Men Modern: On the Causes and Consequences of Individual Change in Six Developing Countries," *American Journal of Sociology*, Vol. 75, No. 2 (September 1969), pp. 208-25.

10. For a complementary point-of-view, focusing on our Christian heritage, see Lynn White, Jr., "The Historic Roots of Our Ecologic Crisis," *Science*, Vol. 155, no. 3767 (March 10, 1967), pp. 1203-1207.

11. These ideas are amplified in Caldwell's "The Human Environment: A Growing Challenge to Higher Education," *Journal of Higher Education*, Vol. 37 (March 1966), pp. 149-55 and *Environment: A Challenge to Modern Society*, op. cit., pp. 149-58.

The U. S. Resource Outlook: Quantity and Quality
Hans H. Landsberg

It will soon be sixty years since Gifford Pinchot published *The Fight for Conservation*, as informative and succinct a guide to the Conservation Movement's views and judgments as one can hope to find. With regard to resource adequacy, it presents a generally somber picture, supported by careful projections based on the idea that the volume of economic resources in the United States is defined by their identified physical occurrence. The lesson that only careful husbanding can stretch the supply is the logical sequel. Governor Pinchot summarizes the findings of approaching resource exhaustion as follows:

> The five indispensably essential materials in our civilization are wood, water, coal, iron, and agricultural products. . . . We have timber for less than thirty years at the present rate of cutting. We have anthracite coal for but fifty years, and bituminous coal for less than 200. Our supplies of iron ore, mineral oil, and natural gas are being rapidly depleted, and many of the great fields are already exhausted.

Later in the book, Pinchot points to our "limited supply" of coal, a substance that he holds to be "in a sense the vital essence of our civilization."

> If it can be preserved, if the life of the mines can be extended, if by preventing waste there can be more coal left in this country after we of this generation have made every needed use of this source of power, then we shall have deserved well of our descendants.

On that last point there is unfortunately no direct way of judging how well we have, in fact, done. Not only is the evaluation of resources and reserves a very imprecise art at any point in time, but criteria and methods themselves undergo change. Thus, the nation's first estimate of coal resources, published by the U. S. Geological Survey in 1909, one year before Pinchot's book, reckoned that 3,200 billion tons had been in existence "when mining first began." This estimate held for four decades but was trimmed to 2,500 billion tons in 1950, and to 1,900 tons in 1953, not because of intervening consumption (not more than 40 billion tons or so, a minute fraction of the amount estimated to exist, has been mined in the entire history of the country), but because of more sophisticated and extensive methods of measurement.

Governor Pinchot would probably judge us kindly on the score of coal consumption, for the American of 1966 used about two and a half tons of coal per year where his forebear of 1910 consumed almost twice as much. The decline was not, however, motivated by thrift or avoidance of waste, as the Conservation Movement understood these terms. Rather, the prime reasons were vastly greater efficiency in burning, especially in steam-electric plants, and the emergence of other energy sources that have almost totally replaced coal in ships, railroads, and homes, and partially replaced it in factories and power plants.

Indeed, in the case of coal, we have come full circle. Today the U. S.

Department of the Interior is investing millions of dollars a year in research that is aimed not at conserving coal but at developing new uses. Two of them, liquefaction and gasification, could, if successful, increase future coal consumption spectacularly. But few considerations, we may be sure, prey less on the Department's mind than the fact, incontestable as it is, that the country's coal supplies constitute a finite resource and thus are subject to eventual exhaustion.

How We Have Made Do—The Big Picture

What has wrought this radical change in our view of things is, of course, the cumulative and joint impact of increased knowledge and improved technology—in short, the forces generally lumped under the broad heading "The Scientific Age."[1] Change induces change. Diminishing returns from exhaustion of resources with better characteristics are staved off not by lucky discoveries, as was once the case, but by advances that are both systematic and cumulative. Moreover, we have learned the advantages of "disaggregation"—that is, the separate utilization of the different inherent features of natural resources, as opposed to their joint use in the form in which they occur in nature. To illustrate the technique and realize its advantages from a conservation point of view, one need only think of the way in which the chemical industry, prominently including oil and gas processing, typically breaks down its raw-material stream.

We have thus enhanced our ability to upgrade old resources (for example, cropland through the addition of fertilizer), to discover new ones (oil, gas, nuclear fission, and so forth), to utilize them more efficiently (coal in power generation, low-grade copper ore, wood waste for pulp mills and building board, and the like), and to adjust to relative resource availabilities (aluminum replacing copper, or air-cooling replacing water-cooling). Consequently, the relative importance of the country's resources as inputs into the economic hopper has steadily diminished. A few gross examples will suffice to support this statement.

At the end of the Civil War, 6.5 million people were employed by the resource industries, which represent the sum total of the agriculture, forestry, and extractive industries (lack of suitable data prevents inclusion of water-associated activities). By 1910, this figure had climbed to 12 million, but it has now dropped to 5.5 million—one million less than it was ninety years ago. Resources now claim less than one tenth of all the labor in the country, instead of the half of a century ago, but this tenth produces five times as much as the half did.

Almost the same relationship is revealed when the output of resource industries is compared with the output of all goods and services. A quintupling in the resource field has been accompanied by a twenty-five-fold growth in the economy's total output. Not surprisingly, prices of resource commodities have, in general, not risen above prices for all goods and services.

A Quick Rundown in Some Detail

One might, therefore, say so far so good. Things have not worked out badly, at least not for the United States. Fossil fuel reserves have held up well, even though we have drawn on them at rates that were unimaginable not so long ago. Because rising yields allow us to grow what is needed on fewer acres, land in crops has been on the decline. And were it not for booming food exports, partly financed by ourselves, the problem of surplus farm land would loom much larger.

The most recent survey reveals that our forests are adding new growth at a substantially faster rate than that at which the annual cut is removing them. In 1962, when detailed estimates were last made, growth exceeded cut by 60 per cent. To be sure, behind this favorable aggregate comparison lurk problems of quality, species, location, marketing, and so on. For example, we still cut more sawtimber softwood—a highly desirable product—than we grow. Moreover, some of this apparent good fortune derives from improved measurement. This would mean that we were better off in the past than we had thought and that part of the apparent improvement is a mirage, but it would not negate the finding that current growth exceeds cut. The products of new technology—metals, plastics, and other synthetic substances—have reduced the demand for forest products; and in some lines, such as pulp and paper, we have been able to rely extensively on imports to supplement domestic production.

Perhaps nothing reflects so dramatically the changing tide of events as the conditions of timber resources. As Harold J. Barnett and Chandler Morse have pointed out, the Conservation Movement's "sense of impending scarcity derived directly from a concern for the future of America's forests, dating back at least to the 1870's."[2] As early as 1877, Carl Schurz, then Secretary of the Interior under President Hayes, forecast a coming "timber famine," with supplies to last only another twenty years. Today the concern for forests focuses on their role as part of the environment rather than as a source of materials.

In the field of nonfuel minerals, we are intermittently plagued by specific shortages—copper, sulfur, tin, and the like—but a stretch of high prices and concern has never as yet failed to engender successful efforts to locate new deposits, to exploit old ones more efficiently, and to promote substitution of more abundant, natural or man-made, materials, sometimes temporarily, sometimes permanently.

The Role of Technology

The current condition of ease regarding sufficiency of quantity is rooted largely in advancing technology, with its twin offspring: efficiency and substitutability. This trend has accelerated in the recent past. Only fifteen years ago, the authors of "Resources for Freedom" (the name under which President Truman's Materials Policy, or Paley, Commission released its finding in 1952) commented that "in the U. S. the supplies of the evident, the cheap, the accessible are running out."

The Commission would probably not phrase it that way today, for there are abundant examples of the nonevident becoming evident, the expensive cheap, and the inaccessible accessible. Broadening scope, increasing variety, and rising volume of man-made products exemplify the nonevident that is becoming evident. So do nuclear power generation and telecommunication by microwave and laser.

Hardness, low-metal content, fine-grained structure, and the non-magnetic nature of part of the deposits made the extensive iron-bearing ores of Minnesota, Michigan, and Wisconsin that are commonly lumped under the generic heading of taconites too costly to mine until after World War II. New processing technology has since made it not merely possible to extract usable material at acceptable costs, but has turned the initial handicap of having to agglomerate the fine particles into pellets into a major advantage, because the pellet feed greatly enhanced the productivity of the industry's furnaces. Similar evidence testifies to the changing circumstances of accessibility. Thus, the deposits of oil in offshore fields, buried under hundreds of feet of water and thousands of feet of ocean bottom, have become accessible. So have many and varied underground ore deposits that have yielded to the search by airborne magnetometer, sensing devices, chemical anomalies, and other new exploration tools.

But while the Commission, from the vantage point of 1967, appears to have underestimated the speed of population growth, of economic growth, and of industrially useful new knowledge and technology, its place in history is secure, for its decisive emphasis was not on the "running out of resources," which had been a popular concept in earlier years, but on resource availability at a cost, on the role of costs as a barometer of scarcity, and on future technology as a factor in determining costs and availability. Thus "running out" becomes a relative matter. Copper may "run out" for fabricator A, but not for fabricator B who, for one reason or another, is able to pay the higher price that reduced availability engenders. At the same time, the higher price is likely to bring closer the threshold at which deposits with poorer characteristics can be commercially exploited. The "running out" process is a dynamic one, subject to changes in direction, and thus is quite different from the straight-line, down-trending concept current early in the century.

Barnett and Morse have suggested that a major cause of this development is the flowering of the scientific advances.[3] In such an environment, there are no diminishing returns from improvements, for the improvement is in turn improved upon before its advantages have been dissipated or squeezed to a zero return. We have reached constant cost plateaus, at which increased amounts of resources are available without cost increases.

Others suggest that the curve of technological improvement will soon begin to flatten out and that we may already be moving along the upper leg of the sigmoid development curve. The bigger part of many technical revolutions, says John R. Platt, appears to lie behind us.[4] We have reached "science and technology plateaus." From horse-and-buggy to the current version of the jet plane is a bigger quantum jump than the impending advance to the SST. The invention of the telephone marked a bigger break with past communications methods than will the transition to satellites.

Perhaps this is so, although the odds in speculating on unknown technology are notoriously long. Nevertheless, no amount of speculation on the kind of plateau we may be approaching can relieve us of the need or impair the usefulness of taking a long look ahead for a test of how well, under carefully spelled-out, realistic assumptions, our resource situation is likely to hold up. Such a look involves a wide array of guesses, the worth of which will depend as much on the effort that goes into making them as on the investigator's success in recognizing and overcoming his biases.

A Look Ahead

Resources for the Future has engaged in making and publishing such informed guesses or projections.[5] I can, therefore, be brief and summarize the picture that emerges for the balance of this century. It is not one to provoke undue concern, at least not on the score of quantity and for this country.

Farm Land

Rising crop yields—based both on further advances in agronomy and on a large-scale catching-up of the bulk of the growers with the best—can confidently be expected to keep land from becoming a limiting factor to food production. A few years ago, contemplation of past history led Resources for the Future to project 1970 corn yields at 70 bushels per acre. Because yields ranged between 53 and 55 bushels per acre in the three years preceding 1961, the year in which we had to make our projections, we thought our prediction a little daring; some scholars who were asked to review what was then a manuscript throught we were very daring. But by 1965 the yield had climbed to 74 bushels and had outrun the projection. The average yield in Iowa had jumped above 80 and in Indiana and Illinois above 90 bushels per acre. Our projected yield of 100 bushels in the year 2000, a faraway guess when made, had begun to move into clearer view. This projection and those for other feed grains stand a good chance of being overtaken before the end of the century. Little can as yet be said about other major crops.

Forests

It is difficult to speak with assurance regarding the long-run adequacy of U.S. forests to supply the domestic market. A few years ago, Resources for the Future had grave doubts that even allowing for a generous drawing on imports, prospective demand could long be satisfied by domestic supply without impairing the size and quality of our forests. These doubts have diminished. Demand continues to lag. Wood prices seem high in comparison with non-wood alternatives, especially when the latter offer advantages in handling and maintenance. Also, there has been a less than buoyant housing market. Moreover, the existing volume of trees now appears larger than was believed a few years ago. The most recent figures (1962) compiled by the U.S. Forest Service show a significantly higher timber inventory than does their previous estimate (1953). For the time being, emphasis has shifted from forest products in the aggregate to adequacy and quality of given species.

Outdoor Recreation

Considerable uncertainty attaches to those uses of land that do not lead to production of commodities. This is true especially for outdoor recreation. Even cautious projections of the use trend of parks and other recreation land translate into very large acreage figures.

On what some might consider quite conservative assumptions regarding both the rate of increase in visits and tolerable density of recreation acreage, Resources for the Future estimated that by 1980 there might be need for 76 million acres for outdoor recreation; and by the year 2000 this need should call for an additional 58 million acres. For comparison, in 1960 there were only 44 million acres of land in national parks, monuments, recreation areas, state parks, and in national forests used primarily for recreation.

In terms of new policies and of magnitude of outlays required, such figures put a wholly new face on a hitherto secondary aspect of land use. On the other hand, until we know more about such factors as the carrying capacity of outdoor acreage for recreation and the potential of private land for such purposes, we must handle these statistics with some sense of detachment. Unfortunately, it will take some time for research to catch up with the speed at which use of this new resource has been growing.

Other Uses of Land

A common complaint of the sixties is the "asphalting over" of America's land. Houses, offices, factories, highways, airports, parking lots, and the like have such high visibility to so many people that their presence and growth tends to distort perspective. It is the view during the occasional airplane ride that restores it.

In cold figures, the 25 million acres or so occupied by the urban population at this time is less than 1.5 per cent of the country's surface. Highways, railroads, and airports take up perhaps 27 million acres, for a grand total of built-up terrain of, say, 50 million acres, not quite 3 per cent of the face of America. By the end of the century, this might grow by 50 per cent, to 75 million acres, due overwhelmingly to expansion of urban land use.

I do not mean to suggest that problems of land use—especially in urban areas—are meaningfully measured in terms of acres. If they were, the task of finding the additional 25 million acres of land that we may need for urban living between now and the end of the century could be entrusted to a child equipped with nothing more than a map and a ruler. Nor does dealing in aggregates, unqualified by reference to land characteristics, do justice to the issue. Pointing to European population densities that typically run five to ten and, in some cases, fifteen times the U.S. density merely shows that other countries have problems too.

On the other hand, nearly 500 million acres are devoted to commercial raising of trees, and about 700 million acres are primarily grazing land (there is room for arguing over proper land classification here, but these rough figures will do for the purpose). Thus, 75 million acres for urban centers and transportation facilities pose less a problem of "space shortage" due to "asphalting over" than of inventiveness in efficient use of the country's surface.

The Demand for Energy

The demand for energy is likely to be three times as high in the year 2000 as it is now, but the entry of new or newly derived energy resources (from nuclear reactors to oil and gas from coal, shale oil, oil sands, and so forth), combined with more efficient utilization and conversion of conventional energy sources, is likely to ward off rising costs. Indeed, we may well be entering an era of slowly declining energy costs. There is unprecedented activity in developing new coal technology to widen the scope of our largest fossil fuel resource; research and development leading to a breeder reactor, which may begin to bear fruit by the mid-seventies, will multiply many times over the country's uranium resources as a basis for power generation.

Metals

Enough deposits of the major metals, supplemented by imports and rising amounts of scrap; have been identified that emergence of sustained supply problems due to inadequate resources seems unlikely given our demonstrated ability to handle ever lower-grade material. This does not, however, insure against shortfalls in times of national emergency—to be provided for through special measures, such as stockpiles. Nor does it offset temporary and, perhaps, even prolonged difficulties like those that have in recent years plagued copper, which is mined in major quantities in countries that are subject to political upheavals or uncertainties. Supply cannot always keep up with quickly rising demand, but it has a habit of catching up, sometimes to a greater extent than is required.

Ability to process low-grade material carries one great advantage: Such material usually exists in very large volume. For example, the previously mentioned taconite ores, most of which are likely to become subject to commercial exploitation during the balance of the century, equal four times the cumulative demand for iron projected through the end of the century. Perhaps a turn to unconventional sources, such as the ocean floor, will help the situation for others, as will substitutions by nonmetallic materials. Thus, despite projected levels of consumption that between now and the year 2000 could cumulate to the equivalent of 60 to 70 times the 1960 consumption for iron, copper, lead, and zinc, 90 to 100 times that for nickel, chromium, and tungsten, and 125 times that for aluminum, it is difficult to envision serious supply problems because of resource limitations.

Water

Judgments about water are often confusing because of fuzzy concepts and poor terminology and complicated because of the attention that must be given to problems of quality. It helps to realize initially that in many of its uses water is either a free or nearly free good and that incentives for economizing are the exception rather than the rule. Thus, projections of future consumption are based more on what people have been led to take for granted as "needed" than on what they would be willing to buy at prices that more nearly reflect cost.

Another aid to understanding is a clear distinction between *withdrawal* of water with subsequent discharge back into the original source and withdrawal followed by consumption, or *depletion*. All uses have elements of both, but the proportions vary greatly. In municipal use, for example, most water—about 90 per cent—is discharged after it has served its function, while irrigation depletes from 60 to 90 per cent, depending upon the circumstances. Since water can be used over and over again, the item to keep one's eye on is, for most purposes, depletion—not withdrawal. Unfortunately, most popular discussion is conducted in terms of water "use," without further definition of the term.

The need for sharpness of definition applies equally to the supply side.

The total supply of surface water—precipitation—is a multiple of what becomes accessible in the form of runoff. The latter is, in turn, normally a multiple of withdrawal, and withdrawal typically exceeds depletion. (Instances where the entire flow is diverted without any return to the source are the exceptions.) Moreover, ground water, as distinguished from annual replenishment, constitutes a separate supply. Finally, there is a variety of techniques for adding to available supply. Some, such as storage, predate the era of recorded history; others, such as desalinization, weather modification, and evaporation control, are undergoing active development. They are paralleled on the demand side by techniques for reducing consumption. Substituting air-cooling for water-cooling, less wasteful irrigation techniques, and a more efficient use generally (for example, having a smaller flow or depletion per unit of service required) belong in this category. As our political and administrative approaches to water management, as well as our costing and pricing mechanisms, receive attention and review, channeling water into the highest-yielding alternatives will assume increasing importance.

Differences in natural endowment and climate have combined with a different mix of use categories to produce a sharp cleavage in situation and outlook between the eastern and western United States, using these geographic terms in the loosest of meanings. Because of the large role played by irrigation, the West (excluding the Pacific Northwest) depletes nearly five times the volume of water depleted in the East. Since it only disposes of about 20 per cent of the runoff available to the East (which is, of course, the reason why the West needs irrigation if it wants to have agriculture), the West depletes about 40 per cent of the water it can count on.

Before long, the West may find water supply a serious obstacle to economic growth if flows are not diverted to uses other than irrigation, prices are not brought into line with costs, and techniques for adding new supplies do not soon become commercially feasible for meeting the needs of cities and industries at prices they can afford.

In sharp contrast, and for the opposite reasons, the East depletes less than 2 per cent of its runoff and faces no long-range physical shortage, provided rainfall deficiencies during the past few years do not represent the beginning of a basic long-term change in climatic conditions. Meteorologists are divided on this issue, and conclusive evidence one way or the other will not be forthcoming for some time. Meanwhile, whatever the ultimate trend, the East faces decisions associated with pricing and allocating water and with encouraging economizing by means other than admonitions and exhortations (though in the face of uncertainty the "muddling-through" approach has the merit of preserving options).

Above all, however, the eastern United States is confronted with growing deterioration of water quality. This increasingly narrows the usefulness of many streams and lakes for purposes that demand clean water. It imposes costs on users that draw their supplies from stretches polluted by others. Moreover, it raises in full not only a host of new technical problems but economic, political, and administrative questions about equitable and efficient remedies to the situation. For those who try to appraise the degree of adequacy of the nation's resources, it opens up a new dimension—the quality of resources.

The size and characteristics of domestic resources, in combination with imports, are such as to exclude any significant limitation to U.S. growth because of resources. This picture would no doubt look different if one were to widen the geographic scope and consider the world, or a major portion of it. The number of critical resource areas would increase, and the time horizon for which one would have a reasonable assurance of adequacy would shrink. Specifically, it is unlikely that these conditions will affect the terms on which the United States obtains its imports sufficiently to alter significantly the general perspective outlined above. Except in the case of food, however, only the most general quantitative appraisals have been made of the resources that the developing countries are likely to need for the decades ahead.[7] Analogies of trends and patterns of material use that have prevailed in Western industrialized nations and extrapolations of short trends in the developing countries can both be misleading. Exploration of future development patterns in terms of claims on specific resources is badly needed, however, if we are to gain a realistic picture of what faces this country in its role as a member of the world community.

Quality of Resources: How Good?

It would be convenient to deal with the quality problem in much the same fashion as with quantitative adequacy. We would, in other words, assess the degree of past acceptability for each of the resources, project the demand into the future, and judge whether the supply will be forthcoming, or whether, where, and when "quality shortages" will develop.

Unfortunately, we can barely begin to measure the state of adequacy at the present. How good or bad the past has been we can deduce, at best, from the presence or absence of comments and protests. Moreover, we are as yet woefully short of methods that can help us pick our way between those who see the population tobogganing toward physical and emotional decay and those who regard the current concern over quality decline as but another phase of modern life with which common sense and technology will in time come to grips.

Technology—Two Sides of the Coin

Technology, it seems has played a cruel hoax on us: It has assured enough, but in the process it has led to degraded quality. Excessive use of the waste-assimilative characteristics of water and air by cities, factories, coal mines, oil wells, chemical-bearing agricultural land, and many other concomitants of life in the industrial age has created a complex technological and economic problem: to devise ways and means other than natural stream and air flow for disposing of waste material, and to determine and apportion the costs and benefits that arise in the process. Undesirable by-products have made their mark on both the rural and the urban landscape. The settings are different but the adverse consequences and the problems of measurement, evaluation, and policy are similar.

Deploring technology's side effects—which range from unpleasant to highly dangerous—is not tantamount to decrying technology as such. In one of his recorded songs, Tom Lehrer, Cambridge's gift to social satire, finds it a sobering thought that at his age Mozart has been dead for two years. Similarly I find it a sobering thought that I would have been less likely to accept the invitation to contribute to this symposium at the turn of the century, for a man in his fifties would at that time have outrun his mean chance of survival. Life expectancy at birth in the United States has since moved from less than fifty to seventy years.

One is apt to view the more disagreeable aspects of modern life, including most prominently those due to the impact of technology, with partiality—often unconsciously. We take for granted that we may drink tap water, eat uncooked fruit or vegetables, and consume milk with no thought of falling victim to a lurking bug. We are reminded of our good fortune only when we travel in parts of the world that require preventive or remedial countermeasures, or when the exceptional case in this country hits the front page. But, customarily, we fail to do much balancing of pluses and minuses. We tend to overlook the fact that the chemical industry produces not only controversial pesticides, but also antibiotics and vaccines; that the automobile whose incomplete fuel combustion fouls the city air does, at the same time, enable us to escape its boundaries and to know the world in a way available a generation or two ago only to the daring or the rich. We are quick to lament the fallen sparrow, but slow to celebrate the fall of "Typhoid Mary."

This is not the same as inviting, or welcoming, or even being indifferent to the negative aspects and abuses that can be or are associated with technological advance. To reconstruct what is in terms of what could have been is generally a misleading venture, for people commonly engage in such reconstruction for the purpose of excising the obnoxious features while leaving untouched those they sanction. They forget or ignore that both are usually part of one and the same fabric. To show that we could have had one without the other requires more than saying so.

Nor can it be taken for granted that accurate and timely anticipation of the adverse consequences of a particular action necessarily produces decisions to prevent them. For example, the failure of cigarette-smoking to decline or of repeated disasters to discourage occupancy of flood plains raises doubts about the level of individual response. Failure to have acted long ago on such matters as provision of adequate, common-carrier urban transport or non-polluting incinerators suggests that we act no more wisely in matters of collective response.

Beyond the need of adequate motivation and appropriate institutions, there is the great difficulty of balancing the gains and the losses. Let us look more closely at the cigarette-smoker, and let us assume that he is well informed about the effects. Presumably the smoker has achieved a balance of gains and losses: The gain from inhalation more than offsets the pain from possible illness and shorter lifetime. Arriving at the balance is likely to involve several elements—among them, the weighing of pleasure *now* against pain *later*, with the distant event, as is customary in such situations, heavily discounted; the reluctance and remoteness of applying to oneself a cause-and-effect relationship that is only statistically demonstrated, a reason for additional discounting; the calculating of odds; allowance for personal habits and characteristics; appeasement through change to presumably less harmful brands. Clearly some such calculus underlies the decision to smoke and how much to smoke.

One might go on to speculate that those smokers who have digested the new knowledge have adjusted to it by setting their daily intake at a level at which they judge reduction would gain them less in future health than they would forego in current pleasure; a level, conversely, at which the improvement in current well-being derived from the extra cigarette, the marginal revenue, is not worth the incremental health hazard, the marginal cost. At that point, the smoker is in equilibrium. This point comes at different levels of smoking for different people, and the motivation—the type of gain extracted—differs widely among smokers. Thus, rationality of decision is not the issue. Rather, what is open to discussion and represents a proper area for education are the value scales on which pleasure from smoking and pain from ill health are traded off.

A serious economic problem arises not when an individual's actions affect adversely only himself (though costs of medical attention will in varying degrees not be defrayed by the individual, and there is, therefore, a public interest), but when those actions affect, primarily and often exclusively, other people. This is the heart of the quality aspect of resources.

Quality Versus Grade Differential
One could argue that to distinguish quality from quantity is merely a semantic nicety; that supply must always be understood as supply corre-

sponding to appropriate specifications; and that if there is not "enough" by whatever the qualitative yardstick, then we have a quantitative shortage, whether it be water, air, iron ore, copper, or softwood sawtimber.

To some extent this is true. For example, within a large excess of aggregate forest growth over aggregate cut, there is too much poor hardwood from small trees and too little good softwood from large ones. Why do we not customarily speak of this as a separate dimension in judging resource adequacy? In part, we do not because there is a market on which poor hardwoods are traded and have, in different uses, found acceptatnce as satisfactory substitutes for good softwoods. Taconite ores are undoubtedly poorer bearers of iron than the traditional ores, but poor quality did not prevent their acceptance as soon as they could be processed at a cost low enough to make their use lucrative in blast furnaces. Copper mines today go after ores that hold only five pounds of metal per thousand. In the end, there is nothing that distinguishes the copper ingot derived from poor ore from that derived from rich ore; all that matters is that their costs be in a range that finds them a market. These grade differentials are handled satisfactorily by the market that reduces the offerings to quantities of some commonly agreed upon standard or equivalent. Provided we have an appropriate processing technique, six tons of .5 per cent copper ore are neither better nor worse than one ton of 3 per cent copper ore.

But one hundred cubic feet of slightly polluted water or air cannot presently substitute for fifty or ten of clean water or air—at least not for most purposes. Given a choice, one could not be indifferent, as in the case of copper. But above all, the choice is not one the consumer, can effectively make, except in the most roundabout way.

Examples of these kinds of quality problems are abundant. There is the discharge of municipal, industrial, and agricultural waste into watercourses, of pollutants into the air; there is disfiguration of the landscape through mining activities, transmission lines, or other symbols of the industrial revolution; there is ugliness along highways, be it beer bottles or billboards, interference with plant life and wildlife through the use of pesticides, disturbance of the atmosphere through vibration caused by fast-flying planes and of the sound waves through indiscriminate use of portable radios.

A new wrinkle in the quantity-quality relationship, best exemplified in the energy field, should be mentioned here. The traditional conservation doctrine maintains that use of natural gas as boiler fuel signifies an "inferior" use of an exhaustible resource. In the past, both the Federal Power Commission and the courts have upheld this viewpoint. As late as 1961, the Supreme Court confirmed the Commission's authority to make end use a factor in deciding upon certification for service (in a case involving shipment of gas from Texas to New York for use as boiler fuel). "One apparent method of preventing waste of gas," said the six-man majority, "is to limit the uses to which it may be put, uses for which another, more abundant fuel may serve equally well."

This was before air pollution became a pressing problem and made natural gas the preferred boiler fuel, given its low pollution quotient. The Federal Power Commission has not yet made this feature a basis for granting electric-utility applications for increased gas deliveries. It does not deny that gas is a less polluting fuel; the "inferior use" argument would sit badly with urban communities today. It does, however, contend that steam-electric plants are not the major villains in the situation and that additional gas would be, at best, a temporary palliative—at worst, a block to more radical remedial action. In any event, appraisal of adequacy can obviously be heavily affected by such changes in judgment.

Economic Characteristics of Side Effects

The "side effect" syndrome has a number of characteristics, all of which distinguish it from simple grade differentiations and make it a highly controversial object of economic analysis and public policy.

Certain effects arise apart from and beyond the primary purpose. Not confined to the user, these affect others. Gains are reaped and costs are incurred, but there is no market that relates the two. Most importantly, the costs that arise are borne not by those that cause them but by others that happen to be around but are outside the process—bystanders, so to speak. Not all the costs of the process end up as costs to the producer; a slice is lodged outside. With inventiveness, but at the peril of losing their nontechnical audience, economists refer to these as "external diseconomies" or "externalities"; less elegantly, one might think of them as "someone else's headache."

Unless these headaches are brought home to the originator in such a way that they are included as costs in his profit-and-loss calculations—or "internalized"—private costs will understate total, or social, costs. Consequently, production decisions will lead to misallocation of resources, for the producer will be faced with production costs that are lower than they would be if he had also to foot the bill for the external diseconomies—the unpleasantness, nuisance, or other aggravation caused to his neighbor or environment.

The cause-effect nexus of such phenomena is often difficult to establish. Sometimes this may be due to the low intensity of the degrading substances or activities or to the low degree of quality deterioration that takes place. At other times, damage may be long delayed in appearing, or it may turn up in areas remote from the locus of emission. Finally, effects seldom occur with laboratory-like purity and in isolation, but are intermingled with a variety of other factors. Thus, presumption is more common than proof. And when the causal relationship can be satisfactorily established, it is often difficult to identify the offender, or when he can be identified, to assess his share in the total effect.

Typically, there is a widely dispersed multiplicity of the offended. In marked contrast to traditional "nuisance" cases that are actionable in the courts, this raises questions of both efficiency and equity in remedial action, if not of the feasibility of starting any action at all.

Changes in the environment are not easily, and often not at all, susceptible to meaningful evaluation in dollars and cents. This impedes comparison with costs incurred or avoided by the producer of the side effect in question, which as a rule lends itself to expression in monetary terms.

There is no answer to "what price beauty?" that would furnish a zoning authority a ready method of weighing the claims of, say, a stone quarry, a wildlife refuge, and a resort hotel where they are competing for the same tract of land. Psychic values are not traded in the market, at least not directly and not obviously. One is, therefore, limited to seeking surrogates and proxies that reflect such values. (For example, movements into and out of specific areas may be prompted by changes in environmental conditions and may be reflected in real-estate quotations.) This search has only just begun. Moreover, there are, as yet, few institutional and administrative arrangements that offer a mechanism for bringing together the offended and the offender, even when both can, in principle, be identified.

For the sake of efficient management, it is frequently desirable that measures dealing with questions of environmental quality be considered for large areas at a time. This is almost a necessity where air and water are concerned. Action then tends to become collective and regional, rather than individual and local. The rationale is that the smaller the community considered, the more the costs will be of the "external" kind. As the area widens, they become internal and, therefore, part of the proper economic calculus. If the decision-making unit is my home, then the costs of my dumping trash in my neighbor's backyard are "external" as far as I am concerned. If the unit is my street, then the costs are "internal."

Thus, one way of catching up with side effects is to extend the area within which they cannot be "external." Decisions made on the basis of rather large areas—the community, the river basin—are likely to produce a result closer to the optimum than the sum total of many individual decisions. One consequence of this spatial relationship, incidentally, is that for reasons of both efficiency and equity the role of the Federal Government as well as that of interstate and regional compacts, commissions, and similar multi-state bodies will inescapably grow larger.

While it may sound as though stressing the size of the decision-making unit as an important element in quality management is a highly academic point, it is actually a very practical one. A good topical illustration is the use of pesticides in crop production. One's balancing of the gains and losses incurred from use of pesticides would differ according to whether one focuses on the individual farmer and his immediate surroundings, the county, the state, a region, the country, or an even larger supranational area. It is one thing to weigh damage to the environment against gains in crop production in a given locality, but quite another to do so in a national or supernational framework. It could be argued that the United States might not now be able to ship one fourth of its wheat crop to India had it not been for the prolonged application of various chemicals to soil and vegetation. Such chemicals not only raise productivity in their own right but permit many other changes in farm practices and organization that jointly form a tight, almost ecological system. Evaluation of gains and losses from use of pesticides, thus, can be seen to depend greatly on the size of the decision-making unit—on where one draws the line.

The Case for Quantification

The above categorizing makes no claim to either comprehensiveness or uniqueness. But it does serve to bring out the principal difficulties that beset improvement of resource quality: identification of gainers and losers, ascertainment and valuation of gains and losses in the absence of a market, and lack of channels and institutions for arbitration of rival claims. If economists have not yet found many answers, they have begun to bring to this relatively new field of concern the integrating element of a common denominator—cost. Its applicability can be exaggerated, but its neglect surely leaves the field open to pressure and emotion. At the very least, even a rough casting of gains and losses into dollars and cents will convey a sense of magnitude that would otherwise be lacking. There is nothing dehumanizing in the process of monetary quantification.[8] Where efforts must be expanded to achieve a given objective, they are not available for alternative uses, and it is only fair that we establish at least the magnitude of what we must forego, so we can gain some idea of whether the environmental change contemplated is worth the price tag. This approach suggests a number of areas that call for better understanding. To a degree, they are corollaries of the characteristics discussed above.

We must learn more about the physical characteristics of the desirable objectives, of the undesirable side effects, and of the relationship of the one to the other. In such studies, attention should be directed not to the spectacular, which is usually accidental and ephemeral, but to the pedestrian, which is usually basic and lasting. From the study of physical aspects, we must move to the dollar values associated with them. Above all, we must ascertain and analyze cost relationships. We know, for example, that it is extraordinarily expensive to remove the final traces of pollution. In water treatment, costs double and triple as we approach a state of pristine purity. In removing successive amounts of coal dust from power-plant smokestacks, the capacity of precipitators must increase proportionately with the added removal efficiency, measured in terms of the remaining dust. Thus, if removal efficiency is to be raised from 96 to, say, 98 per cent, the increase is not 2, but 50 per cent, and consequently represents a steep rise in equipment size and cost. We must, therefore, ask how we determine the point of equilibrium, beyond which additional purity costs more than is gained in terms of health or aesthetics? Where does one reasonably stop? The more we can learn about cost behavior under different conditions, the easier it will become to establish criteria around which compromises can be built, even in the face of the difficulties that beset ascertainment of corresponding benefits.

Indignation over the manifestations of pollution comes easily; remedies do not. It has been estimated, for example, that it would cost some $20 billion annually to return all watercourses to an unspoiled state. This is about what the country spends each year on primary and secondary education. Will such knowledge affect specific decisions? It might, for decisions will tend to be more in accord with explicit value scales, openly arrived at. And these will frequently differ from what is merely presumed.

Measuring Society's Demands
We must find ways of measuring society's demands for improving the quality of resources, the environment. The bafflingly unmeasurable must be made measurable. There are small beginnings today and much groping for answers, for it is clear that in the absence of acceptable measurements the debate will continue to produce more heat than light. Moreover, since funds will be appropriated and spent without greater guidance from any demand gauge, responsibility will remain above all with the resource manager, who must construe a demand schedule out of his own scale of preferences, what he believes are other people's preferences, and what he thinks ought to be other people's preferences. He will get some help from the political process, but that process is clumsy, especially when it comes to detail. Customarily, it permits choices only between approval and rejection between yes and no; rarely between more and less, or among a whole spectrum of alternatives. As a consequence, decisions tend to be reached with little factual knowledge of the values that society as a whole puts on the results of the contemplated action.

Nor does the matter end here. Even though the individual consumer's choice is limited to the range of goods and services that are offered in the market, there *is* choice, both in quantity and in kind. This is not so in most decisions that are arrived at politically. As little as I can have a Federal Government that is part Democratic and part Republican, can I have a river that is both wild and provides storage for water supply and power. Thus, there is a problem of meeting the wants and needs of minorities whose desires are swamped in political decisions.

Finally, we must recognize that the decision-maker can err. Let us assume, for the sake of argument, that cigarette-smoking were considered a form of pollution and its practice made subject to public regulation. In the light of the last few years' experience, there can be little doubt that any restrictions put on smoking would not be in accord with the aggregate of private valuations rationally arrived at—not only, as J. W. Milliman has suggested,[9] because the political process is no freer from imperfection than the market mechanism, but because there is a real conflict between a theoretical cost-benefit calculus, made in all good faith, and one derived from the summation of an individual's preferences. Only by cranking in society's interest in a healthier population as a plus could one hope to redress the balance toward a net gain from restrictive regulation.

All of this demonstrates the need for greatly increased research efforts directed toward methods of ascertaining where in the hierarchy of rival claims people rank quality improvement and similar intangibles. Even without accurate measurements, however, we are not quite lost. Establishing a range of arbitrary quality standards and estimating the costs their imposition would imply is one way out. To initially recommend itself, the cost of an action would have to be at least commensurate with the value of the improvement that is sought or the deterioration that is to be prevented. With the aid of such calculations of alternatives, we can begin to make intelligent choices among policy decisions—intelligent, but not necessarily easy. The cost tag is an indispensable aid: "No intangible has infinite value. All intangibles have cost."[10] Nevertheless, it is not the only nor perhaps always the determining criterion for decision. Still, the magnitude of what one has to forego, which is what cost is all about, is always relevant and usually lurks somewhere in the decision-maker's mind. Instead, it should be explicitly and prominently on the decision-maker's agenda.

Calculation of both gains and losses greatly facilitates dealing with quality changes. Whether it is more efficient to allow degradation to stand, or to reduce or suppress it, the course followed should leave nobody worse off and somebody better off than before. Without cost tags, this is hard to judge.

If the effluent from a paper mill muddies the water for the downstream resident, and the cost of removing the cause exceeds the cost of reducing such disturbance by treatment at the intake, it would clearly be efficient to let the offending effluent continue and to treat the water prior to its further use. In that event, the "winner," the paper mill, could compensate the "loser," the municipality, out of the savings that would accrue from not having to treat the effluent. Thus, both efficiency and equity would be served. The added cost (added, that is, in comparison to the previous condition of pollution without compensation) would most likely be reflected in higher costs of paper, at least initially, which only proves that you do not get something for nothing.

As has been pointed out, most situations of this kind are very complex, involving a multitude of participants, actions, and reactions. But it is easy to see the need for finding ways in which the external cost—in the simplified case above, the nuisance to the city residents—can be gauged and added to the private, or internal, cost, with the result that the polluter's cost will fully reflect the social cost of his activity.

Modifications to Establish Costs

Existing institutions and mechanisms need to be modified or new ones invented to facilitate making the cost of side effects a cost to the originator—that is, "internalizing" them. Imposition of taxes, charges, or other financial burdens on the producer is one way. These might be rigid or flexible so that the punishment could fit the crime. Their rationale lies in the consideration that the use of a congested facility, be this a watercourse, the air, a highway, or a park, should be reduced by putting a price on it.

At times, particularly when it is impractical or too costly to bar free access to the resource, a charge can be levied not on the activity itself but on the agent that causes the adverse effect (a pesticide, a detergent, a fuel), in the expectation that this will promote more sparing use of the offending substance and thus lead to a reduction of the noxious side effects. Also, raising the cost may stimulate the development of new technology, and the charges collected can be tapped for remedying the effects of the activity in question. In other situations, collective, administrative action may be more efficient. Unlike taxes, standard-setting regulations will not, however, produce revenue; also, flexibility will be less easily achieved, and policing and enforcement will present major administrative burdens, if not problems.

Technical considerations may, however, suggest collective action of a different sort—not through regulation—but through doing on a large centralized scale what is harder and more expensive to accomplish through the aggregation of a multitude of individual actions. To illustrate, a dollar's worth of aeration of dirty water performed by a public body according to a carefully laid plan is likely to beat a dollar's worth of waste-discharge treatment undertaken separately by a score of users.

When we can compare meaningfully the costs to society—which are, as we have tried to show, the producer's private costs plus costs to others that are not part of his calculus—with the many-sided benefits that are the counterpart of those costs, we shall have taken a long stride toward evolving a workable policy of preserving the quality of the environment without sacrificing the beneficial effects of advancing technology. Only then will we be able to appraise the present and future adequacy of quality of the resources as we have appraised that of quantity. If this means having the best of two worlds, then the time may be at hand to cease calling economics the dismal science. Until then, the economist will have to insist that the frontiers of cost and benefit measurement be vigorously extended—not necessarily to dictate action but to allow it to be shaped in the presence of the newly gained knowledge.[11]

Notes and References

1. See Harold J. Barnett and Chandler Morse, *Scarcity and Growth: The Economics of Natural Resource Availability* Baltimore, 1963.

2. *Ibid*, p. 80.

3. *Ibid,,* p. 235 ff.

4. John R. Platt, *The Step to Man*, New York, 1966, pp. 185-203.

5. Hans H. Landsberg, Leonard L. Fischman, and Joseph L. Fisher, *Resources in America's Future*, Baltimore, 1963; and Hans H. Landsberg, *Natural Resources for U.S. Growth*, Baltimore, 1964.

6. A cautionary view of prospects for rising yields in developed countries was advanced by Lester R. Brown at the December, 1966, meeting of the American Association for the Advancement of Science. (See *Journal of Commerce*, January 3, 1967; no published version as yet available.)

7. For a recent attempt, see, for instance, Joseph L. Fisher and Neal Potter, *World Prospects for Natural Resources*, Baltimore, 1964.

8. Mason Gaffney, "Applying Economic Controls," *Bulletin of the Atomic Scientists*, May, 1965, pp. 20-25.

9. J. W. Milliman, "Can People Be Trusted with Natural Resources?," *Land Economics*, August 1962, pp. 199-218.

10. *Ibid.*

11. Appreciation is expressed to the Cooper Foundation Committee, Swarthmore College, for permission to utilize material first developed in connection with a talk on conservation presented to a symposium in February, 1966.

Population Pollution
Francis S. L. Williamson

I do not believe that we would still discuss this problem if we did not look hopefully ahead to the technological achievements that may curb—or at least bring to within "tolerable" limits—the tragic, massive, and still-expanding pollution of the air, soil, and water of the earth. This optimism stems from the long overdue consideration of this problem and the implementation of programs dealing with many of its aspects. Environmental pollution, however, is not a priori inexorably linked to human population growth (Daddario, 1968); and we must assume that although numbers of people will increase, the technology now available can and will provide some of the solutions necessary for our health and survival. Additionally, many of us have similar hopes for our less fortunate cohabitants of the earth—those lacking a technology or a freedom of choice. These solutions include the provision in adequate amounts of clean air to breathe, clean water to drink, and clean food to eat. Even if we make the assumption that, as human population growth continues, strict curbs can be simultaneously placed on environmental abuses, we are still confronted with the unresolved problem of population pollution. This I define as the consequences, mental and physical, of life in a world vastly more populous and technologically more complex than the one in which we currently find ourselves. In such a world the goals of healthy and happy human beings, free from malnutrition, poverty, disease, and war, seem to me convincingly elusive. The expression of man's full range of genetic potential is perhaps impossible.

Human Population Growth

I believe there is general agreement among *knowledgeable* men that current trends in the growth of human populations are not only unacceptable but will result in disaster. The current rate of growth, 2% per year (McElroy, 1969), will result in 150 billion people in 200 years. In terms of the time necessary to double the world's population, it represents only about 35 years. As Ehrlich (1968) points out, this "doubling time" has been reduced successively from one million years to 1000, to 200, to 80, and finally to the present 35 years. If the latter rate continues for 900 years, the earth's population will be 60 million billion people, or about 100 persons for each square yard of the *total* earth surface. Unfortunately, we have no evidence that indicates any lessening of this doubling rate.

Of immediate concern is the world food crisis, a subject dealt with at the Plenary Session of the 19th Annual AIBS Meeting. At that session it was indicated that no efforts are presently being made that would avert global famines by 1985 (McElroy, 1969). Ehrlich (1968) has stated that such famines will be prevalent in the 1970s. What we are prepared to consider as "widespread global famine" is questionable, but apparently it is not the 3.5 million people or more who will starve this year (Ehrlich, 1968); nor is it the general agreement that one-half of the world's people are presently either malnourished or undernourished. I agree with those who feel that we must increase food production at home and abroad in an intensive effort to avert famine, but obviously the successes of such an effort will be pitifully short-lived unless population control is achieved.

While there appears to be general agreement that the growth of human populations must be controlled, both in the long-term sense of allowing for survival and in the immediate sense of averting or alleviating famines, there is little agreement as to how this control is to be achieved.

On 7 January of this year, the Presidential Committee on Population and Family Planning proposed a $120 million increase in the federal appropriation for family planning services to make such services available to all American women who want them. At that time the President stated that no critical issue now facing the world, with the exception of peace, is more important than that of the soaring population. He further stated that world peace will probably never be possible if this latter problem goes unsolved, and he noted that the federal investment in family planning activities had risen from $6 million in fiscal 1964 to $115 million in fiscal 1969. This funding may indicate progress, but certainly not of a magnitude proportional to the enormity and urgency of this situation. A value judgment has been made as to the priority of this problem with that of landing a man on the moon, at least regarding funding and the attraction of intellectual effort.

In my opinion the focus continues to be on family planning, not on population control, and this does little more than achieve a reduction in birth rate of an inadequate nature. I find that I must agree with Kingsley Davis (1967) that "There is no reason to expect that the millions of decisions about family size made by couples in their own interest will automatically control population for the benefit of society." As Davis points out, the family planning campaigns in such "model" countries as Japan and Taiwan have hastened the downward trends in birth rates but have not provided population control. Results of the present approach can only be measured as the difference between the number of children women have been having and the number they want to have. For example, the family planning program in Taiwan, assuming that the contraceptives used are completely effective, would be successful if it resulted in the women having the desired 4.5 children each. This represents a sharp drop from the average 6.5 children previously borne to each woman but results in a rate of natural increase for the country of close to 3%. If the social and economic change of Taiwan continues, a further drop in fertility may occur. It may even reach that of the United States, where an average of 3.4 children is currently desired. This would result in Taiwan in a 1.7% per year increase, or a doubling of the population in 41 years, and hardly suggests that our country be used as a model or yardstick for other nations.

The plan of Taylor and Berelson (1968) to provide family planning instructions with maternity care may be a logical step in population control, but I fail to see in what way this plan can alter the basic desire of women in the underdeveloped nations to have more than two children. The natural processes of modernization and education have failed to do this in those nations that are developed. With these facts in mind, it is difficult to imagine the acceptance anywhere that *any* population increase, no matter how trivial, can be tolerated and that the goal must be zero growth.

There is no easy single solution to achieving a zero or near-zero growth rate. Berelson (1969) has recently reviewed the further proposals which have been made to "solve" the population problem. He has appraised them according to scientific, political, administrative, economic, and ethical criteria as well as to their presumed effectiveness. The proposals range from the very nebulous one of augmented research effort to the stringent one of involuntary fertility control. The barriers to acceptance of these criteria, for the truly effective measures, seem insurmountable at the present time. It is my personal view that in the United States a system of tax and welfare benefits and penalties; a liberal, voluntary program of abortion and sterilization (government sponsored and financed, if necessary); attempts at the development in women of substitutes for family interest; and greatly intensified educational campaigns are in order. If the United States is to lead the way, and certainly no other nation appears economically prepared to do so, it seems reasonable that we might begin by abolishing those policies that promote population growth. However, I do not believe we will do these things until economic hardship makes them mandatory. Nonetheless, we are nearing the point of either exercising the free choice of methods of population control still available or facing the compulsory ones that otherwise will be necessary for survival.

In the long interim, however, the emphasis of our efforts can be logically focused on the improvement of the quality of the environment and of the people who are to live here. Here, at least temporarily, we can "do things" with some expectation of success.

The Shift to Urban Life

The rapidly rising number of human beings is not resulting in their general distribution over the landscape but rather in the development of enormous urban centers. In 1800, over 90% of the population of the United States, albeit only some 5-1/2 million people, lived in a rural environment. By 1900, the population of this country was nearly equally divided between cities and rural areas. In 1950, the urban population was 64%; in 1960, 70%; and it is presently about 75%. The projection for 1980 is 78% and for the year 2000 about 85% of the expected 300 million people will be urban dwellers. The number of residents in rural areas has not changed over the last 30 years, and is not expected to vary from its present approximately 53 million persons for the next 10 years. There resides in these data, however, the basic fallacy that what we term "rural" is changing also.

Gigantic urban concentrations are developing within the United States, and these have been termed megalopolises. The three best known have been recently termed "Boswash," "Chipitts," and, for lack of an equally ominous name, "Sag." "Boswash" reaches from New England to Washington, D.C., "Chipitts," from Chicago to Cleveland and south to Pittsburgh and, "Sag," a seaside city occupying the coast of California from San Francisco to San Diego. Demographers and urban planners predict the development of hosts of such "super cities." The Task Force on Environmental Health and Related Problems reported to Secretary Gardner in 1967 that virtually no effort is being made to explore ways of preventing this startling growth. A research program must be inaugurated, they reported, aimed at determining and perfecting measures to shift the focus of future population growth away from already crowded urban areas to parts of the country that are *not now* (emphasis mine) burdened by too many people. Unless such an effort is successful, the pollution control efforts of today, and those planned for the future, could be reduced literally to zero by the sheer increase of people and their correspondingly increased demand for goods, services, and facilities. Similarly, Mayr (1963) earlier pointed out that long before man has reached the stage of "standing room only" his principal preoccupation will be with enormous social, economic, and engineering problems. The undesirable by-products of the crowded urban areas are so deleterious that there will be little opportunity left for the cultivation of man's most uniquely human attributes. This could be what is in store for "Chippitts," "Boswash," "Sag," and others.

It seems that there is not only an urgent need for population control but for planned communities and the de-emphasis of the enormous urban concentrations that compound our problems of coping with environmental pollution.

Urbanization, Pollution, and Man's Welfare

Thus far the data substantiating my remarks are more than adequate. The growth of the world's population is staggering and is attended by increasing urbanization. I still have neglected consideration of man's welfare under these circumstances. The steadily mounting volume of published and unpublished data regarding environmental pollution has focused primarily on the impact of man's activities on his environment and less on the reverse, i.e., the impact of the resultant changes on man himself. Some of these changes are quantifiable, especially those affecting physical well-being. Unfortunately, others affecting such things as mental health and what we refer to vaguely as the "quality of life" are not quantifiable although certainly they are no less real. Obviously, some of these matters cross a number of areas of interest. Consideration of them will be incorporated in the papers of other participants in this symposium.

I would like to consider first some of the quantifiable effects, prefacing my remarks by reiterating the well-known fact that many environmental hazards are so subtle as to be beyond an individual's perception and control. It is less well known that there are frequently some deleterious effects stemming from the most cleverly contrived technological efforts to improve man's general well-being. If we look briefly at selected data from the United States, there is evidence linking air pollution with major respiratory diseases (Task Force on Environmental Health and Related Problems, 1967). Deaths from bronchiogenic carcinoma range from 15 per 100,000 population in rural areas to 30 or more in urban centers with over one million population. Deaths due to emphysema have risen from 1.5 per 100,000 population in 1950 to about 15 in 1964. The correlation of bigger cities with more air pollution with more related deaths seems well-substantiated. Almost half of the people in the United States, 95 million, drink water that is below present federal standards or of unknown quality. Such diseases as infectious hepatitis appear to be directly related to contaminated drinking water, but very little is known about how the agent of hepatitis gets into the water or how it can be removed (The Task Force on Environmental Health and Related Problems, 1967). The concentration of lead is increasing in the air, water, and food, and the blood levels are sufficiently high in many cases to be associated with subacute toxic effects (Dubos, 1965). The accumulation and effects of nonbiodegradable biocides present another serious problem. Documentation is growing that a number of other diseases are associated with environmental pollution, frequently those associated with urbanization.

As alluded to earlier, our best efforts to reduce environmental hazards often have proceeded without adequate knowledge. The development of efficient braking systems for motor vehicles has led to increased exposure of the public to asbestos particles produced by the gradual wearing of brake linings. There is a scientific basis for concern that these particles may promote bronchiogenic carcinoma (Task Force on Environmental Health and Related Problems, 1967). Subsequent to the inoculation of millions of people with a vaccine to prevent poliomyelitis was the discovery that some of the stocks of vaccine, perhaps as many as 25-35%, contained Simian Virus 40

(Sweet and Hilleman, 1960), previously unknown to be resident in the rhesus monkey cells used to culture the virus of poliomyelitis and thus to manufacture the vaccine. The high prevalence of the virus in the cell cultures was compounded by pooling cells from several monkeys. Simian Virus 40 was subsequently shown to be tumorogenic when injected into young hamsters (Eddy, 1962), to possess the capacity of transforming human renal cell lines in vitro (Shein and Enders, 1962), and to result in the production of neutralizing antibodies in 5.3% of cancer patients living in the known limits of distribution of the rhesus monkey (Shah, 1969). Its carcinogenicity in man remains unknown. Poliomyelitis itself is a disease whose spread is enhanced by close human association. Numerous facts support the view that the disease is an enteric infection spread primarily by contaminated excreta (Bodian and Horstmann, 1965).

Without belaboring the matter of pollution and physical well-being excessively, I would like to add that the Food and Drug Administration has estimated that the American people are being exposed to some 500,000 different alien substances, many of them over very long periods of time. Fewer than 10% of these have been analyzed in a manner that might provide the basis for determining their effects, and it has been emphasized that we simply cannot assess potential hazards. The Simian Virus 40 example seems to substantiate this opinion. Nonetheless, severe physical manifestations can ultimately result from repeated exposure to small concentrations of environmental pollutants. These pollutants can have cumulative delayed effects such as cancers, emphysema, and reduced life span (Task Force on Environmental Health and Related Problems, 1967). A three-session symposium of the recent meeting of the American Association for the Advancement of Science was devoted to discussions of such unanticipated environmental hazards, including interactions between contaminants and drugs, food and drugs, and among different drugs.

Does Growth Necessarily Mean Pollution?
Earlier I stated my view that environmental pollution and population growth are not inexorably linked. Assuming that our technology renders the environmental scene once again "pristine" in the sense of allowing for sufficient ecosystem function, perhaps even to the point of eliminating the potential health hazards just mentioned, what are the consequences to man's mental well-being of continued population growth and social contacts? If, for instance, we eliminate the dangerous substances in automobile exhausts and asbestos brake linings, how will we be affected by the increase in vehicles from the present 90 million to the 244 million expected to be present in 30 years? We have no data which allow us to establish levels of tolerance for congestion, noise, odor (perhaps removable), general stress, and accident

threats, including those from traffic. Excessive exposure to high noise levels can impair hearing or cause total deafness, but the effects of daily noise and disruptions of all kinds, in terms of average human tolerance, is largely unknown (Task Force on Environmental Health and Related Problems, 1967). René Dubos states that: "You can go to any one of the thoughtful architects or urban planners . . . none of them knows what it does to the child to have a certain kind of environment, as against other kinds of environments. The whole process of mental development, as affected by physical development of cities, has never been investigated."

Further Social Aspects

I believe it is germane to this discussion to go back to the pioneer work of Faris and Dunham (1939) on mental disorders in urban areas. A brief summary of the data supplied in that study indicates how the incidence of major psychoses are related to the organization of a city. Mental disorders show a decrease from the center to the periphery of the city—a pattern of distribution shown for other kinds of social and economic phenomena such as poverty, unemployment, juvenile delinquency, crime, suicide, family desertion, infant mortality, and communicable disease. Positive correlations are difficult to draw from these data, but they are certainly suggestive and tempting. Each of the chief types of mental disorders has a characteristic distribution with reference to the differentiated areas found within the large, modern city. There is a high degree of association between different types of psychoses as distributed in different urban areas and certain community conditions. It is pointed out that social conditions, while not primary in causation, may be underlying, predisposing, and precipitating factors. Situations involving stress and strain of adjustment may, in the cases of persons constitutionally predisposed, cause mental conflict and breakdown. If social conditions are actually precipitating factors in causing mental illness, then control of conditions making for stress in society will become a chief objective of a preventive program. The study of Faris and Dunham was the first to indicate a relationship between community organization and mental health and to show that urban areas characterized by high rates of social disorganization are also those with high rates of mental disorganization. Finally, it appears that the effect of movement is important to the social and mental adjustment of the person, and precipitating factors in mental breakdown may be found in the difficulties of adjustment to a new situation. Similarly, Dubos (1968) points out that the amount of physical and mental disease during the first phase of the Industrial Revolution had several different causes, one of the most important being the fact that large numbers of people from nonurban areas migrated within a few decades to urban centers. These persons had to make the necessary physiological and emotional adaptations to the new environment.

Our public concern for health, including mental health, has been mainly with frank, overt disease. Since World War II, there has been an increasing understanding of tensions and social stresses, enabling workers in mental health to increase their viewpoints and to include these largely psychologically determined disturbances within their area of interest. The solution of such problems requires the skills of many professions and governmental action nationally and internationally (Soddy and Ahrenfeldt, 1965).

Selection in a Changing World
The concentration of urban life is evidenced by the fact that approximately 70% of our population is crowding into urban areas which represent 10% of the land in the United States. There are presently about 140 million people living on 35 thousand square miles. The evidence reviewed thus far can be reasonably assumed to form the basis for predicting that there will be little or no change in the trend of increasing urbanization. This sequence imposes on man the necessity of ultimately adapting to an environment almost wholly alien to any present today. While our current cities may be no more densely populated than some urban centers have been for centuries, they are infinitely larger and rapidly threaten the existence of all open space. Voluntary population control seems quite unlikely. As long as space and food exist anywhere, it seems reasonable to assume that urbanization will continue until mankind is spread densely over the face of the earth. The luxury of open space appears already threatened and the concept of "getting away from it all" a vanishing one. By 1980, to keep up with today's ratios of people to public space, we will need 49 million acres of national parks, monuments, and recreation areas instead of our present 25 million, and we will require 57 million acres of national forests and 28 million acres of state parks (Task Force on Environmental Health and Related Problems, 1967). It is difficult to speculate what such needs will be in the year 2000, or if at that time it will even be legitimate to consider them as needs.

Dubos (1968) has pointed out that the effects of crowding, safe limits so to speak, cannot be estimated simply from the levels of population density. The populations of Hong Kong and Holland, for example, are among the most crowded on earth, and yet the inhabitants enjoy good physical and mental health. Centuries of crowding have resulted in patterns of human relationships minimizing social conflicts.

The cultural evolution of man from the Neolithic to modern times has taken place without visible biological evolution (Stebbins, 1952). Mayr (1963) points out that Cro-Magnon man differed physically from modern man no more than do the present members of various races one from the other. Crow (1966) views human evolutionary changes as being of such long-term nature as to be considerably less urgent than the problems of increasing population and its relation to natural resources and the quality of life.

Nonetheless, natural selection is important for modern man because it will result in populations of those human beings for whom survival is possible in a uniformly and densely populated world. It is difficult to imagine that time will allow for any considerable shift in man's present genetic makeup, but rather that within the confines of that limitation he must demonstrate the adaptability necessary for continued existence. Such adaptability will necessarily need to be sufficiently flexible to allow for the disappearance of what we now consider basic freedoms and for the increasing regimentation that seems a certain concomitant of future life on earth.

Summary

I would like to summarize by saying that I am optimistic that modern technology can exercise some considerable control over environmental pollution, and that the current ecological crisis in the world makes it seem certain that some progress, perhaps a goodly amount, will be made. I believe that there is less possibility that current trends in the growth of human populations can be changed for a long period of time. Alterations in these trends requires changes in the social and cultural fabric of man and society that are linear in nature, while the growth of population numbers is exponential. Family planning is a start, but it must be followed promptly by other programs much more decisive in character. The United States should take the immediate initiative by abolishing all policies promoting population growth and should use its vast economic and intellectual resources to aid in suitable programs elsewhere. Following our earlier and continuing largess in supplying food and medical services abroad, such accompanying programs of aid in population control would seem to constitute a moral responsibility of considerable magnitude.

In the United States efforts must be made to de-emphasize the trend toward huge urban concentrations, to strive for better planned communities, and thus to alleviate simultaneously the problems of pollution and create greater environmental diversification. Predictive technology must be radically increased, and the liberation of substances into the environment curtailed to allow for *at least* a preliminary assessment of effects.

We are presently unable to adequately evaluate those factors influencing mental hygiene in populations and thus to know what the effects of crowding will be on future generations. However, I think it highly unlikely that those people will either think or react as most of us do today. The prospects for continued life as we presently know it seem to me rather remote. Haldane remarked that the society which enjoys the greatest amount of liberty is the one in which the greatest number of human genotypes can express their peculiar abilities. I am apprehensive as to what these genotypes might be, and in what kind of society they will appear, because the complex environment in which man evolved as the most complex biological species is rapidly disappearing. We must realistically face up to the fact that our biological inheritance, in its currently recognizable form, is not going to persist. I agree that to live is to experience, and that to live well we must maintain ecological diversity, a full range of environmental options so to speak, to insure that a wide range of possibilities exist among men (Ripley, 1968). Nonetheless, a full range of environmental options is different things to different people, and survival in a world restricted in options, of a sort alien to me, brazenly confronts mankind.

Notes and References

Berelson, Bernard. 1969. Beyond Family Planning. *Science*, 163: 533-543.

Bodian, David, and Dorothy M. Horstmann. 1965. Polioviruses. In: *Viral and Rickettsial Infections of Man*, 4th ed., Frank L. Horsfall, Jr., and Igor Tamm (eds.). J. B. Lippincott Co., Philadelphia.

Crow, James F. 1966. The Quality of People: Human Evolutionary Changes. *BioScience*, 16: 863-867.

Daddario, Emilio Q. 1968. A Silver Lining in the Cloud of Pollution. *Med. Opinion and Rev.*, 4: 19-25.

Davis, Kingsley. 1967. Population Policy: Will Current Programs Succeed? *Science*, 158: 730-739.

Dubos, René. 1965. *Man Adapting*. Yale University Press, New Haven.

—— 1968. The Human Environment in Technological Societies. *Rockefeller Univ. Rev.*, July-August.

Eddy, B. E. 1962. Tumors Produced in Hamsters by SV40. *Fed. Proc.*, 21: 930-935.

Ehrlich, Paul R. 1968. *The Population Bomb*. Ballantine Books, Inc., New York.

Faris, Robert E. L., and H. Warren Dunham. 1939. *Mental Disorders in Urban Areas*. University of Chicago Press, Chicago.

Mayr, Ernst. 1963. *Animal Species and Evolution*. Harvard University Press, Cambridge.

McElroy, William D. 1969. Biomedical Aspects of Population Control. *BioScience*, 19: 19-23.

Ripley, S. D. 1968. Statement in Joint House-Senate Colloquium to Discuss a National Policy for the Environment. Hearing before the Committee on Interior and Insular Affairs, United States Senate and the Committee on Science and Astronautics, U.S. House of Representatives. 90th Congress, 2nd Session, 17 July 1968, No. 8, p. 209-215.

Shah, Keerti V. 1969. Investigation of human malignant tumors in India for Simian Virus 40 etiology. *Journal Nat. Cancer Inst.*, 42: 139-145.

Shein, H. M., and J. F. Enders. 1962. Transformation Induced by Simian Virus 40 in Human Renal Cell Cultures. I. Morphology and Growth Characteristics. *Proc. Nat. Acad. Sci.*, 48: 1164-1172.

Soddy, Kenneth, and Robert H. Ahrenfeldt (eds.). 1965. *Mental Health in a Changing World.* Vol. 1 of a report of an international and interprofessional study group convened by the World Federation for Mental Health. J. B. Lippincott Co., Philadelphia.

Stebbins, George L., Jr. 1952. Organic Evolution and Social Evolution. *Idea Exp.*, 11: 3-7.

Sweet, B. H., and M. R. Hilleman. 1960. The Vacuolating Virus, SV40. *Proc. Soc. Exp. Biol. Med.*, 105: 420-427.

Taylor, Howard C., Jr., and Bernard Berelson. 1968. Maternity Care and Family Planning as a World Problem. *Amer. Journal Obstet. Gynecol.*, 100: 885.

The Task Force on Environmental Health and Related Problems. A Report to the Secretary of Health, Education, and Welfare. 1967. U.S. Govt. Printing Office, Wash., D.C.

Environment and the Shaping of Civilization
Lynton K. Caldwell

With the insight of the poet, Matthew Arnold spoke for his time but not for ours when he wrote of "wandering between two worlds, one dead, the other powerless to be born."[1] In Arnold's time the loss of tradition could be regretted, but the shape of the new world yet unborn was hidden. Neither poet nor man of science could know how to relate to it. But the world in gestation in the nineteenth century is now emerging. Its initial outline and its character are beginning to appear and it is a task of our generation to consider what it may become. Will it be a better world or will its already evident tendencies toward the monstrous prevail? Is this new world ours to shape or is it, and are we, analogous to digits in a computer unable to perceive or to control the cosmic program?

We begin with these questions, not to consider if or how they may be answered, but as reminders that our practical way of dealing with this imponderable aspect of the real world poses for us a moral obligation to act as if we could shape our future. We resolve the questions by assumptions of our autonomy and our competence. But we evade the teleological question of predetermined ends only to confront the ontological question of future development.

Our new world emerges with an implicit assumption of our self-actualizing power. The logic of this position implies a corollary responsibility to consider and evaluate the purposes for which resources are used. We are not compelled by logic to determine the ends of our efforts or even to forecast their unplanned outcomes. But it seems irrational to concern ourselves with means to the neglect of ends. For we have already seen the harm that can come from unprecedented and inadequately considered use of power. If there is meaning in the word "wisdom," it surely implies the attempt to use the resources of science not only for immediate purposes, but to shape a future in which human happiness and welfare will be possible.

Man's Future Environment

The shaping of man's future implies the shaping of his future environment. His ability to plan his future depends largely upon his capacity for reason. Disagreement over whether planning of the environment should be comprehensive or incremental reflects differing assessments of human capacity for rational conduct. The difference is one of degree, for no one contends that rationality is unlimited, and few would argue that human behavior is totally irrational. Rationality is always bounded, but incrementalists doubt man's capacity to deal effectively with comprehensive, complex, and long-term developments. They contend that because individual man cannot foresee his future, and societies of men differ among themselves as to what the future ought to be, man as a species is doing the best that he can. He cannot purposefully shape the course of environmental change and should not attempt to do so. His environmental correctives should be confined to specific, immediate, and manifestly harmful effects.

This attitude tends to the conclusion that, whatever its failures, ours is the best possible world. It may not be the best of all possible worlds, but it is the best that is possible for us. We are what we are as a consequence of an evolution over which human rationality has had little or no control. Our expectations of shaping our future, if realistic, must be modest. One may regret that in pursuit of his perceived self-interest man so often degrades the environment that sustains his life—but then, *ecce homo*, this is the kind of creature that the human animal is.

The empirical evidence in support of this conclusion is formidable. We see it on all sides. Continuing disregard of the known causes and consequences of man's misuse of his environment is discouraging. But any conclusion regarding the potentialities of man is tentative. It is a current thesis that man has taken over direction of his evolution. This opinion appears to be shared more widely among physical scientists and geneticists than among social and behavioral scientists. Those who should know man best seem least optimistic about his capacity for collective self-control. Nevertheless, history indicates that human behavior does change and that human societies are capable of planning and sustaining massive, complex, and relatively long-term efforts. Were this not so world wars and space exploration would never have proved feasible. There appears no limit to opinions regarding man's rational capacities. Yet the fact is that we have no verified knowledge regarding man's potential intellect, and no adequate scientific explanation for the evolution of human values.

We are as yet unable to explain the process by which the human brain evolved, separating man from his primate relatives; and we have no basis for assuming that man's evolution is complete. Our knowledge of human evolution is so fragmentary and covers so brief a period of geologic time that we cannot plot a reliable trajectory of man's development. But our knowledge of the forces of evolutionary change is growing, and our technical understanding of man's mental processes, although still rudimentary, is much greater than that of our forebears. If self-understanding is a key to self-control then progress is being made toward a point in human development when man may be able voluntarily to push outward the bounds of his rationality. In brief, as one looks to the future, the limitations of bounded rationality on shaping the environment would seem to be conjectural rather than certain.

In order to improve the quality of man's environment the quality of man himself must also be improved. The upgrading of man and his environment are aspects of a single great and complex process: advancement of the quality of civilization. And it may be argued that neither aspect of the process can occur to a significant degree without the other. The phenomenon of man occurs only in context, and whether one looks outward from man toward his environment or inward from environment toward the nature of man, the *field* in which inquiry takes place is the same. The viewpoint or perspective changes, and the focus of attention shifts, but the man-environment universe, although infinitely extended and complex, is integral and holistic. The amenability of the human factor to purposive self-control is discovered through tests of action. Environment-shaping action is one of these tests and one of the most significant of them because of its contextual relationship to the human condition. Forethought, restraint, and a considered appraisal of alternative means to socially desirable ends are characteristics of the civilized aspects of man. They are qualities of mind and personality that will be emphasized in education of any people who seriously attempt to shape their civilization.

The Process of Civilizing

Civilizing is the process of achieving civilness or civility. The form and substance of civility are not things upon which all men agree. But the essential or basic meaning of civilization is the attainment of relationships under which men are able to live together in communities. Animal and plant communities exist without the assistance of civilization. There are communities of men in which the state of civilization is rudimentary. Yet, the psychobiological distance between the most primitive living men and the most advanced non-human social species appears to be far greater than the distance between the most primitive and most advanced human societies. Man, unlike his fellow creatures, has an aptitude for civilization. His imagination and ambition impell him to refine and complicate his social arrangements and his technology in order to attain his objectives. Given time and an appropriate environment, primitive men have shown that they can become "more civilized," but no ape or insect has as yet demonstrated this capacity.

In the process of becoming "more civilized," man has developed elaborate technologies that are sometimes erroneously identified with civilization itself. Clearly, technology is a major aspect of civilization, and it is through technology that man undertakes to reshape the natural environment better to satisfy his wants. It is what man wants that determines the quality and direction of his civilizing efforts. Technology is the knowledge of means. In a society of self-imposed limitations on perspective, the advancement of technology may become an end in itself. The result is the technological society that Jacques Ellul describes and humanists deplore.

Civilization expresses its dominant impulses through its use of technology, and the consequences of this usage may be seen in its effects upon man-environment relationships. Throughout historic time, deterioration of the viability or self-renewing capability of an environment has presaged a decline of civilization. Evidence from Central Asia, the Middle East, the Mediterranean littoral, and Central America appear to substantiate this hypothesis; and yet, paradoxically, the spectacular advancement of technoscientific civilization in the nineteenth and twentieth centuries has also been accompanied by measurable, verifiable decline in many aspects of man-environment relationships. Skeptics are therefore moved to question the reality of an environmental crisis. Technologists now argue that the environment, in its natural evolved form, can almost if not wholly be ignored. Man can make his own environment. Under plexiglass domes he can lay out golf-courses on the Moon.

The Environment Reveals the Goals

A civilization reveals the nature of its internalized goals and values in the environmental conditions that it creates. Obviously the environment of a civilization does not express all of the values and conditions implicit in a civilized society. Yet if read perceptively, the environment reveals much more than the untrained eye sees. The science of archeology is based upon the reconstruction of past environments, and upon the extrapolation from them of the activities, attitudes, and institutions of the peoples of past civilizations. We cannot be sure of the accuracy of these extrapolations and it is helpful to have written records that verify or supplement material artifacts. We cannot always tell, where natural environments have declined, how much change was caused by man and how much by nature. Did, for example, stream siltation, continental uplift, or both, destroy the harbors of Ionian cities on the Aegean Sea?

But although the physical environment may not tell all that is to be told about the quality of a civilization, neither does it lie, as written records sometimes do. Man may misinterpret, but the physical evidence does not dissemble. In many societies, and not least in the United States of America, one finds great contrasts among the varied uses of the environment. From some viewpoints, American treatment of its environment appears to be violently contradictory. Like magnificent Asian temples rising out of filth and misery, the contrast between the "best" and the "worst" of the American environment is so marked as to suggest a national schizophrenia in environmental attitudes. The analogy may not be inapt. There is ample evidence to suggest that America, as a social system, does express contradictory attitudes toward the environment, as the papers in this volume attest. But this trait is not uniquely American; and it is also true that these contradictions exist within a system that, however complex and contradictory its components, does function as a total integrated society. The contradictions are within the system; they reflect subsystems of the totality. Inconsistent as they may be with one another, such contrasts are not wholly incompatible. The system has accommodated itself to the stress of their differences. In a vernacular phrase, they are "built into the system."

It is this built-in nature of human behavior in relation to the environment that will make the effort for environmental quality in America a difficult and frustrating uphill fight. An attack upon environmental pollution, for example, is in some part an attack upon the prevailing social system. The attack is, of course, focused upon specific and from some viewpoints harmful aspects of the system. But as John Kenneth Gailbraith has remarked in a satirical but all too candid essay, pollution is not a casual or spontaneous activity: "On the contrary, it has deep and penetrating roots in the body politic."[2] And in describing the environmental deterioration of present-day America, Paul Ylvisaker writes:

> Call it by any name—chaos, unplanned growth, ribbon development, social anarchy, slurbs, the decline of American civilization, the resurgence of *laissez-faire*. But recognize it for what it is—a people's *laissez-faire*, which sinks its roots down past any rotting level of corrupt and cynical behavior by the few into a subsoil of widespread popular support and an abiding tradition of private property, individual freedom and "every-man's-home's-his-castle."[3]

The environment of a society as shaped by man is thus not merely an expression of social values, it is a function of the society itself. It is a part of what the society is. To shape the environment of a civilized society means nothing less than shaping the nature of the society. Those who undertake to alter or direct the process of environmental change thereby take a hand in shaping the course of civilization. There are degrees of environmental control, some of which are essentially superficial or cosmetic. But unless even relatively slight changes are integrated into the functional processes of society, the probability of their survival is not high. The flowers will wither in their planters in the downtown mall unless their presence has become a part of the value structure and operational system of the city that sought to improve its image by planting them there.

Styles and Distinctions

The anonymity and uniformity of contemporary man-made environments contrast sharply with the distinctiveness and variety of traditional cities and countryside. Contemporary style in office buildings, airports, luxury hotels, factories, motor expressways, bridges and, increasingly, in the patterns of agricultural settlement, tend to a highly similar, almost common set of qualities. Planned distinctiveness is often attempted, but the leveling logic of technique is not easily offset. It appears that technoscientific culture generates its own environmental style, freed from the assumptions or constraints of traditional cultures. Gestures contrived to provide "atmosphere" in tourist hotels or airports merely confirm the leveling effect of technoscience as man has applied it. Symbolic distinctiveness is often emphasized where loss of variety threatens business based on human interest in change and variety.

Distinctiveness and variety do appear to be human values, but one finds an apparent paradox in contemporary society. Architects, artists, and designers often go to great lengths to assert the individuality of their work. Whether the results are pleasing variety or disturbing discord are perhaps only matters of taste or preference. A result, however, is that eclecticism, rampant at the community level, creates a nondescript sameness as between communities. In traditional societies there was a much higher degree of stylistic uniformity *within* particular communities. But as *among* communities there was greater contrast. By way of example, new additions to older buildings nowadays characteristically contrast violently in style. Variety is added to the immediate environment, but its integrity and distinctiveness are often lost. Widespread, uninhibited heterogeneity results in a generalized sameness. Buffalo, Detroit, Denver, and Seattle are different primarily where nature is still visible. A once-distinctive Boston is becoming more and more like Houston. There have been some successes in accentuating civic distinctiveness. The great arch at St. Louis is one of these. But with few exceptions, all large American cities appear to be the same place.

The implications of this paradox are significant for the task of environmental planning and administration. Implicit in the differences between traditional and technoscientific environments are contrasting latitudes of choice. The constraints upon choice in traditional societies were relatively severe. Yet environmental styles were as distinctive as the images associated with Brittany and Cambodia. The choices that men made in shaping their environments were limited by religion, technology, availability of building materials, patterns of settlement, methods of transportation, agriculture, and trade. These constraints still limit choice, but the latitude of choice has expanded with unprecedented rapidity. Today, that latitude is so wide that contemporary society has hardly begun to explore seriously the range of possibilities available to it.

Traditional society was relatively stable because the choices available to it were few and frequently obvious. In contrast, the choices available to technoscientific society are vastly greater; but many of the possibilities are not perceived by the mass of people or by their leaders. Yet there is also a widespread belief that almost anything can happen. Potential conflicts of interest thus multiply. Growth in technology, in economic wealth, and in population create new opportunities for the enterprising, and new threats to established values. In shaping the environments of traditional societies man appears seldom to have been self-conscious about his choices. The limitations of circumstance, the strength of customary ways, and the relative low pressure of population enabled environment-shaping to assume an almost natural evolutionary course. In the world today, no environment is secure. There is hardly a square acre of earth anywhere that is not vulnerable to someone's plans for change.

Technology's Enlarging View

More than any other factor, science-based technology has enlarged the scope of man's environmental choices. But more than technology is involved. The use of technology in processes that have altered environmental conditions has been highly selective. Technological feasibility is seldom the criterion by which the choice is made in the uses of technology. The real power and limitation of technology lies in its combination with other things—with economic, industrial, or military activities. Technoscience enlarges choice but does not guide it. The effect of technological innovations in combination with other elements is determined by the interactions among the elements. The synergistic effects depend upon the nature of the combinations, seldom upon technology itself. For example, the automobile in so-called less developed countries has not had the impact upon the environment that follows when economics, industrialism, and public policy permit the operation of automobiles by the millions. It was not technologically foreordained for American society to use technology to promote transportation by privately owned automobiles instead of by public carriers. The impact of technology is a systems effect; it is seldom an isolated event.

The environmental conditions of any society, but especially of contemporary technoscientific societies, are perhaps best understood as syndromes of converging causes. This synergistic effect of technology plus economics, plus other factors in society, provides the energy that levels mountains, moves rivers, and creates smog. But this convergent power is usually organized through interrelationships and combinations that are highly resistant to competing interests. Opponents of public works policies of the United States Army Corps of Engineers or Federal Highway Administration have confronted the all but impenetrable strength of these technical-political-economic combinations and have learned how seldom their behavior can be changed by direct frontal attack. Environmental preservationists have fought battle after battle with the corps over specific decisions and policies, but the combination that is the force behind the actions of the corps remains close-knit and strong, as yet unchallenged as an environment-shaping system by any equally powerful alternative.

These technoeconomic and technopolitical combinations have evolved as the primary forces in American society in the making of environmental choices. The choices are those of interested parties, but become by institutional or political default the choices or nonchoices of the whole society. The greater freedom of choice that wealth and technology confer in theory upon contemporary man tends in fact to become illusory. Much of the frustration and anguish of the idealist who would see technoscience used to create better environments results from this paradox. The means that could shape a more healthful, aesthetically pleasing, and convenient environment are used instead in ways that achieve technical objectives, but unnecessarily destroy or impair environmental assets. The latitude of technological choice in meeting the needs of modern society is narrowed by political and economic considerations. The location of factories, dams, highways, harbors, housing developments, and airports, or the necessity for their construction in particular instances, are decided through the application of criteria that do not begin to avail themselves of the full range of possibilities. In brief, although the alibi of technical necessity is often raised in defending environment-impairing choices, the decisive factor is usually economic or political. The choice of technologies in particular instances is seldom governed by technological considerations.

It is evident that criteria for what is good, bad, tolerable, or preferable are largely functions of the total society. These criteria may be, and some have been, influenced by science. In the main they are manifestations of traditional culture and the tendency of society is to apply them uncritically to novel situations. Moreover, the fractionalization of the total culture as a consequence of the impact of technoscience has deprived society of general guidelines or standards by which the results or desirability of technoscientific innovations can be appraised. Freedom of choice thus becomes inability to make discriminating choices. Weakness of constraints on technological choices gives an open field to aggressive and purposive politicoeconomic advantage-seekers. To oversimplify for emphasis, it may be asserted that the two-culture cleavage in modern society adds to the already great difficulties of rational or coherent direction of its future. Expediency thus continues to be a prevailing characteristic of contemporary policy making at a time when available knowledge and techniques are rapidly diminishing the great historical justification for expediency—ignorance.

The Pursuit of a High-Quality Environment

Can we really elect to have a high-quality environment? Does the structure of American society—pluralistic, democratic, historically biased in favor of an "everyman's laissez faire"—permit the shaping of its environment in any way other than by combat and compromise? The question is not whether conflict of interests in the environment can be eliminated. There is no prospect, in a finite world, that they will be. A second practical question is how to raise the levels of information and social concern at which the process of bargaining and accommodation occurs. To improve the human environment, both man and politics must be improved. Men make politics; political institutions influence human behavior; and behavior is heavily influenced by attitudes, beliefs, and values. Purposeful shaping of the environment involves the purposeful shaping of outlooks on life. The quality of the future environment depends, therefore, upon the shaping of attitudes, beliefs, and values through present education.

Some aspects of human conduct are expressions of psychophysical nature. As a civilizing animal it is natural for man to substitute reason and culture for subrational drives, but rational behavior may serve irrational motives. It is, therefore, important to our welfare to understand the nature and effect of physiologically conditioned behavior. If man is a territorial animal, and if he displaces onto the environment aggression generated in his social relationships, knowledge concerning these circumstances could greatly assist development of feasible strategies for effective environmental policy. Yet not all men nor all societies project destructive impulses against the environment. The improvement of man can proceed through education, in the broad sense, while efforts are made also to improve the psychophysical endowment of the human species.

Implications for Education

What are the implications for an educational process that will help to build better environmental relationships in the future? The structuring of the entire process of formal education around man-environment relationships is not necessarily indicated. Many of the attitudes, beliefs, and values that would improve prospects for better environments in the future are equally relevant to other aspects of life. Yet not all educational orientations are equally suitable to help society to set goals and establish priorities for the future. Education limited to information is of little help. The question becomes one of what attitudes, beliefs, and values the system inculcates. In the broadest sense, the issue is what kind of civilization the process of education will produce.

Within this broader context of educational policy an increased and, in some measure, new focus on environmental relationships and policies will be necessary. This basically ecological aspect of research and teaching has long been neglected to our detriment and to our increasing peril. Recent moves to establish centers or institutes for environmental studies in numbers of colleges and universities indicate intention to remedy the neglect. Through the organization of new courses of study and the reorganization of old ones, higher education is better equipping today's youths to perceive and to assess the meaning of environmental change. Only a beginning has been made and much more needs to be done. It is especially important that basic environmental concepts be built into secondary education where they have heretofore generally been lacking. Education is more than schooling, but it is through formal systematic mass education that the greatest single impact on attitudes, beliefs, and values can be made.

In a technoscientific age there is no end to the need for learning. Planned, systematic education now continues through adult life and is increasingly civic as well as vocational in character. With the displacement of traditional culture by technoscience, we are confronted with the necessity of working to obtain our civilization. We can no longer merely inherit it. To preserve the culture of the past, whether in art, in ethics, in historic sites, in landscapes, or in social institutions, requires unremitting effort. It also requires reappraisal; for not all that we inherit is necessarily good.

In the new world struggling to be born it is we who must struggle. The disintegration of traditional culture is a grim and tragic process. We see its consequences in starkest relief in catastrophes that have befallen the ancient civilization of China. Fortunately for us of the Western world, the concepts of self-actualization and of the evolution of man and society are embodied in our culture. Yet, although these internalized concepts may have helped to spare us the misfortunes of China, they have not helped us to be self-actualizing in all respects. Why have they not been more effective in guiding public effort toward better environmental decisions? The explanation lies perhaps in the complexity of our culture and in the particular ways in which these concepts are expressed in our society. More certainly, our educational system has not equipped people to make well-considered environmental choices.

Choosing Valid Goals
We are not yet able to explain why some societies adopt ecologically valid goals and practices and others do not. Simplified explanations are likely to be wrong, but it is possible to draw certain general conclusions from the course

that contrasting cultures have taken without fully understanding the causal factors. For example, although no simple explanation seems adequate to account for the decline of Chinese civilization, the inadvertent overstressing of the environment by sheer numbers of people seems to have been a critical factor. The ethos of China, less complex and more dogmatic than the ideologies of the West, was more congenial to harmony with nature. Yet neither philosophy, bureaucracy, nor science enabled China to avoid the environmental impoverishment that followed a slowly increasing but unremitting pressure of man on the land. In the West, science and technology enabled society to achieve a more productive and better balanced relationship to the natural world even though, paradoxically, the dominant attitudes toward nature tended as much toward hostility as toward harmony. Industrialization and the colonization of the Americas relieved in Europe the inordinate stress of man on his environment that accompanied the decline of Chinese civilization. But we have no assurance that the combination of culture and technology that, with obvious exceptions, has worked well for the West will continue to do so in the technoscientific society of the future.

Two obvious aspects of the historical threshold over which all society is now passing are exponential increases of people and of power. The danger in destructive or misguided attitudes toward nature has become greater today because of the greater means to translate attitudes into action. Guided ignorance in the form of dogma appears to have been a factor in the decline of the old China; unguided knowledge in the form of technocratic optimism appears to have been the characteristic danger to the West. Today, the establishment of guidelines for knowledge in the application of science and technology to the human environment is a task of urgent importance everywhere. The task is urgent because until it is accomplished there will be no adequate basis in theory or principle upon which to base public and international policies for the custody, care, and development of the human environment.

In America, we have no corpus of ecological doctrine in our public life comparable to that which now influences or governs our economic decisions. Our public life is shaped by particular interpretations, or misinterpretations, of self-actualization and freedom to change that tend to contradict the concepts that they are presumed to exemplify. These misinterpretations although deeply rooted in American society are neither uniquely nor necessarily American. They may be changed, and they must be changed, if the shaping of American civilization is to enlarge the public happiness and welfare. Among the attitudes that misinterpret the meaning of human freedom the following are especially familiar and especially harmful to the quality of civilization and its environment: first, an uncritical bias for growth; second, techno-economic determinism; third, cultural relativism; and, fourth, self-centered individualism—the "everyman's laissez faire."

These attitudes share certain negative characteristics significant for the environment-shaping process. None of them imply or require self-restraint or control, none suggest individual or collective accountability, none concede the existence of criteria for evaluating the use of the environment that are independent of individual interest or preference. All of these attitudes suggest resistance to any general pattern of environmental development in society or to any meaningful standards of environmental quality, *per se*. They do not preclude the imposition of social control where a clear and present danger to individual well-being can be proved. But they severely retard the establishment of general principles of ecological policy upon which more specific standards can be based. More critical attention to their effects is therefore needed.

The Urgings of Growth

The "growthmanship" attitude is deeply embedded in American culture. Whether our national obsession with quantitative growth can be transformed into qualitative growth, or growth within a self-renewing or an internally dynamic homeostatic system is conjectural. The most problematic growth of all is that of numbers of people. In America there are grounds for cautious optimism that the national enthusiasm for numbers may someday be displaced by a concern for the quality of human life generally.

Technoeconomic determinism, or the "you can't stop progress" attitude is still firmly ascendant in American life, despite critical attack from both science and aesthetics. Supersonic transport and airports unlimited are only current examples of a national tendency. It is curious that people vigilantly jealous of their rights in relation to government will permit their privacy, convenience, and even health to be jeopardized by costly and unnecessary technological innovation that yields little, if any, social benefit. More strange is the tendency of science-oriented, rational people to accept the metaphysical dogma of technological inevitability. It is, as we have emphasized, a contradiction to the tacit belief of Americans in the self-actualization of the human personality. It is an example of compartmentalized thinking against which education has not yet provided sufficient protection.

Cultural relativism has permeated the social sciences and has strongly influenced ethical and religious thought. The value of a demonstrably valid set of ecological principles by which public policy could be guided would be very great. It could provide a common ground for greater consensus. But it would encounter objections from those who hold that science has nothing to do with values, and that one man's values are as good as another's. Our slowness in exploring the biosocial interface in science has kept us from providing an adequate and convincing answer to arguments over relativity or priority among values in the environment. Political accommodation among conflicting interests therefore tends to occur at too low a conceptual level to give adequate weight to scientific knowledge or ecological wisdom.

The laissez-faire attitude toward the rights of individuals in relation to the environment has suffered some attrition through public action on behalf of public health and safety. Land-use planning and zoning, and emerging pollution control legislation, further constrain individual behavior in relation to the environment. We are beginning to lay a foundation for a legal doctrine of public rights in the environment as distinguished from the specific and discrete prohibitions that have hitherto characterized our environmental policy. Yet at the local level of government and throughout large areas of the country where pressure on the environment has not been felt acutely, the right to exploit the environment for personal advantage is still very broadly construed. Here again culture shapes environmental attitudes. The psychology of the frontiersman is still vigorous and when reinforced by technoscientific capability can be a very potent force, usually in ways harmful to environmental quality.

Pre-Scientific Attitudes in a Scientific World

A characteristic common to all of these foregoing attitudes is that each of them is highly dysfunctional to the effective public control of applied science or technology. They derive from viewpoints formed mostly in the pre-scientific world, although cultural relativism reflects to some degree an inclination to be scientific. Relativistic thinking that dismisses weight of evidence and insists upon incontrovertible proof of the validity of one environmental attitude as against another has abandoned science for a philosophical fetish. In actuality these attitudes do not appear as clear-cut or consistent categories of belief or behavior. They are interwoven in the fabric of our social, political and economic life, and this is why it become so difficult to change them. It is why environment shaping becomes culture shaping, and why attack upon the environmental abuses of our industrial society readily becomes an attack upon certain aspects of the structure of the society itself.

Concluding Remarks

These remarks began with an allusion to the concept of two worlds—the familiar but no longer viable past and the future which, more than a transition from the past, appears to bring a change of state in the human condition. Related to this concept is that of two cultures, popularized by C. P. Snow. Each of these concepts is expressive of the change that science has brought into the world. Both imply discontinuities in culture: chronological, intellectual, and emotional.

The truth of these interpretations of present history is perhaps more poetic than rigorously factual, more qualitative than quantitatively demonstrable. A truth may be substantial without being universal. And it seems true that the *means* to shape the environment of civilized societies belong largely to science; whereas the purposes of men, the standards of beauty, of order, of aesthetic satisfaction, of welfare, and even of some aspects of health belong to the humanities. This separation between the custodians of means and ends in our society creates weakness and discontinuity at the point of social decision. It is in the process of public policy making that the respective contributions of the "two cultures" are needed to form a mutually comprehensible and coherent unity.

The size and complexity of modern society require specialization. In the absence of integrative forces, occupational differences tend to fractionalize society. Communication across occupational lines becomes difficult, and no common set of assumptions or values provides a meeting ground for differing interest. The openness of modern society is deceptive. Freed from barriers of class and caste, it is more subtly fragmented by technoscientific specialization and by the progressive isolation of the traditional culture from technoscience.

Here perhaps lies the answer to the question of why contemporary Western technoscientific society has not dealt more effectively with its environmental problems. Means and ends are separated. The wholeness of man and of society requires a synthesis or integration in orientation toward the world and life that conventional education has not provided. Thus, as we earlier observed, contradictory tendencies of modern American society are built into its social system. And it is this schizoid tendency that most of all makes it difficult for the United States of America to develop a guiding set of environmental policies or to employ more than a fraction of the potential power of science and technology on behalf of human welfare.

Science has placed in the hands of man knowledge and power that makes him responsible for his future; it has not given him the moral compulsion to act responsibly. The substantive values that science and technology serve are articulated in the humanities, but are seldom amenable to scientific verification. It is at this interface between science and the humanities that environmental policy, if made, is made. And it is at this interface also that higher education can contribute to resolving what some observers have called our environmental crisis.

How this task can be accomplished in the colleges and universities is yet to be discovered, and it must also be acknowledged that education alone will not solve our problems. There is no master blueprint equally applicable to all institutions or to all aspects of the educational task. But these elements in that task are universal: first, it is primarily one of synthesis—its basic data will be derived largely from the established disciplines that individually are unable to bring together knowledge relevant to environmental policy in a comprehensive or coherent system; second, its concern is not merely with the appearance of things, but with the purpose, quality, and worth of man-environment relationships; third, it reinforces rather than dilutes efforts in the separate sciences and humanities because it establishes or clarifies their relevance to life; fourth and finally, it emphasizes a truth that is too often forgotten—that through education the civilization of the future is shaped.

Past generations of Americans, and men generally, have understood education as preparation for life. It is that, but that is its smaller dimension. Its larger dimension and equally important task is to *shape* life as well as to help prepare for it. In some degree education has always done this, but often without conscious effort or intention. If man is to be the master of his own ingenuity, and not its victim, he will have to find better ways to relate means to ends, and to evaluate the ends that science makes available to him. In summation, the major task of education and politics is to shape a world in which preparation for life is worthwhile.

Notes and References

1. "Stanzas from the Grande Chartreuse" (lines 85-86), *The Poetical Works of Matthew Arnold*, ed. C. B. Tinker and H. F. Lowry (London: Oxford University Press, 1950), p. 302.

2. "The Polipollutionists," *Atlantic Monthly*, CCXIX (January, 1967), 52.

3. "The Villains are Greed, Indifference—and You," *Life*, LIX (December 24, 1965), 96.

Selected References for Chapter 8

Burch, William R., Jr., *Daydreams and Nightmares: A Sociological Essay on the American Environment.* New York: Harper and Row, Publishers, 1971. A sociological explanation of the recent recognition of environmental crises in America.

Caldwell, Lynton K., *Environment: A Challenge for Modern Society.* 1970. An emphasis on needed changes in man-environment relationships.

Disch, Robert, ed., *The Ecological Conscience: Values for Survival.* Englewood Cliffs, N.J.: Prentice-Hall, Inc., 1970. A collection of essays reflecting humanistic views on environmental management.

Klausner, Samuel Z., ed., "Society and Its Physical Environment." *The Annals of the American Academy of Political and Social Science*, Vol. 389 (May) 1970. A collection of essays focusing on social organizational implications for environmental quality.

Klausner, Samuel Z., *On Man in His Environment.* San Francisco: Jossey—Bass Inc., Publishers, 1971. An analysis of social factors influencing environmental use and policy.

The readings in this concluding chapter have focused on problems of man's environmental setting. It is quite evident that questions regarding environmental ecology are more diverse and less certain than those regarding population ecology. While there appears to be overwhelming agreement that human populations are absolutely too large and growing too rapidly, there is much less accord regarding the current and projected availability of natural resources such as food, land, water, and minerals. Furthermore, whereas alternative strategies for dealing with excessive population growth have at least been catalogued, approximately evaluated, and increasingly implemented (though by no means successfully), appropriate action regarding environmental control is still largely undetermined and uncoordinated. Still, several common themes are seen in the essays contained in this chapter.

Underlying each of these presentations is a concern with the quality of the environment. For example, Landsberg emphasizes the need for evaluating the social costs of particular patterns of resource use. Williamson focuses on the undesirable physical and psychological consequences of uncontrolled technology and population concentration. Finally, encompassing issues raised by the two preceding authors, Caldwell suggests that the factors accounting for current threats to the quality of man's environment may be located in value orientations associated with the development of urban-industrial societies. Taken together, these essays indicate a deep concern over man's inability to shape his environment in such a way that optimum conditions for human survival, individual as well as collective, are maximized.

A second common theme follows from the first, and emphasizes that environmental quality is a collective problem with consequences for entire populations, not simply the apparent violators. Whether the issue in question be the food supply, water and air pollution, or land-population ratios, problems can hardly be resolved on individual or small-group bases. Third, there seems to be a common recognition that population control, if not in itself a partial solution to problems of environmental quality, is at least a necessary pre-condition to the implementation of alternative solutions. The primary force underlying deterioration of environmental conditions is the organization of human activities designed to fulfill the real or imagined exigencies of human survival; smaller and less rapidly growing populations could certainly lessen these pressures.

Finally, all of the contributors to this chapter share an opinion that environmental policy is as yet quite inadequate—where it exists at all. Indeed, each of these essays may be viewed as an attempt to suggest needed innovations or reformulations in socially organized strategies for dealing with issues of environmental quality.

Mechanisms for Adaptation

Though with somewhat greater difficulty than in the preceding chapter, we may again examine the implications of our adaptive mechanisms for understanding the analyses presented above. Views regarding science and technology seem rather mixed. While Landsberg seems optimistic that the quantitative supply of resources is not yet threatened, he recognizes that industrial technology results in considerable environmental pollution and that science as a body of knowledge gives few guidelines regarding optimum resource usage. Williamson agrees that modern technology can provide some control over environmental pollution, but also sees that this same factor contributes to increased rates of population growth and concentration, and in this way creates the conditions for "population pollution." Caldwell clearly recognizes the innovative capacity inherent in this mechanism, but points out that "technoscience" unguided by reasoned policy and values can lead to man's self-destruction. Perhaps the consensus among these writers may be summarized as a recognition of the adaptive potential of science and technology for dealing with environmental problems, but a concerted disappointment with progress achieved thus far.

Symbolic mechanisms also receive some attention from these writers. This is most evident in Caldwell's discussion as evidenced by his explanation of the current status of environmental quality in terms of common value orientations which inhibit collective control of the environment for the public interest. Landsberg, in his examination of resource quality, suggests that private rather than public interests are guiding decisions regarding resource use in the United States. He suggests that truly social (i.e., shared) norms regarding optimum resource use have not yet emerged, and that methods must be developed for evaluating rival claims. A careful examination of the arguments presented by Caldwell and Landsberg will show that the two are complementary: both suggest only minimal public agreement regarding evaluations of appropriate environmental usage. Williamson fails to deal directly with the effects of symbolic mechanisms on environmental quality, but the tone of his discussion would imply an absence of such collective norms.

As with population control, discussed in the preceding chapter, the lack of efficient regulatory mechanisms for promoting environmental quality is a primary concern. This is reflected in the fact that each of these authors presents recommendations for policy formation. However none of the suggestions put forth comes close to being a systematically formulated program for establishing societal control of the environment. Caldwell's statement that we are not yet able to explain why some societies adopt ecologically valid goals and practices and others do not accurately reflects the current state of our knowledge (or ignorance) regarding environmental policy.

Finally, little attention was given to redistribution as a mechanism for improving environmental quality. It is true that some resources, forests for example, and some other aspects of the environment such as housing and landscapes are replenishable and/or alterable. But, given prevailing technological practices and social norms, and the lack of effective public policy, these are at most temporary solutions. Man's environment is best viewed, in the long run, as a closed system, and human survival will ultimately be dependent upon rational usage of existing environmental resources.

Thus we find that problems of environmental quality seem to be potentially responsive to the same three adaptive mechanisms as population problems: science and technology, ideology and culture, and social regulation. But as yet none of these alternative solutions has provided much evidence for a successful attack on the problems in question. The basic issue seems to be whether or not industrial societies can continue to exploit their natural environments, which is undoubtedly necessary for the survival of our present form of socio-economic organization, and yet create a man-made environment fit for human habitation. An affirmative answer to this question would appear to be dependent upon a radical shift in collective views of environmental priorities and the implementation of social strategies for achieving these altered goals.

Epilogue

The argument presented in this volume has been proposed as a reorientation to the study of human ecology. It has depended heavily on earlier formulations of the field by Hawley, Gibbs and Martin, and Duncan and Schnore, and upon the concept of adaptation, especially as reflected in the work of certain contemporary sociologists and anthropologists. While a major consideration underlying the organization of these materials has been the recognition of continuities in the definitional and conceptual bases of human ecology, at the same time it is hoped that the revisions introduced will yield greater specificity regarding the structure and functioning of ecological systems.

To recapitulate: the approach to human ecology followed here focuses on those social processes through which collectivities adapt to external conditions and pressures in their quest for survival. Human ecological systems (see Figure 1, p.   ) are defined in terms of interrelationships among three subsystems: population, environment, and social organization. The primary dynamic feature of the macro-system is evident in socially organized activities that provide means by which the population and environmental sub-systems may be maintained, manipulated, and controlled in the interests of promoting a balance between them, thus maximizing the survival potential of the collectivity. Four dimensions of social organization, here referred to as "mechanisms of organizational adaptation," were singled out by reason of their impact on population and environment. These are the social organizational aspects of (1) science and technology, (2) ideology and culture, (3) power, policy, and social control, and (4) mobility of people and resources. The net result of the operation of these adaptive mechanisms on population and environmental conditions yields levels of ecological adaptation, reflecting not only the independent effects of social organization on the two sub-systems, but also the degree of balance between them.

The studies contained in this volume were selected for their relevance to particular aspects of this approach to human ecology. However, many issues regarding theory and research in the field were necessarily omitted. It is the purpose of this epilogue to address some of these questions briefly, as well as to pursue some of the theoretical and practical implications of the model presented.

Issues in Ecological Theory

As suggested in the Introduction to this volume, perhaps the major deficit in human ecology today is its theoretical basis. A variety of conceptual frameworks have been developed for representing ecological phenomena and relationships among them, but all suffer from one or more of the following problems.

1. Underlying assumptions are either vaguely stated or left completely unspecified.

2. The components of the ecological system are defined only in gross or categorical terms.

3. Statements of cause-and-effect relationships are avoided, the typical preference being for covariance models.

4. In those schemes focusing on adaptation or adjustment, operational definitions of the components and dynamics of this process are lacking.

5. As a consequence of the preceding problems, empirically testable propositions about ecological relationships are seldom evident.

One may counter these criticisms by arguing that most if not all existing schemes for ecological analysis are merely frames of reference rather than explicit theories. Indeed, the model of the human ecological system guiding the argument presented in this volume falls in this same category. But frames of reference (or paradigms) are meant to be transitional stages in understanding a given class of phenomena, eventually to be supplanted by true theories that permit prediction and/or explanation of empirical events. For a variety of reasons, not the least of which is the significance of ecological conditions for the survival of mankind, the development of such theories in human ecology is now overdue.

It is hoped that the scheme presented here will be a step in the direction of productive theory for human ecology. While all the implications of this approach cannot be developed here, several examples will be briefly discussed with the anticipation that they will suggest further lines of inquiry. Perhaps the most significant feature of the adaptation perspective as interpreted here is the explicit premise that man creates and alters the conditions of his existence through his social organization. The history of man's survival on earth is characterized by the development of increasingly complex and powerful networks of social relationships designed to minimize uncertainty in providing the material, interpersonal and psychological requisites for sustained existence. At earlier stages in the evolution of human society, social organization was adapted to the constraints set by external conditions such as climate and terrain, food supply and population size. But through the development of science and technology, a complex division of labor, and extensive corporate relationships (among other organizational phenomena) man has developed increasingly greater capacity to adapt these external conditions to fit his presumed needs. This is not to deny that various aspects of social organization will change in response to external conditions, but these are relatively insignificant in comparison to changes instituted in the opposite direction. In short, social organization is most appropriately viewed as an independent variable in the functioning of ecological systems.

A further advantage of the analytic framework proposed here is the identification of specific components of social organization through which adaptation is effected. Thus it was demonstrated how these adaptive mechanisms are employed by collectivities to maintain, manipulate, and/or control the remaining components of the ecological system, i.e., population and environment. Several implications for the construction of ecological theory are evident. At a "middle-range" level, one may investigate the influence of particular mechanisms on ecological relationships. For example, what are the consequences of differing political systems for control of population and/or the environment? Does the relative absence of coercion in pluralistic democratic (as opposed to totalitarian) systems result in significantly less capacity to control population growth or exploitation of the natural environment? Or, alternatively, is the "growth ethic" characteristic of American ideology necessarily an impediment to the development of a viable balance between the rate of population growth and the availability of resources necessary for subsistence? Similar questions could be raised and investigated regarding the functioning of each of the adaptive mechanisms in question. Such a series of studies could lead to a cumulative body of evidence pertaining to socially organized means of dealing with ecological conditions, yielding both theoretical and substantive payoffs.

Theory at the Macro Level

At the macro-theory level, one may consider the simultaneous influence of all four adaptive mechanisms. Obviously this would be a complicated and demanding undertaking, but one clearly necessary for explaining the composite condition of an ecological system. Throughout this volume it has been stressed that, within any collectivity, the purposes and consequences of these adaptive mechanisms may be incongruent with one another. Occasionally this incongruency may be due to lack of coordination, but more frequently it is the result of conflicts inherent in organization, goals or uses. For example, consider the relationships among urbanization, family-size norms, political regulation and population growth. As population is increasingly concentrated in cities, smaller families become more advantageous and reproductive norms eventually show a corresponding shift downward. At the same time urban social relationships become more secularized, resulting in feelings of alienation and isolation among many urban residents. One consequence of such an orientation may be a feeling of resentment toward mass society, represented most explicitly by national government. Thus popular support for government policy may be difficult to achieve, whatever the benefits to the individual might be. Recognizing this fact, political leaders may be extremely hesitant to adopt and/or enforce any policy that might be interpreted as a threat to individual freedoms, lest they be removed from public office. Perhaps no aspect of individual behavior is so associated with personal freedom as is procreation; thus the historically documented reluctance of most governments to create national population policies. The net result is that, although population redistribution and emerging social norms would seem to favor smaller families and a reduced rate of population growth, congruent population policies have not developed. In short, adaptive mechanisms would seem to be working against one another in this case. This example has been simplified considerably for purposes of illustration, but it does suggest the advantages of considering the simultaneous operation of separate components of social organization. Comprehension of existing levels of ecological adaptation would increase considerably through similar, more rigorous, analyses.

Toward a General Theory of Human Ecology

Empirical investigations of the relative ecological influence of these adaptive mechanisms may ultimately lead to a general theory of human ecology. The principal feature of such a theory would be a hierarchy of organizational solutions to ecological problems. While the information necessary for constructing such a theory probably is not available at present, we do have some suggestive clues for guiding future inquiries. It is now fairly well accepted that the space ship earth is a closed system, and mankind will have to survive—at least for the forseeable future—on resources now present on this planet. This means that the population to be supported in years to come cannot exceed the capacity of these resources, and in effect this rules out redistribution of either population or components of the environment as a long-run solution to the problem of survival. Until relatively recent times the adaptive significance of science and technology was reflected primarily through extensive exploitation and control of the natural environment and creation of a complex manmade environment. A primary consequence was the rapidly increasing capacity to delay human mortality and to support larger and larger populations. But now we are recognizing new ecological implications in science and technology. On the one hand, relatively efficient and effective technological means are available for avoiding conception or aborting pregnancies, and on the other we suddenly realize that through our technological exploitation of the natural environment we are creating serious threats to human health and welfare. This is not to say that science and technology could not be organized in such a manner as to cause minimal disruption of environmental conditions, merely that for the present this has not been the case. Viewed as a mechanism for ecological adaption, then, science and technology show considerable potential. The distressing fact is that this potential has not been realized as yet; population growth continues at dangerously high rates throughout most of the world, and the environments of the industrialized nations, at least, continue to deteriorate.

Conflicting Family Tendencies

The question of whether ecological relationships can be improved through symbolic mechanisms is perhaps the most difficult to evaluate. Extensive evidence suggests that, while collective norms regarding desired, ideal and expected family size are shifting downward in most of the world's populations, they still tend to be somewhat above replacement. Furthermore, traditional emphases on the intrinsic value of children, motherhood, and family life persist. Here we find a curious form of normative conflict whereby the material advantages of smaller families are seemingly recognized, but the symbolic features of the family as a social institution, which support the maintenance of larger families, linger on. We know considerably less about the symbolic connotations of the environment, though some evidence suggests increasing public concern about environmental use and deterioration. Nevertheless, visual evidence, e.g., urban slums, litter strewn highways, oil soaked beaches, would raise serious doubts regarding the extent to which norms fostering environmental preservation are imbedded in the collective conscience. Still, to paraphrase a widely cited observation by W. I. Thomas, *other things being equal*, to the extent that situations are defined as real, they are real in their consequences. Stated otherwise, if the public recognizes the disastrous implications continued high rates of population growth and environmental deterioration have for long-run human survival, this may stimulate a change in behavior reflected by lowered reproduction and greater care in environmental usage. The catch is that other things are *not* equal, which brings us to consideration of the final adaptive mechanism, social regulation through the use of power, policy, and social control.

Social Differentiation

More than any other single feature, contemporary societies are characterized by internal structural differentiation and stratification. One of the principal indicators of the extent of social inequality in a society is the degree to which power is monopolized by certain individuals, groups and organizations or, conversely, diffused widely throughout the population. Present societies, the United States being a prime example, are generally characterized by concentrations of power within a relatively few privileged sub-groups. While the most evident seat of power is still formal political office, sizable influence on public policy and social control is exercized by other interest groups—e.g., the military, the wealthy, business organizations, and the Church. In the United States the influence of these power holders in regulating ecological relationships is manifested in many ways. Consider, for example, the political opposition to formulating a national population policy, the resistance to liberalizing abortion laws, the difficulties in adopting, let alone enforcing, legislation restricting industrial pollution of the natural environment or deterioration of various aspects of the man-made environment, e.g., urban housing. In short, there is an abundance of evidence to indicate that regulatory mechanisms are not operating in the public interest when it comes to creating ecological conditions favorable to collective survival. Private rather than public interests appear to be guiding the direction of ecologically relevant collective decisions. There are indications that this situation may be changing, but as yet results are not encouraging for the immediate future.

The task ahead for those who would seek explanations for ecological conditions may well lie in a detailed examination of the interrelationships among these, and perhaps other, mechanisms of organizational adaptation. Available evidence seems to indicate the somewhat greater overall influence of regulatory mechanisms, though one should not discount the potential for adaptation through symbolic and engineering processes. But at present these are largely speculative inferences, with their veracity and ultimate utility dependent upon extensive and systematic empirical research.

Social Science and Applied Human Ecology
The idea of ecological balance, as well as evaluations of the outcome of processes of collective adaptation, are ultimately dependent upon value judgements. The central issues concern the quality of life man desires for himself, how he ranks this in relation to other societal goals—e.g., national power, exploration of outer space and social equality—and the perceived significance of demographic and environmental conditions. In the present volume, for analytic purposes, the demographic and environmental components of the ecological system have been considered separately. Nevertheless, and this has been emphasized, the ultimate criterion for assessing the level of adaptation within any given ecological system is the balance between population size, distribution and composition, and the environmental resources available for satisfying the survival needs of that population, for the present and in the proximate future.

The role of the social scientist, *qua* social scientist, with respect to these practical questions involves (1) assessment of the empirical validity of charges that there are or are not ecological crises currently threatening the survival of mankind and (2) the analysis of relationships between various aspects of population, environment, and social organization. This first task is equivalent to identification of the problem. But even in this initial stage of inquiry serious difficulties may be encountered. One centers around the definition of survival. Certainly, barring an unexpected catastrophe, no population is going to disappear tomorrow or even next year as a result of ecological imbalances. Many discussions point to the year 2000 as the critical turning point, but one often gets the idea that this date is selected merely for convenience. The point is that survival (or more precisely the failure to survive) suggests particular temporal boundaries, and adequate assessment of ecological problems must deal with them. Furthermore, as emphasized in the Introduction to this volume, survival reflects a qualitative as well as a quantitative dimension.

While some current writers forecast the ultimate self-destruction of human society unless current population pressures and/or environmental imbalances are alleviated, this is probably an overly pessimistic stance. Far more critical is the quality of life to be led should these problems not be resolved in the proximate future. Homo Sapiens, especially in organized group contexts, are able to adapt themselves to many adverse conditions. Examples of this ability to exist, however poorly, are clearly evident in the blighted areas of today's metropoli as well as in the preliterate societies of the ethnographic present. From this perspective, survival is not a matter of life or death, but rather a question of how well man will be able to satisfy his expectations and desires regarding optimal living conditions.

Adjusting the Imbalance

The second task indicated above follows from the identification of ecological problems. It involves two basic questions. First, what conditions in the ecological system are responsible for the ecological imbalance? And, second, how might adjustments in the system be effected such that the imbalance is eliminated or at least reduced below a critical level? The perspective upon which this volume is based would suggest that one look to the four mechanisms of organizational adaptation for the causes of ecological imbalances as well as for the means by which they might be alleviated. This is not to say that the same aspects of social organization constitute both problems as well as solutions. It may well be, for example, that excessive population growth due to high fertility norms may be resolved through technological or political means without dealing directly with normative change. Likewise, environmental pollution due primarily to industrial wastes may be handled by relocating industrial plants without necessarily altering the technology of production. These are empirical questions, with answers dependent upon systematic inquiry and reasoned interpretation.

The point to be stressed here is that human ecology can best serve the public interest if it remains what its founders designed it to be—an empirical science. The primary goal of the discipline thus entails the analysis of the processes through which populations adapt to their environmental settings. Such an emphasis can be pursued only through the skills and knowledge available in the social sciences, thus ensuring them a critical role in providing information crucial to the future course of human society.

Notes On Contributors

John W. Bennett is Professor Anthropology, Washington University, St. Louis, Missouri.

Bernard Berelson is President of the Population Council, New York City.

Donald J. Bogue is Director, Community and Family Study Center, University of Chicago, Chicago, Illinois.

Stanley A. Cain is Charles Lathrop Pack Professor of Conservation and Director, Institute for Environmental Quality, University of Michigan, Ann Arbor, Michigan.

Lynton K. Caldwell is Professor of Political Science, Indiana University, Bloomington, Indiana.

Kingsley Davis is Ford Professor of Sociology and Director, International Population and Urban Research, Institute of International Studies, University of California, Berkeley, California.

Rene Dubos is Emeritus Professor of Pathology, Rockefeller University, New York City.

Otis Dudley Duncan is Professor of Sociology and Associate Director, Population Studies Center, University of Michigan, Ann Arbor, Michigan.

John D. Durand is Professor of Economics and Sociology, Population Studies Center, University of Pennsylvania.

Paul R. Ehrlich is Professor of Biology, Stanford University, Stanford, California.

Ronald Freedman is Professor of Sociology, and Associate Director, Population Studies Center, University of Michigan, Ann Arbor, Michigan.

Jack P. Gibbs is Professor of Sociology, University of Arizona, Tucson, Arizona.

Amos H. Hawley is Kenon Professor of Sociology, University of North Carolina, Chapel Hill, North Carolina.

John P. Holdren is with the Caltech Population Program, California Institute of Technology, Pasadena, California.

Dudley Kirk is Morrison Professor of Population Studies, Food Research Institute and Department of Sociology, Stanford University, Stanford, California.

John M. Krutilla is a senior staff member of Resources for the Future, Inc.

Hans H. Landsberg is Director of the Resource Appraisal Program for Resources for the Future, Inc.

Walter T. Martin is Professor Sociology, University of Oregon, Eugene, Oregon.

John McHale is Director, Center for Integrative Studies, School for Advanced Technology, State University of New York, Binghamton, New York.

Michael Micklin is Associate Professor of Sociology and Epidemiology, Tulane University, New Orleans, La.

Leonard A. Miller is Chief, Regional Coordination Branch, Office of Regional Activities, National Air Pollution Control Administration, Washington, D.C.

Dorothy Nortman is Staff Associate, Demographic Division, Population Council, New York City.

Jack C. Oppenheimer is Assistant to the Commissioner of the National Air Pollution Control Administration, Washington, D.C. and part-time Professor of Law at the George Washington University.

John B. Parr is Professor of Geography, University of Washington, Seattle, Washington.

Leo F. Schnore is Professor of Sociology, Center for Demography and Ecology, University of Wisconsin, Madison Wisconsin.

Alexander Spoehr is Professor of Anthropology, University of Pittsburgh, Pittsburgh, Pennsylvania.

Francis S. L. Williamson is Director of the Chesapeake Bay Center for Field Biology (Smithsonian Institute, Office of Ecology), Edgewater, Maryland.

Index